The Potter's Dictionary

OF MATERIALS AND TECHNIQUES

The Potter's Dictionary

OF MATERIALS AND TECHNIQUES

Fifth edition

FRANK AND JANET HAMER

A & C Black • London
University of Pennsylvania Press • Philadelphia

Fifth edition 2004 (Reprinted in 2012)
Fourth edition 1997 (Reprinted in 2002)
Colour edition 1993
Third edition 1991
Second edition 1986
First edition 1975, Pitman Publishing Ltd

A & C Black Publishers Ltd
an imprint of Bloomsbury Publishing Plc
50 Bedford Square, London, WC1B 3DP
www.acblack.com

ISBN 0–7136–6408–8

Published simultaneously in the USA by:
University of Pennsylvania Press
4200 Pine Street, Philadelphia, Pennsylvania 19104–4011

ISBN 0–8122–3810–9

CIP catalogue records for this book are available from
the British Library and the US Library of Congress.

Frontispiece: Painted dishes by Bennett Cooper
(photo: Bennett Cooper)

This book is produced using paper that is made from wood
grown in managed sustainable forests. It is natural, renewable
and recyclable. The logging and manufacturing processes
conform to the environmental regulations of the country of
origin.

Printed in China.

CONTENTS

LIST OF COLOUR PLATES

AUTHORS' PREFACE TO THE 5TH EDITION

Potters feel proudly in touch with the distant past knowing that fundamentals remain the same since clay was first manipulated. The grand framework of sourcing clay, shaping, simple glazes and the permanence wrought by firing gives a firm impetus to make. Developments are in the fields of specialized processed materials, sophisticated equipment promoting precise control, healthier practices and imaginative expression – ceramics as a vehicle for usefulness, art, politics, social comment, novelty and fun.

This book is for individual makers in ceramics, workshop potters, teachers, students and collectors. It turns a magnifying glass on the fundamentals, e.g. why clay is plastic and how glaze materials function; it demonstrates how the maker can progress when equipped with a well-founded knowledge of materials and an understanding of the ceramic processes effected during the marvel of firing.

The book can be used for detailed study or for quick reference to a word or a process. It is laid out as an index of key words and phrases which give immediate access to short articles. Each article specializes under its own heading and related articles are cross referenced. These allow the reader to choose a path through the information from a particular starting point. Non-technical language is used and numerous illustrations augment the text.

This fifth edition has been completely revised, expanded and updated. Frank and Janet Hamer work closely on every part. Each researches and writes, discusses the other's facts and wording repeatedly until the most accurate and clearest explanations are composed. Building on expansions made in previous editions, this edition presents significantly more comprehensive information on a number of topics. New research has prompted enlargement of the articles on Crystalline glazes, Auto-reduction, Stains, Insulation and specialized forming and firing techniques, as well as new subjects. Additional photographs illustrate the work of today's inventive and skilful potters.

A third colour section breaks new ground by presenting the essential understanding of types of ware—raku, maiolica, crystalline glazes, salt and soda, stoneware and porcelain—in an original visual format. The use of colour in graphs and diagrams brings an added dimension which makes facts readily accessible and connects the rules of process with creativity. These illustrations represent specific situations and must be read only as diagrams in context.

Chemical names of pottery materials and compounds have been brought up-to-date and now accord with international recommendations. Details of this very important change are given in a footnote, see page ix.

Health and safety are now widely and thoroughly covered in official literature. Recommendations and requirements are detailed in most suppliers' catalogues. This edition brings the details together pointing out sensible working practice. Because raw lead and some other toxic materials are no longer used, or indeed available, the articles on the hazards from these are much reduced. Readers wishing to study these materials, especially the historical use, problems etc, must now refer to earlier editions. The space has been used for positive contemporary ideas and visual input via extra photographs, for example under Extrusion.

Much contemporary work crosses the boundaries which once existed between each style and process. This poses problems of classification. Sometimes no accepted new name exists. In other cases a previously general description, like the term fuming, becomes the name for a specific part of a wide field of possibilities. This hijacking of terminology is exciting but presents problems for the compilers of an encyclopedic dictionary! We have tried to make use of both trends to stimulate as wide an appreciation as possible of phenomena and processes. Readers will discover and, we hope, enjoy our attempts to encourage more positive use of some words and open up the meaning of others.

Our thanks and sincere acknowledgements go to our numerous friends who gave help, criticism, advice and information which formed this text:

John Alliston, Stuart Altmann, Peter Barnes, Stuart W. Bennett, Michael Casson, Sheila Casson, Rollo Charles, Sydney Clark, Derek Clarkson, Rosemary Cochrane, John Davey, Jack Doherty, Nigel Edmondson, Derek Emms, Emlyn Evans, Avril Farley, Harry Fraser, Kirsty Gosden, Brian de Graaf, Brian Guest, Peter Hardie, Ian Herbert, B. Hirst, Judith Holden, Tesni Hollands, Sybil Hollingdrake, Mary Hughes, Peter Hughes, Barbara Ineson, Peggy Isaac, Kay Jenkins, David Leach, John Lewis, Avis Loshak, Sue Love, Ron Parker, Pauline Paterson, Colin Pearson, Brian Pugh, Roy Purnell, Ray Scott, Colin Skene, Michael Skipwith, Gordon Slinn, Harry Stringer, Colin Tasker, Frances Tasker, Phillip Tasker, Peter Walcot, Anne Watts, Alun Williams, Nigel Wood, Alistair Young and those whose names have been inadvertently omitted. We enjoyed the cooperation with and acknowledge the help given by Linda Lambert, our editor at A & C Black Ltd, and the excellent copy editing by Jan Mitchell.

Authors of books and publications frequently in use for the early editions were M. Cardew, A.E. Dodd, B. Leach, H.N. Holmes, C.W. Parmalee, D. Rhodes, A.B. Searle, K. Shaw, F. Singer, A. Wedgwood and W.E. Worrall. For the fourth edition we referred often to the *Ceramic Review* and also to writings by J. Gibson, R. Gault, P. Rogers, P. Scott, F. and S.S. Singer and R. Tudball.

Over 150 new and replacement photographs have given the opportunity to include contemporary ceramics which exploit materials and techniques and at the same time to indicate technicalities in areas which readers have requested. It is hoped that this stimulates further work, and provides enjoyable reference. We acknowledge and thank all the potters whose work is reproduced and also the owners of these pots.

Most of the photographs in this edition were taken by the authors. For others, thanks are due to the potters concerned who took and supplied the photographs and to the photographers: Martin Avery, Sam Bailey, Jim Barker, Roger Brann, Stephen Brayne, Laurence Bulaitis, Tessa Bunny, Roger Dorling, Cliff Guttridge, Peter Harper, Michael Harvey, Carrie Herbert, Sam Hughes, Jacqui Hurst, Ben Johnson, Gwyn Jones, Mark Laurence, Dewi Tannatt Lloyd, Robert Meadows, Andrew Morris, Nigel Nicholas, Petra Reynolds, Steve Sparrow, Paul Stubbs, Steve Teague, Bill Thomas, John Wheeldon. The colour photographs are credited in the text.

We wish to thank manufacturers and organizations who gave help, allowed us access for photography or supplied photographs and information, sometimes in great detail.

Arts Centre Aberystwyth,
Borax Holdings Ltd,
British Standards Institution,
Canadian Department of Consumer Affairs,
Canadian High Commission,
Carborundum Ltd,
Cardiff College of Art,
Co-bam Ltd,
Collection Ledbury,
Craft Potters Association,
Design Council,
Edwards and Jones Ltd,
Fordham Thermal Systems Co. Ltd,
Gibbons Refractories Ltd,
Gosling and Gatensbury Ltd,
Gwent Pipe and Firebrick Co. Ltd,
Harrison Mayer Ltd,
The Industrial Pyrometer Co. Ltd,
Kanthal Ltd,
Kanthal AB,
Lotus Pottery,
Marshall Arts Gallery,
Metrication Board,
Mid-Cornwall Gallery,
MPK Insulation Ltd,
National Museum of Wales,
Newport Art Gallery,
New Zealand High Commission,
Orton Ceramic Foundation,
Podmore and Sons Ltd,
Potclays Ltd,
Pottery Crafts Ltd,
J.W. Ratcliffe and Sons Ltd,
Royal Forest of Dean College,
South Wales Potters,
Staatliche Porzellan-Manufaktur,
Stow Potters' Wheels,
Sunderland Polytechnic,
Tastronic Controls,
Taylor Tunnicliff Ltd,
United States Information Service,
WBB Minerals,
Wengers Ltd,
and Wobage Farm.

Frank Hamer   *Croes-yn-y-Pant*
Janet Hamer   *2004*

Standard Abbreviations

At No	Atomic number		cub	cubic
AW	Atomic weight		cwt	hundredweight(s) avoirdupois
BS	British Standard		fl oz	fluid ounce(s)
°C	Degrees Celsius		ft	foot (feet)
CF	Conversion factor		gal	gallon(s)
EMC	Equilibrium moisture content		g	gram(s)
°F	Degrees Fahrenheit		imp	imperial measure
H	Hardness on Mohs' Scale		in	inch(es)
I/G	Inglaze colour		kg	kilo(s) or kilogram(s)
°K	Degrees Kelvin		l	litre(s)
MF	Molecular formula		lb	pound(s) avoirdupois
MP	Melting point		m	metre(s)
MW	Molecular weight		ml	millilitre(s)
O/E	Onglaze enamel			(equivalent to cc)
O/G	Onglaze colour		mm	millimetre(s)
°TW	Degrees Twaddell		oz	ounce(s) avoirdupois
U/G	Underglaze colour		oz pt	ounces per pint
UK	United Kingdom			(correctly weight of one pint in ounces)
US/USA	United States of America		pt	pint(s)
avdp	avoirdupois		qt	quart(s)
cc	cubic centimetre(s) also written cm³		r.d.	relative density
	(equivalent to ml)		wt	weight
cm	centimetre(s)		yd	yard(s)

A Note on Nomenclature

This edition uses and explains the chemical nomenclature recommended by the International Union of Pure and Applied Chemistry. Some allowances are made for potters' particular needs. Monoxide and dioxide are used only where it is necessary to differentiate within an article. Latin and Greek adjectives and endings, like ferrous and ferric, are no longer acceptable internationally so we retain and strengthen the use of descriptive and mineral names like red iron oxide and borax. Because the particular compounds involved in ceramics are few compared with the possible combinations it is acceptable to avoid the complete definitive system where red iron oxide and borax become diiron trioxide and disodium tetraborate decahydrate. We find it unnecessary to include element valency as roman numerals in brackets although this is used in the teaching of chemistry.

There is naturally a knock-on effect into the names of raw materials which gives more accurate descriptions, e.g. potassium feldspar. However, we do make compromises and use semi-mineral names like lime feldspar. We regretfully succumb to the international recommendation to spell sulfur with an f. But we do retain the two names central to ceramics of silica and alumino-silicate.

We dedicate this edition to all those who want to make things with creativity, imagination, and an understanding of why it works the way it does.

A

Aberystwyth International Potters' Festival

The International has taken place alternate summers since 1987 in the Arts Centre on the campus of the University of Wales College, Aberystwyth, Wales, UK. It is organized jointly by the South Wales Potters, the North Wales Potters and the Arts Centre. It developed out of a National Potters' Camp in south Wales organized by SWP and NWP in 1983 which itself was a development of the South Wales Potters' Conferences in different venues dating back to 1969. The International is one of the world's most prestigious ceramic events.

Absorbent

Capable of sucking in water etc by capillary action. Absorbency in biscuit ware is made use of in the glazing process. For tests of absorbency, see **Porosity**.

Absorption is not to be confused with adsorption which involves the collection of molecules of water from the moisture in the atmosphere. See **Adsorption**.

Accelerator

Catalyst. A substance that speeds up a chemical action. In mixing plaster of Paris the setting time can be decreased by adding an already crystalline substance such as common salt, gypsum or previously set plaster. This starts the chemical action which in this case is a crystal growth and is noticeable as setting. One per cent of set plaster will decrease the setting time of a fresh plaster from about 25 minutes to 15 minutes and the time available between mixing and commencement of setting will be decreased from about 7 minutes to 2 minutes.

Acid

To the potter there are acid solutions used in slips and slops, acidic compounds used in bodies and glazes, and acidic gases liberated during firing. An acid is a chemical compound which liberates protons, the positive electrical charges at the centre of atoms. Acids go into solution with non-acidic compounds from which solution new compounds, called salts, may be precipitated. The process may be immediate, e.g.

$$2HCl + Na_2O \longrightarrow H_2O + 2NaCl$$

hydrochloric   sodium   water   sodium
acid   oxide   chloride

(strong acid) + (strong alkali) $\longrightarrow$ (salt solution)

Or it may be slow and require heat, e.g.

$$SiO_2 + CaO \xrightarrow{1100°C} CaO.SiO_2 \text{ or } CaSiO_3$$

silica   calcium   calcium silicate
          oxide

(acid) + (alkali) + (heat) $\rightarrow$ (molten solution which may crystallize upon cooling)

The acid destroys the other compound and itself in a process of neutralization. The non-acidic compounds are alkalis and amphoteric substances.

A common household acid is vinegar. The sting in its taste is the attack by the positive electrical charges of the hydrogen ions seeking neutralization. Acidic solutions, like vinegar, are used to flocculate slips.

Slips that have become too watery and will not settle have probably become so because the water is too alkaline. They can be made to thicken and eventually settle by the addition of vinegar to neutralize the alkali. The acid encourages the clay particles to form box-like structures which link together and become larger particles. The larger particles then sediment. The box-like structure is called 'card-house structure'.

The same structure is used to create the opposite effect in glaze slops composed of non-clay materials. Here a small amount of extremely fine clay is added to the glaze slop and flocculated by an acid. It is usual to use bentonite (about 1% of the recipe) for the clay, and calcium chloride for the acid. Flocculated bentonite gives an extremely open, jelly-like structure which noticeably stiffens the glaze, thereby holding the non-clay materials like flint and whiting. It does not prevent their settling but inhibits this for long enough to facilitate the glazing process. See **Flocculation** and **Fluidity**.

The potter, who is familiar with silica as the hard rock called quartz or as a white insoluble flint powder, does not think of it as an acid or as a possible solution. Molten glazes are, however, solutions and silica is included in these. It can also exist as a solution with water at room temperature. The solution is silicic acid (H_2SiO_3 or $H_2O.SiO_2$). It can be prepared but not by merely mixing silica and water. Silicic acid is a weak acid but its existence shows the acidic tendency of silica.

Another glass-former, boron oxide is well known in solution form as boric or boracic acid (H_3BO_3 or $3H_2O.B_2O_3$). This is a very weak acid and is used as a mild antiseptic. The potter would happily accept boron oxide as an acid but not silica as one. Yet silica has a stronger acid potential than boron oxide.

One must accept the idea of talking about some oxides as acids although they are not acidic solutions in the form in which they are handled. The classification of silica as an acid and of some other oxides as acids under certain circumstances is an important way of assessing their potential in bodies and glazes. During firing they are neutralized by alkalis (fluxes) and other non-acidic oxides to form solutions (glasses). The most stable glazes contain at least twice as many acidic molecules as alkaline ones. See *Acidic oxides* and *Periodic table*.

Flue gases and gases from clay and glaze materials are often potentially acidic. Electric kilns without flues fill the kiln room atmosphere with sulfur dioxide and trioxide, chlorine and fluorine which combine with the atmosphere to form acids. These acids attack the kiln's metal framework and over a period of years the fluorine will etch the workshop windows until they are like frosted glass. This is obviously an unhealthy atmosphere for the potter. See *Health hazard*.

Acidic oxides

Oxides displaying acidic properties in ceramic fusions. They are silica (SiO_2) and phosphorus oxide (P_2O_5).

A number of other oxides, which are mostly dioxides, display some acidic properties in ceramic fusions. However they also display amphoteric properties which make it difficult to assess the unity formulae in which they appear.

Those with strong acidic properties are:

boron oxide	(B_2O_3)
titanium oxide	(TiO_2)
tin oxide	(SnO_2)
zirconium oxide	(ZrO_2)
cerium oxide	(CeO_2)
vanadium oxide	(V_2O_5)
germanium oxide	(GeO_2)

Those with slight acidic properties are:

antimony oxide	(Sb_2O_3)
arsenic oxide	(As_2O_3)
praseodymium oxide	(PrO_2)

Two other oxides display acidic properties in the raw state but change their oxidation during firing to become alkaline in character. They are:

manganese dioxide	(MnO_2)
lead dioxide	(PbO_2)

Manganese dioxide becomes manganese monoxide (MnO) at 1080°C (1976°F). Lead dioxide is part of the lead compound called red lead (Pb_3O_4). It becomes lead monoxide (PbO) at 600°C (1112°F).

Adhesive

Binder. Glue. Any substance added to a glaze to make it remain on the pot before firing. By hardening a friable glaze, it acts as a binder and makes the ware easier to handle in the kiln setting. Adhesives are sometimes put on to a biscuited pot, especially a hard biscuit, to provide a key for the glaze, which will also contain some adhesive.

Any paste or glue will work. Some smell more than others before and during the firing. Gelatinous glues may have the effect of temporarily thickening a glaze slop for the hour or two after being added. Polymer adhesives also give flocculatory effects. See *Flocculation* and *Suspender*. Cellulose pastes and resin gums often give deflocculatory effects.

Adit

Name given to the clay layers, especially when mining or quarrying ball clays.

Adsorption

The action whereby a substance, such as water, is attracted to and concentrated on the surface of a solid. This is an electrostatic action, and results from the atomic charges. It should not be confused with absorption, which is the taking of water into spaces by capillary and gravitational action, as with a sponge. Adsorption comes into the potter's vocabulary with the attraction of water to fully-dried clay, for a description of which see *Readsorption*. The electrostatic charges involved are described under *Double layer theory*.

Agate ware

A decorative ware made from partially blended dark and

light clays which give striations. The effect is sometimes created with surface slips. The name comes from the semi-precious agate stone, a form of crypto-crystalline quartz with striated markings. See also ***Lamination*** and ***Colour plates 47*** and ***81***.

The photographs show porcelain bowls by Jack Doherty and Linda Caswell.

Ageing

Souring. Maturing. The storing of clay in plastic state to improve workability. See ***Workability***. Ageing is used as a synonym for souring although a difference can be inferred. Clay can be aged in damp rooms, in airtight bins or by wrapping in polythene sheets. The intention is to keep the clay damp. A warm atmosphere is acceptable if humid, but frost should be avoided at this stage because it brings the water out of the clay leaving it difficult to deal with by hand methods of wedging and kneading. Weathering is an earlier stage of clay conditioning which uses frost.

Ageing involves the slow penetration of water between clay particles giving a net result of more particles of smaller size. This means a higher plasticity. When the clay is put to age, there should be extra water available in the clay. If this is not done the clay cannot age properly and may be too stiff to use after ageing. It is an easier process to dewater a clay slightly by kneading on an absorbent surface than it is to add water and mix this in.

Another action during ageing is the slow compression of the clay particles. A stack of clay is compressed slightly under its own weight. Particles which are closer together have more strength. They are held together by suction with the seal of water. Providing there is water between the particles, the full plasticity will be maintained. The compressed clay has increased workability.

Compression can be achieved without ageing by vigorous wedging. A good pug mill will also compress the clay but the ideal simulation is a de-airing pug mill. The use of a vacuum causes air pockets to explode and subsequent pugging from the vacuumed state packs the particles together. Once through a de-airing pug mill is said to equal two months of ageing.

Ageing is also used to give clays a rest. Clays which have been overworked, thrown on the wheel, passed through a pug mill with worn blades or cut about in a mixer, become tired. The colloidal attraction between fine particles which gave the clay its strength has been destroyed. Compression by kneading or pugging will bring the particles closer so that a network of strongly attached particles can be set up again.

Ageing is a physical action. Souring is slightly different. It involves organic action. Bacteria break down organic matter releasing amino acids which flocculate the mineral particles. Flocculated particles are attracted to one another and this gives the clay strength. A more prolonged period of ageing and souring allows the acid to penetrate between the finer particles of colloidal size. This promotes a stronger attraction giving a more enduring strength.

A clay which smells like rotting vegetation is therefore prized. Portions are added to other clays to spread the culture. A clay kept specially for handles should always smell. It will be the same clay as the body clay but will have extra plasticity/workability. A gardener's soil disinfectant which encourages bacteria can be added to clays to promote this action. It should be added in a much-diluted form or else it will kill the bacteria.

The longer a clay is aged the better. If mixed from dry materials at least a number of weeks is necessary. Reworked clay is improved by one day's rest though longer is better. Souring takes a matter of months or years. De-airing can simulate ageing but it cannot simulate souring. It produces a very dense clay which does not sour readily. The more open clays produced by the dough mixing method sour more readily. If both processes are used, the clay should be soured first and de-aired afterwards. See also ***Plasticity*** and ***Sour***.

Alabaster
Calcium sulfate. Gypsum. $CaSO_4.2H_2O$. See ***Gypsum***.

Albany slip
A slip glaze made from Albany clay alone or modified with feldspar and other fluxes. The clay is an alluvial deposit of the Hudson River in the vicinity of Albany in New York State.

When used as a glaze it produces a series of rich yellows, blacks and browns over a wide range of temperature from 1100°C to 1300°C (2012°F to 2372°F). It was first developed when the early American potters followed the European practice of refining the body clay to make a glaze.

In Britain, the mud from many of the larger tidal rivers gives similar effects. It can be modified with feldspar, wood ash etc, and gives mostly tenmoku-type slip-glazes for stoneware.

Albarello
The Spanish and Italian decorated maiolica drug jar of the 13th to 18th centuries. Often about 40 cm high the shape is

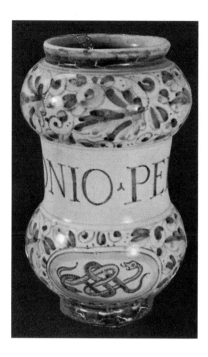

typically a concave cylinder with smaller neck and foot. Shown here are a modern version by Laurence McGowan and a historical example.

Alberta slip
A direct substitute for Albany slip compounded by the Archie Bray Foundation to duplicate the chemical and physical properties of Albany slip.

Albite
Sodium feldspar. $Na_2O.Al_2O_3.6SiO_2$. The second common form of feldspar, the most common being orthoclase (potassium feldspar). Albite is used as a body flux and in glazes as a silicate provider. It is sometimes called white feldspar to differentiate it from orthoclase which is often pinkish, but the term is not specific enough to be used other than between potters in one workshop.

The photograph shows a large, almost pure, albite crystal about 5 cm across. Potter's albite is rarely so pure but contains some of the other feldspars and therefore potassium and calcium oxides are present amounting to perhaps 4% of the whole.

The drawing shows the lattice structure of albite. Oxygen tetrahedra centred on three silicon atoms and one aluminium atom create four-sided rings which link to give crooked chains. The chains are cross-linked by the tetrahedra to give a honeycomb of holes. Sodium atoms occupy the holes in eight-fold coordination. The structure is very similar to that of anorthite, the diagram for which is represented in a complementary way.

It is often possible to substitute albite for orthoclase or cornish stone in bodies and glazes without causing large changes in the result. There must be differences, however slight, because, both chemically and physically, albite is unique. The qualities of albite (sodium feldspar) are most

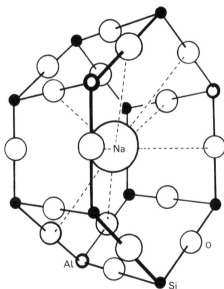

point of approximately 1170°C (2138°F) which is lower than orthoclase's 1200°C (2192°F). Albite is useful as a body and glaze material in combination with orthoclase. It provides extra fluidity without detracting from the overall stability. Above 1200°C, glazes with a high proportion of albite are prone to bubbling due to volatilization. See ***Sodium oxide in glazes***.

Sodium oxide has a higher coefficient of expansion than potassium oxide. Glazes containing albite instead of orthoclase are more likely to craze. They craze because they contract more than the body in cooling. Some adjustment of contraction can be made by simple substitution of albite for orthoclase and *vice versa* in body and glaze recipes. See ***Glaze fit***.

The sodium oxide content of albite tends to be slightly soluble and for this reason albite is often dry ground instead of being ground in water. Prolonged maturation of glaze slops containing albite and clay may involve deflocculation of the clay content by the soluble sodium oxide in the albite. However it is often preferable to purchase a water-ground albite if available, because it is finer.

Alkali

The opposite of acid. Potters call the glaze and body fluxes their alkalis. These are the non-colouring metal oxides which react with the acids in the presence of heat to produce silicates (glasses).

The so-called strong alkalis are:

lithium oxide	(Li$_2$O)
sodium oxide	(Na$_2$O)
potassium oxide	(K$_2$O)

which are soluble in water. The weaker alkalis are partly referred to as alkaline earths or by the more general name of bases. They are:

beryllium oxide	(BeO)
magnesium oxide	(MgO)
calcium oxide	(CaO)
strontium oxide	(SrO)
barium oxide	(BaO)
zinc oxide	(ZnO)
cadmium oxide	(CdO)
lead oxide	(PbO)
bismuth oxide	(Bi$_2$O$_3$)

They are not necessarily weaker in ceramic fusions but are less actively soluble in water. They do not give the same bright colour response in glazes as the strong alkalis. The alkalis are described in relation to the other oxides, amphoteric and acidic, in the section on the Periodic table.

The terms alkali and alkaline oxide are used in this book when describing all the above oxides. The chemist's terms 'base' and 'basic oxide' are avoided because, to the potter, a 'base' is more often part of a pot and 'basic' has the more general meaning of fundamental.

easily understood in a comparison with orthoclase (potassium feldspar).

The alkaline properties of sodium oxide are different from those of potassium oxide and therefore slightly different colour responses occur when albite is used in place of orthoclase. The blue from cobalt oxide is slightly more purple and the green from copper oxide tends more towards blue.

As a flux, sodium oxide is more powerful than potassium oxide but its range is much shorter. Sodium oxide starts its fluxing action about 800°C (1472°F) and begins to volatilize at 1200°C (2192°F). Potassium oxide starts to flux at 750°C (1382°F) and has no upper limit. However, since sodium oxide is a more powerful flux, albite has a melting

Alkalis release negatively-charged hydroxyl ions (OH⁻) when dissolved in water. They have a sting and are corrosive in a similar way to acids while being neutralized by the substances they meet. The soluble alkalis, soda ash and sodium silicate, are used to deflocculate clay for slip casting. See ***Deflocculant*** and ***Periodic table***.

Alkaline earths

Alkaline earth metal oxides. The oxides of the vertical Group 2 of the Periodic table, namely beryllium, magnesium, calcium, strontium and barium oxide. For convenience potters often include zinc oxide from Group 12. See ***Periodic table***.

Alkaline glazes

Glazes with a high content of alkalis. They still contain acidic oxides which form the glass but are usually low in the amphoteric oxides. For this reason they are usually runny. The alkalis present are the stronger alkalis: lithium, sodium, potassium and barium oxides.

Sodium and potassium oxides have high rates of expansion and contraction. Glazes which contain a high proportion of these oxides, especially sodium oxide, are likely to craze. Also these glazes are brittle and can be impractical without the more stabilizing effects of lead oxide and boron oxide. Lead oxide unfortunately modifies the interesting colours obtainable, but small amounts of boron oxide can be used in alkaline glazes to give elasticity. As explained under ***Glaze fit***, boron oxide also has the effect of decreasing the rate of expansion and thus correcting some of the worst crazing. Some crazing seems inevitable if the best colours are to be obtained. Some of the best known colours are: turquoise blue from copper, pink from cobalt, and blue from

iron. They are amongst the brightest and purest of pottery colours. Unfortunately even slight overfiring alters the colour. For example, copper blue loses its brilliance and with higher temperatures becomes green. Eventually with higher temperatures still the colour will be brown.

Alkaline glazes were used effectively on early Egyptian pottery and modelling and on Persian pottery and tiles. The bright sunlight of the area demanded a brightly-coloured ware. Some examples of these wares have been strongly weathered and the glazes have disintegrated. This serves as a reminder that alkaline glazes tend to be unstable. While copper oxide can give a good colour, its poisonous nature in unstable glazes must be overcome if alkaline glazes are to be used on functional wares. Potters primarily interested in colour and decorative effects will find that suitable results are obtained by the principle of keeping the aluminium oxide low in amount, and the alkali or the silica higher than would be found in normal glassy glazes. Vase by Delan Cookson. See also ***Colour plate 16*** and ***Recipe Appendix***.

Alluvial

Material deposited by a river. Clay is often an alluvial deposit. It has been removed by rainwater from its place of origin where it would have been called a primary or residual clay. It settles when the river runs slowly enough, e.g. on a flood plain or in a lake. It is now called a secondary or alluvial clay. In the process of being moved the clay is ground finer, is sorted by particle size and picks up impurities. Hence alluvial clays are usually more plastic, stickier, darker in colour and less refractory than residual clays.

Aluminium oxide

Corundum. Dialuminium trioxide. Aluminium sesquioxide. Al_2O_3. An important oxide in ceramics: it is second only to silica in importance. It is combined with silica in the clay crystal and it is aluminium oxide's presence that causes a flat crystal and thereby gives clay its plasticity. In glazes aluminium oxide is an intermediate oxide and serves to stabilize the combination of fluxes and glass-formers. It affects the stiffness of the molten glaze: too little and the glaze is too runny; too much and the surface remains pin-holed or cratered. It is rarely necessary to introduce pure aluminium oxide into a body or glaze. It is usually possible to introduce sufficient in compound minerals like china clay and feldspar.

Aluminium oxide occurs naturally as the crystalline mineral corundum. Large crystals, tinged by traces of chromium, cobalt, copper and iron are the precious stones ruby and sapphire. The aluminium oxide spinels are also gem stones. The pure crystal of aluminium oxide is second only to diamond in hardness of natural minerals. It is number 9 on Mohs' Scale. Impure corundum which is greatly stained by iron is called emery and is used as an abrasive. Aluminium oxide occurs in hydrated form as bauxite, gibbsite and diaspore. These are easier to crush but become the hard crystal aluminium oxide upon calcination.

From these can be produced a white powdered aluminium oxide and these are also the source of the metal aluminium which is important in light-weight alloys.

Igneous rocks invariably contain aluminium oxide. All the feldspars and feldspathoids are alumino-silicates in which aluminium oxide is combined with silica. This combination results in a slight off-balance of the overall electrical charge which is stabilized by the attraction of another element and the creation of an alkaline content such as potassium oxide or sodium oxide. Clay results from the decomposition of igneous rocks and the kaolinite (clay) crystal is an alumino-silicate with the balance of charges equated by hydrogen.

Aluminium oxide is an amphoteric oxide. It is capable of acting as an alkali or an acid or as a link between the two extremes. The interaction of alkali/acid with heat loosens the solid state structure thus resulting in ceramic fusion. At very high temperatures aluminium oxide acts as a flux. The melting point of silica can be lowered from 1710°C (3110°F) to 1545°C (2813°F) by the addition of 10% aluminium oxide. Aluminium oxide's own high melting point of 2050°C (3722°F) severely limits its activity as a flux at normal ceramic temperatures. It is usual therefore to consider aluminium oxide as an anti-flux. The term 'antiflux' is to be preferred to 'acid' because aluminium oxide is not a glass-former.

In most cases the amount of aluminium oxide in a body or glaze can be controlled by the use of alumino-silicates. The mineral with the highest aluminium oxide content is china clay, followed by the ball clays, feldspars and cornish stones. When pure aluminium oxide is introduced it is for a special purpose.

ALUMINIUM OXIDE IN BODIES. In bodies, powdered aluminium oxide acts as a refractory opener. It cuts down the drying shrinkage on the raw clay and makes the body able to withstand a higher temperature during firing. Its use is restricted by its price. It is a little more effective than silica (flint or quartz) but is more expensive. However in some vitrified bodies it may be preferred to silica on account of its different rate of thermal expansion.

In cases where a higher aluminium oxide chemical content is required in a body, the obvious long-term alteration would be in the choice of a more aluminous clay with a grog of similar material.

ALUMINIUM OXIDE IN GLAZES. In glazes, the function of aluminium oxide is to act as an intermediate oxide linking the alkaline and acidic oxides in stable glasses. Most glazes contain between 5% and 15% aluminium oxide and this is easily dissolved in the glaze. Amounts in excess of this, up to perhaps 25% of the glaze, separate from the molten mass during cooling to give crystalline opacity and a matt surface. Recrystallization of aluminium oxide happens quickly. Time is only a small factor in consideration of alumina matts. The usual consideration is of the aluminium oxide:silica molecular ratio. Proportions of 1:5 and downwards (1:4, 1:3) will result in crystalline glazes.

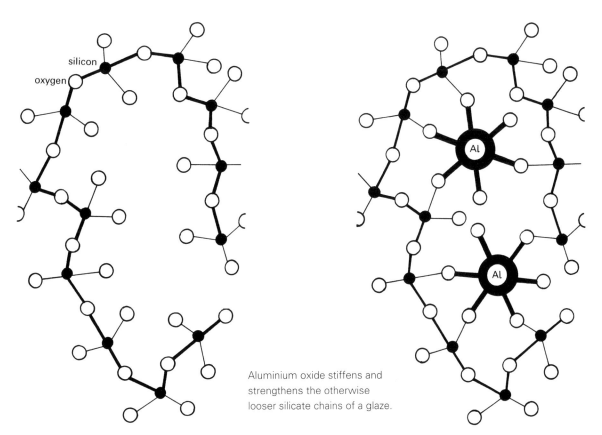

Aluminium oxide stiffens and strengthens the otherwise looser silicate chains of a glaze.

Alumina matts are not difficult to produce. The average transparent glaze can be matted by the addition of aluminium oxide powder. Alternatively the adjustment of a recipe towards the inclusion of more china clay, possibly in calcined form, or of more feldspar, will bring about a matting of the glaze surface and opacity due to crystallization.

Alumina matts can be very beautiful but they can also be very greyish, of poor opacity, pin-holed and crawled. They can be improved in opacity and whiteness by a small amount of zirconium oxide. The crystal quality can be improved by the use of alkaline matting agents like calcium, magnesium and zinc oxides but the addition of these does not give an automatic improvement because their fluxing action might give the opposite result from the one required. The amount of agent required must be established by tests.

In reverse consideration, the fluxing action of zinc oxide can be restrained by the use of aluminium oxide. Zinc matts can easily be very runny glazes because zinc oxide is an active flux. Aluminium oxide helps to hold the glaze during fusion although it is the combination of free silica with the zinc oxide which produces the matting crystals. A safe balance is found in the use of a calcined mixture of china clay and zinc oxide in equal amounts by weight. This matting agent provides aluminium oxide stability and zinc silicate crystals but the effect is not so exciting as zinc silicate crystals alone.

Alumina matts show the action of aluminium oxide as an anti-flux. Increasing the amount of aluminium oxide in a glaze raises the melting point. This effect is very useful and can be achieved simply by the addition of aluminium oxide (or aluminium hydrate) powder. Alternatively, the proportion of the china clay or feldspar in the glaze recipe can be increased.

When the glaze finally melts, the aluminium oxide will be dissolved in the molten glass, but as mentioned above, some aluminium oxide might crystallize out of solution during cooling. If crystallization is an undesirable side effect one should add silica as flint or quartz. Silica is only half as effective as aluminium oxide in its power to raise a melting point but it is cheaper and results in increased shine and transparency. A balance of aluminium oxide and silica is usually required and china clay is therefore used. While some slight opacity and matting of surface might be undesirable, a third effect of an increase in aluminium oxide is a stiffening of the glaze. This cannot be achieved in any similar way.

Aluminium oxide stiffens the molten glaze by hindering the loosening of silica's molecular chains. It introduces itself into these chains and by the six-fold co-ordination of aluminium it becomes widely involved. This is shown by the two diagrams: a loose silica chain and a chain stiffened by aluminium oxide.

Glazes containing little or no aluminium oxide are very runny. They melt quickly and run down the side of the pot. When cool, they often craze, are subject to attack by culinary acids and scratch easily.

The usual pottery practice is to introduce aluminium oxide by approximately 10% of china clay. This will give nearly 4% aluminium oxide to the glaze. If more aluminium oxide is required, more china clay can be added or substituted for some flint, quartz or feldspar until a balance has been found. Glazes can rarely absorb more than 25% china clay and this amount gives a crystalline matt. In this case the total aluminium oxide content of the glaze will be around 20%. Of this, 10% will have been provided by the china clay and 10% by the feldspars.

Lastly, the undesirable effects of too much aluminium oxide are a glaze's over-stiffness and over-stressed surface tension. Over-stiffness means that the glaze cannot smooth over once the surface has been broken. Craters resulting from gassing therefore show as pin-holes in the finished glaze. See **Run**. Coupling this with the extra surface tension of the viscous glaze results in the glaze crawling back from any breaks in the surface which might have occurred before firing. See **Crawling**.

Aluminium trihydrate
Aluminium hydrate. Al_2O_3. $3H_2O$.

Alumino-silicate
Name for any natural or processed compound with aluminium oxide and silicon oxide chemically combined and forming the main structure. Thus all clays, feldspars, feldspathoids and glazes are alumino-silicates.

Amakusa
Japanese equivalent to **Cornish stone**.

Amblygonite
Lithium alumino-fluophosphate. $Li.AlF.PO_4$. A lithium ore which has had some experimental use as a glaze material. It is an active flux and gives phosphoric opacity but can only be used in limited amounts because it causes blistering. It requires oxidation.

Amorphous
Having no definite form, that is, non-crystalline. Glazes are called amorphous glasses when they have not had time to crystallize on cooling.

One of the characteristics of amorphous solids is that they do not have definite melting points. Instead they have softening, melting or maturing ranges over which they slowly soften and eventually become liquid. Crystalline solids have a definite melting point below which they are solid and above which they are liquid.

A glaze is complex and contains many different substances which have different crystalline states. The melting range of a glaze is dictated by the different melting points of the constituents and their interaction on one another in eutectic combinations. The glaze becomes a liquid which on cooling becomes an amorphous solid.

Amphoteric
Intermediate. Capable of acting as either an acid or an alkali

according to whichever opposite is presented. In glazes the amphoteric substances are important as a bridge or link between the acidic glass-formers and the alkaline fluxes. They act as stabilizers sometimes giving valuable stiffening to the glaze and, if in excess of what can be dissolved, they often create crystals. The potter's most important amphoteric substance is aluminium oxide. See *Aluminium oxide*.

There are many oxides which in a wide use show amphoteric properties. However, in ceramic use they tend to act as either acid or alkali. They are listed and described under *Periodic table*. The important ones are boron, iron and chromium oxides which are sesquioxides (R_2O_3), and the opacifiers titanium, zirconium and tin oxides which are dioxides (RO_2).

Anagama

The inspiration to wood-firing potters which centres on the cult of the firing and products from the ancient Japanese anagama or cave kilns. High temperatures, up to $1300°C$ ($2372°F$), were achieved in wood-burning kilns in south China as early as the 3rd century BC. The techniques spread via Korea to Japan by the middle of the 5th century AD. The chamber of the kiln, the flue and the firemouth were dug into a sloping hillside. The main chamber could be 6 to 10 metres at a slope of $30°$ and was lined with mud and bamboo. The firing took several days.

In the tradition of anagama, wood-fired pots are now admired for the evidence they bear of searching flames, intense heat, incidental ash deposits and scars from surrounding pots.

Analysis

A method of describing a substance by its different parts. An analysis is made in two ways: qualitative, which determines only the nature of the parts present, and quantitative, which determines also the amount of each part present. The latter gives a percentage composition of the substance, but may group similar parts together for convenience.

An analysis provided by a supplier of potter's materials is always a convenient combination of qualitative and quantitative analyses and should be understood as such. This convention assists in making comparisons between different materials.

There are three main types of analysis. They describe the chemical content, the mineral content and the physical properties of a substance. The chemical content is given by chemical, ultimate and fired analyses of which the ultimate is the most useful to the potter. The mineral content is given by rational and proximate analyses which assist in appreciating the properties of the raw material. The physical properties listed in a mechanical analysis are those of grain and particle sizes.

Analyses assist assessment of a material in different ways but do not obviate the necessity for practical tests. In order to contrast the information given by the different analyses, an imaginary 'clay-like' material has been taken as an example. Six analyses are given of this sample material and comments made upon each analysis. The items and numbers are simplified to clarify the examples. The analyses are: chemical, ultimate, fired; rational, proximate; mechanical.

CHEMICAL ANALYSIS. Analysis of a material expressed in single elements or convenient compounds. For example an analysis of limestone could express the calcium carbonate as $CaCO_3$, as CaO and CO_2, or as Ca, C and O. The material to be analysed may be merely a mixture, e.g. iron oxide and silica, or may be a complex compound, e.g. cornish stone.

To be of value to the potter, the chemical analysis needs to be quantitative and preferably expressed as oxides. It then becomes, for his purpose, the same as an ultimate analysis and the potter is able to read this as compounds which give the material its fired character.

The items in a chemical analysis are usually listed in the order of abundance and the list often concludes with items which have been traced but not isolated or measured.

The following comparative example of a chemical analysis is given in single elements. The same sample given as oxides is seen under Ultimate Analysis (see below). This chemical analysis shows that the material does not contain the elements sulfur, fluorine and chlorine which could give gassing troubles.

Oxygen	51
Silicon	26
Aluminium	12
Iron	5·5
Potassium	2·5
Calcium	1
Hydrogen	0·75
Carbon	0·25
Titanium	
Magnesium	
Manganese	
Sodium	

ULTIMATE ANALYSIS. A type of chemical analysis expressed as proportions of metal and non-metal oxides that are involved in the ceramic fusion. Elements and oxides which do not enter the fusion may be grouped together as volatiles, sometimes called 'H_2O etc' or 'loss on ignition'. The oxides listed do not necessarily exist in the material but are arrived at from a previous analysis.

For example if the mineral cryolite Na_3AlF_6 is used in a glaze, the bonds between the three elements sodium, aluminium and fluorine are replaced with bonds to oxygen giving sodium oxide and aluminium oxide, and liberating the fluorine gas. The oxygen is taken from the kiln atmosphere and therefore enters the calculation as an extra. If 100 grams of cryolite are used, this takes up 22·9 grams of oxygen when it decomposes. Thus 100 grams of cryolite produces 44·3 grams of sodium oxide, 24·3 grams of aluminium oxide and liberates 54·3 grams of fluorine. This is a total of 122.9 grams. The potter is not interested in the amount of fluorine, provided that he can expel it from the kiln. His ultimate analysis would therefore read: Na_2O 44.3%, Al_2O_3 24.3%, loss 31.4%.

The word loss is quite literal. This represents a loss of weight which has been paid for. The others represent what is used. The ultimate analysis, therefore, is of use to the potter in comparing the cost of one material with another because it defines what will eventually enter the fusion.

Most books on ceramic calculations use the system of a conversion factor. This will be seen to coincide with the ultimate analysis after taking into account the acquired oxides. For example, the conversion factors for the sodium and aluminium oxides in cryolite are 0.443 and 0.243 respectively. These factors are multiplied by the weight of cryolite to discover the weight of oxides obtained.

The comparative example of an ultimate analysis shows how it can help in estimating the value as a glaze material.

SiO_2	59
TiO_2	1
Al_2O_3	19
Fe_2O_3	9
CaO	1
MgO	0.5
Na_2O	0.5
K_2O	2
Loss	8

In comparison with a feldspar, it is relatively high in aluminium oxide and low in silica. It will therefore be fairly refractory. The iron oxide content indicates that, when fused, it will be dark in colour. There are no details about volatiles. For these one must refer to the chemical analysis.

FIRED ANALYSIS. A type of chemical analysis in which all elements have been converted into ceramic oxides. Volatiles are discounted and the remainder is recalculated as a percentage. This analysis is used for calcined materials.

The comparative example of a fired analysis would be:

SiO_2	64.1
TiO_2	1.1
Al_2O_3	20.6
Fe_2O_3	9.7
CaO	1.1
MgO	0.6
Na_2O	0.6
K_2O	2.2

RATIONAL ANALYSIS. Analysis of a material expressed as proportions of theoretically pure kaolinite (called clay substance), quartz and either feldspar or mica. The rational analysis is ascertained by a combination of physical and chemical processes and therefore gives information about the raw material and some indication of its firing behaviour. It does not guarantee that the substances listed are present in the form given. For example, the alumino-silicates not calculable as clay substances are attributed to either feldspar or mica and theoretically combined with discovered bases. The truth is that both feldspar and mica are usually present but analyses containing both would be difficult to compare.

The rational analysis is more useful to the potter than the similar proximate analysis which is calculated entirely by theory from a chemical analysis. The rational analysis is of most use when coupled with a mechanical analysis and an ultimate analysis.

The following is the comparative example:

clay substance	52
feldspar	20
quartz	20

It shows that a large proportion of the material is a true clay substance and therefore the material can be expected to behave as a clay in terms of plasticity and drying shrinkage. Any material with over 45% clay substance on the feldspar basis of analysis or over 30% clay substance on the mica basis can be considered as a clay. Note that this analysis does not include the colouring oxides and free fluxes. For these reference must be made to the ultimate analysis.

PROXIMATE ANALYSIS. Analysis of a material expressed as proportions of kaolinite, feldspar and quartz. It is conceived entirely theoretically from the chemical analysis and is therefore not so accurate an indication of character as is a rational analysis.

The comparative example shows similar amounts to the rational analysis and would be considered in the same way:

kaolinite	49
feldspar	19
quartz	21

MECHANICAL ANALYSIS. Analysis of a material expressed as grain and particle sizes. The sizes may be coarse gradings expressed as mesh size or extremely fine particles measured in micrometres. When the analysis is all in fine measurements, it is called a particle size analysis.

Often the analysis states only what percentages are above and below a given size but more important are the analyses which define the largest and smallest sizes and the distribution in between. The value of this distribution is seen when choosing between two grogs of apparent similarity. They may both be graded as '60's to dust', meaning that all the material will pass through a 60's mesh. However one may be nearly all dust with a little coarse 60's grade of grog while the other contains an even amount of all sizes gradually varying from 60's to dust. These two grogs, apparently the same from description, would give different properties to a throwing clay.

If the mechanical analysis is coupled with a rational analysis, it will give the particle size of the different constituent minerals. For example, the free silica in a rational analysis of a clay is given a mechanical analysis of between 80's and 100's mesh size while all the clay substance, feldspar etc is graded finer. In this case it follows that sieving at 100's mesh will remove what is obviously a quartz sand. This is useful information if the clay is to be used both as a body clay and in a glaze. If the clay has to be sieved to remove roots etc, the quartz sand can be left in for texture and throwing character by using a sieve coarser than 80's. For the glaze, which may not require this amount of silica, the sand can be removed by sieving at 100's mesh or finer.

The comparative example gives a mechanical analysis for the material as a whole. This is expressed as percentages of material which are composed of particles of equivalent spherical diameter less than the given sizes.

0·1	1·0	10	25	50	100	micrometres
2	26	45	60	80	87	per cent

Retained by 100's mesh: 10%

From it one can deduce that although by the rational analysis the material appears to be a clay, this material is rather coarse. Only 26% of the material is of particle size below one micrometre and most potting clays would have between 30% and 70%. Also there is little ultrafine material below 0·1 micrometre. Most potting clays would have 10% to 30% of their material below this size. The 10% retained by 100's mesh is contrastingly low. The material would be easy to process for glazes and it could probably be used unprocessed in bodies.

Anatase

TiO_2. Natural titanium oxide. Anatase is one of the three oxide ores of titanium. The other two are rutile and brookite. They are chemically alike but different in crystal form.

Anatase crystals appear to be brown, bluish and black but they are free from the iron impurity which colours rutile. Anatase is a source of white titanium oxide. See ***Titanium oxide***.

Andesine

One of the plagioclase feldspars. It is mostly sodium feldspar but contains up to 49% lime feldspar.

Anhydrite

Natural calcium sulfate. $CaSO_4$. See ***Calcium sulfate***.

Anhydrous

Without water. The term usually implies that there existed some water chemically combined in the crystal structure, as in kaolinite, borax and aluminium hydroxide. The term anhydration is sometimes used to describe the ceramic change whereby clay is turned into pot by the removal of bound water.

Anorthite

Lime feldspar. $CaO.Al_2O_3.2SiO_2$. One of the twelve true feldspars. It is based upon calcium oxide which has a high melting point so that this feldspar has a melting point of 1550°C (2822°F). It could be used in glazes to introduce calcium oxide, aluminium oxide and silica but these can be more profitably introduced separately when their amounts can be adjusted.

Anorthite crystals are part of the devitrification occurring in lime matts. The lattice is a series of squarish rings each composed of oxygen tetrahedra. Half of the tetrahedra are built around aluminium and half around silicon. The rings form crooked chains. Between these chains are large holes which can accommodate calcium in eight-fold co-ordination as in other feldspars.

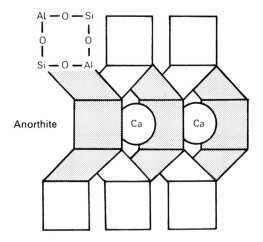

Anorthoclase

Sodium orthoclase. Sodium microcline. $NaKO.Al_2O_3.6SiO_2$. A feldspar which is chemically halfway between albite and orthoclase. There are two crystal structures. See ***Feldspars: types of***. The term anorthoclase is also used for any variable feldspar which cannot be considered 90% albite or orthoclase, and in this sense is synonymous with the potter's term 'mixed feldspar'.

Anorthosite

Plagioclase feldspar. A natural, white, ultrabasic mineral combination of anorthite and albite feldspars with good progressive fusion characteristics. It is particularly useful in fast-fire porcelain.

Anti-flux

A term used throughout this book to express the action of minerals or oxides in glazes and bodies. An anti-flux obviously does not act as a flux but hinders the fluxing action. Most refractory minerals hinder fluxing in the early stages of fusion but these are not described as anti-fluxes. Rather, the term has been reserved for action which deserves special consideration, e.g. calcium oxide which is a strong flux above 1100°C (2012°F) but hinders fusion before this temperature is reached. Although it is chemically alkaline and will become part of the molten glass at

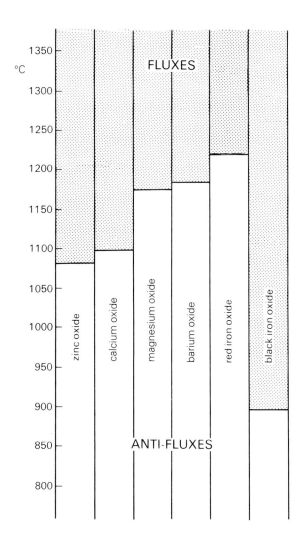

The presence of alkali causes the amphoteric oxide to present itself as the opposite—that is, as an acid or anti-flux. In the absence of powerful alkaline fluxes, the amphoteric oxides present themselves as alkalis towards the acidic silica. However, they usually require temperatures higher than the alkaline fluxes.

The case of the amphoteric red iron oxide is particularly interesting. Because it is such a common oxide and present in large amounts, its influence has been studied and the effects are often very noticeable. It should be remembered that red iron oxide is susceptible to even slight reduction which changes it partially to black iron oxide, a distinct flux. See **Iron oxide**.

The molecular structure of red iron oxide is similar to that of aluminium oxide. However it is less compact and therefore it is more susceptible to the effects of heat and interaction. It melts at a lower temperature than aluminium oxide and acts as a flux towards silica at temperatures over 1300°C (2372°F). In most glazes it begins to decompose at 1220°C (2228°F) creating some black iron oxide (FeO) and a spinel structure of $FeO.Fe_2O_3$ which has some alkaline tendencies. Therefore from this temperature upwards red iron oxide becomes progressively active as a flux even without deliberate reduction. See **Periodic table**.

Antimonate of lead

Naples yellow. $Pb_3(SbO_4)_2$. This is a poisonous creamish yellow paint pigment which was once used to introduce antimony oxide into lead glazes. See **Poison**.

Antimony oxide

Diantimony trioxide. Stibium sesquioxide. Sb_2O_3. An oxide with various properties which depend upon its combination with other oxides. Antimony is a semi-metal—that is, it behaves sometimes as a non-metal and sometimes as a metal. The oxide therefore has some properties which belong to the non-metal oxides and some properties which belong to the metal oxides. It is a glass-former. It is also a modifier and opacifier, as are many amphoteric substances, and it modifies lead oxide to produce a yellow colour.

Antimony occurs freely in nature but is usually mined as the ore stibnite (Sb_2S_3). China, Mexico and the USA are the main sources. The ore is roasted to oxidation or first melted and then oxidized. It is used in lead alloys and as a paint colourant. Antimony compounds are poisonous. See **Poison**.

In glazes which are rich in lead, 1% of antimony oxide will give a bright yellow colour. In a slip to be covered with a lead glaze, at least 8% of antimony oxide is required to give a yellow. It is more usual to introduce the antimony oxide into a glaze already combined with the lead oxide as antimonate of lead. Five per cent will be required and the glaze must also contain lead. The combination of lead and antimony oxides is sometimes referred to by its paint colour of Naples yellow. The addition of small amounts of iron oxide will make the colour more orange.

In leadless glazes, antimony oxide gives an opacity

temperatures below 1100°C, its inclusion in a glaze does little to improve fusion or lower the melting temperature. Small amounts (up to 1%) might have some fluxing action, as indeed all impurities would have, by virtue of the phenomenon called interaction. However, larger amounts could be correctly called anti-flux. Their inclusion at these lower temperatures is often to provide a more stable glass.

Similar effects will be experienced with magnesium oxide, barium oxide and zinc oxide. Each of these is a strong flux in its own temperature range.

Other anti-fluxes are the acidic opacifiers: the oxides of tin, titanium, zirconium and cerium. In very small amounts (up to 1%) they could give some fluxing by interaction but their normal action is against the fusion which they do not fully enter.

Amphoteric oxides also exhibit anti-flux properties. This is as one would expect of an oxide behaving as either alkali, acid or both. Arsenic oxide, antimony oxide, bismuth oxide, chromium oxide, red iron oxide and aluminium oxide each inhibit fusion when present in certain amounts at certain temperatures and in relation to other oxides.

As a general rule it could be said that amphoteric oxides act as anti-fluxes when more powerful fluxes are present.

because it does not dissolve. At least 10% is required. The result is not particularly exciting and is therefore considered an expensive way of producing an opaque glaze. Its redeeming quality is that it can sometimes modify or mellow an otherwise harsh colour.

There is a tendency for antimony oxide to volatilize at stoneware temperatures.

Anvil

A pebble or piece of wood used to beat pot walls. The anvil is used inside the pot, a beater or paddle is used outside. The process compresses the clay, thins the pot wall and enlarges the pot. To assist the clay to stretch without cracking, the anvil is often 'pecked'—that is, it has its surface covered with small chipped holes. See also ***Paddle and anvil***.

Apatite

$3Ca_3(PO_4)_2.Ca(Cl.F)_2$. Natural calcium phosphate and fluoride/chloride of igneous origin. The ultimate formula varies between $9CaO.P_2O_5$ and $3CaO.P_2O_5$. It is a source of calcium phosphate for bodies and glazes but the fluorine and chlorine often cause trouble. Bone ash is a better source.

Applied decoration

Usually refers to clay pieces which are added to pottery as decoration and therefore have no part in the functional forms of the pottery. See ***Sprigging***. The term is also used for transfer printed decoration.

The two photographs right show a detail of cut-out leaf shapes applied to a platter by Pauline Paterson and cut-out shapes making a coastal picture on a tile, 'Chough Rock' by Diana Barraclough.

Arabian lustre

A transmutation lustre.

Argonite

$CaCO_3$. See ***Calcite***.

Arenaceous rocks

Arenite. Sandstones. Rocks composed of layers of previously existing sand in which the grains have been cemented together by siliceous, calcareous or ferruginous solutions. Drifts of sand from these rocks occur in rivers and lakes of the locality and sometimes provide a source of opener giving interesting textures.

Argentite

Silver ore. Silver sulfide. Ag_2S.

Argillaceous rocks

Mudstones. Rocks composed of sedimented and compressed material of very fine particle size. Argillaceous rocks often contain a proportion of clay. The ground rock is not likely to constitute as a clay but may be useful in glazes. See also ***Albany slip***.

Ark

Storage tank for clay or glaze slips. The slip is prevented from settling by continuous mechanical stirring. The ark shown was at Cardiff College of Art. The guards have been removed to show the paddles.

Arsenic oxide

Diarsenic trioxide. White arsenic. As_2O_3. A glass-forming oxide which is often present in small quantities in glazes. It is rarely deliberately introduced by potters but is occasionally used for its amphoteric properties as a modifier. In small quantities it is capable of absorbing unwanted colouring in transparent glazes. However, it does not itself easily dissolve, and may give opacity at low temperatures. Arsenic compounds are poisonous.

Asbestos

Calcium magnesium silicate. $CaMg_3(SiO_3)_4$. Since the danger of asbestosis has been recognized, asbestos has been completely phased out and replaced by ceramic fibre. Old kilns might still have asbestos as door seals and electric element tail packing. See also *Silicosis* and *Health hazard*.

Asbolite

Asbolan. Cobalt ore containing manganese and iron impurities. It was the source of underglaze blue for Chinese porcelain. It is the only cobalt ore that is an oxide and safe to use. The other cobalt ores contain arsenic.

Ashes

The non-combustible remains of animal (bone) and vegetable matter used by the potter as a source of body and glaze fluxes. The commonest uses are of bone ash in bone china body, and vegetable and wood ashes in stoneware ash glazes. See also *Bone ash* and *Wood ash*.

The ashes provide fluxing and other oxides. The main oxides involved are those of calcium, phosphorus, potassium, sodium and aluminium with silica and many trace oxides. Although the original matter is organic (that is, with carbon being the most important element and hydrogen, nitrogen and sulfur also involved) the potter is seeking the inorganic content. Thus from a large bulk of wood the potter collects a relatively small amount of ash.

Even so, the ash is only a half-way stage between the original matter and the required oxides. Vegetable ashes contain carbon, sulfur, fluorine and chlorine. Bone ash contains carbon and fluorine. The burning of the original matter is not intended to, and in fact cannot completely, create a new material composed of required oxides and non-volatile compounds. The burning is a preparation, a controlled calcination, which removes the bulk of unwanted carbon, hydrogen and sulfur, and renders the material to a usable form. The elements involved have reached stable states for dry conditions as oxides, carbonates, sulfates, phosphates, chlorides and fluorides.

Some unwanted compounds can be removed by washing the ash but most will be removed during the firing when the presence of silicates will cause decomposition of the compounds to oxides and volatiles.

The accompanying chart shows how the original elements reach the ceramic fusions as oxides.

It will be seen from the chart that wood and vegetable ashes are the most complex. A few contain sufficient silica to fuse to a glass alone, but the majority of ashes contain mostly fluxing oxides. Wood and vegetable ashes are therefore considered as fluxes, especially for glazes. They also introduce colouring and crystallizers which give textures. See *Table 2*.

Many wood ashes contain a large proportion of monovalent oxides which give strong fluxing action at stoneware temperatures. If sufficient ash is used, and it is the glaze's only flux, it creates the decorative effect known as stringing. This is seen in the photograph of a stoneware jar by William Marshall.

Two example recipes are given for wood ash glazes to be fired at 1250°C (2282°F). The first is to go on biscuit:

feldspar	50
china clay	10
quartz	10
wood ash	30

The second recipe is for a slip-glaze and contains a second (divalent) flux to stabilize the fusion:

feldspar	30
ball clay	30
wood ash	30
whiting	10

Astbury

John and son Thomas. Early 18th-century Staffordshire potters who incorporated into their work various ideas which developed English earthenware. Starting with the precision of red stoneware, John Astbury used coloured sprigging, including some freely executed work, and covered this with the traditional lead glaze. The use of white clays for sprigging led the Astburys to make white ware and to add flint to the clay to make a denser body when fired. See **Creamware**.

Atmosphere

Air surrounding pottery during forming, drying and firing. A potter working with nature, rather than under controlled factory conditions, watches the weather to judge the drying qualities of the atmosphere and estimates the pressure and wind for the firing. See **Drying**. Kiln atmosphere is dealt with under **Oxidation** and **Reduction**.

Atom

The smallest part of an element that retains all the properties of that element and that can take part in a chemical combination or reaction. In a chemical formula, one atom of an element is represented by the chemical symbol. In a compound containing more than one atom of the same element the number of the atoms appears large before, or in small type, below and after the chemical symbol. For use, see **Formula: chemical**.

An atom consists of a positively charged nucleus at the centre with orbiting negatively charged electrons. The number of electrons determines the identity of the atom as an element and the number is called its atomic number. The electrons create an electron cloud surrounding the nucleus. This cloud has many symmetrical configurations given schematic representation as balloon-like extensions from and around the nucleus. The significance of these configurations is in explaining the way in which atoms absorb energy and the manner in which different atoms are bonded in molecular structures.

The power of an atom to combine with other different atoms is called its valency. This power depends upon the number of electrons and their theoretical allocation to layers or shells surrounding the nucleus. Each shell holds a particular number of electrons and so it is the filling or partial filling of these shells which dictates the atom's character. See **Valency**.

The potassium atom has 19 electrons, one of which is in the outer shell. The calcium atom has 20 electrons, two of which are in the outer shell. The next ten elements in ascending order with 21 to 30 electrons also have only one or two electrons in the outer shell because the extra electrons are packed into the shell beneath. This gives rise to a whole set of extra properties while retaining properties in common with potassium and calcium. The extra properties include more than one valency and the ability to change the colour of light. See **Periodic table** and **Colour**.

The first diagram shows a theoretical potassium atom. At the centre is the nucleus of 19 protons of positive charge with 20 neutrons which are electrically neutral. Around this nucleus revolve 19 electrons of negative charge. The atomic number of potassium is 19, the same as the number of electrons. Potassium is an active element because it is willing to part with the single outer electron. The other

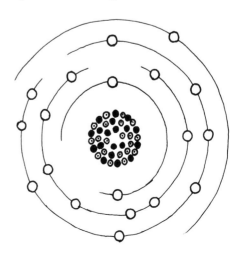

shells of electrons are complete and not easily disturbed. Having parted with this electron, the atom has an excess of positive protons and is attracted to a negatively-charged atom, probably the one to which it has given its negatively-charged electron.

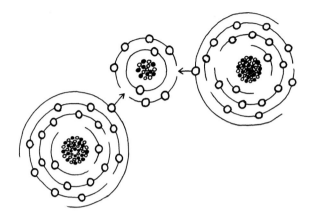

The second diagram shows how potassium quickly reacts with oxygen to form potassium oxide. Two atoms of potassium are required, each providing one electron, to complete the outer shell of 8 electrons on the oxygen atom. Therefore in one molecule of potassium oxide there are two atoms of potassium and one atom of oxygen and the chemical formula is K_2O.

Atomic number
Proton number. The number of electrons orbiting the nucleus of an atom. It is also the number of protons inside the nucleus. Atomic numbers are used to put the different elements in an order from which can be deduced the probable properties of the elements. See ***Periodic table***.

Atomic weight
Relative atomic mass. The average weight of an atom of a specified element. The weight is expressed as a number of atomic mass units (symbol A). The international system is based upon $12 A$ as the accepted weight for the carbon 12 isotope.

This edition retains the abbreviation AW for atomic weight. Atomic weights are used to calculate molecular weights. In turn, these are used to discover the effective number of molecules which will enter a ceramic fusion from a given recipe. See ***Formula: unity***.

Attic pottery
Athenian pottery produced during the classical period, 700BC to 400BC. The only rival pottery of the time was made at Corinth. The forms are expressions of intellect rather than of use of plastic media. In the most admired pieces, the potter showed complete control creating severe shapes on which detailed scenes were skilfully painted. It was the painter who signed the work and this ware is the earliest known signed pottery. At the same time there were productions with freer interpretations of form and decoration. These were mostly for export. The decoration of Attic pottery is invaluable as historical documentation of costume, rituals and legends.

Pottery painted with contemporary scenes had earlier been popular in the Mycenaean period, 1600BC to 1100BC, but had become outmoded by the introduction of the geometric style at the beginning of the Classical Iron Age. Interest in pictorial decoration, especially mural painting, was revived by trade with Egypt and western Asia. Attic pottery then developed through distinct stages known as Black-figure, Red-figure and White Ground, each style using greater control of painted detail than the preceding one.

The slips for the decoration were finely levigated and had additions of iron oxide and fluxes. They vitrified during firing, and were sometimes reduced to produce the darkest lustrous effects. Glazes were not used.

Automation
See ***Instrumentation***.

Autoreduction
Inglaze reduction. Local reduction. A method of reducing a glaze in an otherwise oxidized firing by including in the recipe an oxygen-greedy material which steals oxygen from the colouring oxides. For example, silicon carbide activated by the heat and action of the surrounding molten glaze seeks oxygen to become silicon oxide (silica) and carbon dioxide. The oxygen is taken from the iron and copper oxides and to a lesser extent from manganese and chromium oxides. This can be expressed as:

$$SiC + 4CuO \longrightarrow SiO_2 + CO_2\uparrow + 4Cu$$

If the reducing agent is finely ground, it will be thoroughly dispersed through the glaze and close to colouring metal oxides which will thus be reduced. The amount of agent required is not large, typically less than 1% of the glaze recipe. Naturally the glaze composition also has a large effect upon the colour with this process. Stabilizers are used as with reduction firings. See **Copper oxides: reduction**.

Silicon carbide (SiC) is the most used autoreduction agent. Also used and being developed are: silicon (Si); silicon monoxide (SiO); graphite (C); boron silicide (B_4Si); aluminium (Al). Recent work by Richard Slade in the UK using silicon proves that excellent reduction results are obtainable in both earthenware and stoneware including earthenware lead glazes. He also shows that oxidized and reduced effects can be simultaneously produced on a single ceramic piece fired in oxidation. Copper reds and iron celadons are achievable and manganese oxide and chromium oxide can be given a bluish cast. Silicon has an advantage over silicon carbide in that it does not create bubbles as a side effect. See **Silicon carbide**.

Aventurine glazes

Aventurine is a feldspar containing tiny haematite crystals that catch the light and give it sparkle. Aventurine glazes contain tiny crystals usually associated with iron or other colouring oxide. These crystals catch the light and sparkle with varying colour. The crystals are not large enough to be seen individually. They are the beginnings of crystallization, which takes place on cooling when there is more colouring oxide than will remain dissolved in the glaze.

For aventurine effects, lead glazes, low in aluminium oxide, are the most popular. Some alkaline glazes which are low in aluminium oxide give aventurines at stoneware temperatures. Tests should be made with increasing amounts of colouring oxide to find the correct addition. Too little will not give any crystals. Too much will give crystals which make the glaze opaque and matt. The speed of cooling also influences the crystal growth. Some aventurine glazes contain as much as 30% red iron oxide. See also **Devitrification**, **Galena** and **Crystalline glazes**.

The following recipe used by Beatrice and Robert Pearson uses soluble material in order to achieve the necessary alkaline balance. It fires between 1200°C and 1230°C (2192°F and 2246°F) and is very fluid.

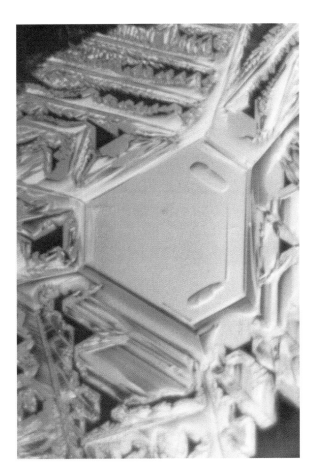

cornish stone	33
china clay	6
flint	8
gerstley borate	6
true borax	13
sodium bicarbonate	18
red iron oxide	16

The photograph shows an enlargement (×250) of aventurine crystals.

Azurite

Natural basic copper carbonate. $2CuCO_3.Cu(OH)_2$. A weathered ore of copper which is easily identified by its bright turquoise-blue colour. It occurs with malachite (the green ore) and can be found amongst the wash-out from mines. See **Malachite** and **Copper ores**.

B

Bag

Bag wall. The wall which divides the combustion space from the pot space in a kiln. Its purpose is to deflect the flame as it enters the chamber and thereby stop the creation of a hot spot amongst the pots nearest the heat source.

Baidunze

Petuntse. Chinese name for the equivalent of cornish stone. It is a variable feldspathic mineral and was used to fuse the white clay, kaolin, in the making of porcelain. Baidunze is a corruption of the Chinese for 'white bricks', in which form it was transported from the quarry to the pottery. This is similar to the English origin of the term 'ball clays' which were transported in balls. See **Cornish stone**.

Baiting

Periodic kiln stoking.

Ball clay

Blue clay. A highly plastic clay, usually light in colour, which is the basis of many potting bodies. Alone, it tends to be too fine and slippery for use, but additions of sand, grog and coarser and less-plastic clays actually improve workability. Ball clay is a general term for many clays. It comes from the practice of digging the clay out of the open pits in convenient blocks of about 12 kg, called balls. These clays are always plastic, are mostly cream and vitrify in the 1100°C to 1200°C (2012°F to 2192°F) range.

Ball clays are usually accepted as once-removed kaolins. They contain a high proportion of kaolinite, the pure clay mineral, but also contain free silica, and the oxides of potassium, sodium, calcium and magnesium as mica and associated cations. The presence of these fluxes brings down the vitrification range of the kaolinite to 1100°C to 1200°C. A few ball clays will withstand 1300°C (2372°F) and a few actually deform before 1100°C (2012°F).

Fortunately few ball clays have collected iron oxide and titanium oxide as impurities and therefore most are cream burning.

Mention should be made of blue and black ball clays which colours describe the raw clay. This is no indication of the fired colour. The blue and dark grey colours are due to the presence of carbonaceous matter. The black ball clays were once considered to be more plastic than the white. It is true that some carbonaceous matter improves plasticity. All ball clays, however, contain some carbon. It is usually less than 1% which gives no difficulties in the firing. Some contain as much as 3% which must be carefully burned out during the firing. See **Black core**. Ball clays, excellent in other respects, have been reported with 10% carbonaceous matter. Such clays must be difficult to fire but may be acceptable for high temperature blends which can be soaked and remain 'open' at 750°C (1382°F) to burn out the carbon.

Ball clays have extremely fine particles, many of colloidal size. This accounts for their plasticity. It also means that suspensions of ball clay settle very slowly. Ball clay slurries are also difficult to dry off to plastic consistency. As the water moves out from between the particles, these are pulled together to form a waterproof layer through which further water cannot pass. Without admixtures of other coarser materials and the use of excessive doping, it is impossible to filter-press a ball clay. Ball clays are therefore sold 'plastic as dug' or in dry powder state. The powder state is often airfloated to allow heavy foreign particles to fall out, a process similar to winnowing but involving the collection of the lightest material.

The fine particle size and purity of the clay content means that ball clays respond well to treatment with deflocculants and flocculants. Ball clays are an important addition to casting slips to provide fluidity with bulk and green strength.

Plastic ball clays contain a large percentage of moisture which is necessary to surround all the particles. Water can account for 25% to 35% of the weight of a plastic ball clay. This is a considerable bulk to eliminate in drying so it is not surprising that ball clays contract about 10% (linear) in drying from plastic to dry. They also shrink a further 10% to 15% (linear) in firing to vitrification.

The British ball clays are located in the south-west of England and are said to have originated with the granites of the south-west peninsula. They were deposited in their present locations in the Cainozoic Era some 30 to 70 million years ago. In one pit there are a number of very different ball clays in overlapping lenses or veins. They are documented by number and by general names like 'top', 'rough' or 'brokes bottom', which become their specific trading names.

The photographs show the strata of an open-cast ball clay pit and digger and dumper excavation. Both pits are owned by WBB Minerals, of South Devon, who supplied the photographs.

Ball clays are often described as aluminous or siliceous. Aluminous ball clays contain 30% to 40% aluminium oxide. Siliceous ball clays contain 60% to 80% silica. A comparison of a group of ball clay analyses will show a wide variety of chemical composition. The following ultimate analysis shows the ranges:

SiO_2	40–80%
TiO_2	2%
Al_2O_3	15–40%
Fe_2O_3	6%
MgO	1%
CaO	1%
K_2O	3%
Na_2O	1%
Loss	5–10%

Ball clays are often included in glazes to assist suspension

of the slop and provide adhesion before firing. They introduce aluminium oxide and silica as does china clay but they are not so white. While an ultimate analysis is desirable when calculating a glaze's unity formula, the following unity formulae for ball clays will be found reasonably accurate for small amounts. See also ***Particle size***.

Average ball clay: MW. 387 $Al_2O_3.4SiO_2.2H_2O.0·1K_2O$
Aluminous ball clay: MW. 267 $Al_2O_3.2SiO_2.2H_2O.0·1K_2O$
Siliceous ball clay: MW. 696 $Al_2O_3.9SiO_2.2H_2O.0·2K_2O$

Ball mill
Pebble mill. A grinding mill used for the fine grinding of glaze and colour minerals. The balls are natural or manufactured pebbles which fall onto one another and thus grind the materials.

The drawing shows the ball mill manufactured by Cobam Ltd.

The mill consists of a steel drum which rotates about a horizontal axis. It is lined with stone, porcelain or steel plates and is charged and emptied through a sealing door in the side. The mill, containing a charge of minerals, pebbles, airspace and usually water, is rotated at a critical speed which tumbles the pebbles in a continuous cascade. The drum may be up to 2·5 m in diameter.

Small mills employ a porcelain jar instead of a steel drum. See ***Jar mill***.

Barilla
The ash from burnt glasswart marsh plants. It was used as a source of sodium oxide for glass-making during the 18th century. Sea plants yield sodium carbonate upon being burnt. The sodium is derived from the sodium salts in the sea. Land plants yield potassium carbonate and calcium phosphate. See ***Sodium carbonate***.

Barium carbonate
$BaCO_3$. A barium compound occurring as the mineral witherite. Barium carbonate is also prepared from the

mineral barytes by precipitation. Both are used in glaze recipes to introduce barium oxide. In glaze slops the precipitated carbonate is preferable because it is lighter and more easily suspended. It is also introduced into slips to combat the scum which occurs on unglazed ware. See **Poison**.

In glazes barium carbonate is used because it is relatively insoluble whereas the desired barium oxide reacts with water. It is intended that, during firing, the carbonate decomposes to become the required barium oxide and carbon dioxide. Barium carbonate is the most difficult of the carbonates to decompose. It is strangely necessary to use some reduction in order to deprive the carbonate of some of its oxygen. Thus deprived, an unstable compound is produced which breaks down, releasing the desired oxide. The equation is:

$$BaCO_3 + CO \xrightarrow{900°C} BaCO_2 + CO_2\uparrow$$

(stable)   carbon   (unstable)
         monoxide $\hookrightarrow BaO + CO\uparrow$
                               barium oxide

The temperature required for this decomposition is at least 900°C (1652°F). The reduction therefore comes after the usual period of oxidation of carbonaceous matter. Reduction need not be heavy but temperature alone will not suffice to effect the change. If the carbonate is not decomposed, it becomes involved in the melt as an opacifier with anti-flux properties. This gives matt effects but not the matt effects associated with the oxide. In prolonged firings and active fusions, the carbonate will slowly dissolve and decompose. The small silky crystals promoted by barium oxide will then appear upon cooling if the balance of the glaze is conducive to their growth.

The following is a barium carbonate oxidized glaze for 1250°C to 1260°C (2282°F to 2300°F) used by Emmanuel Cooper.

feldspar	35
china clay	5
flint	5
barium carbonate	40
zinc oxide	15

Barium carbonate is varyingly reported as soluble and insoluble. It can be accepted as insoluble in pure water and hence can be used in glaze batches. However, glaze slops that contain a flocculant to deter sedimentation are slightly acidic. Some barium carbonate will become soluble in such a suspension as it exchanges its acid radical with the flocculant. The previously soluble flocculant will be precipitated as the insoluble carbonate. For example:

$$CaCl_2 + BaCO_3 \longrightarrow BaCl_2 + CaCO_3\downarrow$$

calcium   barium   barium   calcium
chloride   carbonate   chloride   carbonate
(soluble)   (insoluble)   (soluble)   (precipitate)

The barium chloride will continue the action of the flocculant though weaker than the calcium chloride. Only a small amount of barium carbonate is involved and providing water is not siphoned off, the compound will produce barium oxide in the final glaze. The calcium compound will act as a flux. The amount is too small to be noticed.

This same process of anionic radical exchange is used with clay for two different reasons: to get rid of scum on unglazed fired ware and to prepare clays which are to be used for casting slips.

Soluble calcium salts, and to a lesser extent magnesium salts, crystallize on the surface of ware during drying. If these crystals are broken by handling, the finger-prints show after firing either as white prints or as dark over-fluxed prints. This is called scum. The commonest salt is calcium sulfate and this can be rendered insoluble by the addition of barium carbonate. See **Scum**. The radical exchange equation is:

$$CaSO_4 + BaCO_3 \longrightarrow BaSO_4 + CaCO_3\downarrow$$

calcium   barium   barium   calcium
sulfate   carbonate   sulfate   carbonate

The barium sulfate remains in solution but it does not cause scum. Barium chloride ($BaCl_2$) can also be used.

Clays to be used for making casting slips must not contain natural flocculants that act against the required action of the deflocculants. Clays which contain calcium sulfate, which is a strong flocculant, are therefore difficult to make into casting slips. The addition of barium carbonate effects the exchange previously described. The resulting calcium carbonate is insoluble and barium sulfate is a less active flocculant. Clays which are intended for use in casting slips are often treated in this way so that deflocculation can take place without interference from soluble salts. The weak action of barium sulfate can be neutralized by the sodium deflocculants. See **Deflocculation** and **Casting slips**.

Barium compounds

To introduce barium oxide into bodies and glazes it is usual to use barium carbonate. However, the soluble barium sulfate has been used in paste bodies and paste glazes. The compounds used by the potter are:

barium oxide	BaO
barium carbonate	$BaCO_3$ (mineral: witherite)
barium sulfate	$BaSO_4$ (mineral: barytes)
barium chloride	$BaCl_2$
barium hydroxide	$Ba(OH)_2$ (mineral: baryta)

Barium oxide

BaO. An auxiliary flux in earthenware frits and high-temperature stoneware glazes. It is also introduced for its crystallizing properties which give excellent satin matts. Barium compounds should be treated with care because they are poisonous. Barium oxide is soluble in water and is introduced into glazes via a frit or in barium carbonate.

Barium oxide does not occur as a mineral. It is an unstable oxide which reacts with moisture. The minerals of barium are barytes (barium sulfate), witherite (barium carbonate) and barytocalcite (carbonate with calcium). The metal barium quickly tarnishes in the air. It melts at 850°C (1562°F) but the melting point of barium oxide is 1923°C (3493°F). The oxide is refractory and enters fusion by virtue of its instability and hence interaction with silica. Its instability is one of attraction rather than dispersion so it is resistant to reduction. Its bond with other compounds is strong once formed. Its bond with carbon dioxide in the compound barium carbonate ($BaCO_3$) is so strong that the carbonate does not decompose with heat alone but requires some reduction. See **Barium carbonate**. Potters have been known to use barium sulfate in paste glazes. It is not to be recommended because sulfurous fumes are released during firing.

Barium oxide is the heaviest of all the divalent oxides used as fluxes, and as such it is often considered a high-temperature substitute for lead oxide. It has similar properties of body attack and high shine, but it cannot be used as the only flux, as can lead oxide.

Barium oxide's fluxing action is dependent upon its method of introduction into the glaze and the other glaze constituents. Like calcium, magnesium, strontium and zinc oxides, the other divalent oxides, barium oxide is proportionately most active by interaction and when it is only a small percentage of the total glaze. Increased amounts give no advantage for its use; calcium oxide gives more dependable results. However, there is an optimum point at which it forms beautiful small crystals during cooling. These give a satin-like matt surface. It is for this matt surface rather than the fluxing action that barium oxide is usually required.

The fluxing action of barium oxide is unusual. It will act as a flux for all temperatures, if it is in a frit with sodium and potassium oxides. Such frits need first to have been fused above 1200°C (2192°F). Without this close association in a frit, barium oxide as a flux is limited to temperatures above 1175°C (2147°F).

Below 1175°C barium oxide retains its crystalline form and opacifies the glaze. Up to 20% barium carbonate in the recipe gives opacity and matt surfaces with increasing form-ation of crystals. At the higher temperatures the crystalline matt is created by devitrification. The two effects are slightly different. In both cases, boron tends to destroy the matt surface. Preferred fluxing oxides are of potassium, sodium and calcium. See **Colour plate 16** and **Recipe Appendix**.

Bars

Pyrometric bars. Short rods composed of the same materials as cones and designed to bend after subjection to determined amounts of heat-work. They are shaped with sections both triangular and square, and are approximately 2·5 cm long. They are produced for use with the Dawson Kiln-Sitter (*trade name*). See **Instrumentation**. Some potters use the small cones as horizontal bars.

In kilns with limited space or inconvenient shelf position, a U-shaped piece of high temperature insulation brick can be cemented at the inside of the spyhole. This supports the ends of a single bar which is visible across the hole.

Bullers bars (*trade name*) now replace Holdcroft bars in the UK. Bullers bars are 5·7 cm long and of near-square section. There are 42 bars in the range. These are related to temperatures from 590°C to 1525°C (1094°F to 2777°F) when heated at 80°C per hour (144°F/hr). See **Table 9** and also **Cones**.

Barytes

Barite. Calk or calk-stone. Barium sulfate. $BaSO_4$. The commonest and most important barium mineral. It is found associated with lead ore and in veins of calcite and fluorspar where it can be identified by its weight. It is much heavier than the two other 'spars' and is known as 'heavy spar'. It is variously coloured and crystalline. Sometimes there are large flat crystals which form rosettes and are known in America as desert roses.

Josiah Wedgwood was probably the first to realize the

potential of barium oxide as a body and glaze constituent. In 1775, after some ten thousand trials, he successfully produced his Jasper ware which was 40% barytes.

Barytocalcite

$BaCO_3.CaCO_3$. Double carbonate of barium and calcium. This is an idealized mineral found in association with lead ores. In practice it is a variable replacement of barium by calcium and given local names like alstonite $((Ba,Ca)CO_3)$. See **Poison**.

Basalt

A basic (alkaline), extrusive, igneous rock—that is, one which contains between 45% and 55% silica contained in plagioclase feldspars and mafic minerals. There is no free silica. Basalt originated as a flowing lava sheet which, as it cooled, contracted into compact masses often in hexagonal columns as in the illustration.

Basalt is very hard, heavy, of fine crystalline texture and a dark grey colour from its iron content. It melts to a fluid glass between 1150°C and 1250°C (2102°F and 2282°F) mainly because of its calcium oxide content. It requires further feldspar and free silica to turn it into a practical glaze which will always be dark in colour. See also **Mafic minerals**.

Basalt is very difficult to grind but powder can sometimes be obtained from road-metal quarries. Alternatively, chips of basalt can be used for decorative effects when melted on to tiles fired horizontally.

Basalt ware

A black unglazed stoneware originated by Josiah Wedgwood. In this ware approximately 50% of clay is vitrified and coloured by 50% of iron and manganese oxides. See also **Black**.

Base

Alkali. A chemistry term for a substance which is the opposite of an acid and reacts to neutralize the acid and form a salt. Bases are metal oxides and they are listed under alkali. The term 'base' is often avoided in this book in favour of 'alkali' which, although strictly narrower than the term base, is less open to confusion. A base to a potter is more often a part of a pot.

Similarly, the term 'basic' is avoided in its scientific sense and the term 'alkaline' used instead. Basic often means fundamental or a starting point for further work to the potter considering glaze recipes.

Bat

Batt. Batten. A common word with many meanings in the pottery. It implies a flat surface and is used for kiln shelf, pot board, detachable wheel head and pot beater. Shelves are mentioned under **Refractory**. Beaters are described under **Paddle and anvil**.

Pot boards are made from any suitable material which is slightly porous. Plain wood and wood composition boards are popular. Dense substances like glazed tiles or painted boards do not allow the base of a pot to dry and are one of the causes of base cracks. Wheel-head bats need not be porous if they are only a means to throwing and moving pots. If pots are allowed to dry on the bats then the bats should be slightly porous. Chipboard and waterproof plywood are best. If pots are left on the bat to dry they should first be separated from the bat by a wire otherwise base cracks may occur in drying or later in the firing.

Most potters use round wheel-head bats and stick these to the wheel head with soft clay or locate them by means of studs in the wheel head and corresponding holes in the bats. A central stud and one other has been found to be the best method. Alternatively, square bats can be located within a framework of similar material glued or otherwise fastened to the wheel head. The drawing is of the popular Lotus wheel head (*trade name*). Waterproof plywood discs fit into a recessed head with a location key.

Also illustrated is a bat of fired clay. It is held in both hands by its loop handle and used for batting out sheets of clay for press-moulding.

Bat wash

A slurry of refractory material used to prevent kiln furniture from fusing together or pots fusing to shelves or to their lids when fired in position. The ideal wash is one which is not affected by interaction with shelves, furniture or the ware during firing. It should also be relatively cheap, and should be easy to make up into a wash which stays put during setting, and, lastly, it should easily wash off the foot rims, lids etc of the finished ware.

A mixture of aluminium trihydrate two parts, china clay one part will be found excellent for most purposes both oxidized and reduced. A flint wash was popular until the hazards from silicosis were understood. See **Silicosis**. Aluminium oxide, zirconium silicate and sillimanite are effective but expensive. Salt glaze does not always need a wash, depending upon the body temperature. If one is used, any combination of aluminium oxide and silica is avoided and pure aluminium oxide or pure silica is used. Also lime washes of whiting and water are used for salt glaze and in some cases a few thicknesses of newspaper on the kiln shelf gives sufficient lime (calcium oxide) to prevent the pots from sticking.

Batch

Mill batch. Charge. Body batch or glaze batch refers to the total of the materials weighed out to a recipe for that particular mixing.

Bauxite

Aluminium hydrate. $Al_2O_3.2H_2O$. Mineral source of aluminium and its oxide. It is used as a bat wash etc both raw and calcined and is sometimes added to glazes to give mattness. Variations of hydration are called diaspore ($Al_2O_3.H_2O$) and gibbsite ($Al_2O_3.3H_2O$).

Beading

Excessive crawling in which the glaze rolls back on itself to form a series of globules on an otherwise bare pot. See **Crawling**.

Beating

See **Paddle and anvil**.

Bell beaker

An early type of Bronze Age pot. The Beaker Folk were bronze traders who traded throughout the western sea approaches of Europe from 2000BC. It has been suggested that they also traded in beer and that their beakers were the first beer mugs.

The beakers have a small, flat base, swelled body and conical top which is as wide as, or wider than, the rest of the pot. Some of the beakers have handles. They hold from one to four pints. The term bell beaker is reserved for the pots of the original traders. The pots of the later settlers are simply called beakers. The illustrations show a beaker and part of the corded decoration.

Bellarmine

Grey beard or Bartmanner. A salt-glazed beer bottle with a relief bearded face on the neck. All sizes were made from about 15 cm to 60 cm. Bellarmines originated at Cologne in the mid-16th century and were made in the Rhineland, in Flanders and in London up to the end of the 17th century. It is said that the face was modelled deliberately to insult Cardinal Bellarmine but this is not so. Bottles with modelled faces, like jugs with faces, were made long before the Cardinal lived. The name was a nickname to describe the bottle and insult the Cardinal, though a likeness may have been attempted on later work. It is possible that the first Bellarmines made in Britain were made by John Dwight.

Bentonite

A highly plastic clay originating in the decomposition of volcanic ash. It is extremely fine and can be dispersed widely through bodies and glazes, in which it is used to impart plasticity and an ability to keep a glaze slop in suspension. Up to 2% can be added to bodies and will improve plasticity. Up to 1% can conveniently be added to glazes when the slop water is also made slightly acidic by the addition of calcium chloride solution. With the increasing interest in raw glazing, bentonite has become an important glaze material. As much as 10% is used in glazes often replacing some or all of the china clay. Its sticky nature holds the glaze on the raw ware yet allows thorough drying through the flocculated structure.

Decomposition of igneous rocks under different humidities and pressures resulted in the formation of different silicates. The most important to the potter is kaolinite of the kaolinite group. Kaolinite is the mineral crystal of clay. Next in importance is probably the feldspar

group with free silica (quartz). Not often mentioned is the montmorillonite group which has a structure similar to kaolinite and produces mixtures of high plasticity. Bentonite is one of the montmorillonites and is often called a clay, although strictly it is not one.

It is usually accepted that bentonite decomposed from volcanic ash and occasionally from lava. Kaolinites and montmorillonites occur in the same decompositions but there is always an overwhelming dominance by one or the other. Most of the world's bentonite comes from Central North America near Fort Benton but there are deposits in other parts of the world, notably in Italy and South Africa.

The difference between a kaolinite and a montmorillonite is in the molecular structure. Both have layers but in kaolinite the repetition unit is gibbsite-silica and in the montmorillonite it is silica-gibbsite-silica. See diagram.

In kaolinite the layers are held together by weak hydroxyl bonds from the gibbsite of one layer to the silica of the next (H in diagram). In montmorillonite there are no hydroxyl bonds available on the outside of the layers. The outsides are composed of the oxygen atoms of the silica. The layers therefore have no hold on one another and can slide past one another. This gives the montmorillonite mineral, bentonite, its greasy feel. Bentonite is used as a lubricant in well drilling. Its swelling properties, described next, are useful to seal off wet porous rocks which are encountered.

Because there is no bond between the layers it is possible for water to enter and divide the particles. This happens

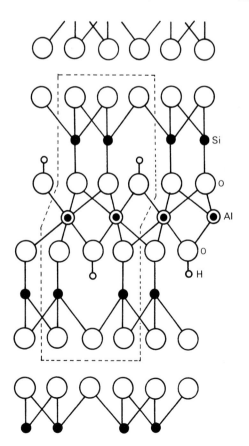

when bentonite is put into water. The particles of bentonite separate to colloidal size and in some cases almost down to molecular units. The result is that bentonite can absorb a vast amount of water. One kilogram of bentonite can accommodate 2·5 litres of water and still not be liquid. Compare this with ball clay, 1 kg of which with 1·4 litres of water makes an average slip. Bentonite swells and produces not a clay but a greasy mass with obvious lubricating properties. Bentonite is one of the minerals in fuller's earth which is used for cleansing by absorption of grease, dye etc.

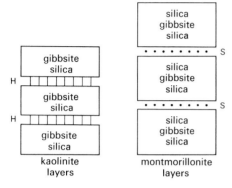

kaolinite layers

montmorillonite layers

The idealized bentonite would have the formula $Al_2O_3.4SiO_2.H_2O$. Usually some of the silicon has been replaced by aluminium. This leaves a deficiency in positive charge. The deficiency is made up by the presence of sodium or calcium cations on the surface of the layers. These provide exceptionally weak bonds joining the layers (S in diagram). Sodium cations actually keep the layers at a wide distance apart which helps water to penetrate quickly. The best bentonites for pottery purposes are therefore sodium bentonites. The calcium bentonites can be converted into sodium bentonites by cation exchange.

The sodium bentonites are obviously deflocculated and provide excellent lubricants to improve plasticity of clays. The addition of up to 6% of bentonite to a clay of low plasticity will improve plasticity but it does not necessarily improve the workability range. See **Workability range**. Stoneware bodies can be prepared from refined fireclays by the addition of 2% to 3% bentonite. If this is added at blunging stage, then it will assist in the flow properties for sieving and levigation. However it will increase the time required for settling.

Porcelain bodies which contain little other plastic material, and are to be used for throwing, require 6% of bentonite. A perfectly white quality of bentonite will be required. Some bentonites vitrify or even melt above 1200°C (2192°F) and discolour white bodies.

Bentonite has a high cation exchange capacity. This means that it reacts dramatically to the presence of acids and alkalis. The presence of an acid induces strong polarity in the particles producing a flocculated or cardhouse structure. This is useful in glaze slops to inhibit the tendency of larger and heavier particles, like flint and lead frit, to settle out of suspension. Just 1% or 2% of the recipe is sufficient bentonite and this can be flocculated with calcium chloride solution. When an amount of bentonite powder is wetted it expands into large slippery flocs which do not blend into a glaze slop. It is therefore necessary to combine first the dry bentonite with the other dry ingredients before adding the water. Care must be taken not to create a dust. See **Health hazard**.

Beryllium oxide

BeO. One of the alkaline earth oxides which acts as a high-temperature flux. It has been used in some porcelain glazes and as an opacifier and modifier at lower temperatures. Alone, it is a refractory with a melting point at around 2500°C (4532°F). It is practically insoluble in water but is poisonous. As a flux it must rank as one of the most expensive, costing fifty times as much as calcium oxide which is more effective.

Beryllium oxide is found only in beryl, the mineral silicate ($3BeO.Al_2O_3.6SiO_2$) of igneous origin. Beryl stained with chromium is called emerald. A bluish variety is called aquamarine. See also **Poison**.

Bi

Bis. Di. A term used in chemical nomenclature to indicate a combination with two atoms or two molecules. For example, carbon dioxide (CO_2) has two atoms of oxygen: lead bisilicate ($PbO.2SiO_2$) has two molecules of silica.

Bianco sopra bianco

(White on white.) Italian name for a style of maiolica which was further used on Bristol Delft. The colour of the common white tin glaze had degenerated to a dirty colour by the use of cheaper ingredients. Cobalt oxide had been used to enliven the white effect but this only resulted in a pale greenish blue for the commonest wares. By making particularly white and opaque glaze and painting this onto the standard white glaze an effective light decoration was achieved and was used successfully on plate borders. In an attempt to enhance the effect, the background glaze was further darkened, and the charm and delicacy of the style was thus lost.

Binder

Glaze binder. See **SCMC** and **Suspender**.

Biotite

See **Mica**.

Bisc

Bisque. Hard biscuit. Unglazed fired pottery. The words bisc and bisque are used to imply the industrial method of a high temperature firing of the unglazed ware to be followed by a lower temperature glaze firing. The individual potter uses it in relation to raku pots which are separately biscuited to a temperature higher than that to which the raku glaze is fired.

The advantages of bisc firing are:

1. The ware is harder and easier to handle for glazing.
2. Firing cracks are likely to show and money and time are thus saved in not glaze firing these pieces.
3. Any warpage arising from shrinkage can be controlled by setting the pieces in sand during bisc firing.
4. Shrinkage is complete and the glaze firing can be more economically set.

The disadvantage is that with coarse clays it is difficult to get a sufficiently thick layer of glaze to adhere to the ware because the porosity of the ware is very low. In this context, most clays used by individual potters would be considered coarse because the comparison is with industrial clays.

Biscuit

To fire ware unglazed in preparation for glazing; also the unglazed fired ware. It is an overall term but individual potters imply the use of a temperature lower than the following glaze firing and use the term bisc or bisque for the industrial method of high-temperature biscuit firings. Meaning literally baked twice, it comes from the early 17th-century introduction from France of tin glaze with its necessity for an extra firing. Previous to this the British potter had used only a single firing of raw glazed ware.

The advantage of biscuit over bisc is that biscuit is more porous and it is therefore relatively easy to get a glaze to adhere to it before firing. If the biscuit ware is very porous it is easy to glaze because it quickly takes in the water of the glaze slop leaving the layer of glaze on the surface of the ware. The more porous the biscuit, the faster it is possible to glaze a batch of pots. The lower the temperature of the biscuit firing, the greater the degree of porosity. The lowest feasible temperature is about 750°C (1382°F) at which point the clay has become pot and has enough physical strength to survive in one piece.

Soft biscuit, besides meaning soft (low) temperature, can be taken literally. Low firing gives physically soft ware which is mechanically weak. As porosity is lost through the increase in temperature, so strength is gained. The pores in the body are filled with melted silicates which on cooling set hard and bind together the particles around the pores. Each clay behaves differently and will have its own temperature at which it is sufficiently strong to be easily handled yet sufficiently porous to be easily glazed.

Potters have their own preferences within the practical temperature range for biscuit firing which is from 850°C to 1000°C (1562°F to 1832°F). Some kilns may even cover this range in temperature differences in parts of the same firing. Potters often use the tongue test to determine how porous the biscuit is. The colour of the ware is some indication but it is confirmed by a quick touch with the tongue which is a very sensitive instrument.

The illustrations show enlarged sections through:

1. very soft biscuit where the clay particles are only sintered;
2. ideal porous biscuit which has the particles fastened together but large pores to give porosity;
3. dense body where the glassy matrix has almost filled the pores. The progressive breakdown of the clay particle can be seen and the other body constituents assisting this fusion, viz fluxes and free silica, are diagrammatically shown as small circles. Note how the body also shrinks.

For details of biscuit firing, see **Firing**.

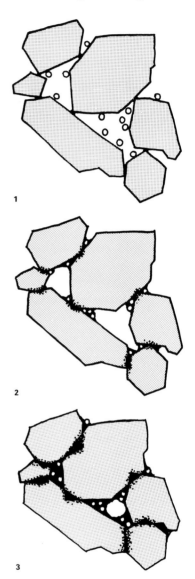

Biscuits

Unfired disc setters used under pots to prevent sticking. Being unfired they shrink with the foot rim, thereby saving distortion. They may be made from body clay or refractory clay.

Bismuth oxide

Bi_2O_3. An amphoteric oxide which acts as a flux in ceramic fusions. It is usually introduced in small amounts as a modifier of colourings.

Bismuth occurs as sulfide, oxide and telluride but is mostly recovered from tin, lead and copper ores. It is a low melting point metal and is used in low melting alloys. Nitrate salts are used in medicine.

The pure metal can be polished like silver. A thin layer deposited on the glaze by reduction gives a mother of pearl lustre. Bismuth nitrate is dissolved in resin and oil for application to glazed ware. The organic materials burn out in the 700°C to 800°C (1292°F to 1472°F) range and leave the pure metal. This lustre medium is used as a carrier for other lustre colours.

Bizen

The Japanese centre of wood-fired pottery production. The local clay had a high iron content which necessitated firing at a lower temperature. To compensate for this, the firing was taken slowly, even up to 60 days. Close packing, the play of flames, and deposits of ash and salt created a unique surface.

Black

When studied critically, a black colour will be seen to be a dark brown, blue or green. Transparent or semi-transparent glazes are easily stained by the addition of the strong colouring oxides which give brown, blue and green.

The fully matured transparent glaze dissolves and uniformly disperses the stain, thus providing a depth of colour which is rich. Transparent shiny glazes give the best black glazes. Opaque tin glazes and crystalline glazes etc can only be a dark grey.

Similarly with bodies and slips, the darkest colour develops with glassiness. Vitrified bodies, like that of the black basalt vase by Colin Pearson illustrated (below), are distinctly black, but non-vitrified bodies and slips can only be a dusty dark grey. The photograph of 'Black Venus' (right) by Jude Jelfs shows a medium-temperature vitrified-slip coating. See **Recipe Appendix**.

A matured transparent glaze covering a black slip always gives a good black colour. The following recipe is for a black slip to go under a transparent glaze at 1120°C (2048°F):

ball clay	76
manganese oxide	8
red iron oxide	8
cobalt oxide	8

For an unglazed black slip which will vitrify at 1250°C (2282°F), the following recipe can be used:

ball clay or body clay	75
whiting	12
red iron oxide	8
copper oxide	2·5
cobalt oxide	2·5

Colouring oxides can be added to existing glazes to give a black colour. The oxides will give extra fluxing action which should be counteracted by some china clay. Half the weight of the colouring oxides is a suitable starting point for the amount of china clay. The following recipes are balanced with the colouring oxides.

The first is for a black shiny glaze for 1120°C to 1150°C (2048°F to 2102°F):

feldspar	30
china clay	15
lead bisilicate	45
manganese oxide	5
red iron oxide	4
cobalt oxide	1

An alternative colouring is:

manganese oxide	9
copper oxide	1

The next recipe is for 1200°C (2192°F). This glaze has a fine crystalline surface with some separation of oxide as speckles:

feldspar	50
china clay	15
flint	5
whiting	15
cobalt oxide	5
manganese oxide	5
red iron oxide	5

See also **Tea-dust**.

Nickel and chromium oxides are often used in the production of calcined black stains. They may also be used in glazes without calcination and help to produce neutral blacks. Two examples of colouring to be added to existing glazes are given:

nickel oxide	2	1
red iron oxide	5	6
cobalt oxide	5	3
manganese oxide	2	–
chromium oxide	1	5

Black core

Blue core. The dark grey centre which shows in the section of some fired bodies. It is caused by local reduction. The black colour is black iron oxide possibly with some carbon. In ivory and cream bodies the colour is a pale grey often lighter in colour than the oxidized surround.

Black core occurs when the carbon inside the body has not been successfully burnt out. All clays contain some carbonaceous matter. This oxidizes to give carbon dioxide at temperatures above 750°C (1382°F). Oxygen enters the pores of the body, combines with the carbon and escapes as a gas. If insufficient oxygen is present in the kiln atmosphere, then the carbon cannot burn (oxidize). However, at this temperature it is exceedingly greedy for oxygen and will achieve oxidation by taking oxygen from any red iron oxide which may be present. The result is black iron oxide. The equation is:

$$2Fe_2O_3 + C \longrightarrow 4FeO + CO_2\uparrow$$

2Fe$_2$O$_3$	+	C		4FeO	+	CO$_2$↑
red iron oxide		carbon		black iron oxide		carbon dioxide

At 900°C (1652°F) the black iron oxide becomes an active flux and is immediately involved in the early stages of vitrification. Later oxidation will be unable to reoxidize this black iron oxide which is combined in a melt. The vitrification continues through the firing and is one cause of premature breakdown.

The lack of sufficient oxygen between 750°C and 900°C by an unclean atmosphere or by too rapid a firing can lead to breakdown, bloating etc at higher temperatures. See **Breakdown**. Black core is often a fault arising in the biscuit firing that does not show itself until the glaze firing.

Black-figure ware

Early classical Greek pottery which was decorated with a partially reduced ferruginous slip. The figures were painted in solid black upon a lighter ground. Red and white slips were sometimes added and details were drawn on by sgraffito through the black slip. See **Attic pottery**.

Black-hard clay

Any type or colour of clay at the stage between leatherhard and white-hard. It is the stage at which clay looks its darkest colour with the edges just beginning to look whitish. With earthenware clays and some stoneware clays most of the shrinkage has now taken place. Any drying cracks are likely to have formed already, even if they are not visible, and further drying can be relatively quick. Alternatively, this is the ideal stage for the application of slip glazes composed of wood ash and clay. Stoneware clays are usually stronger at this stage than when white-hard. The slight wetting received in glazing only strengthens the clay further, yet drying can be swift after glazing. See also **Drying**.

Blacksmith's scale

Iron spangles. Finery cinder. Fe$_3$O$_4$. The lustrous blue flakes produced when hot iron is hammered. It is a source of speckles for clays and glazes because it does not immediately dissolve during the firing. See **Iron oxide: types**.

Blakeley's tuning fork

This is a device similar to Steger's bending bar for measuring the stress between body and glaze.

Blistering

Unwanted gassing of a glaze resulting in bubbles and the craters of burst bubbles. Blistering occurs where the glaze has not had time to smooth out before it sets.

The bubbles are gases originating in the glaze or in the body beneath. See **Bloating**. With the rise in temperature and its attendant interactions, many gases are liberated, e.g. sulfur dioxide from crocus martis above 900°C (1652°F), oxygen from manganese dioxide at 1080°C (1976°F) and fluorine from cornish stone above 1150°C (2102°F). Also some constituents begin to boil and volatilize, e.g. lead oxide above 1150°C and sodium oxide above 1200°C (2192°F).

To overcome blistering: cut down the amount of offending material, alter the firing cycle and alter the viscosity of the molten glaze.

It is sometimes possible to replace glaze materials with more practical ones though often with some loss of character. Feldspars can often be substituted for cornish stone, iron oxides for crocus martis etc.

The firing cycle can be altered to include a slower maturing of the glaze towards top temperature. Possibly a slightly lower top temperature but a longer firing may smooth out the glaze. The introduction of oxygen in the later stages often helps to clear gases out of the chamber and clean up glazes. A soaking at top temperature or, better still, an extended cooling down the first 50°C or 100°C (90°F or 180°F) allows the bubbles to escape and the glaze to heal over.

A stiff glaze often traps bubbles in it giving it a frosted opacity. See **Stiff glazes**. The stiffness when molten is called a glaze's viscosity. It is possible to alter this viscosity by adjustment of the glaze recipe. A glaze which is fluid allows the bubbles to escape quickly and also heals over the scars. See **Viscosity of molten glazes** and **Surface tension**. It should be remembered that bubbles try to rise vertically. They take longer to escape from overhanging surfaces near the base of swelling forms and from inside foot rims. A slightly thinner glaze layer may be necessary.

Bloating

The unwanted blistering of the body caused by trapped gases. The defect occurs in stoneware and between body and slip in slipware.

During firing, many gases are liberated from the body. Most of these escape through the body pores and if

necessary through the molten glaze. If the body pores are blocked by a stiff fusion of body-glaze layer or by a stiff vitrifying slip, the gases cannot escape. They then build up pockets of gas behind a 'plastic' barrier which is distorted to accommodate the gas bubble.

The gases involved are carbon monoxide and dioxide which escape from 700°C to 900°C (1292°F to 1652°F); sulfur in various oxidations from 700°C to 1150°C (1292°F to 2102°F) and fluorine from 700°C to 1300°C (1292°F to 2372°F).

The greatest trouble arises from carbon which has not been completely burnt out at biscuit stage. If there is only one 'through' firing then the biscuiting part of this may have been rushed. The result is carbon still trapped in the body and unable to oxidize because sealed from the outside atmosphere. See **Black core** and **Firing: biscuit**. This carbon eventually oxidizes by taking oxygen from iron oxide. The reduced iron oxide acts as a body flux, the body is softened by over-vitrification and the carbon oxides create bloats.

This defect is emphasized in stoneware where the body is intentionally reaching vitrification. In earthenware, with the exception of slipware described later, the gases usually manage to escape from the still-porous body and the worst effect from black core is a blistering or milder pin-holing of the glaze.

Sometimes a clay contains so much gas that it cannot be fired satisfactorily. Gases which are liberated after the body has become vitreous are obviously difficult to disperse. One answer lies in the lower temperatures for the firing which do not involve vitrification and gassing.

Vitreous slips should be used on one side of the body only and it may even be necessary to leave one side unglazed. This was common with some 17th- and 18th-century English slipware which was raw glazed. The soft-firing lead glaze fused before the carbon had burnt out of the body. In a few examples which are glazed all over, some interesting reduced colourings were sealed. These have reoxidized around the craze lines. There is also unfortunately some bloating.

Blue

This colour has always been popular on pottery and was one of the earliest colours used in glazes. It was achieved in early Egyptian and Persian wares by cobalt oxide in lead glazes and copper oxide in high-alkaline glazes.

Cobalt oxide usually gives a blue colour in glazes and bodies. The blue varies in hue according to the predominance of lead oxide or boron oxide. Lead oxide gives an inky blue with a slightly greenish tint. Boron oxide and alkaline glazes give purply blues of the royal blue and willow blue type. Cobalt oxide is very dependable and can be used at high temperatures. It bleeds slightly into the glaze as it forms the cobalt silicate colourant. To overcome the bleeding, a more permanent stain is used which is prepared as cobalt aluminate and known as matt blue. This must be produced prior to addition to the glaze.

An even more dependable stain, which again must be prepared first as a colourant, is produced by a combination of vanadium oxide and zirconium silicate.

The copper oxide blue in glazes is only obtainable under special conditions. The blue is the result of copper silicate in combination with an alkali-silicate (using lithium, sodium, potassium, barium and/or calcium oxides). The presence of magnesium, lead, boron or aluminium oxides kills the pure blue colour. Some copper-blue glazes lose their pure blue colour when overfired. They turn green or, if seriously overfired, brown. See **Colour plate 16**.

The delicate blue of Yingqing porcelain is derived from 0·5% of iron oxide in heavy reduction. Jun blue is an optical effect caused by the scattering of light. See **Jun**, **Cobalt oxide**, **Vanadium stains** and **Alkaline glazes**.

Blue and white

A term implying white porcelain with painted blue decoration. It usually refers to Chinese porcelain which had been perfected to a white translucence by the 13th century and was painted with cobalt blue. The Mongolian Yuan Dynasty (1280–1368) is famous for the introduction of a particularly pure cobalt ore from Persia.

The Chinese porcelains were later copied in Europe and are also called 'blue and white'.

Blue core

See **Black core**.

Blunge

To mix materials and water thoroughly. Blunging is done in an octagonal or hexagonal tank with a central vertical shaft. On this shaft are fastened radial blades or paddles. These are set at an angle so that, when the shaft rotates, the blades force the mixture downwards. The resulting creamy slurry is run out of the tank by a tap at the bottom. It can then be sieved, settled etc.

The drawing shows the principle of the blunger and the photograph a 30 cm octagonal blunger manufactured by Gosling and Gatensbury Ltd.

A development is centrifugal blunging which uses a small, high-speed impellor at the base of the tank. The second drawing shows the highly-efficient impellor made by Edwards and Jones Ltd.

Boccaro

Unglazed red stoneware originally from 17th-century China. Now used as a name for any vitrified red clay ware especially when such ware is domestic pottery and has at least some unglazed parts, often with relief decoration. The photograph is of a tiny Chinese teapot. See also *Yixing*.

Body (1)

The clay part of a pot as opposed to any additional parts such as slips, glazes and colours. Since the clay ceases to be clay and becomes ceramic during firing the term 'body' is a useful one, in contrast to glaze, in the discussion of actions taking place during firing or in discussing the final result.

Body (2)

A clay for a special purpose. It is created by blending different clays or by adding to clays other minerals, such as feldspar and flint, in order to produce a desired workability or finished result. A body is the result of man's technology. A clay is the natural product, though possibly simply processed to make it homogeneous.

Body constituents

The different materials used in compounding and blending pottery bodies. They can be classified as clays, fluxes, hardeners and openers. Natural clays often contain fluxes, hardeners and openers. Some of these may be undesirable and may be removed during preparation.

Instead of starting with a natural stoneware clay which has the properties required, one may create a blend with a ball clay for plasticity and raw strength, a china clay for whiteness and refractoriness, and a fireclay for refractoriness and texture. To this clay blend will be added the fluxes, hardeners and openers.

The fluxes used in bodies are feldspathoids such as cornish stone, feldspar and nepheline syenite, or in the soft maturing bodies may be frits. The frits themselves melt and flux the free silica in the body to produce a molten glass which fills the interstitial spaces. On cooling the larger particles are thus cemented together by a glassy matrix.

The hardeners are the free silicas which may be added as

flint, quartz, silica sand and cristobalite. Silica is hard but is fluxed during the firing and then gives its hardness to the resulting glass.

The openers are used to give texture and workability. They are grog, fireclay, and organic matter such as sawdust, cereal husks, chopped straw and cow dung.

In the preparation of a body it is usual to blunge the clays, fluxes and hardeners together, the proportions being determined by dry weight. The blunged slurry is sieved and dried to plasticity by filterpress or drying troughs. The openers are usually added at the wedging and kneading stage or at the pug mill, the proportions being determined by dry weight of opener to plastic weight of clay. The use of clay mixers which mix dry powders together with water to a plastic state without the intermediate state of slurry has meant that openers can be added from the start. In these cases the proportions are dry weight of opener and dry weight of clay. If working from someone else's recipe for a body it is advisable to discover how the proportions, especially of openers, are calculated against the other constituents.

Body-glaze layer

Intermediate layer. Interface. The part of a fired pot where the glaze meets the body. It is seen in section as a gradation from body to glaze. Sometimes it is darker than either the body or the glaze. This layer is more strongly defined in stoneware and porcelain where the higher temperature and longer firing give greater opportunities for this to take place.

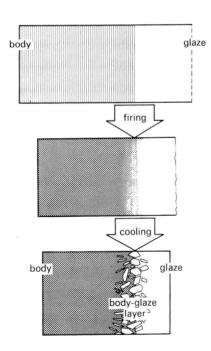

The layer begins to form as soon as the fluxes in either body or glaze begin to melt with the silicates. If the melt is soft enough it will envelop not only adjacent particles in its own substance but also in the neighbouring one of body or glaze. As the glaze becomes molten some of it will soak into the body if the body is sufficiently porous. It will immediately begin to flux the body surrounding the cavities which it has entered.

The body-glaze layer often contains more aluminium oxide than the glaze because it has more clay in it, and therefore on cooling it forms crystals. These crystals are often the place where other crystals start their growth in a crystalline glaze. Thus a prolonged soaking during firing can help to produce crystals.

A thick body-glaze layer acts as a cushion to absorb the stress between body and glaze. The deliberate formation of this layer is some insurance against crazing, and to a lesser extent, shivering. Such a layer would be termed a buffer layer.

A thick body-glaze layer develops in porcelain. Here it can be twice the thickness of the glaze remaining as pure glaze. Thus a strong compression of the glaze can be cushioned and the overall strength of a glazed piece of porcelain can be double that of its unglazed counterpart.

Bog ore

A general name covering a variety of ores which are the result of precipitation. Lakes, marshes and other areas of land-locked water often contain iron in solution. The iron is precipitated as the end product of a series of reactions which starts with the decomposition of vegetable matter. The precipitate is at first the colloidal state iron hydroxide ($Fe(OH)_3$ or $Fe_2O_3.3H_2O$) and later the ore limonite ($2Fe_2O_3.3H_2O$). Pure deposits can be won as rich ores.

Sand and other silt often become involved in the deposition resulting in sedimentary rocks called ironstones. These sometimes contain sufficient iron to be worth recovery. Others provide horizon markers in coal mining and have descriptive names like 'black band' and 'clay ironstone'. They often weather quickly to a crumbly state and are useful as glaze constituents. See ***Iron oxide***.

Boiling point

Normally means the boiling point of water at 100°C (212°F). However all liquids have a boiling point. Glazes, in their liquid state during firing, boil periodically as the different compounds, which are mostly oxides, reach their individual boiling points. At a certain temperature, as an oxide boils it becomes vapour in the same way that water becomes steam. It does not require much liquid to make a lot of vapour and create a lot of bubbles which froth the glaze.

All glazes boil during melting, or more correctly some constituent of the glaze boils. This results in bubbles which spoil the smooth surface of the glaze. The vapour must be cleared by a higher temperature and/or a prolonged firing otherwise the bubbles may be trapped in the glaze. If they do get to the surface and burst, the resulting crater also needs time to heal before the glaze stiffens and sets. Materials which are likely to give trouble are previously fritted to a higher temperature than the one at which they will be used.

Bole

A fine red clay occurring in the countries of the eastern Mediterranean. It is used as a pigment and in the compounding of enamel colours. It is relatively pure as a clay, approximating kaolinite plus iron oxide.

Bone ash

Ground calcined bones, usually cattle bones. It is one source of calcium phosphate; others are phosphorite and apatite. It is used as a flux in bodies where the calcium oxide does the fluxing and the phosphorus oxide acts as a glass-former in the melt and also checks over-rapid fusion. Its stiff glassy character is seen combined with that of feldspar in bone china. Bone china contains 45% to 50% of bone ash. A small amount of carbon remains in bone ash when calcination is controlled and this carbon assists the raw plasticity of the body.

A typical analysis of bone ash would be calcium oxide 55%, phosphorus oxide 40%, with the remainder composed of fluorine, silica and alkaline oxides. An acceptable formula for bone ash is $Ca_3(PO_4)_2$ ultimately $3CaO.P_2O_5$ which proportion could vary to $13CaO.4P_2O_5$.

Bone ash is used in glazes as an opacifier. In spite of its large percentage of calcium oxide its fluxing action is checked somewhat by the phosphorus oxide which produces a stiff melt. It can be used to assist tin oxide so that less tin oxide is required, especially where a less shiny surface is acceptable. It creates an attractive soft mottling and also encourages the glaze to flow away from modelled high spots making relief decoration more effective. However, bone ash can be a cause of crawling and blistering. Small amounts are said to assist the formation of a good jun glaze by introducing phosphorus. The quality of depth in Song glazes is attributed to phosphorus and could have come from bone ash.

Bone china

A British porcelain in which the body is first fired to translucent state without a glaze. The glaze firing is at a lower temperature. For the bisc firing, the body is supported in powdered aluminium oxide to inhibit warping.

The ware was developed in the late 18th century by Josiah Spode to meet the demand for a white translucent ware which arose with the importation of Oriental porcelain.

Calcined ox bones are used to provide a viscous body flux. A typical bone china body is composed of:

china clay	25
feldspar	25
bone ash	50

This body is very short when plastic and fragile when dry. It is most suitable for slip-casting but with plasticizer (bentonite 6%) can be press-moulded. It is bisc fired to 1280°C (2336°F) and glaze fired below 1080°C (1976°F).

The winged jugs by Sasha Wardell were first fired to 900°C (1652°F) to harden them for smoothing with dry, fine-abrasion paper. They were then fired in an electric kiln to 1260°C (2300°F) supported on an open shelf by aluminium oxide powder. Using a series of maskings with tape, the jugs were sprayed with underglaze and glaze before firing to 1000°C (1832°F). The pieces were finished with dry abrasion paper. See also *Slip-casting*.

Bone-dry clay

Clay which has been dried beyond the naturally dry state which it reaches in the air. Dry clay contains water equal with the atmosphere but bone-dry clay has had this water removed. To achieve the bone-dry state, the clay is heated to over 100°C (212°F), the boiling point of water. In the early stages of a firing, this is called water smoking. See *Drying*.

If bone-dry clay is allowed to cool it will take up moisture from the atmosphere by a process of adsorption and capillary action. A slight expansion will take place which sometimes leads to unequal sizes of adjacent parts, stress and cracks. See *Readsorption*.

Boracite

Stassfurtite. $6MgO.MgCl_2.8B_2O_3$. A complex and variable mineral of magnesium and boron which is used in frits. It occurs associated with gypsum, rock salt and anhydrite in Germany.

Boracitis

A word concocted by J. W. Mellor in the early 1930s to describe the unwanted action of boron oxide. Additions of small amounts of boron oxide to a glaze have beneficial effects as an anti-craze. This is described under *Glaze fit*. However, there is an optimum amount for this benefit and this amount is different for each glaze recipe. Above this point further additions of boron oxide have the opposite effect and can cause crazing. The effect is due to the loss of elasticity in the glaze. An elastic glaze has the capacity to absorb the stress between body and glaze which a more brittle glaze cannot achieve.

Borate

A chemical compound which includes the element boron. Boron, oxygen and hydrogen are capable of forming over fifty different lattice structures and of involving other elements in those structures. This book mentions only those naturally-occurring compounds which are the source of boron oxide in glazes. Their descriptive mineral names are used rather than their complex scientific ones and they are given the general name of borate.

In describing borates in this book, the formulae are divided into oxides for ease of reading. This is not acceptable to chemists because it implies that separate molecules exist which, of course, they do not in a compound.

The following is an explanation of some of the simpler borate nomenclature:

1. Borax is usually written as $Na_2B_4O_7.10H_2O$ which implies that there is a sodium, boron and oxygen lattice into which water, as hydrogen and oxygen, is integrated. Potters prefer to see it written as $Na_2O.2B_2O_3.10H_2O$. They ignore the water which they know will burn out during firing and see the borax as sodium and boron oxides thereby viewing its potential in a glaze.

2. Borax was known as sodium pyroborate because of its volcanic origin. Preferred structural names are: disodium tetraborate referring to the two and four atoms of sodium and boron per molecule ($Na_2B_4O_7$); and sodium diborate referring to the two boron oxide molecules ($Na_2O.2B_2O_3$). The term 'hydrated' before (or 'hydrate' after) means simply 'with water of crystallization'. More specifically, 'deca-hydrate' explains how much water.

3. $NaBO_2$ is called sodium monoborate because there is one atom of boron per molecule. It is also called, non-specifically, sodium metaborate which means simply that the sodium is with boron and implies a sense of change. If the formula is multiplied by two, one achieves: $2NaBO_2 = Na_2O.B_2O_3$ which is referred to as sodium orthoborate because there is a straight or equal balance of molecules, sodium oxide:boron oxide.

4. BO_2H is called metaboric acid. The 'meta' here implies the half-way position between boric acid and boron oxide. See *Boric acid*.

5. B_2O_3 is called simply boron oxide in this book because B_2O_3 is the only oxide form theoretically involved in glazes. Specifically, diboron trioxide or boron (III) oxide would be correct. Boron sesquioxide is still acceptable but boric oxide is no longer recommended.

6. Some other borate minerals are:

kernite	$Na_2B_4O_7.4H_2O$	$= Na_2O.2B_2O_3.4H_2O$
pandermite	$Ca_4B_{10}O_{19}.7H_2O$	$= 4CaO.5B_2O_3.7H_2O$
boracite	$Mg_6Cl_2B_{14}O_{26}$	$= 5MgO.7B_2O_3.MgCl_2$

Borax

Tincal. $Na_2B_4O_7.10H_2O$ or $Na_2O.2B_2O_3.10H_2O$. A crystal-line mineral which is the source of boron oxide with sodium oxide. It is used in making low-melting glaze frits without lead oxide. Borax occurs naturally as a precipitate from lakes and marshes in California. Tincal is the name for Asian borax. Lower phases of hydration are also found and have the mineral names rasorite and kernite with the formula $Na_2O.2B_2O_3.4H_2O$.

Borax is the chief source of boron oxide for glazes but because it is soluble in water it is necessary to introduce it into the glaze batch in a fritted form. Strictly speaking, once the borax has been dehydrated and incorporated in a frit it is no longer borax but the term borax frit is used to indicate its origin and is obviously less cumbersome than any alternative.

Borax decomposes upon heating to form sodium metaborate, boron oxide and water:

$$Na_2B_4O_7.10H_2O \longrightarrow 2NaBO_2.B_2O_3 + 10H_2O\uparrow$$

The sodium metaborate/boron oxide combination is also written $Na_2O.2B_2O_3$ and is therefore referred to as sodium diborate. This end product has a melting point of 741°C (1366°F) when it is known as fused borax. For clarification of the nomenclature, see **Borate**. The simplest borax frit has the formula $Na_2O.2B_2O_3.3SiO_2$ and is useful in the glaze range 900°C to 1100°C (1652°F to 2012°F) over which it is itself maturing. See **Boron oxide** for use in glazes.

Borax frit

A frit made from borax and silica (or silicate). The borax provides sodium oxide and boron oxide. The sodium oxide is a flux; the boron oxide is a flux and a glass-former. Both flux the silica at a low temperature to produce a molten glass. This is shattered with water and ground to a powder. If a silicate is used there will be aluminium oxide present also.

There are many possible unity formulae for borax frits. The simplest is:

$$Na_2O.2B_2O_3.3SiO_2$$

Borax frits are used with feldspars and clays to compound leadless glazes. The frit melts in the 850°C to 1000°C (1562°F to 1832°F) range thus originating the fusion of the glaze. Pure borax cannot be used in a glaze slop because it is soluble in water. In fritted form it is insoluble. See **Boron oxide** for use in glazes.

If borax frit is being prepared for use in a lead (low sol) glaze, it is never fritted with the lead oxide. Lead silicate must be prepared separately from the borax frit in order to render the lead oxide insoluble. See **Low sol** and **Double fritting**.

Boric acid

Boracic acid. Trioxoboric acid. Sassoline. $B(OH)_3$ or H_3BO_3 or $B_2O_3.3H_2O$. A boron mineral occurring as waxy white crystals around some Italian hot springs. It is also manufactured from borax and is used as a mild acid antiseptic for the eyes. Its use in pottery is in the preparation of borosilicate frits.

Boric acid is soluble in water and therefore must be fritted with silicates before it can be used in a glaze slop. When subjected to heat during the fritting process, the boric acid decomposes to boron oxide (B_2O_3) and water (H_2O). The equation is:

$$2B(OH)_3 \xrightarrow{100°C} 2BO_2H + 2H_2O \uparrow \xrightarrow{200°C} 2B_2O_3 + 3H_2O \uparrow$$

Time, as well as temperature, is an important factor in this dehydration process.

Borocalcite

See **Colemanite** and **Calcium borate**.

Boron oxide

Diboron trioxide. B_2O_3. A glass-forming oxide which is one of the most useful of glaze constituents. It melts at a low temperature and is therefore suitable for low-temperature glazes where it acts both as a glass-former and a flux. It rarely occurs alone in nature but is available as a series of borates in combination with water, sodium oxide, calcium oxide and magnesium oxide. These minerals are mostly soluble in water and hence they are incorporated in frits before being used in glazes. Boron oxide itself is hygroscopic and freely soluble in water. See **Borate**.

In glaze theory it is considered that there is a molecule of boron oxide (B_2O_3) and that this becomes linked in endless chains with itself and silica (SiO_2). To achieve the boron oxide chain one must melt the crystals of boron oxide. Melting begins at 300°C (572°F) when the crystals start to break down. The molecule B_2O_3 goes through a series of divisions into sub-oxides with partial melting until full fusion is reached at 700°C (1292°F). A useful glass is now formed from the chains of boron oxide and this does not recrystallize on cooling. It is an amorphous substance and as such has no melting point but a melting range. Remelting will be in the range 570°C to 600°C (1058°F to 1112°F), which enables boron oxide to be used as a low-temperature flux (alkali) as well as a glass-former (acid).

Boron oxide frits and glazes were developed as an alternative to lead glazes to overcome lead poisoning. It is possible to make glazes melting as low as 750°C (1382°F). However boron oxide is also extremely useful in combination with lead silicates. In fully fused glazes it decreases the solubility of the lead oxide and it extends the firing range of lead silicates. It assists the glaze balance and is well known as an anti-craze. See **Glaze fit**. Lead oxide increases the elasticity of boron oxide glazes and the combination of the two produces a range of finishes and colours. As a generalization, the boron oxide gives harsher colours than lead oxide.

Boron oxide is a glass-former and therefore works in a similar way to silica in the glaze. It provides part of the glass network into which are incorporated the other oxides. One of its greatest merits is its low melting point and it is often used for this property. Its theoretical introduction into glazes is simple. It can be substituted for some of the silica on a molecular basis. See **Equivalent**. Small amounts (0·1 equivalents) make appreciable differences in the melting point of the glaze. With matt glazes it is better to substitute the boron oxide for some of the aluminium oxide. However the low melting point of boron oxide makes the theoretical consideration of matts difficult. Once the boron oxide has melted it naturally assists other actions and therefore has some interaction with the alkalis which would cause the crystalline matt.

BORON OXIDE AND RECIPE ADJUSTMENTS. Boron oxide is a glass-former (acid) but also acts as a flux (alkali). Its sesquioxide formula tells us that it is indeed amphoteric and will act accordingly. Potters often have difficulty in putting it into its proper place in unity formulae. Its correct place is with the amphoteric oxides but one must realize that if the equivalents of boron oxide exceed 0·05 it is difficult to relate the formula to others which contain none.

In most glaze adjustments the boron oxide to be added will be part of a frit. It will be necessary to know the unity formula of the frit if one is to calculate from formula to new recipe. If one is making one's own frit, it is better to keep the frit recipe and formula simple. If the soluble parts are rendered insoluble and the frit is soft enough to grind there is no advantage in fritting more than is necessary of the glaze recipe. See **Frit**. Some frits of very simple unity formula, e.g. $Na_2O.2B_2O_3.3SiO_2$, are available commercially for potters who wish to work by calculation, but what starts as an intention of simple substitution can become complex when related to compound minerals in the recipe for the glaze batch. See also **Formula: unity** and **Calculations**.

Most potters regard theoretical substitution as difficult and prefer the simple addition of a frit. In this case the frit should be chosen with regard to the composition of the glaze. Assuming that the glaze is as required except that it needs to be softened slightly, one would choose a frit containing the same oxides as the glaze. If the glaze is a limestone, clay and sodium feldspar glaze the simplest

course is to introduce a frit which also contains calcium, sodium and aluminium oxides as well as the boron oxide and silica. The introductory tests should be done with a mixture of the glaze and frit at one end of a line blend and the straight glaze at the other. If in doubt as to the choice of frit, one should first try the most popular standard frit available. It is likely that this has been developed for general occasions which one's own case will fit. If the original glaze has no especial merit, then the addition of any frit will probably bring some interest.

BORON OXIDE AND NEW RECIPES. One often starts with someone else's glaze recipe and adjusts this empirically to one's own potting. The word frit alone in a recipe has little value and could mean a material melting at 750°C or 1100°C. In the absence of detail as to which frit to use, start by using a frit in a line blend. Boron oxide frits are various and are manufactured for most situations. The manufacturer's advice should be sought as to which frit will be suitable for the temperature range, colour, clay etc.

For temperatures up to 1150°C (2102°F), a line blend is easily prepared. Most frits within their suggested temperature ranges begin to look like glazes with the addition of 10% china clay. If this is taken as one end of a line blend and the other end is 90% feldspar with 10% of china clay, then a suitable glaze requiring minor balancing by silica and whiting should be possible.

For temperatures above 1150°C (2102°F), it is better to start without the frit and introduce this only as necessary to improve glaze surface, shine, colour, range, balance and anti-craze.

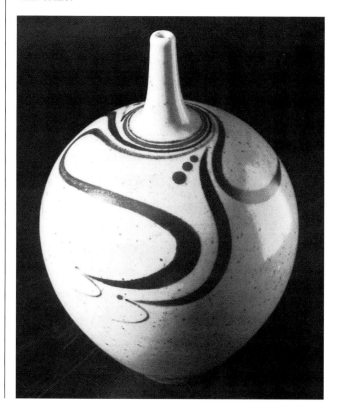

Bottle
Illustrated on page 36 is a large stoneware bottle by David Frith who uses a poured glaze over wax resist technique also shown in **Plate 44**. The second bottle is by Derek Clarkson and shows painted iron oxide decoration.

Bottle kiln
A familiar name for the bottle-shaped, up-draught, brick-built kiln which was developed in Stoke-on-Trent. From the late 18th century to the mid-20th century scores of these kiln structures dominated the skyline in the Stoke Potteries area. See **Hovel kiln**.

These kilns were notoriously inefficient. Only 5% of the heat input actually heated the ware. They also polluted the atmosphere around the Potteries with the smoke from the coal fires. Their demise was inevitable with the introduction of more efficient kilns and the clean air legislation.

Boulder clay
A clay of glacial origin containing boulders. Some of the boulders are massive while others are only small pebbles. Sometimes there are more boulders than there is clay but some deposits are workable as clay and provide a fairly uniform and smooth clay. It is a fusible clay suitable for soft-fired earthenware.

During its transportation the clay was ground, split and weathered. It also gathered impurities which were equally fine. It settled in lakes dammed by ice or was washed out of melting glaciers at the end of the last glacial period.

Because it is full of impurities of similar size to the clay, it cannot be purified by sieving. The impurities make it vitrify at approximately 1100°C (2012°F) and melt by 1300°C (2372°F). It is therefore suitable for low temperatures as a body or higher temperatures as a fusible slip, possibly with the addition of some wood ash or soft frit.

Bowl
The examples shown are a salt-glazed bowl by Walter Keeler, a trailed and painted earthenware bowl by Bennett Cooper, an engraved porcelain bowl by Margaret Frith, a deep blue bowl with resin gold lustre by Mary Rich, a smoked-lustre maiolica bowl by Edgar Campden, the underside of a

smoked-lustre bowl by Marianne de Trey and a stoneware bowl with oxide decoration by Andrew McGarva.

Boxing

Putting bowls or cups together rim to rim to prevent warpage during drying and firing. From cheesehard state the drying is more uniform because insides and rims are protected. Boxing is also used in stoneware glaze firings when bowl and small plate rims are unglazed.

Brass

A class of alloys incorporating copper and zinc. Brass filings are used by potters to speckle clays and glazes. After oxidation the zinc oxide becomes a powerful flux and the copper oxide a strong stain.

Braunite

Mn_2O_3. The anhydrous form of the ore manganite. It is present in sedimentary clays.

$$Mn_2O_3 + H_2O = 2MnO(OH)$$

Breakdown

The actions of decomposition, disintegration and deformation, especially when they are undesirable. The commonest use is to describe the deformation of bodies caused by over-fluxing. The special case of breakdown caused by iron oxide is treated under a sub-heading.

Clays deform when they are over-fired. They collapse and might even melt to a glass. At this point the silica and silicates of the clay have been successfully fluxed by alkaline oxides. The alkaline oxides could be present in the feldspar, in the sand, in chalk or limestone flour, and in the salts. Throughout a firing, from the completion of the ceramic change at 600°C (1112°F), the body fluxes are working on the silicates. The action is desirable. It causes vitrification which is the creation of glassy parts within the body. These weld the whole together into the strong structure of the finished product. See **Vitrification**. The process becomes breakdown when it has developed too far. Here the glassy parts completely surround the solid parts so that the solid parts have lost frictional contact. Under the force of gravity or the force of gases, the solid parts slide past one another and the desired form is lost.

The natural body fluxes are the oxides of potassium, sodium, calcium, magnesium and iron. Potassium and sodium oxides start their action around 600°C (1112°F) and the work they do progresses steadily. They are ideal fluxes because with them the maturing range is long and progressive so that a slight under- or overfiring is not ruinous. A good clay for earthenware and stoneware will contain in the region of 1% to 3% of potassium and sodium oxides. Depending upon the kaolinite content of the clay, this is sufficient to vitrify the clay in the range 1000°C to 1300°C (1832°F to 2372°F).

Calcium and magnesium oxides are active only above 1100°C (2012°F) and 1170°C (2138°F) respectively. Their actions are then such that coupled with the previous action of the potassium and sodium oxides they produce a very rapid vitrification. The action is so quick that it is difficult to fire such a body with accuracy. It is soon overfired with resulting breakdown. The content of the calcium and magnesium oxide is rarely more than 1% but some brick shales, brick marls and estuarine muds contain up to 4% of magnesium oxide which causes a very rapid breakdown at around 1200°C (2192°F).

It will be seen that clays containing more than 1% of calcium oxide or magnesium oxide, coupled with aluminium oxide content below 25% are likely to be unsuitable for temperatures above 1100°C (2012°F). These are therefore the earthenware potting clays. This statement ignores prepared earthenware bodies for the industrial high bisc and low glost method.

The clays which are low in calcium and magnesium oxides, and those which contain over 25% of aluminium oxide, are the stoneware clays.

BREAKDOWN DUE TO IRON OXIDE. Iron oxide presents a special case. Its presence in a clay can result in premature breakdown.

All clays contain some iron oxide. In china clay it is only 0·1% but most ball clays and fireclays contain 2% and red clays contain 5% to 8%. The critical amount is around 1·5%, above which the iron oxide must be regarded as a possible fluxing force.

If the iron oxide were all red iron oxide (Fe_2O_3), there would be no fluxing action from it. Red iron oxide is a refractory amphoteric oxide with no fluxing action in the presence of stronger fluxes like the oxides of potassium and sodium. On the other hand if the iron oxide were all black iron oxide (FeO), there would be strong fluxing action from 900°C (1652°F) upwards. Black iron oxide is an alkaline flux.

The state of red iron oxide or black iron oxide is established by the atmosphere inside the kiln. An atmosphere with surplus oxygen, called an oxidizing atmosphere, will give oxygen to the iron oxide to create the red state:

$$2FeO + O \longrightarrow Fe_2O_3$$

Whereas an atmosphere short of oxygen, called a reducing atmosphere, will take oxygen from the iron oxide to create the black state:

$$Fe_2O_3 + \underset{\substack{\text{carbon} \\ \text{monoxide}}}{CO} \longrightarrow 2FeO + \underset{\substack{\text{carbon} \\ \text{dioxide}}}{CO_2}$$

Black iron oxide (FeO) is greedy for oxygen, but it is not so greedy as carbon monoxide (CO). If there is a limited amount of oxygen available, the carbon monoxide will claim it. Thus by controlling the kiln atmosphere one controls the iron oxide content of the body and establishes either the red or the black state. One also thus controls whether the iron oxide will act as a flux or not.

By reduction, therefore, one can perhaps double the body fluxes. The following is an example analysis of a stoneware clay. Note how the fluxes total either 2·5% or 4·5% according to whether one uses an oxidized or a reduced firing.

Aluminium oxide	28%		
Silica	57		
Iron oxide	2		⎫
Calcium and magnesium oxides	0·5	⎫ 2·5	⎬ 4·5
Potassium and sodium oxides	2	⎭	⎭
Loss on firing	10·5		

Clays suitable for oxidized firing arc rarely ideal for reduced firing. The exceptions are the white bodies with less than 0·5% iron oxide content.

Iron oxide is an acceptable flux if used intentionally. It requires the presence of some calcium or magnesium oxides to give elasticity to vitrification. Iron oxide, with only potassium and sodium oxides, tends to give brittle glasses and hence brittle bodies.

Breakdown occurs with the unintentional use of iron oxide as a flux. At any temperature above 900°C (1652°F) it will not be possible to reoxidize a reduced iron oxide. Above 900°C the black iron oxide acts as a flux and at least half of it will be involved in a melt. One cannot expect it to change to red iron oxide and undo the fluxing action it has achieved. Therefore in bodies which have been reduced, one can only expect about half of the iron oxide to be still available for return to red iron oxide by oxidation.

For the production of a fully oxidized ware, like red stoneware, it is necessary to fire slowly with deliberate oxidation of the atmosphere by the provision of clean air passage through the kiln. The danger of accidental reduction then comes from impurities in the clay. All clays contain impurities which are burnt out in the firing. Carbonaceous matter is burnt out by oxidation before 900°C. Sulfur is oxidized betwen 900°C and 1150°C (1652°F and 2102°F). Oxygen enters the pores of the body, and combines with the sulfur in the action of burning or oxidation. The new compound is sulfur monoxide. This is a gas. The gas escapes through the pores into the kiln atmosphere where it takes up more oxygen to become sulfur dioxide. The sulfur dioxide escapes from the kiln through a flue or cracks round the door etc. One can smell these gases in the workshop atmosphere, especially from an electric kiln without a flue.

If the body has become semi-vitrified before this burning out period, then the oxidation is impeded. The sulfur, excited by the heat, turns to other sources of oxygen. Iron oxide is a ready source because it can be persuaded to part with some oxygen as has been previously explained. Hot sulfur is as effective as carbon monoxide. The result is a sulfur gas, monoxide or dioxide, and black iron oxide. A simplified equation would be:

$$2Fe_2O_3 + S \xrightarrow{900°C} 4FeO + SO_2 \uparrow$$

red iron oxide   sulfur   black iron oxide   sulfur dioxide

The newly-formed black iron oxide acts as a flux and produces molten glass which fills the pores in the body. The sulfur gases cannot escape because the pores are blocked. Yet as the sulfur gas is formed there is rapid expansion from the solid state. The result is bloating which is a bubble of gas pushing aside the sealed and softened body in an attempt to escape.

Once started, this action accelerates. It is assisted at temperatures over 1100°C (2012°F) by calcium oxide, if this is present. Bloated bodies are often a black, cellular froth within. The black is reduced iron oxide.

Black core is another factor often assisting this premature breakdown. If the body has a black core this contains reduced iron oxide due to insufficient oxidation between 750°C and 900°C (1382°F and 1652°F). At 900°C the reduced iron (black iron oxide) acts as an unintentional flux.

It is difficult, if not actually impossible, to keep a body so completely oxidized that there is no formation of black iron oxide at all. The red bodies which burn to the brightest colour are the ones containing very little carbon and sulfur.

Bristol

(England). Famous for Bristol delft from about 1650 to 1750 and for Bristol glazes when zinc oxide was introduced to replace the poisonous lead oxide in the 19th century. Bristol glazes were developed for all temperatures from 1150°C to 1300°C (2102°F to 2372°F). Zinc oxide is an active flux above 1100°C (2012°F) and can also be used to produce opaque and crystalline effects. Many of the early Bristol glazes were of this type. See *Zinc oxide*.

The photograph is of a Bristol-glazed jug by Janet Hamer using the following recipe for 1250°C (2282°F). This recipe gives a similar result to the old Bristol stoneware but suffers from the usual defect of zinc glazes in that it easily crawls if applied too thickly.

feldspar	65
china clay	9
flint	3
whiting	8
zinc oxide	10
titanium oxide	5

See also *Recipe Appendix*.

Brongniart

Alexandre (1770–1847). Director of the Sèvres porcelain factory from 1800 to 1847. He was an eminent geologist and mineralogist who turned potter and thereby brought to pottery the scientific reasoning which was developing at the close of the 18th century. He complemented the work of English potters like Whieldon and Wedgwood who moved towards the scientific approach in pottery making from the simpler rule-of-thumb approach. Brongniart is known as the father of ceramic chemistry and is best known for the Brongniart formula for converting slop measure to dry weight. See *Formula: Brongniart's*.

Bronze

A class of alloys incorporating copper and usually tin or aluminium. Phosphor bronze contains copper, tin and phosphorus. Bell metal contains copper, tin, zinc and lead. Gun metal contains copper, tin and zinc. Bronzes are physically hard but filings will melt in a pottery firing and can be used for speckle staining in bodies and glazes. See also *Brass*.

Bronze lustre on the surface of a glaze can be obtained with chromium and lead compounds in a special reduction firing. Bronze-effect glazes can be produced in oxidized stoneware and porcelain using the fluxing action of manganese oxide with or without copper oxide, feldspar and/or clay.

The porcelain bowl is by Peter Wills. His bronze glaze fires successfully up to 1285°C (2345°F) oxidized. See *Recipe Appendix* and also *Manganese oxide* and *Colour plates 29* and *38*.

Bronze Age pottery

Pottery made during the periods when metals were first used. Bronze (copper and tin) was important but gold and copper were also worked. Iron was not used until later because it required a higher temperature to soften the ore. The change to iron occurred with the development of more efficient furnaces and naturally coincides with improved pottery kilns.

The earliest Bronze Age was in Egypt starting perhaps 5000BC and spreading through the eastern Mediterranean and eastern Europe from 2600BC. In western Europe and eastern Asia the era is from about 2000BC and in all places lasted about 1500 years. The Ages typify a period of expanding trade, agriculture and stock rearing.

Bronze Age pottery of the eastern regions, from Greece to the Far East, shows a diversity and multiplicity of forms. In the Mediterranean area, the decoration was painted. See *Crete* and *Mycenaean*. The pots are free and expressive of life, but towards the late Bronze Age one can see that they were influenced by bronze objects.

The Western potters permutated well-tried forms which were few in number. They were able to keep a more plastic expression in their work and were not influenced by bronze objects. The decoration is textural patterning, sometimes scratched but mostly impressed. The pot shown on page 41 is a drinking beaker from South Wales, *c.* 1600BC. The decoration is produced by a notched rocker tool. See also *Bell beaker*, *Cinerary urn* and *Pygmy cup*.

Brookite

TiO_2. Natural titanium oxide. Brookite is one of the three oxide ores of titanium. The other two are rutile and anatase. They are chemically alike but individual in their crystal structure.

Brookite crystals appear to be coloured but are colourless within and are the source of the white titanium oxide. See *Titanium oxide*.

Brown

Brown colours are easily achieved in bodies and glazes by additions of iron oxide and manganese oxide either alone or in combination. The browns can be modified with zinc oxide and nickel oxide.

Iron oxide gives colours ranging from yellow through reddish browns and rusts to dark browns and blacks. Manganese oxide gives colours from gingery orange to purply brown. In glazes, some very rich, deep, reddish browns can be obtained which sometimes contain metallic speckle at the surface, by a combination of the two oxides. See *Iron oxide*, *Manganese oxide* and *Colour plate 67*.

Brown mouth

The dark rim of a pot resulting from the iron in the body showing through the glaze. If the glaze is fairly liquid during firing it tends to leave a thinner layer on the rim. The iron oxide of a dark body-glaze layer will then force its way through the thin layer of glaze to the surface. The term brown mouth is especially used to describe the Chinese Guan ware of the Song dynasty.

Buffer layer

Glaze-body interface. Glaze-body interlayer. Engobe layer. A controlled body-glaze layer. In certain circumstances it may be desirable to encourage the development of the body-glaze layer to create resistance to crazing or shivering or to improve colour and crystallization. The deliberately created layer is a buffer layer. The interlayer absorbs the stress between body and glaze. Normally a longer firing at the same temperature, called soaking, will do this but may be undesirable because of its effect upon the body as a whole. See *Body-glaze layer*. The only way is to create the body-glaze layer artificially or at least assist its formation by a wash of soft flux on the biscuit before the glaze is applied, or more popularly by an engobe attached to the raw ware.

The engobe would be approximately half body and half glaze and not necessarily the same body and glaze. As with normal slips, the opportunity to introduce a colour should not be missed. Also the use of a white buffer layer assists the formation of clean colours, especially iron colours in

stoneware. The white surface reflects the heat back into the glaze and fuses it more while protecting the body slightly. At the same time it is fusing the two together as a body-glaze layer, which it is intended to do, and introducing clean or white crystals into the iron layer of the glaze to give good rust colours on cooling. A buffer layer of this type is very useful on the rims of dark coloured stonewares producing not only a good colour but also preventing the thinner rim from becoming over-vitrified and too brittle. Some buffer engobes are more refractory than the body and may be desirable in cases similar to the one just quoted.

In testing different buffer layers one must remember to note the difference in body-glaze layer and body breakdown as well as colour differences. If the body and glaze are not fitting properly so that crazing or shivering is occurring, the buffer layer can be used to act as a cushion for the stress. The normal buffer engobe is a 50/50 mix of body and glaze. Free silica in the form of sand is often removed or alternatively it is carefully studied in test sections to see that it is becoming involved in the melt. If it does not become involved but remains as crystalline silica, it is subject to the silica inversions and could cause more difficulties.

Bullers rings

(*trade name*). Firing trial rings. Pyroscopes compounded from minerals which interact upon one another over a wide temperature range producing a progressive shrinkage. They were introduced in 1910 by Bullers Ltd of Hanley but are now produced by Taylor Tunnicliff Ltd of Longton. The ring is really a flat disc about 6·5 cm in diameter with a convenient hole in the middle by which it can be easily withdrawn from the kiln on the end of a hooked rod. The diameter is measured on either an Index gauge with an extended pointer or a Vector gauge between two converging guide rails. An average of three diameters gives a mean value. This value can be related to a temperature if necessary. However, to get consistency of results in a sequence of firings, users of Bullers rings are encouraged to describe firings in gauge-read numbers. There is a natural temptation to convert these numbers to temperatures but the original values relate directly to the heat-work of the firing and are therefore a more accurate description. Rings are effective for the range 960°C to 1420°C (1760°F to 2588°F) and can be withdrawn and the heat-work calculated as a temperature at any time during a firing. They are not returned to the kiln. New ones are withdrawn for each reading that is required.

Unlike cones and bars, the rings are not in themselves related to temperatures. Cones and bars are selected for specific points in a firing and only give indication when this point is reached. Rings can be removed at any time and indicate what is happening. They help the fireman to take correct action during the firing and are especially useful with tunnel kilns. Cones and bars indicate end points of firings and are useful for post-firing diagnosis.

Bung (1)

A removable stopper closing or filling a kiln spyhole. When viewing cones, the eyes must be protected from the glare. See *Safety*.

Bung (2)

A pile of saggars. In the kiln, saggars are stacked vertically one on top of another, the top one often having a lid. The rim of each saggar has a wad or snake of refractory clay to give a firm seating, seal the saggar if necessary, and provide a soft joint which will split apart easily after the firing. Bungs are arranged with varying gaps between them to direct the flames through the kiln.

Burners

Installations to achieve the efficient burning of gas or oil for kiln heating. Both gas and oil burners fall into two main groups: those relying upon atmospheric pressure and those relying upon boosted pressure to supply the necessary air for

Principle of the atmospheric gas burner with LPG type gauge.

Principle of forced-air oil burner with low-pressure oil and high-pressure primary air.

combustion. Kilns with atmospheric gas burners are independent of an electricity supply but oil burners always require electrical power for either the oil pressure or boosted air.

The hydrocarbons of gas and oil require oxygen for combustion. Air is only 20% oxygen and therefore a large volume of air is required. For example, coal gas requires six times, natural gas ten times, propane twenty-three times and butane thirty times its own volume of air to burn completely. A gas or oil burning freely does not involve sufficient air to burn completely. The hydrogen burns first and the remaining carbon is seen as smoke. A device to mix the fuel with air before burning it is therefore essential for smokeless efficiency.

Kiln burners usually need two categories of air: primary and secondary. Primary air is mixed with the fuel before it is ignited. Secondary air joins and mixes with the fuel at the flame stage. The use and control of two supplies gives flexibility. Primary air is fed with the gas or oil through the burner. This primary mixing ensures a stable flame but is insufficient to burn all the fuel. The full burning is achieved with the help of the secondary air thereby giving control of oxidation or reduction of the firing by admitting excess or restricting the air. A general rule is that more primary air always shortens a flame and that less primary air lengthens it.

Primary air may be supplied either at atmospheric pressure drawn into the burner by the pressure of the fuel or it may be supplied under extra pressure (forced air).

Secondary air may be supplied either by being drawn in at the burner port or at a separate secondary port by the pull of the chimney, or alternatively by blown air at these ports supplied by a fan or compressor (forced draught).

Primary air is controlled by opening and closing holes at the burner and by varying the pressure or amount of forced air. Natural draught secondary air is controlled by opening and closing the damper at the base of the chimney thus drawing more or less air in at the burners. A forced draught is controlled by varying the pressure at the compressor or varying the speed of the fan.

The simplest atmospheric gas burner operates on the Bunsen principle. The gas enters the mixing tube via a jet directed along the axis of the tube. There are adjustable air holes alongside the jet through which air is drawn. The gas pressure must be sufficient to push itself and the entrained air out to the end of the tube, otherwise the flame travels back down the tube to the jet in a back-fire.

More sophisticated burners make use of the Venturi principle whereby the mixing tube begins to narrow upstream of where the gas jet enters and then widens downstream to the open end. This restriction increases the gas speed thus entraining more air in at the primary air holes. This ensures a more stable flame with the higher calorific gases of butane and propane.

The gas and air mixture should burn with the flame at the end of the tube but if the gas and air settings are not correctly balanced the flame can burn back down the tube to the jet in a back-fire or lift off the end of the tube and burn in unstable manner partway up the kiln burning space.

The back-fire occurs when there is too much air in the mixture and the gas pressure is very low. Thus it occurs mostly with coal gas but not with LPG. It is remedied by reducing the amount of primary air when gas pressure is low. Coal gas is usually pressured up to only 5 cm (2 inches) of water, natural gas up to 25 cm (10 inches), liquid petroleum gases between 0·03 and 1·05 kilograms per square centimetre (0·5 and 15 pounds per square inch). See *Table 41*.

Flame lift-off occurs when the gas pressure is high and there is too little primary air mixed with the gas. A strong secondary air current carries the unburnt mixture away. It is remedied by increasing the amount of primary air and/or reducing the amount or speed of secondary air if this can be done. There is also a design feature of a burner known as the flame retaining nozzle. See drawing on page 43. This is a cup-shaped end to the tube. The sudden widening slows down the mixture at the burner mouth which encourages the flame to remain at the burner. When available gas pressure is low it can be advantageous to use a forced air system. Here the primary air is blown through the burner and is used to entrain the gas into the tube where it is mixed with the air before burning. So much air can be introduced by this method that secondary air might not be necessary and the burner can be sealed into the pierced brick of the kiln wall at what is known as the quarl. The quarl is often shaped as a flame retaining nozzle. In a sealed kiln where the forced air is also a forced draught, there is no need for a chimney to effect draw. Of course a vent of some description is necessary to evacuate the spent fumes. Control of such a burner is by variable speed fan or blower or by altering the air pressure fed to the burner.

When kilns have little natural draught or a natural draught that is constantly changing because of the environment, a forced draught is necessary. This supplies controllable secondary air and ensures continuous uniform burning of the gas, whether this has forced primary air or not. Forced draught is often made to enter the port or burning space obliquely so that it creates a spiralling of the flame. This improves the mixing of gas and air.

A packaged burner, as the name implies, is a burner complete with all necessary valves, governor, gauges, blower, electrical controls, pilot light and often ignition device and safety solenoid valve. The whole is ready-assembled in an integral casing and only needs gas supply and electricity connections. Each packaged burner carries its own blower separately controlled.

Most gas burners can be fitted with sparking plugs and flame failure devices. See ***Instrumentation***.

Oil must be atomized into a fine spray so that it can combine quickly with oxygen in combustion. Smoke results if the spray is not fine enough or if insufficient oxygen is present.

Oil passed through a very small jet under high pressure can involve sufficient primary air for first burning and a good natural draught can provide sufficient secondary air. Such a burner is acceptable once the kiln is hot. However fine jets block easily and such a burner has limited adjustment.

Most oil burners operate with forced primary air spiralling inside the burner and atomizing the oil as it emerges from a jet under low pressure. Typical pressures are 0·05 to 0·35 kg/cm^2 (1–5 p.s.i.) for the oil provided by gravity or pump, and 0·3 to 0·5 kg/cm^2 (5–20 p.s.i.) for the air giving a wide range of burning. See ***Table 41***.

Secondary air can be natural draught, a separate blower at the burner port or separate secondary port, or integrated in the burner itself.

Burning off

A casual term for the removal of bound water in the ceramic change.

Burning out

The removal of unwanted matter by heat in the kiln. Some colours are applied to glazes with gums and oils. These are not part of the final colour required but merely convenient carriers for the colour when it is applied. The gum etc is burnt out before the colour melts to form its ceramic state. Also in many clay and glaze materials there is unwanted carbon, sulfur and fluorine. This is burnt out by oxidation at temperatures above red heat. If not burnt out, these unwanted materials would damage the body, glaze or colour with bloating, bubbling, blistering and discolouration. See also ***Hardening on***.

Burnishing

Polishing leatherhard clay by rubbing with a hard object like a smooth pebble, the back of a spoon or a strip of spring steel. Pinched and coiled pots are often burnished. Thrown pots can be burnished after turning by reversing the spin of the wheel and laying flat the torn roughness created by the turning tool. The globular jar and bottles are by Christine Gittins. For making details see ***Colour plate 32***.

Butterfly
A particular type of glaze crawl in which a piece of glaze leaves its place and folds back on itself to give a double thickness next to a bald patch. See ***Crawling***.

Bytownite
One of the plagioclase feldspars. It is mostly lime feldspar but contains up to 25% sodium feldspar.

C

Cadmium

Cd. A metal, the sulfide of which is a common orange and yellow pigment in paints and ceramics. The oxide (CdO) also occurs in glazes but is not deliberately introduced although its presence has some modifying effect upon colours.

Cadmium sulfide (CdS) gives brilliant yellows. In combination with cadmium selenide (CdSe) a range of oranges and bright reds is possible. These colours are fugitive. The selenium volatilizes easily so that the firing must be rapid. Also the colour must be protected from the effects of oxidation by a suitably reducing atmosphere. Coloured glazes are made but most use is in onglaze colours. See **Poison** and **Metal release**.

Cake

A slab of clay, usually from the filter-press as in the photograph.

Calamine

Mining name for zinc ores especially zinc carbonate.

Calcine

To purify by the action of heat, from the use of the word to describe the burning of lime (calx). The potter uses the term to describe the preparation of a material by heat, usually in the region of 700°C (1292°F). For example, the calcination of china clay produces an alumino-silicate for use in glazes and bodies which has the same ultimate chemical content as china clay but is without the properties of a clay. See **Molochite**.

Calcining is not the same as fritting which involves melting and the creation of complex silicates. Calcining is essentially a purifying process although two or more materials calcined together can create new compounds.

Calcining can be done on a small scale by putting the material in a pot for the biscuit firing. The sintered mass is then crushed in a mortar and sieved if necessary.

Calcite

Calcspar. CaCO₃. Crystalline calcium carbonate occurring in many forms as spar crystals, stalactites, chalk, marble etc. As clean crystals it occurs as white veins and pockets in limestones and is often mistaken for quartz. However, it is much softer than quartz and can be scratched with a penknife, which quartz cannot. Being soft it is easily ground for use as calcium carbonate in glazes.

Nail-head spar, dog-tooth spar and Iceland spar are different varieties of the calcite crystal. Aragonite is chemically identical but of a different crystal structure.

Calcium borate

Ca(BO₂)₂. The anhydrous state of borocalcite. See **Colemanite**. Calcium borate is the theoretical combination of one molecule each of calcia and boric oxide (CaO.B₂O₃). In reality, colemanite is a much more variable structure.

Calcium borate crystals occur as partial devitrification in some glazes and create attractive blue flushes. See **Clair-de-lune** and **Jun**.

Calcium carbonate

Carbonate of lime. CaCO₃. A stable and insoluble (in water) compound of calcium which is used to introduce calcium oxide (CaO) into bodies and glazes.

Calcium carbonate is the chemical name. The potter's materials which are almost pure calcium carbonate are whiting, limestone, marble and chalk.

Calcium carbonate decomposes by 825°C (1517°F) to give calcium oxide and carbon dioxide. The carbon dioxide escapes without difficulty leaving the calcium oxide in the body or glaze.

$$CaCO_3 \xrightarrow{825°C} CaO + CO_2\uparrow$$

Calcium chloride

CaCl₂. A highly soluble and deliquescent crystalline compound. It is used to flocculate clay suspensions.

Four teaspoonsful of concentrated solution of calcium chloride are sufficient to flocculate up to 100 g of bentonite. This expands the bentonite in a box-like jelly structure which holds non-clay minerals and inhibits their sedimentation. See *Flocculation*.

Calcium fluoride

Fluorspar. Blue John. CaF_2. See *Fluorspar*.

Calcium minerals

The element calcium accounts for approximately 4% of the earth's crust but it does not occur as a native metal. It is always combined with other elements in compounds of which there are many. Calcium is essential to animal life as the constituent of bones, shells and teeth.

The most common of the calcium compounds is calcium carbonate which the potter uses as a source of calcium oxide for glazes. A list of the calcium compounds used in ceramics follows:

calcium oxide	CaO
calcium carbonate	$CaCO_3$
calcium chloride	$CaCl_2$
calcium fluoride	CaF_2
calcium phosphate	$Ca_3(PO_4)_2$
calcium sulfate, anhydrite	$CaSO_4$
calcium sulfate, gypsum	$CaSO_4.2H_2O$
calcium borate	$Ca(BO_2)_2$
dolomite	$CaMg(CO_3)_2$
wollastonite	$CaSiO_3$

Calcium oxide

Lime. CaO. A readily available and extremely useful body and glaze material. It is used as a filler in low-temperature bodies and glazes; and as a flux in high-temperature glazes. Large amounts encourage crystalline growth during cooling.

The pure oxide (CaO) is also called quicklime. It reacts with water combining with it to produce calcium hydroxide, called slaked lime, ($Ca(OH)_2$). Calcium oxide is therefore introduced into bodies and glazes in the insoluble form of the carbonate ($CaCO_3$) and the borate ($Ca(BO_2)_2$). See *Calcium carbonate* and *Calcium borate*.

Calcium oxide is often introduced into bodies, but whether it is introduced or is already present, it is necessary to involve it in part of the fusion. If it is not involved somehow in a silicate, a glassy part of the body, it remains as the very absorbent quicklime. This can happen with very low-fired porous bodies which naturally absorb moisture from the air. The quicklime does so with attendant swelling which is enough to cause flaking or even complete shattering of a finished piece of work. See *Lime blows*.

Calcium oxide, which is involved in the fusion, brings to a body some noteworthy properties. It has a high rate of contraction which is valuable in earthenwares to prevent crazing of the glaze. Malms or true marls contain up to 20% which accounts for their successful use for maiolica ware

fired at 1050°C (1922°F). Calcium oxide also prevents warping and gives whiteness. It is introduced into some low-temperature pressing bodies for these reasons.

However, calcium oxide cannot be used in vitreous bodies or those to be fired above 1100°C (2012°F). Above 1100°C, it becomes an active flux and is therefore not practical in bodies. The rapid fluxing action makes the body mature too rapidly. It is therefore difficult to successfully fire because a kiln will contain too many pieces that are under-mature and too many that are overfired and distorted. Clays naturally high in calcium oxide do not make good stoneware bodies and are therefore used mostly in the 1000°C to 1080°C range (1832°F to 1976°F).

Again, in glazes, the actions of calcium oxide can be divided into low and high temperature by the 1100°C (2012°F) mark. Below 1100°C it is not active as a flux although small amounts sometimes give some interaction. Generally it will be found to be an anti-flux but one whose action is not strong. It readily involves itself in glassy fusions with sodium, potassium and lead oxides, and brings to glazes a hardness and acid resistance that is worth its introduction. It helps to involve lead oxide and thereby reduces solubility. It also stabilizes the sodium oxide and silica combination. Up to 10% can often be absorbed in earthenware glazes with little loss of shine and great improvement in durability. It may make lead glazes more susceptible to crazing but it increases the craze resistance of glazes which are high in sodium and potassium oxides.

Large amounts of calcium oxide, perhaps as much as 35%, in soft earthenware glazes encourage the growth of crystals. See *Lime matt*. Calcium oxide in boron oxide glazes also encourages the formation of calcium borate devitrification giving a decorative flushing or milkiness to the glaze without upsetting the high shine of the boron oxide glaze. The amount of calcium oxide here need not be larger than 5% in some glazes.

Calcium oxide begins its fluxing action at 1100°C (2012°F) and from then upwards it is an active and practical flux for all glazes at all temperatures and atmospheres. Its own melting point is 2570°C (4658°F) and with silica alone, whose melting point is 1710°C (3110°F), it cannot produce a molten glass below 1400°C (2552°F). However, in combination with or in interaction with other fluxes, the calcium oxide can produce fluid melts. A typical recipe for a transparent stoneware glaze for 1250°C (2282°F), which uses calcium oxide as the main flux in interaction with potassium and sodium oxides, is:

mixed feldspar	50
china clay	15
quartz	15
calcium carbonate	20

An important point about calcium oxide is its stable structure during a firing. The melting point of the metal calcium is 852°C (1566°F) but the melting point of the oxide is 2570°C (4658°F). The ions of calcium and oxygen

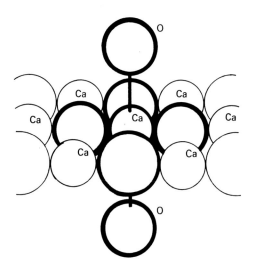

make a strong bond, each in six-fold co-ordination as shown in the drawing.

In interaction with other oxides, and especially over 1100°C (2012°F), these bonds can be loosened. Hence its fluxing action, but it is impossible to completely separate the calcium from the oxygen by reduction below 2200°C (3992°F). Calcium oxide is therefore suitable for all glazes and is unaffected by deliberately or accidentally reducing atmospheres. There are in fact no difficulties in its use, but there is one remaining property that should be taken into consideration.

Calcium oxide is a bleach whose effect is sometimes surprising. Where the colouring oxide is small in amount, the result can be interestingly alkaline with copper blues and cobalt mauves. This happens in lime matts. However calcium oxide cannot cope with strong colours.

With oxidized iron oxide (red iron oxide) a bleaching effect is noticeable. Up to 3% of iron oxide is bleached to a yellow in lime matts. Here the iron oxide presents itself as an alternative to silica because there is a surfeit of calcium oxide. Instead of calcium silicate ($CaO.SiO_2$) a spinel type of combination, which could be called calcium ferrite ($CaO.Fe_2O_3$), is formed.

Reduced iron oxide (black iron oxide) is not affected because calcium oxide cannot combine with it. It is unlikely to be available either, because, as soon as oxidized iron oxide becomes reduced iron oxide it is an active flux and combines with the silica. Its fluxing action can take place at 900°C (1652°F) which is long before calcium oxide becomes active.

Oxidation and reduction therefore have an effect upon iron glazes in which the main flux is calcium oxide, not because the calcium oxide is changed but because in one case it links with iron oxide (red), and in the other the iron oxide (black) is already committed and not available.

For this reason calcium oxide is an excellent flux for reduced iron glazes like the clean-coloured celadons and blue-black tenmokus; but it is not a suitable flux for oxidized tenmoku because the crystals of calcium ferrite cloud the colour of the iron dissolved in the silicate.

Calcium phosphate

Tricalcium phosphate. $Ca_3(PO_4)_2$, ultimately $3CaO.P_2O_5$. Phosphorus oxide is combined with calcium oxide in its occurrence in rocks, the soil, plants and animals. It is introduced as calcium phosphate into bodies and glazes from apatite, phosphorite, vegetable ashes and bone ash. Small amounts in glazes give flushes or cloudy opacity. Larger amounts give opacity, a dull surface and blisters. In bodies, calcium phosphate gives controlled vitrification as in bone china. See **Bone ash**, **Phosphorus oxide** and **Colloid: glaze**.

Calcium sulfate

Anhydrite. $CaSO_4$. The anhydrous state of gypsum which is found as a salt in Germany. It is soluble in water and is used as a flocculant to prevent the rapid settling of glaze slops. See **Flocculation** and **Gypsum**.

Calculations

Most of the calculations which the potter is called upon to do depend upon straightforward addition, subtraction, multiplication and division of known numbers. The numbers are obtained from recipes, by weighing or by looking them up in the appropriate lists, as in the Tables of this book. Often the numbers are inserted into a formula. See **Formula** in this book. Two examples are worked here along with examples involving the unity formulae of glazes which require a series of stages. For the use of unity formulae see **Formula: unity**, and **Computer glaze calculations**.

EXAMPLE OF FINDING A MOLECULAR WEIGHT. In this example the molecular weight is required for albite feldspar. The chemical formula is:

$$Na_2O.Al_2O_3.6SiO_2$$

The first step is to find the atomic weight of each of the elements involved. These are given under **Element** and again in **Table 17**. The small numbers below the formula refer to the number of atoms of the preceding element. The large number 6 indicates that the whole of the molecule SiO_2 is present six times. See **Formula: chemical**.

$$
\begin{aligned}
Na_2O &= (23 \times 2) + 16 &=& \quad 62 \\
Al_2O_3 &= (27 \times 2) + (16 \times 3) &=& \quad 102 \\
6SiO_2 &= 6 \times (28 \cdot 1 + (16 \times 2)) &=& \quad \underline{360 \cdot 6} \\
& & & \quad 524 \cdot 6
\end{aligned}
$$

The molecular weight for albite is therefore $524 \cdot 6$. A list of the molecular weights of common minerals is given in **Table 30**.

EXAMPLE OF CONVERSION OF PERCENTAGE GLAZE RECIPE TO BATCH RECIPE. Given the percentage recipe:

borax frit	75
feldspar	15
china clay	10

calculate the actual weights required to make 40 litres of glaze slop at 90°TW.

Table 19 equates 90°TW with r.d. 1·45, therefore the total weight of 40 litres of slop will be:

$$40\,\text{kg} \times \text{r.d.}\ 1\cdot45 = 58\text{kg}$$
(wt of 40 litres of water)

The total amount of dry material is discovered by using Brongniart's formula. This states that the dry weight content is equal to the apparent dry weight multiplied by the relative density of the dry materials divided by this relative density minus one.

$$(\text{total wt minus wt of same volume of water}) \times \frac{\text{r.d.}}{\text{r.d.}-1}$$

The formula is explained under **Formula: Brongniart's**. The relative density of the glaze materials approximates 2·5 and this is a typical average for most of the leadless materials. See **Tables 10 to 16** and **30**. Therefore the total dry weight of 40 litres of glaze slop will be:

$$(58\,\text{kg} - 40\,\text{kg}) \times \frac{2\cdot5}{1\cdot5} = 30\,\text{kg}$$

and the amount of the water will be:

$$58\,\text{kg} - 30\,\text{kg} = 28\,\text{kg} = 28\,\text{litres}$$

All that remains to be done is to apportion the total weight of 30 kg in the percentages of the recipe. This is done by using the formula:

$$\frac{\text{recipe amount} \times \text{total weight required}}{\text{total of recipe amounts}}$$

borax frit $\dfrac{75 \times 30}{100} = 22\cdot5\,\text{kg}$

feldspar $\dfrac{15 \times 30}{100} = 4\cdot5\,\text{kg}$

china clay $\dfrac{10 \times 30}{100} = 3\cdot0\,\text{kg}$

$$\overline{30\cdot0\,\text{kg}}$$

Most potters will have discovered that with leadless glazes approximately equal weights of dry material and water give a workable slop and that the volume of water used is approximately 0·75 of the final volume of slop.

EXAMPLE OF FINDING THE UNITY FORMULA OF A GLAZE. To find the unity formula one starts with the glaze recipe and uses either the chemical formula for each material or an ultimate analysis of each material to discover which oxides are entering the glaze fusion and in what proportional amount. Both methods are shown.

Given the glaze recipe:

albite	35
lead monosilicate	57
wollastonite	8
	100

METHOD 1. *Stage 1.* Ascertain the chemical formula and molecular weight of each material. See **Table 30**.

albite $Na_2O.Al_2O_3.6SiO_2$ MW 524·6
lead monosilicate $PbO.SiO_2$ MW 283·3
wollastonite $CaO.SiO_2$ MW 116·2

Note that the chemical formulae have been separated into the constituent oxides which are to be considered as entering the fusion. If there are volatiles, e.g. CO_2, these are also listed separately.

Stage 2. Divide the recipe amount by the appropriate molecular weight. This gives the number of molecules of each oxide which is present in the glaze, or at least gives a series of numbers which proportionately represent this.

$$35 \div 524\cdot6 = 0\cdot0667$$
$$57 \div 283\cdot3 = 0\cdot2012$$
$$8 \div 116\cdot2 = 0\cdot0685$$

The resulting numbers tend to be small decimals. This can be avoided by appropriately inflating the recipe numbers by multiplying each by 10,000 and the molecular weight by 10. Decimal places are then ignored and the numbers are more manageable.

$$350\,000 \div 5246 = 67$$
$$570\,000 \div 2833 = 201$$
$$80\,000 \div 1162 = 69$$

Stage 3. These numbers represent the number of molecules of each material. The number of molecules of each oxide is discovered by reference to the chemical formulae. Only albite with its six molecules of SiO_2 requires special care. All the others become straightforwardly interpreted. Thus:

albite provides 67 Na_2O, 67 Al_2O_3 and 6×67 SiO_2
lead monosilicate provides 201 PbO and 201 SiO_2
wollastonite provides 69 CaO and 69 SiO_2

When this is written in the usual layout it becomes:

67 Na_2O
201 PbO   67 Al_2O_3 672 SiO_2
69 CaO
337

The RO group of oxides is totalled (337) and all the numbers are divided by this figure to bring the RO group to unity and the other groups into proportion. This is the unity formula:

$$\left.\begin{array}{l} 0\cdot199 \text{ Na}_2\text{O} \\ 0\cdot593 \text{ PbO} \\ \underline{0\cdot205 \text{ CaO}} \\ \overline{0\cdot997} \end{array}\right\} 0\cdot199 \text{ Al}_2\text{O}_3 \qquad 1\cdot994 \text{ SiO}_2$$

METHOD 2. *Stage 1.* Ascertain, from the suppliers, the ultimate percentage analysis for each material. If there are volatiles which are lost in the firing, these are included at this stage.

albite:	SiO_2	66
	Al_2O_3	21
	Na_2O	9
	K_2O	3
	CaO	1
lead monosilicate:	SiO_2	21
	PbO	79
wollastonite:	SiO_2	50
	CaO	49
	Al_2O_3	1

Stage 2. Multiply each item by the appropriate number (amount) in the recipe. Volatiles can now be ignored.

SiO_2	$66 \times 35 =$	2310
Al_2O_3	$21 \times 35 =$	735
Na_2O	$9 \times 35 =$	315
K_2O	$3 \times 35 =$	105
CaO	$1 \times 35 =$	35
SiO_2	$21 \times 57 =$	1197
PbO	$79 \times 57 =$	4503
SiO_2	$50 \times 8 =$	400
CaO	$49 \times 8 =$	392
Al_2O_3	$1 \times 8 =$	8

Stage 3. Repeated oxides are totalled and the amounts are divided by their respective molecular weights:

SiO_2	2310		
	1197		
	$\underline{400}$		
	$\overline{3907}$	$\div \quad 60\cdot1$	$= 65\cdot0$
Al_2O_3	735		
	$\underline{8}$		
	$\overline{743}$	$\div \quad 102\cdot0$	$= 7\cdot3$
Na_2O	315	$\div \quad 62\cdot0$	$= 5\cdot1$
K_2O	105	$\div \quad 94\cdot2$	$= 1\cdot1$
CaO	35		
	$\underline{392}$		
	$\overline{427}$	$\div \quad 56\cdot1$	$= 7\cdot6$
PbO	4503	$\div \quad 223\cdot2$	$= 20\cdot2$

Stage 4. When this information is put together in the usual layout it becomes:

$$\begin{array}{ll} 5\cdot1 & \text{Na}_2\text{O} \\ 1\cdot1 & \text{K}_2\text{O} \\ 20\cdot2 & \text{PbO} \\ \underline{7\cdot6} & \text{CaO} \\ \overline{34\cdot0} \end{array} \qquad 7\cdot3 \text{ Al}_2\text{O}_3 \qquad 65\cdot0 \text{ SiO}_2$$

Stage 5. The RO group of oxides is totalled (34) and all the numbers are divided by this figure to bring the RO group to unity and the other groups into proportion. This is the unity formula:

$$\left.\begin{array}{l} 0\cdot150 \text{ Na}_2\text{O} \\ 0\cdot032 \text{ K}_2\text{O} \\ 0\cdot594 \text{ PbO} \\ \underline{0\cdot224 \text{ CaO}} \\ \overline{1\cdot000} \end{array}\right\} 0\cdot214 \text{ Al}_2\text{O}_3 \; 1\cdot911 \text{ SiO}_2$$

There is a noticeable difference in the two unity formulae produced by these two methods. The first method is easier and sufficiently accurate for most cases. The second method is more accurate but takes longer to do. It is needed when a material has no chemical formula that can be used, unless a simplified formula and molecular weight are created from its ultimate analysis. This is done by giving it its own unity formula. Unity can be based on any convenient oxide since the molecular weight is calculated from the formula and it will always be proportionate.

EXAMPLE OF CONVERTING A UNITY FORMULA INTO A RECIPE. In this calculation, one starts with a unity formula and by use of chemical formulae and molecular weights one projects a recipe of desired materials. The materials chosen must contain suitable oxides in suitable proportions.

Given the unity formula:

$$\left.\begin{array}{l} 0\cdot3 \text{ K}_2\text{O} \\ 0\cdot1 \text{ MgO} \\ \underline{0\cdot6 \text{ CaO}} \\ \overline{1\cdot0} \end{array}\right\} 0\cdot4 \text{ Al}_2\text{O}_3 \qquad 4\cdot0 \text{ SiO}_2$$

Stage 1. Suitable materials are chosen which will give the appropriate oxides. They are written so that the proportions of their constituent oxides can be seen:

orthoclase	$=$	$\text{K}_2\text{O}.\text{Al}_2\text{O}_3.6\text{SiO}_2$
dolomite	$=$	$\text{CaO}.\text{MgO}.2\text{CO}_2$
whiting	$=$	$\text{CaO}.\text{CO}_2$
china clay	$=$	$\text{Al}_2\text{O}_3.2\text{SiO}_2.2\text{H}_2\text{O}$
flint	$=$	SiO_2

Stage 2. The amounts of molecules in the unity formula are satisfied by amounts (molecules) of the desired glaze materials:

		K_2O	MgO	CaO	Al_2O_3	SiO_2
0·3 orthoclase	=	0·3			0·3	1·8
0·1 dolomite	=		0·1	0·1		
0·5 whiting	=			0·5		
0·1 china clay	=				0·1	0·2
2·0 flint	=					2·0
		0·3	0·1	0·6	0·4	4·0

Stage 3. The molecular amounts of materials are converted to actual comparable weights by multiplying each one by its own molecular weight:

orthoclase	0·3	×	556·8 =	167·04
dolomite	0·1	×	184·4 =	18·44
whiting	0·5	×	100·1 =	50·05
china clay	0·1	×	258·2 =	25·82
flint	2·0	×	60·1 =	120·20
				381·55

Stage 4. To bring this recipe to a comparable percentage, each amount is multiplied by 100 and divided by the total (381·55). The percentage recipe reads:

orthoclase	43·8
dolomite	4·8
whiting	13·1
china clay	6·8
flint	31·5
	100·0

Cane clay

A refined fireclay often sandy in texture but less refractory than fireclay. The fired colour is that of cane or straw.

Cane clay was used for relief modelled pottery in the late 18th and early 19th century. Its pastry colour was effectively used to produce lidded serving pots which imitated pies when flour was taxed in the early 19th century.

Carbon

Carbon is present in most clays and even when only 1% or 2% of the clay, it gives the clay a grey colour. This colouration is removed by careful firing in the oxidation period. See *Firing*. If the carbon is not removed it may cause discolouration of the ware or possibly bloating. See *Black core*. Surface clays tend to contain carbon introduced by the roots of plants. Clays which were once surface clays, like fireclays and some ball clays, contain a high percentage of carbon.

Carbon sometimes builds up on pots in the early stages of a firing by wood, coal, oil and gas. This is caused by incomplete combustion and is called sooting. The carbon later burns effectively producing heat, if sufficient oxygen can enter the kiln above 700°C (1292°F). Carbon not oxidized in this way can discolour glazes. Soft leadless glazes are quickly spoilt once they begin to melt.

Carbonization

The chemical alteration of organic material by the removal of oxygen and oxides to leave only carbon as in the production of charcoal and the slower production of coal. The term has been extended by potters to mean the impregnation of a porous body, and in some cases a glaze, by finely divided carbon as smoke. The result is a velvety black body. The example is a Greek raku panel. See also *Smoking*.

Carbon monoxide

CO. A combination of one atom of carbon with one atom of oxygen as a colourless, odourless but highly poisonous gas.

Carbon monoxide is created in kiln atmospheres to achieve reduction. Carbon-bearing fuel is burned, using oxygen, to heat the kiln, and when fully burned, oxidized, produces carbon dioxide. When the supply of oxygen is restricted the monoxide is formed. This gas seeks for more oxygen and takes it from the metal oxides available in the clay and glazes thus producing the effects of reduction. See *Reduction: atmosphere*.

If this procedure is inexpertly controlled excess carbon monoxide will leak from the kiln. Partly closing a damper in the exit flue to restrict the air also limits the escape of fumes and causes pressure to build up in the chamber. Leakage of fumes must be avoided and all kilns must be vented adequately to outdoors.

One per cent of this gas in the air can cause death. The initial effects on the human system may not be felt immediately but they lead to dizziness, drowsiness, nausea, irritability, headache and a predisposition to accidents. The gas interferes with the supply of oxygen to the body and especially the brain. The red blood cells take up the carbon monoxide in preference to oxygen. If the air breathed contains only 0·01% of carbon monoxide as against 20% of oxygen the blood will carry only half its normal amount of oxygen. If the amount falls below one-third the victim loses consciousness.

Carolina stone
See **Cornish stone**.

Casserole
A lidded, oven-cooking dish for meat and vegetable stews. It is intended as oven-to-table ware, that is, for cooking in and serving from.

The casserole shown is by Pauline Paterson.

Cassiterite
Tin stone. SnO_2. The ore of tin which is a crude form of the tin oxide known to potters as a white opacifier. The ore contains impurities of arsenic, bismuth, copper, iron and zinc. It occurs in igneous acid rocks often within quartz veins. The crushed raw ore and also the tin-containing slurry from tin mines have been used in glazes and as a decorating pigment.

Casting slip
A clay and water suspension used in the process of slip-casting. The suspension is poured into porous moulds and poured out again when a sufficient layer of clay has adhered to the sides. The resulting hollow form is dried, fettled and fired etc.

There are five requirements of a casting slip:

1. It should contain all the ingredients to form a good pottery body when fired.
2. It must be sufficiently fluid to pour into the moulds and fill all details.
3. It must be capable of taking an accurate impression of the mould.

4. It must be reasonably permeable so that as a layer of clay builds up on the wall of the mould, more water can pass through it to increase the thickness.
5. The newly-formed cast, although still wet, must remain firm until it has hardened sufficiently to keep its form as a clay.

The requirements are met as follows:

1. The casting slip will contain many minerals. At least two clays will be used to give a more controllable balance. There may be feldspathic minerals to act as viscous fluxes; flint or quartz for whiteness and hardness; sand or grog for texture and hardness; and cristobalite for glaze fit. It is necessary that a precise sequence is followed in the preparation of a slip in order to get the desired end result. An example sequence is described later.

2. Fluidity can be achieved by a watery slip but this gives difficulties in the amount of water to be absorbed by the moulds. The usual practice is to use deflocculants which enable a fluid slip to have high density. See **Fluidity** and **Deflocculation**. A litre of deflocculated slip will weigh 1·7 kg to 1·9 kg and still be fluid. An equally fluid slip made without the aid of deflocculants could not contain this weight of materials and would only weigh 1·45 kg to the litre.

3. It is pointless to have a fluid slip if it is mostly composed of coarse particles. The majority of the slip should pass a 120's sieve. It may permissibly then contain some grog or other coarse material which should not be coarser than 60's. Too coarse a material will settle during casting giving a non-uniform composition

4. Most natural clays are permeable. However when deflocculated these same clays become impermeable. See **Flocculation**. A balance must be chosen between deflocculation and natural state to allow sufficient permeability. Permeability of the slip is assisted by the non-clay ingredients of the recipe. Pitchers made specially from a flocculated body are sometimes added for this purpose. A permeable body also means that the casts can dry out quickly. There is an advantage in workshop space saved if production is large.

5. Suspensions 'set' slightly when allowed to rest. The phenomenon is a property of all clay suspensions and of some other suspensions. See **Thixotropy**. The property is destroyed by some deflocculants but not by others. A balance of two deflocculants must therefore be used.

PREPARATION OF CASTING SLIP. It will be seen that a casting slip is a compromise of many factors. While scientific in approach, the workshop practice is inevitably one of trial and error, assessment and adjustment. To discover the ideal slip for one's own production, one must decide first upon the quality of the finished ware and establish the body recipe. A test amount of approximately a litre should be mixed as a thick creamy slip of known amounts of dry materials and water. For convenience, the coarse materials like grogs can be omitted at this stage.

The slip is progressively deflocculated with a combined deflocculant made from:

sodium silicate 140° TW	30 ml
sodium carbonate	30 g
hot water	60 ml

The amount of this combined deflocculant, which is added at each step of the test, should be accurately measured with a burette. At each addition of the decided amount of deflocculant, the whole slip is very thoroughly stirred. It is then poured through a funnel and the time taken for this operation is measured. A watch or clock with a second hand is necessary. The funnel should hold all the slip at once. It can be successfully made from an inverted plastic bottle with the base removed. It is also possible to measure the deflocculant without a burette by using a small, deep-bowled measuring spoon.

The results of the test show as seconds taken to drain the funnel related to the progressive additions of deflocculant.

It is not necessary to plot a graph unless the steps taken have been too large. In this case a graph will help to locate the optimum point more accurately. An overdose of de-flocculant brings the effect into reverse. See **Deflocculant**. It should be pointed out that one will not make use of full deflocculation because this would destroy the permeability and make casting impossible. Again a graph will help to locate a suitable point of deflocculation which will give latitude for slight inaccuracies of measurement.

The amounts must now be calculated as a batch recipe. The deflocculant amounts can be calculated by taking the amount of solution used to get the desired effect as a fraction of the amount of solution originally prepared. The amount of deflocculant materials is this same fraction of their starting amounts.

There follows a description of the preparation of a batch of casting slip. It is a light-coloured body to fire to 1000°C (1832°F) biscuit and 1200°C (2192°F) glaze. It illustrates a typical method and recipe. The batch recipe is:

china clay	10	kg
ball clay	20	kg
potash feldspar	12·5	kg
flint	5	kg
whiting	2·5	kg
grog 60's/dust	20	kg
distinguishing stain	60	g
sodium silicate 140°TW	60	ml
sodium carbonate	60	g
water	20 +	litres

Approximately half the water is put into a blunger and approximately a quarter of the clay is added. This is blunged for a few minutes while the sodium silicate and sodium carbonate are dissolved in very hot water. About a quarter of this solution is added to the mixture and blunged for about five minutes. The remaining water is now added together with the distinguishing stain which has been mixed with hot water and passed through a fine sieve (120's to 200's). The remainder of the clay and the deflocculant solution are added and blunging continued for about half-an-hour. The slip should now be extremely fluid.

The feldspar, flint and whiting are now added and the whole slip blunged for another half-an-hour. It is now sieved through a 120's mesh. There remains the grog to be added. This should be separately screened for size. It is added to the slip and blunged in thoroughly by use again of the blunger or by hand blunging. At this point it may be found necessary to readjust the fluidity of the slip by adding still more water. The amount required may be small or it may be a litre. The types of ball clay and grog will affect this.

Industrially it is normal practice to work to an accurate density. In small workshops it is safer to err on the side of fluidity and compensate for this by additional casting time. The above slip should make up at approximately 170 g per 100 ml. See **Slop weight**.

It may be necessary to adjust future batches for density and deflocculation. It is difficult to rebalance existing slips except by adding water. The use of slips, their troubles and remedies is dealt with under **Slip casting**.

ADJUSTMENT OF CASTING SLIP. A number of defects arise in cast ware which require diagnosis and corrective measures. The assessments should be read in conjunction with the articles on **Deflocculation**, **Thixotropy** and **Fluidity**. Adjustment amounts are often quite small. Faults and adjustments required are summarized below:

1. *Wreathing or livering, which is a rippled or uneven surface on the inside of the cast, and roping, which is when this unevenness is in raised lines:*
The slip has insufficient thixotropy. The sodium silicate should be reduced and if necessary the sodium carbonate increased to maintain a working fluidity. Swilling the remaining slip around the mould before draining may help to overcome the trouble.

2. *Cast buckles:*
The cast has been removed from the mould too early.

3. *Cast warps:*
i. The cast has been removed from the mould too late.
ii. The cast has freed itself from one side of the mould but remained attached to the other, possibly due to the angle at which the mould was resting.
iii. The drying has not been uniform.

4. *Cast is flabby and distorts when handled:*
i. Casting time has been too long owing to a wet mould or a

slip which contains too much water and insufficient sodium silicate.

ii. Equally, of course, if the slip has been deflocculated to its maximum, it produces an impervious layer during casting which also increases casting time and gives flabby casts. In this case, decrease both de-flocculants.

5. *Pin-holes in the surface of the cast on the mould side:*

i. The slip has insufficient fluidity and/or contains air bubbles. The water and/or the deflocculants should be increased.

ii. The slip was not poured into the mould with sufficient force to 'wet' the mould wall. The whirler should be spun faster.

6. *Check marks which are horizontal lines on the ware:*

The slip was poured into the mould too slowly and probably with a pause. The mould must be filled quickly.

7. *Cast is brittle at leatherhard and dry stages:*

The thixotropy is too low so that the cast does not 'set' properly. The dry strength is too great which makes the cast brittle. In both cases the sodium silicate should be decreased.

8. *Flashing or casting spot which is a discolouration on the finished ware:*

The discolouration is due to an area of different composition and is where the slip first hit the mould. At this point, if the mould is very porous, a thin slip breaks up into clay and non-clay particles. The pressure of the slip hitting the mould should be reduced by introducing the slip through a pipe. The fluidity of the slip should be decreased by decreasing the amount of deflocculant used, especially the sodium silicate.

Castor ware

Romano-British pottery made at Castor, Northamptonshire. The colour varies from a yellowish grey to a slate blue and is the finest of the Romano-British wares. It was not glazed; decoration was added in the form of freely and elaborately trailed white slip depicting figures, animals and scenes.

Catalyst

A substance which assists a chemical or a physical change to take place in another substance. It may speed up the rate of change or enable the change to take place more easily but after the change the catalyst itself is unchanged. The oxides of aluminium, calcium, iron, magnesium, potassium and sodium all act as catalysts assisting the conversion of the quartz phase of silica into the cristobalite phase.

Catenary curve

A curve made by a chain hanging from two fixed points. If this line is used in an inverted form it gives an arch which is extremely strong when used in building. A catenary arch used over a kiln chamber directs all the thrust of its weight

within the base. There is therefore no need for buttresses or angle iron bracing across the arch.

Celadon

A grey-green to grey-blue stoneware and porcelain glaze. The glaze is a feldspathic type. The colour is derived from a very small amount of red iron oxide which in the reducing firing has been changed to black iron oxide. Celadon ware originated in China, developing from dark, grey-green thickly glazed Yue ware to its artistic maturity in the Song Dynasty. The name was derived from Céladon, a shepherd in the 17th-century French play *L'Astrée* who wore grey-green ribbons and cloak. The classic celadon glaze is thickly applied and semi-translucent. This quality is shown best over deep and shallow carving in the body which exploits the varied depth of colour. The glaze is very viscous when molten in the firing and prone to crawling. Sudden drops in temperature, a danger with heavy reduction, must be avoided. A more transparent, pale bluish glaze fired on porcelain, like the Chinese Yingqing, is also included as a celadon. See *Iron oxide in glazes* and *Recipe Appendix*.

The photographs show Margaret Frith engraving a porcelain bowl to be glazed later with celadon glaze; and an engraved stoneware bowl by Janet Hamer.

Celestine
Celestite. Strontium sulfate. $SrSO_4$. The slightly soluble strontium mineral associated with clay shales and salt deposits.

Celsian
Barium feldspar. $BaO.Al_2O_3.2SiO_2$. One of the true feldspars. See *Feldspar: types of*. It is very rare and available only as hand-picked specimens.

Celsius
°C. Centigrade. Degrees Celsius are units on the Centigrade scale where the freezing point and boiling point of water are 0°C and 100°C, respectively. The scale is named after Anders Celsius, the 18th-century Swedish astronomer, who introduced the centigrade thermometer in 1742. A century later, Lord Kelvin took the principle of the centigrade scale and extended it to an absolute scale beyond the temperatures associated with water. See *Kelvin*.

Ceramic change
The change from clay to pot, upon which the whole pottery industry is founded. Clay can be dried and reconstituted to plastic state *ad infinitum* but once it has been subjected to 600°C (1112°F) it is no longer clay but a hard material which cannot be disintegrated and dispersed by water. The ceramic change involves the removal of hydroxyl groups (OH) from the clay lattice and water (H_2O) from the adsorbed layer attached to the broken ends of the lattice.

Chemically these two items are expressed as water in the acceptable formula for clay which is $Al_2O_3.2SiO_2.2H_2O$. The removal of the two molecules of water in the formula leaves a bonded alumino-silicate which is often referred to as metakaolin. See *Clay: the crystal structure of*, *Firing* and *Water (bound)*.

The ceramic change is a slow process. First, the attached water molecules are sheared from their positions at the ends of the clay lattice. Second, the hydroxyl groups within the lattice are loosened and removed. These immediately become water vapour. The bound water thus released in the ceramic change can amount to 14% of the weight of dry clay. It is not surprising, therefore, that this water can be seen as water vapour escaping from the vents of muffle kilns. These vents have previously dried after the removal of the pore water during the water-smoking period.

The first stage of the ceramic process approximates 450°C to 550°C (842°F to 1022°F) although with some fireclays it begins about 100°C (180°F) earlier. The second stage takes over at 550°C and lasts till 700°C (1292°F). The whole presents a steady process of water liberation starting gradually at a point somewhere between 350°C and 450°C (662°F and 842°F) and increasing to a maximum at 600°C (1112°F) after which there is a rapid decrease in liberation trailing off to 700°C (1292°F).

The ceramic change presents little danger from explosion by steam pressure because the pores of the body are open. As the heat enters the body, the water which seals the passages is released to the outside.

Ceramic fibre
General name for the silicate fibre material first developed for use in jet engines and then used for general high-temperature insulation including kilns. It can be bought as blanket, paper, board, rope and in many pre-formed shapes. See *Insulation*.

Ceramics
Keramics. Clay products made permanent by heat (the ceramic change); also the study of this subject. The word comes from the Greek *keramos* meaning potter's clay and the ware made from it, but it is used to describe non-clay refractories which are changed or formed by heat and also many silicate products. It is often used by the individual potter when the name 'pottery' seems too limiting a description of the work.

Ceramics became a subject of study during the late 19th century when courses were established in many European countries to train chemists and engineers specifically for the pottery industry. Previously the chemists and engineers had first gained their knowledge in other spheres and had then been employed by the potteries.

Prior to the college courses, the only scientific pottery training had been at Wedgwood's and Sèvres, which were two of the earliest potteries to be organized with scientific control.

The early use of the word ceramics to describe a subject of

study was entirely biased towards technology. At the present time, ceramics describes the whole range of pottery and claywork with equal emphasis also given to the skills of designing and making.

Cerium oxide

CeO_2. One of the lanthanide oxides in the amphoteric area of the periodic table. It is an acidic anti-flux with properties similar to tin oxide. It is very refractory and does not dissolve easily. It therefore remains as an opacifier in glazes fired below $1000°C$ ($1832°F$). At higher temperatures it begins to dissolve. It is a suitable substitute for tin oxide at low temperatures.

Cerium oxide gives yellow colours in combination with titanium oxide. In slow-maturing glazes the two oxides can be added to the glaze and will satisfactorily combine. Approximately 3% of cerium oxide is required with 5% of titanium oxide. The colour will withstand high temperatures.

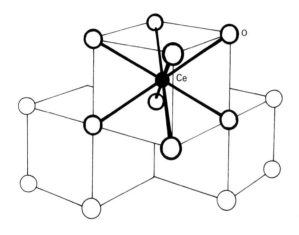

Cerium oxide is used as a stabilizer in the production of yellow stains using vanadium and antimony oxides.

Chalk

Calcium carbonate. $CaCO_3$. The softest of the limestones. It was deposited as a calcareous mud and hence is extremely fine in texture. It varies in colour with impurities of iron. It is a source of calcium oxide in glazes. See **Limestone** and **Calcium carbonate**.

French chalk is not chalk in the same sense. This is talc: magnesium silicate.

Chamotte

Grog. Ground, fired fireclay or other refractory clay. Through its use in Scandinavia, the term chamotte ware or chamotte is also used to mean artistic wares produced in a coarsely-grogged clay especially one containing a lot of plastic fireclay. It is a more romantic name than the English equivalent of saggar-marl ware. See **Grog**.

The photograph shows a detail of 'Death', a wall sculpture by James Milroy.

Charging

Packing a kiln or filling a blunger or grinding mill. A charge is a measured amount of material to be put into the mill etc.

Chattering

The rhythmic rippling which appears when turning. It occurs when the clay is too hard or too soft, or is not uniformly leatherhard. Blunt and unsuitable turning tools also cause chattering. A tool that is too flexible on a hard clay or one that is too stiff on a soft clay sets up a series of waves which become accentuated.

It is possible to use chattering as a decorative feature, in which case it is deliberately encouraged to occur. This can be done effectively when turning plaster of Paris plate moulds.

To overcome chattering the tool should be resharpened and held at a new angle to cut across the chatter. Alternatively, reverse the wheel and use a loop or smaller, pointed tool to cut a series of lines through the chatter before attempting to cut away the whole surface.

Cheesehard

The stage at which the clay has dried sufficiently from its plastic state to be carefully handled without deformation. It is the softest stage at which a pot can be shaved or turned on a wheel or lathe. The next stage in this setting up or stiffening is leatherhard when enough water has dried out for the clay particles to touch one another and the form is almost rigid. Nearly all drying shrinkage has taken place by the leatherhard stage.

Chemical symbol

A shorthand way of writing the name of an element by using the initial letter or two letters of its English or Latin name. The symbol represents the element, e.g. Si means silicon. The symbol is also used to denote one atom of an element when it appears in a compound. For example, SiO_2, which is silicon dioxide, usually called silica, has one atom of silicon to every two atoms of oxygen. The symbols are standardized and accepted internationally. See **Tables 17** and **30**, and **Formula: chemical**.

Chequer

The pierced floor of a kiln through which the flames reach the chamber. The chequer pattern results from the use of standardized bricks supported by other bricks on end to give flues underneath the floor.

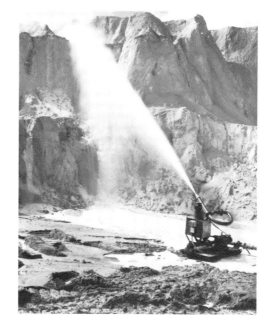

China

British porcelains and white earthenwares are often loosely called 'china'. The term comes from the habit of naming imports by their country of origin. Chinese porcelain was 'china' and so also were its European imitations and derivatives. Today china has a specific meaning amongst potters and implies a translucent white body covered with a glaze fired at a lower temperature than the body.

A development dating from the 18th century is bone china which uses calcined ox bones to provide a viscous flux for the body. See **Bone ash**. A 20th-century development is translucent china or non-bone china which uses mineral fluxes in a similar way to the soft paste porcelains.

China clay

Kaolin. The purest natural clay. Its composition is approximately equal to the mineral kaolinite and it is therefore given the same chemical formula of $Al_2O_3.2SiO_2.2H_2O$. It is used in bodies to give whiteness, to clarify colours and to control vitrification. In glazes it gives fluidity control at slop stage, viscosity control during the molten stage and adds stability to the final glaze.

China clay is an essential ingredient in making porcelain body and bone china body. See **Porcelain** and **Bone china**.

During the 17th century, Europe was searched for white clays with which to make porcelain. The imported Chinese porcelain had created the demand for a European product. Suitable clays were eventually discovered in France and later in England and Bohemia. They were called kaolins like the Chinese clays but while of similar chemical composition they had different physical properties. Unlike the Eastern kaolins, Western kaolins are not very plastic. Some American kaolins are of sedimentary origin and have a little more plasticity.

China clay contains very little iron oxide and titanium

oxide. Therefore it is white in its raw state and remains white through the firing. It is used for whiteware bodies and is indispensable for translucent white porcelain. Its whiteness also helps to clarify the colour of other clays, red and buff clays for example, which are improved by the addition of some china clay. Many prepared red bodies have this addition.

China clay is high in aluminium oxide and average in silica content. It is therefore a refractory clay. Its relatively large crystals melt slowly giving it a long maturing range. It is vitrified by 1770°C (3218°F) at which point it deforms. It was used as a standard of refractoriness by Dr Hermann Seger and became cone number 35. In bodies it is used to introduce controlled vitrification, as in porcelain. It is also used as a refractory for heat treatment furnaces. In glazes it is used to introduce aluminium oxide and silica to control glaze viscosity during firing and give stability to the final structure.

China clay has large crystals in relation to other clays like red earthenware and ball clays. There is therefore a relatively low total surface area to the particles and it requires little water to bring the dry clay to plastic consistency. In some cases as little as 15% moisture content is sufficient. The resulting plasticity is poor. As the water dries out of the plastic clay, the contraction is naturally small compared with more plastic clays. In some cases it is as little as 2% linear contraction, plastic to dry. Similarly, firing shrinkage is low, but this is to be expected when the clay is fired to a point which is a long way below vitrification. These properties are of use in blending bodies.

China clay originated as granite which decomposed to clay, quartz, mica and feldspar. See *Clay origin*. Most china clays are won from their original position as granites and are called primary clays. Secondary china clays have been washed away from these locations and deposited as sediments. In the process they have often been subjected to a process of natural levigation, which allows the heavier particles, of quartz, mica and feldspar, to settle out and the finer particles, which are mostly clay, to be carried further before settling.

China clays which are still *in situ* are won by being washed from the parent rock with power hoses. The slurry is levigated and settled in a series of channels with riffles as traps for the heavier particles.

Many new methods which are less wasteful of space and china clay are being introduced to separate the sand and mica from the clay. The eventual pure clay slurry is filter-pressed and usually dried and pulverized. The three photographs are of automatic washing out, hydrocyclones and filter-press at the works owned by WBB Minerals of Newton Abbot, England.

The kaolinite content, that is, the idealized clay mineral content of the decomposed granite, is as low as 5%. The 'by-products' are therefore commercially important. The eventual clay claimed might account for 10–40% of the original rock. The by-products will be 50–80% quartz sand and 10–20% mica. The china clay will contain approximately 88% kaolinite and 12% mica and quartz.

An ultimate analysis, typical of a china clay is:

SiO_2	46·6
Al_2O_3	38·3
TiO_2	0·1
Fe_2O_3	0·4
CaO	0·3
MgO	0·3
Na_2O	0·3
K_2O	0·7
Loss	13·0

China stone

A pure white cornish stone used in bone china recipes. About 25% is used with 25% of china clay and 50% of bone ash. See *Cornish stone*.

Christmas glitter

Loose crystals found on the surface of salt or soda glazes. Excessive salt or soda which cannot integrate with the body during the firing since the available alumino-silicate has already formed a covering of glaze.

Chromite

$FeO.Cr_2O_3$. Natural chromium iron ore occurring in ultrabasic igneous rocks and the source of chromium oxide for paints, dyes and ceramics. The oxidized form, $Fe_2O_3.Cr_2O_3$, is called iron chromate and is used as a grey colourant in ceramics.

Chromium oxide

Cr_2O_3. The only stable oxide of the metal chromium. It is purchased as a prepared green powder which has a strong staining power in glazes giving mainly greens (up to 2%) but also reds under special conditions. It can be used at all temperatures but above 1200°C (2192°F) some of the oxide will volatilize.

Colours from chromium oxide have a different appearance in daylight from their colours in artificial light, more than is found with colours from other oxides.

Chromium oxide is found in combination with iron oxide in the ore chromite. The metal chromium is used with iron (ferro-chrome) to produce steels. The compounds of chromium are used in paint pigments, dyes and ceramic colours. The oxidized form of chromite, called iron chromate, gives an opaque grey colour in ceramics. Brush-work under glazes can be interesting where the chromium oxide remains stable and opaque, and the iron oxide bleeds into the glaze.

Chromium oxide is an amphoteric oxide and therefore plays different roles in ceramic fusions, depending upon the circumstances presented. It is not easily dissolved in fusion and often gives the appearance of an opaque pigment dispersed in the glaze. Apparently it is slow to act as either a flux or an acid but small amounts (up to 1%) can be dissolved in most glazes. In these cases the chromium oxide is probably fulfilling a linking role partially combined with the fluxes and partially with the acids. It gives a green colour known as chrome green which is not a single hue but a range. It will be appreciated that the particular role which the chromium oxide is fulfilling determines its colour and therefore the properties of the other oxides are important.

Chromium oxide acts as an acid and dissolves more easily in combination with the strong flux lead oxide. It then gives reds and oranges known as chrome reds or chrome coral pinks. Zinc oxide acting amphoterically in lead glazes extends the chrome orange colour.

Chromium oxide acts as a flux and dissolves in combination with the acidic tin oxide. Here it gives a crimson pink colour known as chrome-tin pink. The colours from chromium oxide can be tantalizingly variable. Consistent results will only be obtained by separate preparation of the colouring as a stain.

CHROME GREEN. Chromium oxide gives greens under most conditions. Amounts up to 1% disperse and dissolve fairly easily and give bright greens in alkaline glazes, drab greens in boron glazes and yellowish greens in lead glazes. Amounts below 0·5% give yellow in lead glazes. Amounts up to a maximum of 3% give opacity and greyish green colours. The oxide powder is often quite a rich blue-green colour but it is impossible to keep this colour in glazes without the assistance of cobalt oxide. Chromium oxide can also be used to stain slips and bodies. Amounts up to 5% give different grey greens.

CHROME PEACOCK GREEN. The drabness of many greens can be enlivened by the addition of cobalt oxide. Both chromium and cobalt are strong oxides. Only 1% of each is required to give a bright colour. Boron oxide, or boron and sodium oxides, glazes give the best results. This is a useful addition to the colouring range for potters who use alkaline frit glazes.

CHROME RED. Small amounts of chromium oxide dissolve well and give a bright red colour below 900°C (1652°F) in combination with lead oxide and silica. The presence of aluminium oxide detracts from the quality of red and therefore it is not easy to produce a satisfactory glaze for pottery. However, it is easy to produce exciting red and orange glasses for filling hollows in horizontally-fired tiles. The firing needs to be fully oxidized to achieve the red colour. These glazes are not suitable for raku because they blacken if reduced.

Prepared lead silicates give excellent colours with very little, or preferably without any, feldspar, clay and minerals containing aluminium oxide. Chromium oxide is introduced as potassium dichromate which provides a stabilizing extra flux to carry the chromium oxide into finer dispersion. The presence of sodium oxide turns the red to yellow. Potassium dichromate is soluble in water, therefore only the required amount of water should be added to the glaze. It is also poisonous. A suitable recipe is:

lead bisilicate	90
china clay	5
potassium dichromate	5

CHROME ORANGE. The red colour from lead oxide and chromium oxide becomes orange and then yellow with firings of approximately 950°C (1742°F) and 1050°C (1922°F), although duration of firing is another very important factor. The orange colour can be extended in the temperature range upwards and maintained even in glazes containing aluminium oxide by the presence of zinc oxide and iron oxide. It should be noted that these oxides are also amphoteric oxides. The colour is not quite the same orange but is rather harsh in colour and distinctly opaque. It relies upon the brown of the zinc and chromium oxides being heightened by a clean red iron oxide. The following recipe is an example for the 1100°C to 1150°C (2012°F to 2102°F) range:

feldspar	30
china clay	10
flint	5
whiting	6
lead bisilicate	40
chromium oxide	2
zinc oxide	5
red iron oxide	2

CHROME-TIN PINK. Chromium oxide also produces reds in combination with tin oxide. Here the chromium oxide acts as a flux and enters a loose structure of the normally inert tin oxide. There is therefore no temperature limit with this combination. The resulting colour is a harsh crimson.

Only a small amount of chromium oxide is required. The maximum is 0·5% and less than 0·1% will give results. The amount of tin oxide can vary from 4% to 10% with equal results. The best soft pinks are obtainable with lime matt glazes containing less than 5% of tin oxide and less than 0·1% of chromium oxide. The example recipe is for a glaze firing at 1220°C (2228°F). At this temperature the chromium oxide becomes volatile and some will travel to adjacent pots in the kiln. It is impossible to keep other tin oxide glazes in the same firing from becoming flashed with pink. The original glaze does not seem to be thereby depleted in colour. See also **Recipe Appendix**.

cornish stone	48
china clay	14
flint	5
whiting	28
tin oxide	5
chromium oxide	0·1

Chuck

Chum. A thrown and/or turned clay form which is centred and stuck onto the wheel-head where it is used to hold a pot for turning. The chuck should be in a fairly soft cheese-hard condition in which it is slightly sticky and thus grips the pot.

When not in use, a chuck is stored to keep it in cheeseburial but the best pottery examples come from the Middle Bronze Age of South Wales, Britain, 1400BC to 1000BC. The one illustrated shows the typical collar and decoration of pecked bands.

hard state. Wrapping it in polythene to exclude the air is excellent.

Some potters use a plaster chuck which sits in a cup-head. Also rubber chucks are available which are ready-centred on their own wheel-heads.

Chun
See *Jun*.

Cider jar
A storage jar for cider with a draw-off tap.

Cinerary urn
A pot used for burial of cremated remains or part of the remains. Sometimes it was inverted over the remains and may have been part of a ritual of transporting them. Cinerary urns are found throughout the world and are usually associated with the first large communities. Prior to this the more isolated villages and nomadic groups used inhumation and later peoples tended to have religious beliefs which inhibited cremation.

Cinerary urns vary in size from the pygmy cups, only 5 cm tall, to enlarged food vessels 50 cm tall. Many Western cultures from Bronze Age to Roman used this method of

Cistercian ware
Sixteenth-century earthenware, some of which was made by the Cistercian monks. It is thinly potted ware of deep red clay with a dark shiny glaze containing iron and manganese oxides. Most pieces are multi-handled small mugs, the forerunners of the tygs of the next two centuries.

Cizhou
Tz'u-chou. A collection of stoneware kilns in northern China famous for decorated pottery using white and dark brown slips with sgraffito, carved and brushwork decoration. Bowls, bottles, jars and pillows presented surfaces to decorate over the period from the 7th to the 13th century. The name is used quite generally for all northern Chinese wares of Cizhou type. The photograph on the next page shows a piece from the 13th century.

Clair-de-lune flush

A 19th-century romantic term used to describe the pale blue striations found in Chinese stoneware glazes and emulated by softer glazes in western Europe. The striations are chains of crystal nuclei which have isolated themselves from the molten glaze.

Black iron oxide in high alkaline and low aluminium oxide glazes; phosphorus oxide in stoneware glazes; and calcium borate in hard and soft glazes are some of the sources of flushes. See also *Jun, Colloid* and *Calcium borate*.

Clam

Clam up. Clem. Clag. To smear clay slurry over kiln brickwork, especially the wicket, which is rebuilt for each firing. The words clam and clay have the same origin in the Greek word *gloios* meaning a sticky substance.

Clay

Hydrated silicate of aluminium. A heavy, damp, plastic material that 'sets' upon drying and can be changed by heat into a hard, waterproof material.

There is the idealized clay mineral called kaolinite which is always considered to be of chemical purity though of variably-sized crystals; and there is the clay which all potters know as their fundamental material which seems to bear little relationship to an idealized substance but is a variable, responsive material.

The properties of clay upon which pottery depends are the workability which allows forming and retention of form; and the property of ceramic change to a new material by heat.

Clay is used for other things as well as pottery. Ceramically it is used for bricks, tiles, sanitary ware, electrical insulators and heat insulators. It is also used in cosmetics and as a filler in rubber and paper.

Clay is here covered under the following sub-headings: ORIGIN OF CLAY; TYPES OF CLAY; CHEMISTRY OF CLAY; PHYSICS OF CLAY; THE CRYSTAL STRUCTURE OF CLAY; CLAY IN GLAZES. For clay and heat: see *Firing*. For clay preparation: see *Preparation of clay*.

ORIGIN OF CLAY. Clay is a mineral with a crystal structure, but the individual crystals are too tiny to be seen with the naked eye or even through a magnifying glass. Most people would describe clay as a mud, deposited by rivers in lakes and the sea. However, before it can be thus transported it originates as a pure mineral in decomposed igneous rocks. The decomposed rock is no longer the hard igneous rock of the original but is a soft disintegrating rock which, if exposed, is weathered and washes away. During transportation by a river, or by ice or sea, the clay is ground, picks up impurities, loses associated minerals and is finally settled into areas of similar particle size. See *Levigation*. The result is a clay stratum of progressive variation from fine to coarse with possible change of colour and composition also. This is a typical clay bank. Sedimentary clays rarely show a uniformity over a wide area. This is why blending of different clays is necessary to keep a constant product.

Clays which occur in their place of origin are called primary clays. They are the end product of a chain of reactions and are therefore also called residual clays. The only common examples are china clay and bentonite. Clays which have been transported from their place of origin and settled elsewhere are called secondary clays or sedimentary clays. Ball clays, red marls and stoneware clays are of this type. See also *Kaolinite* and *Disordered kaolinite*.

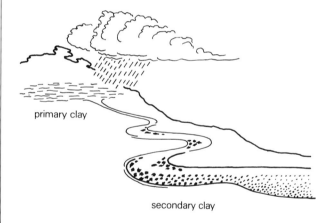

All present clays originated as deep-seated igneous or metamorphic rocks. Hot magma was pushed up from below. It did not reach the surface and therefore cooled slowly in large masses. These were often domes of rock, created where the magma was trapped, preventing further upward movement. These domes are the granite bosses which form upland areas today, like Dartmoor. While cooling and still in a thermoplastic state, the future clays were subjected to hypogenic action. That is, a recreative action from below. This consisted of hot gases including carbon dioxide, water, boron and fluorine.

By a series of substitutions, the gases were able to decompose a potentially hard rock into a soft one which included clay. The hard rock included the mineral feldspar which by hydrolization becomes clay, silica and a salt. The accommodation of hydroxyl ions within the feldspar forms aluminium oxide into a sheet. By later substitutions and accommodations to this sheet a laminar crystal results. The clay (kaolinite) crystal is just such a crystal. Highly siliceous rocks like granite have an end product of clay (kaolinite), quartz, mica and other silicates. The kaolinite is not likely to be more than 25%.

The sheet structure of aluminium oxide, however, is capable of being the basis of more minerals than kaolinite. The end result is dependent upon the original rock composition and the humidity and pressure etc of the hypogenic action. Montmorillonites, micas and chlorites are silicate minerals of similar plate-like structure to kaolinite. However, only the montmorillonite mineral called bentonite resembles clay in its plasticity. The other minerals exist as impurities in clay and give to a clay some of its individuality.

Simplified origin of clays

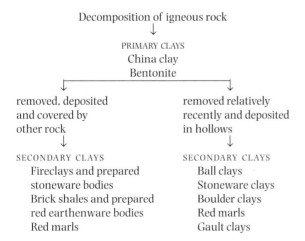

TYPES OF CLAY. Clay can be classified in many ways and each classification can be sub-divided again and again. For example, one of the sedimentary clays is ball clay which can be further classified by the area from which it comes. In each area, it will be found that there are a number of pits and each pit might contain ten or twenty differentiated clays lying in seams or veins, and as isolated pockets. The following divisions are offered as a guide to clay nomenclature and are therefore given the general name of types.

1. *Primary clays*, also called residual clays, are clays which can be mined from the position in which they decomposed from the parent rock. The most important primary clay is china clay which decomposed from feldspar and succeeded in remaining free from colouring impurity. Its attraction is its whiteness. The second important primary clay is bentonite. Apart from bentonite, the primary clays tend to be relatively large in particle size and hence low in plasticity. See **China clay**.

2. *Secondary clays*, also called sedimentary clays, are clays which have been deposited in their present position by the action of water or ice. This category covers most clays. In their removal from parent rock or previous residence, these clays were subjected to abrasion, frost action, leaching and other weathering. Inevitably these break up the particles producing finer clays and hence more plastic ones. Secondary clays are more plastic than primary clays. Most secondary clays contain impurities of which iron is the most common giving a grey, cream or brown colour. They have also collected organic matter which may also give a darkened colour and cause the clays to smell. See ***Disordered kaolinite***.

3. *Plastic clay* is a classification of a property which can be possessed by any clay. It assumes better than average plasticity. Some clays, notably ball clays, are highly plastic and are used as additions to clays low in plasticity. All clays can have their plasticity improved by high-speed blunging, adding plasticizers, and de-aired pugging. Plastic clays are also called long clays and fat clays. They are strong clays and withstand vigorous handling during forming. Naturally plastic clays are also strong at cheesehard and raw state, and usually after firing if fired correctly. Ball clays and most red clays are plastic clays.

4. *Short clays*, also called lean clays, are non-plastic clays or, more correctly, clays of low plasticity. Clays with large particles are naturally low in plasticity and require treatment to improve it. Clays which contain a large proportion of non-plastic material, like sand, are also naturally short. Short clays have no strength in the forming process and usually little at cheesehard and dry state, although this property does not follow automatically. They may or may not be strong after firing. Fireclays and specially prepared bodies for pressing are often short clays.

5. *Shales* are previously sedimented clays which have been subjected to pressure. The clay particles orientate themselves to resist this pressure by lying across its path. The result is a compacted clay with a tendency to break into small flat flakes. Shales subjected to extremes of pressure with heat produce slates. Shales weather and are removed into nearby deposits often as highly plastic clays which show their earlier quality. Such shales can be crushed and blunged to produce excellent plastic clays. Fireclays and brick clays are often shales in deposit state.

6. *Refractory clays* are those which will withstand a high temperature without deformation. Their use is in making fire bricks, kiln furniture etc, and blending with other clays to improve firing behaviour. They are often the purer clays containing little iron but it does not follow that all light-coloured clays are refractory. China clay, fireclay and prepared crank mixtures are refractory clays. Fireclays and crank mixtures are often added to bodies for the textural effects they give as well as their refractory properties.

7. *Fusible clays* are the opposite of refractory clays. They will not withstand high temperatures but break down with heat and melt before 1300°C (2372°F). They are almost invariably dark-coloured, either black or brown, but some cream ball clays are fusible. They are used as clays for low temperatures because they are often highly plastic. They have become plastic by repeated removals but have also collected impurities in the form of fluxes. They are also used alone or with wood ash as slip glazes for stoneware. Some red marls, gault clay, boulder clay and most estuarine muds are fusible clays.

8. *White clays* are usually prepared bodies which include china clay for whiteness and some ball clay for strength and plasticity. Other additions are flint, feldspar, plasticizer, and cobalt stain to bleach any tendency to look cream.

9. *Grey clays* usually contain iron oxide in reduced state. They often contain a high percentage of organic matter which keeps the iron oxide reduced and gives a black colour by its carbon. Grey clays burn pink or cream-white. Many fireclays and ball clays are grey in the raw state.

10. *Red clays* are not bright red but a rust red from red iron oxide. Natural clays can contain up to 8% of iron oxide but even 2% will give a strong colour. The iron oxide and other collected impurities cause red clays to vitrify before 1200°C (2192°F).

11. *Coloured clays*. Natural clays fire to white, cream and brown, but clays can be stained with metal oxides and prepared stains to give other colours. The colour at raw stage is not necessarily the colour developed after firing when the colouring material has formed silicates. See **Oxides: colouring**.

12. Raku clays have the capacity to withstand thermal shock. Almost every clay can be made into a raku clay by suitable additions of grog, sand etc. See **Raku clay**, **Fireclay** and **Crank mixture**.

13. *Earthenware* clays are many and various. All clays can be used for making earthenware in the sense that, for earthenware, the clay is fired to provide a strong product which is porous and is covered by a waterproof skin of glaze, therefore giving the best opportunity for the full expression of free, rich and varied forms.

Red earthenware clays are the red clays mentioned above. In Britain, these are the red clays of a pleasant, fine, sandy texture and are amenable to forming by any process: throwing, turning, pressing, slabbing and coiling. They are the least inhibited by specific requirements and can be used in combined forming techniques. When glazed, their colour can be used to add richness. See **Red clay**.

Buff earthenware clays are used for tin-glazed ware. Traditionally the true marls are used and these fire to a soft pink or an ochre buff. Stoneware clays and coloured ball clays are also used but they lack the capacity to put a compression onto the glaze. See **Marl**. Some buff clays are also used for slipware. White earthenware clays are prepared bodies blended from china clay, ball clay, flint, feldspar etc. They are usually produced for a specific forming process and are given sufficient plasticity for this process but with most emphasis given to whiteness and fired durability. For this ware, the system of high biscuit firing followed by lower glaze firing was perfected. See **Creamware**, **Bisc** and **Glost**.

14. *Stoneware* clays are those which progress to maturity over a wide temperature range. It is therefore possible to fire them to the dense state of stoneware without undue deformation. See **Vitrifiable clay**. Natural stoneware clays are related to ball clays but contain more impurities of sand and colouring. Fireclays of the plastic variety are often used or added to ball clays to produce stoneware bodies. See **Stone-ware clay**, **Fireclay**, **Underclay** and **Crank mixture**.

15. *Porcelain clays* are usually specially-prepared bodies. To achieve whiteness, the purest materials are used. This usually results in a short body. A porcelain clay is rarely textured. If grogged it will be with its own body. See **Pitchers**. The translucency of fired porcelain is obtained by the almost total vitrification of the body. Unlike stoneware, a porcelain body is homogenous. It does not contain particles of various sizes like grog and sand. It is therefore able to vitrify completely and high fired porcelain integrates with the glaze to produce a thick body-glaze layer. See **Porcelain**, **China clay** and **Bone china**.

The illustrations (overleaf) show a clay mine and the loading of tipper wagons on the site in South Staffordshire owned by Potclays Ltd of Stoke-on-Trent, who supplied the photographs.

CHEMISTRY OF CLAY. The potter accepts clay as a medium of many properties. The chemist sees clay as a complex mixture and combination of minerals. The chemist gives an analysis of clay in two ways. One way separates the oxides, lists them and possibly gives amounts. The other tries to give some idea of the clay's properties by grouping the oxides as clay content, feldspar, mica etc. See also *Analysis: chemical and rational*. For example, a boulder clay could be analysed as:

aluminium oxide	23
silica	62
iron oxide	1
calcium and magnesium oxides	3
potassium and sodium oxides	2
loss on firing	9

Or it could be given the analysis:

clay content	50
feldspar	15
free silica	29
plus	
iron oxide	1
limestone	5

The clay content is the theoretical clay which is based upon the clay crystal structure with the formula $Al_2O_3.2SiO_2.2H_2O$. This gives theoretical clay a composition of:

aluminium oxide	39·5
silica	46·5
water	14·0

It will be noticed that there is a theoretical 14% of water. This is in the form of hydroxyl groups (OH) in the gibbsite layer and therefore many chemists prefer to describe the clay crystal by the formula $Al_2Si_2O_5(OH)_4$. They also call it hydrated aluminium silicate.

This 14% water in the crystal structure is called bound water. In plastic clay there is also water in the holes between the particles, called pore water, and water called water of plasticity which allows the particles to slide past one another. See *Water*.

In dry state, 100 kg of clay contains 14 litres of bound water. This water is locked in the crystal and present as hydroxides (OH). During the firing, these are released and become water, which in turn becomes steam. The steam escapes slowly over a period starting before 450°C (842°F) intensifying up to 600°C (1112°F) and tailing off to 700°C (1292°F). The bound water can escape as steam without causing trouble because the pores of the clay are open at this temperature. It is very unlikely that any pot would burst from the escape of this water although 14 litres of water give 23 cubic metres of steam. With muffle kilns the water vapour will be seen escaping from the kiln at this temperature. See *Ceramic change*.

Dry clay also contains pore water. This remains in the pores and does not dry out because there is water in the atmosphere. This pore water could equal another 14 litres in 100 kg of 'dry' clay.

Plastic clay contains more water still. This is the water of plasticity. In extreme cases this water of plasticity could account for 30% of the weight of plastic clay but 20% to 25% is more normal. Plastic clay based upon the theoretical clay would have the formula:

$$Al_2O_3. 2SiO_2. 2H_2O. 2H_2O. 5H_2O.$$

And a percentage composition of:

aluminium oxide	26
silica	30·5
bound water	9·25
pore water	9·25
plasticity water	25

Seen thus, it is not surprising that there is shrinkage from plastic state to fired body.

The following are analyses of typical clays. They give percentage amounts of oxides after the ceramic change and therefore do not include water.

	China clay	Fireclay
Aluminium oxide	44	41
Silica	53	55·5
Iron oxide	1	2·3
Calcium/magnesium oxide	1	0·7
Potassium/sodium oxide	1	0·5

	Ball clay	Stoneware clay
Aluminium oxide	37·5	32
Silica	56·5	63
Iron oxide	2	2·2
Calcium/magnesium oxide	0·5	0·6
Potassium/sodium oxide	3·5	2·2

	Brick shale	True marl	Etruria marl
Aluminium oxide	26·5	15	21·5
Silica	62	64	65·5
Iron oxide	6·5	4	9·5
Calcium/magnesium oxide	3·5	14	1·5
Potassium/sodium oxide	1·5	3	2

PHYSICS OF CLAY. The physics of clay is concerned with the size and shape of the clay crystal and resulting agglomerate particles; and the effects arising from these. The effects concern plasticity and shrinkage.

The shape and form of the clay crystal are dependent upon its lattice structure. Each sheet of aluminium silicate structure contains thousands of atoms. Thousands of sheets, layered on one another produce a clay crystal. The layers do not fit over one another in exact repetition but are slightly displaced since there is no reason for exact location. However, the overall crystal has a roughly hexagonal appearance and is of course flattish as in fig. 1.

Fig. 1 represents an average-sized clay crystal. The true size is about 0·5 micrometres across. This diagram is therefore 100,000 times too large. On the same scale, the smallest clay crystals are like the solid hexagon in fig. 1 and the largest crystals about the size of this page. China clay and some fireclays have the large crystals. Ball clay has the smallest crystals.

These crystals must not be confused with clay dust or grains. These crystals are so small that they are invisible to the naked eye. Many hundreds of crystals make up a grain of clay dust. In comparison with the clay crystal in fig. 1, a hole in a 60's mesh sieve would be a square with sides as long as a lawn tennis court.

Because of the electrostatic forces of attraction and the compression that clays at rest have undergone, the larger grains are often replicas of the smaller crystals. That is, they are flattish and roughly hexagonal. Therefore whether one is considering the largest grains or the smallest crystals, the theory remains the same. Variation will be by amount of effect. In the explanation of strength, plasticity etc which follows, the word particle is used to describe the individual pieces of clay involved.

Water of plasticity is the lubricant between the particles see fig. 2. If there is plenty of water, the particles can slide past one another without difficulty. In such a case, there is little friction. A very soft, wet, plastic clay is in this state. When there is less water between the particles, there is some stickiness, like a wet pack of cards. In this case, the friction gives strength. A stiff plastic clay is in this state. As the water dries out of clay, the particles are brought closer together. The clay object becomes a solid. See also **Adsorption**, **Drying** and **Water** for an explanation of water involvement.

2

1

clay particles

3

4

5

6

7

The water gives plasticity because the particles are able to hold onto one another. The contrast of a plastic material like clay and a non-plastic one like sand is shown in fig. 3. The clay particles can hold onto one another by suction. The water between the particles gives the necessary seal. There is also some electrostatic attraction. See **Thixotropy** and **Plasticity**.

Fine clays are more plastic than coarse ones. This refers literally to the particle size. As will be seen by reference to fig. 4, for the same amount of overall movement, two adjacent coarse particles must slide further past each other. The fine clay is shaped by a total of small adjustments. Fig. 5 shows that the fine clay will also shrink more than the coarse clay during drying. The fine clay also contains more water. See also **Plasticity** and **Workability**.

Fig. 6 shows why fine clays are stronger than coarse clays. In an equal bend, the fine clay has less displacement to accommodate per particle, than has the coarse clay.

Fig. 7 shows how a clay will shrink more in one direction than in the other providing that all the clay particles are lying flat upon one another. In fig. 7 they are stacked in neat rows but the effect is the same if they are stacked brickwise. If we assume that the gaps which the water fills are of equal width, there are six gaps in direction A but only two in direction B. As the water dries out, there must be more shrinkage in direction A than direction B. This situation occurs in pots.

Clay particles position themselves with their flat faces opposing the direction of pressure. An extreme example of this is seen in compressed clays which have become shales. However in all potting use, the particles are being asked to rearrange their relative positions. Rolling and press moulding lays the particles flat along the clay sheet. This gives strength. In kneading clay, the particles are placed concentrically. This gives a circular strength which is useful on the wheel and is further added to by the centring process. During opening of the clay in throwing, the base of the pot is compressed. This lays the particles flat across the base giving strength. It also makes the larger drying shrinkage through the thickness of the base rather than across the base. The firing shrinkage also follows this course. A compressed base is less likely to crack than an uncompressed one. The uncompressed one often tears apart in what is called an S crack. See **Crack**. Many other minor idiosyncrasies are explained by understanding which way compression was applied. For example, lids which are thrown upside down often shrink more than the pots they were measured to fit.

In a pinched pot, fig. 8, the particles line up in the pot wall parallel to the wall sides because the pressure of the fingers is at right angles to the pot wall. In throwing, fig. 9, the clay is lifted and therefore the pressure is upwards as well as inwards. The outer hand is probably below the inner one putting a diagonal pressure on the particles.

In throwing, the hands describe a slow spiral up a pot in a clockwise direction—clockwise seen from above on an anti-clockwise wheel. The particles will follow this course which coincides with the throwing rings. The line of greatest shrinkage therefore becomes a steep twist at right angles to the throwing rings. See fig. 10.

This shrinkage is responsible for the twisting in the firing of thrown teapot spouts and tall pots. The twist follows the direction of the throwing spiral, taking the pot further on in a clockwise direction. This is often baffling to the beginner who expects the twist to be in the opposite direction as if it were associated with regaining a position once held as if by elasticity. This it is not.

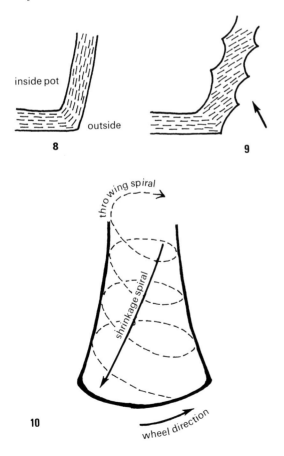

The properties of clay, described as plasticity and strength, which give to clay its workability character, are further described under **Plasticity** and **Workability**. Clays can be improved in workability by blunging, ageing, souring and de-airing which divide the clay grains into smaller particles and improve the lubrication between particles. The processes are described under **Ageing**, **Blunging** and **De-airing**.

THE CRYSTAL STRUCTURE OF CLAY. Oxygen is the commonest element in the earth's crust, in the sea, and in the atmosphere. It is not surprising to learn that oxygen is the linking force in clay. The clay crystal is composed of alternate layers of silica and gibbsite. Each layer has oxygen as its major constituent forming the structure. Each silica layer is fastened to a gibbsite layer by oxygen links. The combined silica-gibbsite layer is attached to others by hydroxyl bonds to form crystals. This is the kaolinite or clay crystal.

The structure is in sheets and can therefore be conveniently represented by a series of two-dimensional diagrams. As an indication of scale, 6 million of these diagrams side by side would equal 1 cm. Fig. 1 shows the silica layer. This is a hexagonal structure which is not exactly regular. There is slight variation in the silicon-oxygen-silicon link which is not a straight link but is more often an angle. Each oxygen atom requires links with two silicon atoms. The hexagonal structure allows this and promotes a sheet structure which can continue indefinitely on all sides but cannot extend from the oxygen atoms above or below. In this respect it is like the diagram which is flat on the page. However, each silicon atom requires links with four oxygen atoms and in this sheet there are links with only three. There is also not yet sufficient oxygen to give the common silica formula of SiO_2.

Fig. 2 shows how each silicon atom obtains its fourth oxygen atom. This is positioned above each silicon atom thus forming a little three-sided pyramid out of the four oxygen atoms with the silicon atom fitting snugly inside. See **Silica structure** for a diagram.

The original layer shown in fig. 1 is now shown in dotted

Clay

68

Clay

2

4

outline. There are now too many oxygen atoms to give the common formula SiO_2. This is because the top layer of oxygen atoms shown in fig. 2 are as yet not attached to the requisite number of other atoms (their valencies are unsatisfied). The mineral silica known as quartz would result if the unsatisfied atoms of oxygen were to link up with more silicon and so on upwards. However this possibility is inhibited in clay by the presence of aluminium which forms the next layer called the gibbsite layer. The silica of figs. 1 and 2 is also called the Si_2O_5 layer and the tetrahedral layer.

aluminium

3

Fig. 3 shows the strictly regular gibbsite layer. The presence of aluminium in six-fold co-ordination with oxygen (links with six oxygen atoms) makes a stiff and regular lattice. Part of this lattice is composed of the oxygen atoms from fig. 2, here shown as dotted outlines. Their valencies are now satisfied by a link with silicon below and two weaker links to aluminium atoms above. The other oxygen atoms of this gibbsite layer have their unsatisfied valencies occupied by a hydrogen atom each. The total atoms in the composite sheet represented by figs. 1, 2 and 3 are $Al_8Si_8O_{36}H_{16}$ which when rationalized gives $Al_2O_3.2SiO_2.2H_2O$.

The gibbsite layer is sometimes called the octohedral layer, because the six oxygen atoms surrounding each aluminium atom, when considered in terms of packing

together, form a three-dimensional figure which has eight sides. The gibbsite layer is rigid. The silica layer is not rigid. If it were, it would not be able to fit exactly into the gibbsite layer. The slight flexibility of the hexagonal structure allows it to adjust to the requirements of the layer above.

The hydrogen atoms of the gibbsite layer do not form a rigid bond but are able to oscillate in their attachment between these oxygen atoms and other oxygen atoms in an adjacent layer. The adjacent layer is another composite sheet above of identical make-up. The hydrogen oscillation holds the two layers together by what is called the hydroxyl bond.

A clay crystal is therefore a pile of alternate silica and gibbsite layers held together by common oxygen atoms and hydroxyl bonds. Because of the third dimension of the crystal lattice it is impossible to produce a simplified side view which corresponds exactly with the plans of figs. 1, 2 and 3. However, a simplified diagram can be drawn which fulfils the conditions of valency as expressed in the sheet structure. This is done by superimposition as in fig. 4. This figure shows the silica and gibbsite layers linked by oxygen atoms and the composite layers held by hydroxyl bonds.

CLAYS IN GLAZES. Clay is often included in a glaze recipe to provide glaze slop suspension, adhesion to the pot and stiffening to the maturing glaze.

Clay in the glaze slop settles slowly. If the water is acidic, and it is usual to add some calcium chloride to make it so, then the clay is flocculated and produces an open mesh of particles. This mesh hinders the settling of non-clay minerals like flint and feldspar which would otherwise settle quickly. See **Calcium chloride**.

Dry glaze on pottery awaiting the firing is in powder form. Clay in the glaze helps to bind this together giving it strength. About 10% of china clay is usual in a glaze and serves this purpose as well as others. Glazes without clay are very friable.

Pure clay is aluminium oxide and silica. In the glaze, silica provides glass and the aluminium oxide provides a stiffening. Clay is high in aluminium oxide and therefore glazes containing 20% and more of china clay tend to be stiff matt glazes. See *Aluminium oxide* and *China clay*.

Clays are chemically similar to glazes. Both are alumino-silicates but glazes melt because they contain fluxes in sufficient quantity to engage all the silica in fusion. A few clays, notably estuarine muds, contain an abundance of flux. These clays can be used as clay for pot-making providing the firing does not exceed about 1050°C (1922°F). However they are more often used as glazes, either alone as slip glazes, or as the main glaze constituent tempered with flint and/or wood ash. Most estuarine muds show this property and examples of these clays are the Albany slip of the United States and Nottingham marl of Great Britain.

Clobbering

The practice of adding extra decoration to someone else's pottery with or without permission. It was done mainly in the 18th and 19th centuries to increase market value of the ware. Some antiques are given a face lift in this way. The term is obviously not intended to be complimentary.

CMC

Carboxymethylcellulose. See *SCMC*.

Cobalt carbonate

$CoCO_3$. A compound of cobalt which is used for colouring slips and glazes. Upon heating to the region of 800°C

(1472°F) it decomposes into cobalt oxide and carbon dioxide.

$$CoCO_3 \xrightarrow{\text{800°C}} CoO \ + \ CO_2 \uparrow$$
$$100\% \qquad\quad 63\% \quad\ 37\%$$

Because the carbonate is only 63% effective blue stain (CoO) it is easier to use than the more concentrated cobalt oxides, black and grey. It is a lighter powder and can be spread more evenly through the glaze thus avoiding the tendency to specking which is common with cobalt oxide.

The release of the carbon dioxide gas is automatic and without incident except where very low-melting glazes or fluxes are used, e.g. raku glazes and enamel colours. Here the gas may cause some blistering. It should be noted that the oxides also may cause blistering. This difficulty can be avoided by previous calcination and fusion.

Cobalt carbonate may be added to glazes in amounts up to 1·5% and gives shades of blue. See also *Cobalt oxide*.

Cobalt oxide

CoO or CoO_2 or Co_2O_3 or Co_3O_4. A general name for a number of compounds of cobalt and oxygen which have been used as blue stains for pottery for nearly two thousand years. Cobalt oxide is an extremely strong ceramic stain. In fact it is the most powerful colouring oxide. Less than 1% dispersed throughout a glaze is sufficient to give a very strong blue. The blue varies from a violet to a green according to the other oxides present. Most potters find its strong colour too pure and monotonous and therefore modify it with other colouring oxides such as iron and manganese to give a softer slate blue. Other blue stains are now commercially prepared without cobalt oxide but the ease with which the cobalt oxide gives blue ensures its continuing use. It is unaffected by oxidation or reduction and is not volatile even at 1400°C (2552°F). It can be easily stored and handled, and it can be used effectively over the entire range of pottery-making.

Cobalt is a metal which occurs as ores in combination with nickel, arsenic, sulfur and manganese. The most rewarding deposits are in Canada and southern Africa. The oxide is extracted from the ore by roasting or as a by-product recovered from nickel ore. The purest oxide marketed contains traces of nickel and iron oxides. It is not advisable to attempt to roast one's own ore or to use raw crushed ore because of the arsenic and sulfur content. Cobalt metal is used in steel and chromium alloys. Cobalt salts are used as driers and the oxides are used in paint pigments and pottery stains.

Cobalt oxide is usually purchased as black cobalt oxide (Co_3O_4). This is a stable form at room temperature which liberates its excess oxygen during firing above 800°C (1472°F) to form cobalt monoxide (CoO). Cobalt monoxide is the stable form at higher temperatures and the one which combines with the silicates and borates to give a blue colour. Other convenient forms are cobalt sesquioxide (Co_2O_3) which is grey but contains only 90% effective stain against the 93% of the black oxide, and cobalt carbonate ($CoCO_3$) which is mauve in colour and is only 63% effective stain content. The acidic cobalt dioxide (CoO_2) also exists but is not marketed for pottery use because the other forms are sufficiently stable for storage and are convenient in use. Cobalt oxide is also marketed as silicates, alumino-silicates and aluminates for use as glaze and body stains, and in underglaze colours etc.

Cobalt monoxide is a powerful glaze flux, equalling the strong alkaline oxides of potassium and sodium. It is therefore very active in a glaze and dissolves readily in most glazes, especially high alkaline and boron glazes, although it has a high melting point alone (2860°C or 5180°F). As it dissolves in the glaze it diffuses over an area. It is therefore impossible to keep a hard edge to underglaze painting in cobalt oxide. The edge will inevitably bleed slightly into the surrounding glaze.

Cobalt oxide is a very powerful colourant and only a small amount is needed to stain a glaze. This small amount would eventually spread throughout the glaze but in most firings there is insufficient time for this to occur and the result is that the glaze appears patchy or speckled around the separate particles of cobalt oxide. A deliberate speckle is easily obtained by adding the cobalt oxide to the already sieved glaze and stirring it in without further sieving. To avoid a speckle one must grind the colour with part of the glaze and sieve the whole glaze at least twice through a fine mesh (120's). Alternatively, the use of cobalt carbonate helps to spread the colour because it is a less powerful colourant for its bulk than is cobalt oxide.

To obtain a blue glaze one has merely to add cobalt oxide to the recipe. A strong blue will be obtained by only 0·5% if the glaze is one that fuses fully, e.g. a transparent earthenware glaze. Even 0·05% (one two-thousandth part of the glaze) is perceptible in transparent and semi-transparent glazes. Glazes which are opaque tend to require more colourant because only the colour at the surface of the glaze is seen. Opaque tin glazes are fully stained to a deep blue by 1% cobalt oxide. Crystalline glazes, especially barium matts, are capable of absorbing as much as 10% cobalt oxide before the colour becomes blackened. Too much cobalt oxide gives an unpleasant inky blackness in all glazes. Excesses of cobalt oxide appear on the glaze surface as metallic patches. The effect is misleadingly known as 'ironing'. The following recipe contains its limit of cobalt oxide. It is a crystalline barium matt glaze for use in combination with vitrifying slips and other matt glazes at 1200°C (2192°F):

feldspar	50
china clay	10
soft borax frit	10
barium carbonate	20
magnesium carbonate	4
cobalt oxide	6

Slips and bodies require more stain than glazes. Approximately 5% cobalt oxide in a slip gives the same intensity of blue as 1% in a tin glaze. However, 10% is still the limit. This gives a very deep blue which is almost black and is partly due to the fusion of the slip and partly to the fact that the cobalt oxide is not forming a full silicate. This is the same as the 'ironing' of the glaze. This proportion of oxide gives enough fluxing to render the slip almost a glaze at temperatures above 1200°C (2192°F). It should be noted that it is not cobalt oxide itself that is blue. In fact the cobalt oxide (CoO), if isolated, would be found to be a red crystal! Any attempt to get a red powder at room temperature is thwarted by the occurrence of the black and grey of the other cobalt oxides. Attempts to get a red crystal in the glaze are thwarted by the active combining of the cobalt oxide with silicates. The result is always a blue colour modified by the pull of the other atoms within the silicate chains. For this reason a cobalt blue slip or body appears grey in the raw state and changes to blue during the firing.

It is possible to use a very weak stain to counteract the tendency of some white clays to appear cream coloured. The cream colour is due to traces of iron oxide which the cobalt oxide over-rides with its opposite colouring. If too much iron is present the result is a muddy colour. Only about one part of cobalt oxide in 20,000 parts of clay is required but the total used represents the largest use of cobalt in the ceramic industry. Traces of cobalt oxide are also used in low solubility glazes to counteract yellowish tinges.

It is possible to produce a variety of blues from cobalt oxide as can be seen by any collection of Chinese blue and white porcelain. All are typically cobalt blues but they range from a purple-blue to a green-blue. The fluxing oxides in a glaze determine the character of a glaze's surface shine, transparency etc. They similarly affect the colouring. With a lead glaze the cobalt oxide gives a middle blue. This blue is brightened by the strong alkalis and given a purplish overtone with a particularly interesting feeling of depth. Boron oxide has a similar effect. The purple tinge can be further extended in high alkaline glazes where magnesium oxide is present but only a very small amount of cobalt oxide is needed. This gives some delightful soft mauve colours. It is possible to get these colours in crystalline stoneware glazes by overlapping a cobalt-stained glaze with a white crystalline glaze. The underneath glaze should contain magnesium oxide as talc or dolomite, approximately 10%, and cobalt oxide, approximately 0·1%. The upper glaze may be a dolomite matt or a lime matt with approximately 5% of tin oxide. The tin oxide helps to keep the colour clean. Pink also appears in barium glazes.

Greenish blues are obtained in combination with rutile and in the absence of boron oxide and tin oxide. In reduction an emerald type of green occurs. The presence of zinc and magnesium oxides and extra aluminium oxide have been known to help.

The strong blue is not to everyone's liking. After the first excitement of the pure colour many potters modify it with other colouring oxides. Iron oxide, manganese oxide and nickel oxide give subtle slate greys. Zinc oxide gives greys and greens. Uranium oxide gives greens and blacks. Bright modifications are obtained in high alkaline glazes with copper oxide and chromium oxide giving turquoises and peacock blues.

As with all colourings, consistent results are best obtained by first calcining the colourant separately. However cobalt is probably the most dependable colour that the individual potter will use and only the extreme variations will require separate preparation as a stain. See **Colours**.

Coffee pot and coffee jug
See also **Spout, Lid**, **Handle** and **Teapot**. Examples shown (left) are by Roger Michell and Joanna Howells. See **Recipe Appendix**.

Coiling
Hand-building a pot using 'snakes' of plastic clay. The term is extended to cover many techniques in which the 'snake' varies from a thin strip to a large thick sausage which is squashed and added with a pinching technique. Each coil is usually integrated with the previous one so that its separate identity as a coil is lost. Only rarely are coils left showing the method of construction and then it is as a decorative feature. Coiling is usually done from the base upwards to the rim but wide bowls are often coiled upside down starting at the rim. Either way, the process is one of organic construction and the feeling of steady growth and expansion is expressed. The photographs are of coiled vessels by Carolyn Genders and (overleaf) Jonathan Keep. See **Recipe Appendix**.

Pre-Columbian American pottery and West African pottery are usually quoted as good examples of coiling. Historically, most Neolithic and Bronze Age peoples produced good coiled pottery and continued to do so for large storage jars when the wheel became used for smaller repeat items. Western Asia, the Mediterranean and northern China can provide some excellent examples.

Some potters use a turntable of some kind on which to build the pot while they remain in one place, but others prefer to walk around the pot as coils are added and the pot is scraped and shaped. Combinations of coiling and throwing, or coiling and turning are used and give their own particular qualities.

Tools used in coiling are simple, being coarse combs; hard scrapers of metal, plastic or natural shells and seed pods; and beaters and pebbles used in a paddle and anvil technique.

Most clays are suitable for coiling. Coarse clays are popular because their texture can be fully exploited. Coarse clays with some fine highly plastic content coil well and dry quickly and uniformly. Sandy and short clays can be made suitable for coiling by the liberal addition of bentonite but it may also be necessary to use some slurry to help one coil to join to the next. The more plastic clays can be worked in soft plastic state without use of water or slurry.

Colemanite

Borocalcite. Hydrated calcium borate. Priceite. Pandermite. $2CaO.3B_2O_3.5H_2O$. A variable, crystalline mineral providing calcium and boron oxides in relatively insoluble form. It occurs in the western USA associated with ulexite. Colemanite is variable from $CaO.2B_2O_3.6H_2O$ to $2CaO.3B_2O_3.5H_2O$. The mineral pandermite which comes from Turkey is $4CaO.5B_2O_3.7H_2O$. Colemanite is a useful means of introducing boron oxide into a glaze without recourse to fritting. About 10% of the glaze recipe is the usual limit for colemanite and this amount actually improves the brilliance of colour and the gloss. It is a popular glaze material but users need to be aware of its disadvantages as well as advantages.

Colemanite is a powerful flux in glazes. It introduces calcium oxide which begins its action at 1100°C (2012°F) and boron oxide which begins to fuse at red heat (600°C or 1112°F). It is especially useful in low- and middle-temperature glazes where its fluxing action begins at approximately 900°C (1652°F). In glazes for the 1000°C to 1100°C (1832°F to 2012°F) range it gives some opacity. Above 1100°C the colemanite becomes a very active flux giving bright shiny glazes.

One advantage of colemanite is in the production of leadless glazes without using commercial or self-made frit. However, an important use is in combination with lead to form low-sol glazes which are craze-resistant. These glazes can have an attractive bright shine and a longer maturing range than simple lead glazes or leadless glazes.

In stoneware glazes, the introduction of colemanite instead of calcium carbonate will render the glaze more fusible at the same temperature or will lower the melting point of the glaze.

In coloured stoneware glazes, the two distinct fluxing actions of the boron and calcium oxides produce a time lapse between a first fusion and a second or final fusion. Between these two there is time for the glaze to smooth itself out at the surface. The second fusion breaks this surface in a characteristic mottling. The effect is most striking on semi-matt glazes but shiny glazes also may still retain some of this texture.

Boron oxide has a low coefficient of expansion. If boron oxide is introduced into the glaze, the whole glaze will contract less upon cooling after firing. This glaze is therefore less likely to craze. Colemanite is therefore used in small amounts to balance a glaze and at the same time to correct slight crazing. See *Glaze fit*.

Colemanite is the only mineral which contains boron oxide in insoluble form and is therefore valuable for introducing boron oxide, along with calcium oxide, into raw glazes. In all other cases, boron oxide is obtained from soluble minerals which must be fritted before being introduced into the glaze slop. Even so, some colemanite will be found to be slightly soluble and the calcium oxide, possibly assisted by the boron oxide, will act as a deflocculant on clay and clay content minerals in the glaze slop. The glaze will then be thinner than required and will not settle sufficiently to have the extra water siphoned off. This will happen only with glazes which are stored and is no worse than similar trouble with wood ashes. It can be countered by the use of calcium chloride solution or vinegar.

The name borocalcite is often used for calcium borate $(Ca(BO_2)_2)$. This crystalline combination of boron and calcium oxides sometimes occurs as devitrification in glazes. It can be responsible for some attractive blue flushes, especially in glazes covering dark bodies. See ***Clair-de-lune flush*** and ***Jun***.

The major disadvantage of colemanite is its tendency to encourage crawling. Minor disadvantages are: its creation of a flushing opacity if unwanted; its creation of a dull opacity when used in large amounts; and the tendency for some colemanites to dissolve partly in the glaze slop. For these reasons colemanite is often limited to 2% or 3% of a glaze.

Colemanite encourages crawling by loosening the glaze layer during the firing prior to fusion. Colemanite contains water as part of its crystal structure. Decomposition between 700°C and 800°C (1292°F and 1472°F) liberates this water and the vapour loosens the glaze layer. When the glaze melts, its surface tension pulls the glaze into separate areas leaving bare patches. See ***Crawling***.

Colloid

Colloidal particles are those of a finely divided substance when these are dispersed throughout another substance. Colloidal particles exhibit characteristics which are not associated with the same substance in larger particles. For example:

1. What is really a transparent substance can produce a milky blue opalescence in a glaze.
2. A substance that is more than twice as heavy as water produces a suspension in water that will not settle.

The finely divided particles are called the dispersed phase or discontinuous phase. The substance through which they are dispersed is called the dispersion medium or continuous phase. Both phases together are called a colloid. A colloid is half-way between a suspension, such as a glaze slop, and a true solution.

The degree of fineness involved is from 10^{-4} cm to 10^{-7} cm (0·0001 cm to 0·0000001 cm). This includes particles smaller than the wave-lengths of visible light. Therefore they cannot be seen separately by the naked eye even with the help of a magnifying glass but require an ultramicroscope or an electron microscope to identify them. Though one colloidal particle is invisible to the naked eye the collective qualities of many particles give a visual effect.

COLLOIDAL CLAY. A clay's plasticity and strength is dependent upon the fineness of the clay particles. Colloidal particles give excellent plasticity for their bulk and when flocculated by amino acids create a colloidal gel which gives strength. See ***Sour***.

All particles of a substance tend to have the same predominant electrical charge resident on the surface. The particles thus repel one another if dispersed in a liquid.

The finest clay particles are of this type and in some very plastic ball clays may account for 30% of the bulk. Slips made from such clays settle exceedingly slowly. The particles move around in the water repelled by one another and moved by the water molecules, which are also in motion. The force is from all sides and is sufficient to counteract gravity. Warming a slip will help to settle it by increasing the motion and causing some collision of particles. Particles which have collided become one larger particle. A larger particle is not able to move so far with the same force and if it is large enough, the force of gravity has the greater exertion and it will sink. The activity of colloidal particles in a liquid is known as Brownian motion.

Suitable electrolytes weaken the layer of electrostatic charges surrounding each particle with the result that the particles no longer repel one another. They are therefore able to aggregate or produce flocs. Thus a clay slip which will not settle can be persuaded to settle by the addition of a small amount of acid. The acid is referred to as a flocculant. Calcium chloride is a popular flocculant but vinegar will also work. Unlike with a deflocculant, it is not possible to add too much flocculant. However, an excess beyond the amount required for the result is wasted or may have undesirable side effects with other materials. The settling is called sedimentation. The aggregation of particles is called flocculation. See ***Flocculation*** and ***Deflocculation***. For use of colloidal slip see ***Terra sigillata***.

GLAZE COLLOIDS. Another colloid which the potter encounters is that of particles dispersed in a finished glaze which give a colour effect.

These colloidal particles may have a colour of their own which is the native colour of the substance. This colour depends upon the ability of the colouring element to absorb part of the visible light spectrum so that we see the remaining part of the spectrum reflected, and this is the colour which we see. See ***Colours***.

Colloidal particles may also have a colour which is created by their small size. They may have no colour at all in the bulk state, being transparent, but because the particles are smaller than some light wavelengths, they interfere with some of the light waves and create a coloured effect. This occurs when such particles retain their identity and do not become part of the molten glaze. These can be considered as separate particles in suspension in a liquid even when the glaze has set. The fired glaze is therefore a colloid composed of a dispersed phase of solid or gas in a dispersion medium which is also solid. The particles may be transparent crystals, nuclei of crystals, amorphous solids, or gas, but because they are separate entities they have a surface different from the surrounding glass. This surface bends the light waves with the result that the glaze appears opaque instead of transparent. The photograph (overleaf) shows an enlargement of a calcium borate flush.

Most potters are familiar with opacity due to suspended

bubbles which can be seen through a magnifying glass. If the bubbles are of the ultrafine dimension which cannot be distinguished through a magnifying glass the glaze is a colloid. These bubbles collectively disperse the light and give a frosted opacity inside the glaze although the surface of the glaze may be shiny. Sulfur, fluorine and chlorine if not driven off as gases during firing may be present in sulfates, fluorides and chlorides in colloidal state. These are entrapped in the glaze and give an opalescent quality. Carbon also as carbon particles and monoxide gas gives smokey appearances. The glass-former phosphorus oxide does not always become part of the random chain of oxides which makes a molten glaze. Instead it remains as isolated particles dispersed in the glaze. When the glaze cools these particles, although transparent, produce a blue opalescence.

The darker bodies which provide a good background to blue opalescence are often the bodies which release sulfur, fluorine and chlorine. It has been suggested that these gases are part of the colloid in classical Jun and Guan wares.

The colour seen in the semi-opacity of these glazes is not that of a crystalline solid but is the result of scattered light. The violet and blue light is scattered more than the other colours and therefore a glaze appears semi-opaque and bluish. The red, yellow and green light passes through the glaze. Some of these colours are deflected, so that depending upon the angle of viewing, the glaze appears opalescent and variable.

The metals gold, silver and copper in colloids also produce colouring. A small amount of metal is capable of dispersing through a large amount of glaze. The colour varies with the particle size. Cassius purple is produced by colloidal gold and tin. The classical Chinese *sang-de-boeuf* is a colloidal copper glaze which is predominantly red. However it does contain yellow and blue colours which show the colour variations caused by particle size. The middle band of possible sizes gives various reds but finer sizes give yellow and coarser ones give blue. Prolonged controlled firings are needed to produce particles of the same size and isolate a single colour.

Glazes which depend upon colloidal effects require accurate firing. They also appear to change their characters during storage in the slop state. The phenomenon, as yet, is not satisfactorily explained but the softer copper colourings of peach bloom are particularly affected and change month by month as the glaze slop matures.

The flanged bowl by Derek Emms combines the colloidal copper red, seen here as the darker crescent within the bowl, with the light blue opalescence of nuclei dispersal. See ***Jun***.

Colours

Ceramic colours. Metal oxides and prepared stains used to colour bodies, slips, glazes and enamels. Some clays are naturally coloured by iron and manganese. So are some glaze materials. But potters often require other colourings and use a white-burning clay and colourless glaze to which they add colouring materials. The simplest of these materials are the colouring metal oxides like cobalt oxide giving blue and copper oxide giving green. There are also other compounds of these metals used as carbonates, sulfates, chlorides and hydrates which decompose to become oxides during the firing. Lastly, there are specially prepared compounds, usually called stains, which do not decompose but remain as individual very fine specks of colour. The original colour of an oxide or other compound is not necessarily an indication of the colour when fired. Cobalt oxide is dark grey or black yet it gives a blue colour in bodies and glazes. But prepared stains change very little in colour and therefore present a good indication of their final colour.

It is usual to add up to 15% of a prepared stain to a slip or body and up to 10% to a glaze. Metal oxides and other compounds require differing amounts because some have stronger colouring power than others. See ***Oxide: colouring***.

THE THEORY OF COLOUR. Colour is a sensation experienced when pulses from light of particular wavelengths reach sensors at the back of the eye. White light is composed of many different wavelengths, the spectrum of different colours, added together. If some of these colours are subtracted the eye sees the sum of the remaining colours. Coloured ceramics, in common with other coloured things, absorb sections of the light spectrum so that they appear to be the colour of the remaining part of the spectrum which reaches the eye. If an object absorbs all the light then that object appears black.

The item responsible for this absorption of light energy is the colouring metal atom whether it is isolated as a metal or linked to oxygen as an oxide or involved in a silicate or other structure. See **Atom**.

Within a coloured ceramic body or glaze less than 10% of the atoms are actually coloured. Most of the atoms either totally reflect the light and appear white or allow the light to pass through and are transparent.

The electron cloud surrounding the nucleus of a colouring atom has many possible configurations, each one absorbing different energy pulses, that is, colours of light. Since a particular configuration is determined by the magnetic pull of adjacent atoms to which the colouring atom is united, it follows that combinations with different atoms, those of different elements, will produce different colours. For example, the pure metal copper absorbs the blue and green sections of the spectrum and therefore looks red. Pure metal copper gives the red in *sang-de-boeuf* glazes.

When copper is chemically combined with oxygen to give copper oxide there is a rearrangement of the electron cloud and the atom now absorbs all the light energy so that copper oxide looks black. When this same copper oxide is linked up in the silicate chain of a glaze, the electron cloud is changed again and the red and blue sections of the spectrum are absorbed so that the glaze is green in colour. See diagram. Different glaze fluxes impose different distortions of most electron clouds along the silicate chains thereby influencing the copper atom and creating variations of the green colour from grassy green to turquoise.

All the colouring atoms in ceramic situations are influenced in this way and by creating combinations of two or more colouring atoms a wide range of colours is possible.

The iridescent colours of a lustre are not produced by colouring atoms but are the result of interference with the light reflected from the lustre surface. See **Iridescence**.

OXIDES AND PREPARED STAINS. During the fusion and setting of a molten glaze when new bonds are established between different oxides, the colouring oxide shows particular preferences. The general pattern for all colouring oxides is to establish first a link with titanium oxide. If this is not close enough or is absent, preference is given to tin oxide, followed by boron oxide, silica, the other colouring oxides, the glaze fluxes and, lastly, aluminium oxide. It is unlikely therefore that aluminium oxide will be in close contact with a colouring oxide in the final glaze. For example, cobalt oxide in a glaze will not link up with aluminium oxide to produce the particular purple that this combination can give. The cobalt oxide will always be surrounded by and attached to some other oxides including silica, and therefore will give a blue colour. See **Glaze: physics of**.

To achieve the purple colour it is necessary to create the link between the cobalt and aluminium oxides first in isolation. This creates cobalt aluminate stain which is one example of the very stable structure known as a spinel. See **Spinel**.

The intention in creating a stain is to produce a compound in which the oxygen atoms are very closely packed together and shelter the colour atoms. This makes the stain resistant to the acidic attack of molten glass and thus limits the break-up of the compound and the loss of the particular colour for which it was created.

There are other stains which are not strictly spinels because they involve other valency combinations and these are called spinel types. Chromium-tin pink stain is one. They are not quite so stable as spinels.

And lastly, there are complex compounds of up to six oxides some of which are not colouring oxides but stabilizers. Stabilizers balance the electrical neutrality of the compound making it less susceptible to the pull of outside atoms allowing the colouring atoms to maintain the same electron cloud configuration even in widely differing glazes. Typical stabilizers are tin, titanium, zirconium and zinc oxides.

Ceramic stains are prepared by mixing together the appropriate oxides or materials in calculated amounts and calcining them so that the chemical combination takes place. This sometimes occurs without melting but sometimes high temperature fusion is necessary. The resulting material is finely ground to produce the stain powder. See **Periodic table: colouring oxides**.

COLOURING BODIES AND GLAZING. The principle of colouring a body or glaze is simply a matter of adding one or more colouring oxides, carbonates etc and/or prepared stains. The most economical ceramic to colour is a transparent glaze in which all the colouring matter is visible and effective. Next is an opaque glaze, then a vitrified body or slip and, lastly, a soft-fired non-vitrified body. Here only the colour at the surface is visible and there is no benefit from the wetting effect of a glassy environment. Fifteen times the amount of colouring might be needed in a soft-fired body to achieve the colour strength of a transparent glaze. A list of oxide colours is given under ***Oxide: colouring***. See also ***Stains***.

As a general rule it will be found that the RO type of colouring oxide is the easiest to use. It always gives a colour and since it acts as a flux is readily assimilated into a ceramic situation. When the amount is large the recipe may need to be adjusted slightly. Colouring oxides with the larger amounts of oxygen, R_2O_3, RO_2, R_2O_5 show increasing reluctance to produce colour except in specific situations. These situations often involve preparation as stains prior to use. They are also increasingly refractory and do not assimilate well. With some of the more refractory stains it is necessary to add some soft glaze and/or rebalance the glaze recipe by decreasing the amount of china clay. See ***Stains***.

Prepared stains give the same colour in varying strengths in bodies and glazes, but colouring oxides vary in colour according to their environments. Thus red iron oxide in most cases gives the reddish brown colour but when surrounded by calcium oxide it is yellow and when involved in a fusion it is a dark brown. Copper oxide is associated with green which is true of its involvement in oxidized glazes but in the non-vitrified environment of bodies it gives black speckling, browns, tans and even pinks. See articles on individual oxides and colours. Whether oxide or stain, there are factors other than amount which affect the colour and should always be borne in mind when comparing results. These are: the composition of both glaze and body even when the colour is in only one of these; the kiln atmosphere; the firing temperature and duration; the type of light, artificial or daylight, and the predominant colour of the environment in which the results are viewed.

Prepared stains and colouring oxides are finely ground and, in powder form, should be handled with care since they quickly become air-borne dust. Some contain toxic materials and silica. See ***Health hazard***.

Compound

Chemical compound. Two or more elements so united as to create molecules of an entirely new substance with different characteristics from the constituents. For example, the soft metal aluminium and the gas oxygen unite to form the extremely hard crystal aluminium oxide (Al_2O_3) which is used as an abrasive. In order to form a compound, the constituents must be present in determinable numbers of atoms which will form an electrically balanced unit. Therefore a glaze is not a compound although it contains many different compounds.

Compression

Pressure inwards. The state of being pushed to decrease size. Glazes in a state of excessive compression may shiver or

flake off. On the other hand if the body exerts some stress of compression on the glaze this acts against any tendency to craze with the periodic expansion and contraction of the body and glaze with heat, or moisture. A glaze can withstand ten times the amount of stress under compression as under tension before rupturing. Some compression is thus desirable providing it is not so great that it causes shivering. Cristobalite is introduced into earthenware bodies to create this stress which is then called the cristobalite squeeze.

Computer glaze calculations

When a potter needs to reformulate a glaze recipe, the computer takes the tedium out of the calculations from recipe to unity formula to fired percentage composition and back to recipe. The user does not need maths skills or understanding of the methods of calculations involved. However, an appreciation of what happens in the firing and how to interpret this in terms of materials is necessary. The time taken is reckoned in minutes compared with the same number of hours spent with pencil, paper and a host of reference books. All that is needed is one small disk (and a computer).

Although potters can create their own simple programs which reduce time spent on calculations, proven programs are marketed. The basic computer program is for the conversion of a glaze recipe into a unity formula and/or a fired percentage composition of its oxides. In these forms it is possible to compare one glaze with another however different might be the materials in the recipes. Adjustments can be made to unity formula and percentage composition in the light of these comparisons. The computer program converts from the adjusted formula or composition to a new recipe. All programs which are marketed do this, some in more user-friendly manner than others, and all offer other features and facilities. Comments on these follow. Purchasers must decide what features are required remembering that, as with any technology, it is necessary to start simply and upgrade as one's understanding increases. Compatibility must be checked. See ***Appendix of Suppliers***.

DATA ADDITIONAL TO THE BASIC PROGRAM. A more complete program will give such useful information as: relative density of dry recipe ingredients; coefficient of expansion of the finished glaze; projected softening and melting temperatures; projected viscosity at different temperatures; ratios of the different oxide groups

$$R_2O:RO$$
$$R_2O + RO:SiO_2$$
$$Al_2O_3:SiO_2$$

with ratios both molecular and weight; health hazards.

The success of any recipe is dependent upon factors not in the control of the computer like clay body, glaze application and kiln. Firing temperature and cycle alone are usually considered by programs. Some programs can deduce further characteristics and predict possible problems from the data which has been fed in. Alternatively, other programs can diagnose where problems have arisen when an unsuccessful recipe is presented.

Sometimes all these details, instructions and warnings are available in different languages all on one disk.

FACILITY TO UPDATE. Variable materials like feldspars are often blended by the suppliers to maintain a consistent supply of the material but specifications change from time to time. The program must be able to accept alterations or have a large capacity to introduce new materials with all their data and keep these in memory.

Many programs give a total cost for a batch recipe and often include major world currencies. The memory must be kept up-to-date.

REFERENCE. The computer disk is more than just a program. It can contain an amount of information about the materials in its store. This information is used in the calculations and predictions. Where the information is independently accessible extra information about the structure of the material, its source and processing are included and thus the disk becomes an important source of reference.

VISUAL. A few programs actually consider presentation rather than simply listing information. Ingredient amounts are put into boxes which makes the process more like actual glaze mixing. Different amounts of materials and oxides are shown as lengths of bars across the screen. These bars can be altered visually rather than by number. Graphs for two and three variables show the positions for different recipes entered, maintaining memory of those previously plotted as more are added.

ASSISTANCE WITH CHOICE OF MATERIALS. When deriving a recipe from input of unity formula or oxide percentage there is always less freedom to choose one's materials than one would like. Complex materials introduce unwanted oxides. Some programs expect the user to choose the materials and offer suggested quantities to fulfil the requirements. The program assists by deducting the material amounts as entered, showing what is still to be accounted for. Some programs decide the materials and juggle the amounts as necessary. Some suggest a list of materials and expect the user to put these in priority order or suggest a proportion in which suitable materials should be considered. These do not necessarily work out exactly every time and compromises are explained. Re-runs or a step-by-step override might be necessary.

Some programs will calculate blends of recipes and comment on suitable options.

STORAGE. Some programs have space on the same disk to store each final recipe once given a code. These can be accessed by their attendant features of origin, type, temperature, body match, material, colour and so on. Other programs expect the user to supply disks for storage of recipes.

INTERNET. For some programs additional advice and interpretation is available from the originator via the Internet. There are also available more glaze recipes than one could ever use. Details of new materials are also available here for updating a program.

Conduction

Transference of heat through solids by the interaction of their atoms and molecules. In the kiln the pottery is heated through its solid mass by conduction, the heat having arrived at its surface by convection and/or radiation.

Cones

Pyrometric Cones. Elongated three-sided pyramids, 2 cm to 8 cm tall, which are placed inside a kiln as a measurement of heat-work.

The cones are made from ceramic minerals and are similar in composition to glazes. With heat the cones soften and eventually bend over. If more heat were applied the cones would melt into a glass. It is the action of bending over, also called collapsing and squatting, which is important. This action can be viewed from outside the kiln through a spyhole and thereby the potter has knowledge of what heat-work is taking place inside the kiln. Because the cones are made from ceramic minerals their actions relate directly to pottery, but they are used by workers in other heat-treatment fields.

By having cones of different compositions, it is possible to have cones which collapse with different amounts of heat-work. Each cone is given a number corresponding to a temperature at which it will collapse through heat-work if that temperature is arrived at through a specified cycle. Cones are therefore more accurate than electric pyrometers which measure only temperature without relation to time. For example, a Harrison cone 5 which is given the temperature of 1205°C (2201°F) would collapse at about 1185°C (2165°F) if fired extremely slowly taking, for instance, three days. Prolonged soaking would give a more marked difference. Correspondingly the cone would be able to survive to a temperature in the region of 1220°C (2228°F) before collapsing if the firing were rapid, say three hours. Bodies and glazes would be affected in a similar way so the cone 5 would be a better indicator than an electric pyrometer. Conversely, it is more accurate to refer to a glaze as a cone 8 glaze than as a 1260°C (2300°F) glaze. The glaze materials are related much more closely to a cone composition than they are to an abstract temperature. The only disadvantage in this is the difference in cones number 8 from different manufacturers.

For example, cones number 8 are available as follows. The squatting temperatures are those quoted by the manufacturers. More complete lists are in **Tables 4 to 8** at the end of this book where it will be noted that the rate of temperature rise is also quoted.

Type of cone	°C	°F
Standard Seger	1280	2336
Miniature Seger	1295	2363
Standard Harrison	1260	2300
Large Orton	1263	2305
Small Orton	1300	2372

ORIGIN AND TYPES OF CONE. The form of the pyrometric cone was adopted by Dr Hermann Seger in 1885, for use in testing the refractoriness of materials. The idea of pyrometric cones had been used previously at Sèvres around 1880 and some 600 years earlier in China. Seger's cone was 6 cm high and the base was a triangle with 1·3 cm sides. The effects of heat penetrating a cone obviously meet first within the narrow upper part of the cone and fusion progresses down the cone. A cone therefore bends slowly and gives time to study the effects.

Dr Seger followed the experiments on natural materials with compounded ones and devised a series of cones based upon a progression in the unity formula he had invented. The cones were given numbers and each was linked in a relative way with a given temperature. However Dr Seger was not concerned with making cones which would collapse at predetermined temperatures. He was interested in producing an accurate scale of refractoriness against which natural materials could be measured. This method of describing refractoriness is still used. A material is given a cone number rather than a temperature to describe the limit of its ability to withstand heat.

Dr Seger took his formula for feldspar as a starting point. This was $K_2O.Al_2O_3.6SiO_2$. He altered the alkaline oxide to include calcium oxide and by reducing the potassium oxide content he was able to alter the aluminium oxide:silica ratio to 1:10. It is worth noting that this ratio is a common one in glazes. The aluminium oxide equivalent was now 0·6 molecules and the silica 6 molecules. This cone was therefore given the number 6 and corresponded to the slow

maturing point of feldspar at 1200°C (2192°F) or a quicker firing to 1250°C (2282°F).

By adding 0·1 molecule of aluminium oxide and 1 molecule of silica at each step the progression of cones was numbered upwards in ones. Each step was subsequently found to relate approximately to 25°C (45°F). Dr Seger next worked downwards progressively to number 1 with additions of iron oxide and, later still, alterations were made to the alkaline oxides. To denote the change of alkaline oxide, the cones were given the suffix A with the number.

Later still, someone else extended the range below 1A and the numbers given were 01A, 02A etc. These numbers therefore increase down the temperature scale whereas Seger's numbers increased up the scale. Also they do not refer to any molecular equivalents within the recipes but are merely numbers.

Different composition, different cone sizes and some different sections have been tried since the original series was produced. The original recipes have been altered to produce a more consistent step between the numbers and to achieve exact temperatures at end points after specified temperature increases. Specified increases vary from 20°C (36°F) per hour to 600°C (1080°F) per hour.

The types of cone popularly in use are Orton cones made in the USA, Seger cones made in Germany and Harrison cones made in the UK. Harrison cones were previously known as Staffordshire and British Standard cones. Miniature cones approximately 2·5 cm in height are available and are very useful in small kilns where space is limited. They are also used in the Dawson Kiln-Sitter as are the small bars of similar composition. See **Bars**.

CONES IN USE. Because a cone measures the heat-work rather than a temperature, it is a more accurate indicator of the completion of a firing than is an electric pyrometer. To make full use of a cone, it should be set at a slight angle into a base socket. A piece of refractory clay is excellent and holds a cone securely. The correct angle is 82° from the horizontal but often the cone is tilted further in order to determine exactly in which direction it will collapse. This is useful in a tight packing of pots when one can predict that it will collapse into a space and not touch a pot. Seger cones should be set with the impressed number on the side that will be on top when the cones have collapsed. Orton and Harrison cones are set to collapse over a side leaving the number on one of the two outside faces. After the firing it should be possible to read the cone number should there be any doubt as to the temperature reached.

Cones should be placed in the kiln thoughtfully if they are to be accurately used. Placing close to a spyhole during one firing and then deeply in the kiln for the next will not give consistent firings. The same position should be sought every time. Cones are not easy to see above 1200°C (2192°F) but silhouetting them against a space helps. In muffle kilns this is easy but where they are to be sheltered from the action of flames by a refractory box they cannot be so placed and are difficult to see. A mental note should be made of what the cone looks like in position. This will help in discerning it when the kiln is hot. Sometimes it is necessary to use a place close to the spyhole. Providing this is consistently done, the firings should be the same. Spyholes which are above half-way, in most kilns, tend to have hot air coming out of them. This may be a disadvantage for viewing but it prevents the cones from being chilled by the entry of cold air. See also *Safety*.

The cone is more important than a pot. To misposition the cone in order to get a pot in the kiln could result in spoiling the whole firing.

Cones are also used as a check on different parts of the kiln to assess what has happened. These cones are not visible during the firing but are recovered on drawing the kiln. Rings are also used for this purpose.

It is common practice when firing by visible cones to set three cones next to one another. One cone will be the one for the correct firing temperature and the others will be the consecutive ones above and below this. Thus there is a warning of about 20°C (36°F) when the first cone collapses and the potter knows that he must watch the second or firing cone in order to be accurate. The third cone should remain standing as proof that the kiln was not overfired. Cones that have not collapsed cannot be used again because they have been subjected to an amount of heat-work and would not be accurate.

Inaccuracies occur if cones are fired too rapidly during the early stages of a firing when binders are burning out. Heavy reduction early in a firing also makes the cones inaccurate. In both cases the cones form a crust which delays collapse. Cones affected in this way will appear discoloured after firing. Cones which contain iron can be identified by their brown colour in raw state. These are affected the opposite way by reduction and collapse too early. Cones containing iron are intended only for fully oxidized firings. Crusting sometimes accompanied by bloating occurs when cones are set close to incoming fierce flames, or in sulfurous atmospheres or in atmospheres containing water vapour as in salt glazing. These crusted cones remain erect beyond their correct end point then collapse suddenly from the base without curving. These cones never appear shiny although collapsed.

Opinions vary amongst potters about the setting and use of cones. Some start the cone vertical while others start it at about 50°. Starting the cone in an already inclined position precipitates the end point. A variation of 10°C (18°F) could occur in extreme settings. Setting vertically can mean that when a cone does collapse it goes very quickly. This can be a nuisance because one may miss it. Some potters count the cone as down when it is pointing horizontally like a crooked finger while others wait until the tip is bent over and is level with the base. It seems sensible to count the end point of the cone as the latter because this will give a longer time in which to view the bending. Cones progressively speed up in collapsing. Thus the second part from half-way down represents less temperature rise than the first part. Cone manufacturers count the end point as when the tip is bent over and is level with the base.

Consistency of use is however more important than method. Where more than one person is setting and firing a kiln, an agreed method in detail will be required to maintain consistency. In laboratory work the angle of setting and the length of cone which protrudes from the mount are carefully measured. The Orton Foundation has done much research in this field and has introduced the self-supporting cone to overcome some of these variables.

Continuous kiln

The first type of continuous kiln was presumably one used for raku but here there is intermittent setting and stoking. The first truly continuous kiln was the tunnel kiln at Vincennes in use for enamel firing in the second half of the 18th century.

Tunnel kilns are economical. The ware passes on trucks or a moving hearth through the tunnel, the centre section of which is at the top temperature and remains so. An air movement from exit end to entry end is used. The air which cools the ware becomes preheated for the burning. The hot fumes from the burning preheat the ware entering.

The use of low density insulation in tunnel kilns has resulted in economical use on a daily basis. Kilns can now be heated up in less than an hour and need to operate continuously only for the working day. It is no longer necessary to keep them operative overnight.

The illustration of the tunnel kiln is diagrammatic only. A kiln would have many more than five trucks to be efficient and some kilns are 70 metres long.

Contraction

Decrease in size due to temperature change. In pottery, this means a decrease in size with a drop in temperature, and it is important in the understanding of glaze fit and ovenware.

Each mineral, clay, feldspar etc and each oxide involved in ceramics has its own rate of contraction. The overall result is proportionately cumulative and therefore the contraction rate of a piece of pottery can be altered by altering its chemical composition. See **Glaze fit**.

Contraction is exactly reversible by a reversal of the temperature change. The reversed result is called expansion. Contraction should not be confused with shrinkage which is usually assessed as a one-way decrease in size, starting with the drying of clay and bodies and ending with vitrification in the firing.

Convection

Transference of heat by moving air. In the kiln the convection agents are the flames or hot gases which move from the heat source and transfer their heat to objects against which they impinge.

Conversion factor

CF. A number used to discover the amount of oxide that will enter a fusion from a raw material. For example, the CF for black copper oxide (CuO) is 1·0 because all the material enters the fusion as CuO. Therefore 100 grams of black copper oxide would ultimately put into a glaze 100 x 1·0 = 100 grams of CuO.

However, the CF for red copper oxide (Cu_2O) is 1·11 because this takes up oxygen during firing to increase its bulk and becomes CuO to enter the fusion. Therefore 100 grams of red copper oxide would become 100 x 1·11 = 111 grams of CuO.

Compare this with copper carbonate ($CuCO_3$) the CF of which is 0·645 because there is a loss of carbon dioxide during firing. Therefore 100 grams of copper carbonate would become 100 x 0·645 = 64·5 grams of CuO.

There may be other reasons for wanting to use Cu_2O or $CuCO_3$ but assuming that the only reason is to get CuO to enter the fusion, then by using the CF it is possible to discover the most economical. If all three cost the same then Cu_2O is obviously the best value.

A list of conversion factors appears in **Table 30**.

Cooling

See **Firing**.

Copper carbonate

$CuCO_3$. (Also the basic carbonate $CuCO_3.Cu(OH)_2$.) A useful source of copper oxide for staining bodies and glazes. See **Copper oxide.**

The equations of decomposition are:

$$CuCO_3.Cu(OH)_2 \xrightarrow{200°C} CuCO_3 + CuO + H_2O \uparrow$$

$$CuCO_3 \xrightarrow{500°C} CuO + CO_2 \uparrow$$

The conversion factor of copper carbonate is 0·645. This means that only 64·5% of the copper carbonate becomes a staining oxide. The carbonate is therefore a less powerful stain than the oxide and more carbonate than oxide is needed to get equal staining power. The carbonate is therefore able to disperse through a body or glaze more uniformly than the oxide and is used where the slight speckle of the oxide is unwanted. This property is useful in brushwork decoration. To convert a copper oxide amount in a recipe to a copper carbonate amount, multiply by 1·55.

Copper lustre

A film of metallic copper on the surface of the glaze. The effect is produced by heavy reduction of from 2% to 8% copper oxide or carbonate in the glaze.

The bird by Janet Hamer illustrated shows the lustrous effect achieved by cooling reduction from 1220°C (2228°F) in a gas kiln.

The glaze is fired oxidized with intense intermittent reduction during the cooling cycle until the glaze has set around dull red heat. Copper lustre is very popular on low-fired raku pieces fired as low as 750°C (1382°F). Here the reduction is effected on the piece after withdrawing from the kiln. See **Raku**. Soft glazes firing between 900°C and 1000°C (1652°F and 1832°F) are often used but inglaze copper lustre can be achieved with glazes firing up to 1220°C (2228°F). Reduction is achieved by relighting the burners and adjusting the damper, or by introducing wood into the kiln. Slivers of wood can be introduced into an electric kiln through the spyhole. This causes little damage to the elements as the power is switched off before reduction is begun. The following glaze fired to 960°C (1760°F) gives good full copper lustre. Less copper carbonate and lighter reduction gives a ruby lustre. See **Ruby lustre, Lustre** and **Colour plates 1, 2, 3, 4** and **15**.

china clay	10
soft alkaline frit	70
lead bisilicate	16
copper carbonate	3
bentonite	1

There is also the copper lustre produced by transferring copper from a refractory paste on to the glaze surface. See ***Transmutation***.

Copper ores

There are over ten workable copper ores in which the copper is combined with oxygen, sulfur, carbon and the metals iron, lead, tin and zinc. The oxide and carbonate ores are the result of weathering during deposition or exposure of a lode.

The oxide ores are tenorite and cuprite. Tenorite is a black colour. Cuprite is a deep red colour.

The carbonate ores are malachite and azurite. Malachite is a bright emerald green colour and azurite is a bright turquoise blue.

Cuprite, malachite and azurite are easily distinguished in rock exposures and as small pieces amongst the wash-out debris of old mines. Tenorite, being black, is not easily found and has usually disintegrated. All are easily crushed by hand pestle and mortar, and provide colourant for glaze and brushwork.

The chemical formulae are:

tenorite	CuO	black
cuprite	Cu_2O	deep red
malachite	$CuCO_3.Cu(OH)_2$	bright green
azurite	$2CuCO_3.Cu(OH)_2$	bright blue

Copper oxides

CuO and Cu_2O (previously called cupric oxide and cuprous oxide). Both oxides are strong colouring oxides in glazes and give green to black and red-brown. In bodies the colour varies from fawn to green depending upon the amount of vitrification. Five per cent copper oxide in a slip is equivalent in colour to 2% in a glaze.

The metal copper occurs as native copper, but mostly it is combined with oxygen, carbon, sulfur and the metals iron, lead, tin and zinc. There are over ten workable copper ores of which the oxide and carbonate ores are the most beautiful and also useful to the potter. See ***Copper ores***. Copper is used in electrical conductors, wires, terminals etc; as roofing; for pipes and boilers; and in the alloys brass, bronze, bell metal etc. These metals are easily oxidized before or during a firing.

Metal filings will give strong speckle stains to bodies and glazes. Potters' merchants market the two copper oxides and copper carbonate.

Copper was the first metal to be worked by man. Copper was known in Egypt in 3000BC. Copper oxide was used in early glazes giving the turquoise of Egyptian faience, the green-blue of Islamic pottery and the greens of Chinese lead-glazed tombware, glazed Roman cups and of English medieval jugs.

Black copper oxide is CuO. Red copper oxide is Cu_2O and varies from deep red to dull brown because other states of this sub-oxide down to Cu_4O are present. Copper carbonate ($CuCO_3$) is pale green: the basic carbonate is a deeper green. They are both called green copper carbonate and sometimes erroneously green copper oxide.

All the above oxidize to black copper oxide and give a green colour when dissolved in glass. Amounts up to 2% give increasingly strong greens. Five per cent gives a black which so fills the glaze that the surface is metallic. The black copper oxide will often come off the surface of the finished glaze onto the fingers when a black copper glaze is touched. Since this oxide is soluble in fruit juices, glazes strongly stained by copper oxide should not be used for food because the copper is poisonous. Copper oxide also upsets the stability of lead glazes making the lead content soluble. See ***Metal release*** and ***Conversion factor***.

The colour of the green varies according to the flux or combination of fluxes in the glaze. Rich grass greens varying from bluish to yellowish occur with the oxides of calcium, boron, potassium, magnesium and barium. In high-magnesium glazes, small amounts of copper oxide give soft mottled pinks. Turquoise blues are possible with barium, sodium and lithium oxides while lead oxide gives soft apple greens. See ***Recipe Appendix*** and ***Colour plate 16***. Combinations with iron oxide give excellent yellow-greens and with cobalt oxide, blue-greens. When copper oxide is present in extremely small amounts, bright yellows sometimes occur. The colour is fickle and not easy to reproduce. See ***Colours***.

Copper oxide dissolves readily in the molten glaze causing bleeding and decorative spreading of colour from a slip or pigment motif. However, black copper oxide is still a strong stain and the particles tend to give a speckled colour in all but the most runny glazes. Copper carbonate, which is less powerful in colouring, is used to overcome this speckle.

COPPER OXIDE IN REDUCTION. Copper oxide is very susceptible to changes in the kiln atmosphere and post-firing alteration in raku down to as low as 400°C (752°F). The oxygen is withdrawn from the black copper oxide by the oxygen-greedy carbon monoxide. See ***Reduction***. The equation is:

$$2CuO + CO \rightarrow Cu_2O + CO_2 \uparrow$$

The copper oxide can also be reduced completely to metal state by further reduction:

$$Cu_2O + CO \rightarrow Cu_2 + CO_2 \uparrow$$

Thus while black copper oxide gives green glazes in oxidation, reddish browns are achievable by partial reduction, and bright red glazes with reduction to copper metal.

The reddish browns vary from a deep dull red through brown to a purplish brown depending upon the amount of copper oxide, the glaze composition and the reduction. The colour tends to be rather opaque if more than 1% copper oxide is used but with amounts less than 1% the colour looks cleaner. A yellow is possible with amounts below 0·2%.

The brightest reds are achieved by the complete reduction to metal copper. The amount of copper oxide in these glazes is less than 0·5% and the glaze needs to be alkaline. If such a glaze were oxidized it would hardly have any colour at all. The red colour is stabilized by the presence of tin oxide. The small amount of tin oxide, around 1%, fired higher than its normal use, and reduced, breaks down completely. The white tin oxide is reduced to black tin oxide and some is further reduced to the metal itself. Black tin oxide becomes part of the glaze structure thus affecting the environment of the copper atoms. The metal tin attaches itself to any crystals of pure copper and sometimes provides a nucleus on which a copper crystal can grow. In all cases the re-oxidation of the copper will be inhibited.

An even smaller amount of iron oxide is sometimes added to assist the process of assimilation. Iron oxide does not reduce to the metal state but as black iron oxide it captures any stray oxygen which might re-oxidize the metal copper thus preserving the colour.

Copper red glazes require a thickish layer to achieve a strong colour. The resulting glazes are attractive and known as *flambé* and *sang-de-boeuf*. See **Colloid, Autoreduction, Striking in** and **Colour plate 82**.

Copper oxide can also be induced to produce a copper metal surface on a glaze. See **Copper lustre** and **Raku**. It is also involved in producing bronze effects. See **Colour plate 38**.

Cordierite

Magnesium alumino-silicate. $2MgO.2Al_2O_3.5SiO_2$. A natural mineral in the USA but usually synthesized for making oven and hob ware. The exact formula stated above is not duplicated to avoid a sudden deformation during firing. Cordierite is used for very-fast-fire kiln shelves. See **Flameproof ware**.

Cornish stone

DF stone. Carolina stone. A feldspathoid which is used as a flux in bodies and as a major constituent in glazes. It contains feldspar, quartz, kaolinite, mica and a small percentage of fluorspar. It melts in the range 1150°C to 1300°C (2102°F to 2372°F) to a stiff glass which is opaque with suspended fine bubbles. It is often used as a substitute for feldspar because it introduces a number of alkalis which give additional properties.

A few Swedish feldspathoids approximate the composition of cornish stone and are used as substitutes when the original is unobtainable.

Cornish stone is not a single mineral and cannot be given a chemical formula. It is a crushed igneous rock with similar properties to those of feldspar but varying greatly in actual composition. Hence its many names, some of which are linked with a single quarry source. It can be described as a complex and variable alumino-silicate closely related to the feldspars and considered by many potters as a mixed feldspar with impurities. Cornish stone is important in that however variable it may be, it is almost free from iron and thus is nearly white. The purple variety of cornish stone is coloured by fluorspar but this burns to white (colourless) also.

Cornish stone originated as an igneous rock of the acidic type, like granite, or possibly as a sedimentary silicate rock which underwent granitization. The result in either case was a crystalline rock containing feldspar, mica and free quartz with often some fluorspar. The slow decomposition (kaolinization) of this rock has started when it is considered to be cornish stone and it is therefore slightly softer and easier to grind than a feldspar.

Such a complex and variable material as cornish stone cannot be given a single unity formula. Each specimen can be given an analysis from which a formula can be calculated. An acceptable unity formula follows but it must be understood that this can only be accurate for one specimen, the analysis for which is also given.

$$\left.\begin{array}{l} 0·42\ Na_2O \\ 0·25\ K_2O \\ 0·31\ CaO \\ 0·02\ MgO \end{array}\right\} \quad 0·92\ Al_2O_3 \quad 7·6\ SiO_2$$

SiO_2	72·92	K_2O	3·83
TiO_2	0·02	CaO	2·08
Al_2O_3	14·95	MgO	0·09
Fe_2O_3	0·05	CaF_2	1·07
Na_2O	4·13	Loss	0·86

The foregoing specimen would be considered a 'hard purple' variety with similar properties in a fusion to those of a sodium feldspar. It melts over the range 1180°C to 1240°C (2156°F to 2264°F). To show the wide range of cornish stone, a unity formula for a 'soft white' specimen is also given. Notice that the aluminium oxide and silica contents are very high, making this a harder material to melt and correspondingly stiffer. It melts over the range 1250°C to 1350°C (2282°F to 2462°F).

$$\left.\begin{array}{l} 0·07\ Na_2O \\ 0·49\ K_2O \\ 0·36\ CaO \\ 0·08\ MgO \end{array}\right\} \quad 1·7\ Al_2O_3 \quad 12·0\ SiO_2$$

Sample unity formulae are sometimes given with

aluminium oxide unity, a method reserved for clays and body materials to establish comparison with kaolinite. If a sample formula has $1 \cdot 0 \, Al_2O_3$, it is wise to total the alkalis as a check on which unity has been used.

The varieties of cornish stone are due to the different parent rocks and to progressive stages of decomposition whereby the feldspathic content becomes clay mineral (kaolinite) and quartz. During this process, the alkaline (fluxing) content becomes soluble and is washed away. The fluorspar, which gives the purplish colour, is also dissolved and removed. In the early stages of decomposition, the rock is hard and purplish in colour. It contains more feldspar, and thus more flux, and it will melt at a lower temperature than the rock in its later stages of decomposition. As the rock decomposes, it becomes physically softer and whiter but its melting point becomes higher (harder). Thus the anomaly, which is mentioned under *Hard (2)*, is that hard purple cornish stone is softer (melts at a lower temperature) than soft white cornish stone. The hard purple is therefore the stronger flux for bodies and is easier to melt in glazes.

The side effects from the release of fluorine gas from purple stones are deterioration of kiln linings etc, and harmful gas in the workshop. See *Fluorspar*. Suppliers of cornish stone now process some by flotation to remove the fluorspar and also the ferreous micas. The defluorinated cornish stone is known as DF stone.

Cornish stone is partly kaolinized and contains 5% to 12% kaolinite. It therefore responds to flocculation and deflocculation when in a glaze slop and assists glaze grip before firing. However, the clay-like property can also cause pre-firing cracks which give crawling. This occurs with a glaze which already contains a high proportion of clay in the recipe.

Paradoxically, cornish stone is sometimes substituted for some feldspar in a glaze recipe to cure crawling. Here its property in molten state is required. Although similarly stiff in molten state to a pure feldspar, cornish stone has not the same high surface tension because of the interaction of its more numerous alkalis. This wide spread of alkalis ensures a gradual maturity and a wetting action when molten.

Costrel bottle

A bottle with lugs near the neck by which it can be slung on a thong, carried by the fingers, or held for drinking. It originated in post-classical Greece, was also used in Persia, and the form had reached China by the 6th century. There are various forms; some are tall, some fat, some flattened and some barrel shaped. They were used by travellers and harvesters until recent times. See also *Pilgrim flask*.

Cottle

Cockle. Cockling. Expendable wall of card, plastic or clay to contain poured plaster until it has set.

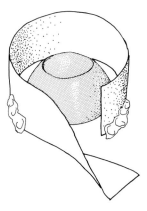

Crack (1)

To make the first opening of a kiln after firing. As the kiln cools it is clammed up at red heat to give uniform cooling over the dunting period. It is cracked when dunting and other thermal shock hazards are passed.

Crack (2)

An unwanted break in a piece of pottery. It should always be remembered that cracks are caused by physical stress and that some stress is always present in a pot resulting from the expansion, contraction and shrinkage the pot has experienced. Cracks occur when the stress is greater than the pot can withstand.

General points in the analysis of any crack are as follows:

1. The position of the crack on the pot is related to the form of the pot. The design of the pot controls the form and therefore the stresses. A badly designed pot, with awkward angles etc, of unequal section, is likely to crack although it may be made from ideal materials. A well-designed pot made from infamously awkward materials may survive. Two pots which are similar but not identical may be on each side of an unknown safety line. One may crack; the other remain sound.

2. If one takes liberties in pottery-making, one must expect differing results. Potters talk about good-natured clays and well-disposed glazes but this only emphasizes that they can be otherwise. A variation in body, form, method of making, method and speed of drying, firing temperature, firing cycles, slip or glaze will result in a variation of product. The variety may include a crack.

3. Cracks in raw ware arise from faults in the making of the pots, and these can be overcome however difficult the clay may be to deal with. The design—that is, the form—is all important, and achieving the design means working with the clay and not against its nature. Uniform consistency of clay, before and after making, uniform thicknesses and uniform drying are the ideal principles.

4. In finished ware one should look where the crack started to understand when it happened. The wider end of the crack was the starting point. If the crack started at the rim, the fault is likely to have been somewhere at the raw stage. If in the base, the crack usually occurred in the firing and could be caused by the materials, the type of firing and the type of setting used.

5. The edges and faces of the crack are another indication of when the crack occurred. Frayed edges and rough faces on the two sides show that the crack occurred relatively slowly and probably at the making and drying stages even though it may be that the crack did not show until after firing. A glaze on such a crack will be seen to have rolled back from the edge and rounded itself. On the other hand, if the edge of the crack is sharp and the faces of the crack are smooth, the crack is a kiln crack. If glaze around the crack has smoothed itself and is rounded at the edge, the crack must have occurred early in the firing and the glaze during fusion crawled back from the edge. If the glaze is sharp-edged, the crack must have occurred after the glaze had set during the later stages of cooling.

6. Whether a crack is hairline or wide is a matter of amount of stress. A differentiation should not be so much in width as in whether there is sideways displacement as well as parting. Fine dunts may be undiscernible but are discovered by touch when the finger catches upon an edge. In this case there is a displacement. Displacements are usually firing cracks. Cracks which are partings without displacement, even if apparently happening in the glaze firing, are usually from an earlier process, e.g. a biscuit dunt or a drying crack.

The illustrations show typical cracks and a brief comment is made on the causes. The reader is often referred to other items in the book for details.

CRACK A. The crack is at right angles to the rim and is wider at the rim and peters out below.

Crack A in raw ware:
1. The design is poor giving a structurally weak pot. Probably the rim is too thin to contain the stresses in the remainder of the pot.
2. Method of working was incorrect for the clay used. Probably the drying was too rapid and unequal.
3. If the crack is in newly-thrown clay and shows while still on the wheel or soon after removing, it is likely to be insufficiently prepared clay or possibly tired clay or over-

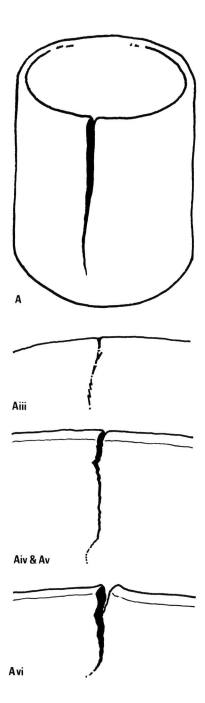

short clay. If the clay has had extra sand or grog added this may have made the clay too short for the type of throwing used. This crack has the appearance of a fibrous tear. Illustration A iii.
4. If the crack is in the rim of a plate or dish, especially a press-moulded dish, the clay was probably over-wet unequally in some way. Also the drying which followed was too rapid for the clay to equalize its moisture content. Illustration A iv.
5. If a slip coating has been poured or brushed inside the dish it was done when the dish was too dry. Illustration A v.
6. If a slip coating was used and the dish was too damp then some distortion will have taken place. Illustration A vi.

7. If the crack is hairline, it could be that the pot has been waiting for firing over a period which involved dry weather followed by wet weather. The resulting crack is a result of readsorption and the phenomenon is described under **Readsorption** in this book.

Crack A in biscuit and glazed ware:
8. The crack is probably the development of one that was latent at the raw stage. The stress at the raw stage may have ruptured the clay without visible signs at the surface. Such cracks are called latent or dormant cracks and no matter how careful the firing they are forced to develop. Mishandling of raw ware when packing a biscuit kiln may have induced cracks, but the cause should first be sought as poor design, rapid drying, unequal drying, incorrect method and readsorption.
9. Stress in the raw ware which could be successfully contained by careful drying and firing may have been over-emphasized by too rapid a firing in the early stages of biscuit.

CRACK B. The crack is at right angles to the rim but is wider below the rim and almost undiscernible at the rim. It starts at the base or some other feature.

B

Crack B in raw ware:
1. Very rare but could result from a thin base and unequal drying.

Crack B in biscuit ware and glazed ware:
2. The crack is a cooling dunt caused by the crystalline silica in the body. The crystalline silica undergoes an inversion or change of crystal structure. This is accompanied by a change in size which proportionately affects the body of the pot but not the glaze. Stress within the body, or between body and glaze, may be sufficient to rupture the pot. See **Dunting: cooling dunts.**

CRACK C. The crack is at right angles to the rim and the sides are almost parallel. The crack originates at a star-shattering in the base. See crack F.

C

Crack C in raw ware:
1. The wall and the base are unequal in thickness, with the base probably too thin for the pot. It is also likely that the base was left too wet after throwing and that drying followed immediately and was too rapid. This could occur where a wet pot was left on a very absorbent surface.

Crack C in biscuit ware:
2. The crack is a development of one that already existed at the raw stage.

Crack C in glazed ware:
3. This type of crack is most common on glazed ware and is a cooling dunt caused by a thick glaze layer inside the pot. It does not matter that the glaze is crazed and therefore one would expect it not to force the pot body apart. There existed a point during cooling when the glaze was too large for the pot surrounding it. It is most likely to occur where the pot is glazed inside only and the base is thinner than the walls.

CRACK D. The crack is clean and sharp-edged. It divides the pot into two almost equal pieces. It is common on stoneware and porcelain bowls, especially refires, where it is discovered on opening the kiln. The parts are unlikely to fit together perfectly because distorted.

D

Crack D in raw ware:
1. A crack of this sort is virtually impossible because cracks in raw ware tend to avoid the foot rim.

Crack D in biscuit ware:
2. A rare possibility of a cooling dunt caused by a cold draught on an inverted bowl.

Crack D in glazed ware:
3. The clean break through body and glaze shows that the crack took place after the glaze had set. It is classified as a cooling dunt caused by the crystalline silica in the body. The crystalline silica undergoes a change in size and proportionately changes the size of the body. The glaze, which is not crystalline, does not change and stress results. Also, the difference in thermal contraction between body and glaze without consideration of crystalline silica inversions causes stress. See **Dunting: cooling dunts** and **Silica inversions**.
4. In consideration of the above stress between body and glaze there is a factor which exaggerates the danger of a crack occurring. It is the over-densification of the body. Overfiring the pot brings the body nearer to its total vitrification point, makes it more brittle, and hence less able to absorb the stress. Refiring pots, even to the same temperature, continues the vitrification process beyond its original point. Already dense ware is forced to be adversely affected and become over-glassy and brittle. During the firing, a bowl is likely to distort and go oval which concentrates the stresses upon cooling.
5. An over-dense body tends to fuse itself to the kiln shelf unless a very efficient bat wash is used. The foot rim becomes fastened to the shelf upon cooling and, since the shelf is likely to contract less than the pot body, the pot is torn apart starting at the foot.

CRACK E. The crack is a hairline crack which runs across the base in a straight line. It almost invariably continues up the side of the pot at least as far as the thickness of the base. It may continue up both sides of the pot. It is closely related to cracks D and F and occurs on glazed ware only. It is not to be confused with cracks G and H which are more commonly confined to the base.

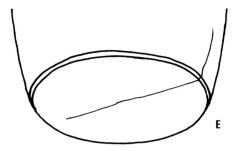

Crack E in glazed ware:
1. The glaze is obviously too big for the body so that the base of the pot is trying to squeeze the glaze. If the stress is great enough the body ruptures itself. The crack would be classified as a cooling dunt resulting from the different contraction rates of the body and glaze. See **Dunting: cooling dunts, Glaze fit** and **Silica inversions**.
2. If the crack occurs months or even years after the pot has been made, it is likely to be called the result of thermal shock. The cause of the stress is still the difference in contraction rates between body and glaze but not directly attributable to crystalline silica. See **Thermal shock** and **Glaze fit**.

CRACK F. The drawing shows star shattering of the base seen from underneath. The actual pattern of the star varies considerably but there is usually a main crack with subsidiary ones at approximately right angles. There is often a fifth crack making the star as in the example shown.

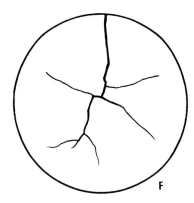

Crack F in raw ware:
1. If the base of a thrown pot is too thin in relation to the walls, it could crack in this way.
2. If the base of a thrown pot was left over-wet and then possibly dried quickly the stress of (1) would be exaggerated.

Crack F in biscuit ware:
3. Cracks in biscuit would be developed from cracks in the raw ware and in this case should have been discernible at raw stage.

Crack F in glazed ware:
4. The star is closely related to cracks D and E. In this case the glaze layer inside is usually thick, even thicker than the base of the pot. The fluxing action of the glaze on the thin base makes the base almost vitrified and hence brittle. In cooling, if the body contracts more than the glaze, even by a small amount, it is too brittle and weak to compress the glaze. The body ruptures and the crack probably continues up the side to the rim as in crack C.

CRACK G. The crack is straight or nearly so. In most cases it is related to crack H. In raw ware and biscuit, it is only a hair crack but in glazed ware there is likely to be some slight sideways displacement as if one side of the crack had curled up and the other side down.

G

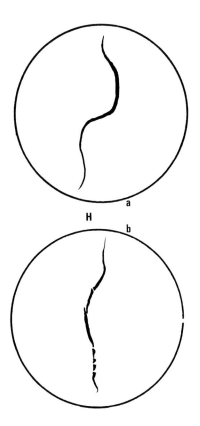

H

a

b

Crack G in raw ware:
1. The crack is the result of unequal drying in some way. For example, the pot was not cut from the wheel-head after throwing but was allowed to dry on the wheel-head or bat. The pot was cut under but not lifted clear from the wheel-head or bat. The pot was lifted clear but was placed on a pot board that was not sufficiently porous to allow the base to dry. These cracks can sometimes be patched at the dry stage by using some very soft and sticky body clay.

Crack G in biscuit ware and glazed ware:
2. The crack is really a drying crack and occurred much earlier although being only a hair crack it was not discovered at the raw stage. In glazed ware the crack sometimes goes the whole way through the base. In this case the glaze will have rolled back from the crack with rounded edges or, if the glaze is very runny, it may have run through the crack and appeared underneath. The crack, if small, can sometimes be patched at biscuit stage with biscuit stopping or pitchers. This is a ground fired body which is mixed with water to form a paste that can be pushed into the crack. The stopping should be allowed to dry before glazing. Stopping of cracks after biscuit is effective only if the following glaze firing is at a lower temperature than or only slightly more than the biscuit temperature.

CRACK H. This base crack is known as an S crack because it often forms an S across the base. The two illustrations show the crack as seen from (a) inside the pot and (b) underneath. It occurs in thrown ware. The crack, if seen without the glaze covering, looks more like a tear than a sudden crack. Where there is a glaze, this may or may not have flowed into or away from the crack, dependent upon the properties of the glaze and shrinkage cycle of the clay. In these cracks the glaze is no indication. The character of the crack itself is sufficient evidence.

Crack H in raw ware, biscuit ware and glazed ware.
The cause is the same throughout. It is the unequal shrinkage of the clay in the base and walls of the pot. Shrinkage starts as the clay dries and continues as the pot fires and is matured or vitrified. The shrinkage is equal in all directions only when the clay particles are haphazardly mixed. This does not happen in a pot. The clay particles are disc-like plates which align themselves across the pressure. There is always some pressure in a pot wall caused by the

fingers inside and out. The clay shrinks proportionately to the gaps between the particles and therefore if the particles are all lying in one direction there will be a concentration of the shrinkage. In the diagram H(c) the clay particles are vastly enlarged in a section of a pot to show how there are as many gaps between particles through the wall of a pot as in its height. In this exaggerated case the shrinkage on the pot wall thickness (w) would equal the shrinkage in height (x). The slight angle of the particles is caused by the lifting action of the throwing. See ***Clay: physics***.

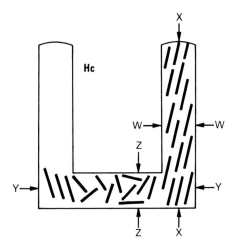

X

Hc

W→ ←W

Z

Y→ ←Y

Z X

No harm comes to the pot wall by this shrinkage; in fact it is strengthened. The base should be similarly subjected to pressure across its thickness resulting in the alignment of particles in a flat way across the base. However, in the diagram, the base has not been subjected to sufficient pressure. The particles are haphazardly arranged and show only a slight tendency to alignment from the pressure received at the opening up stage of throwing. This pressure has only emphasized an arrangement of the particles vertically because the pressure was outwards from the centre. Shrinkage on this base will be greater at y than at z. The result will be an S crack.

To overcome the S cracks requires a change of throwing technique to include a compression of the base. The term compression is used in this sense. Some potters beat the bases of the pots as soon as the pots can be inverted but this is likely to be too late for most clays. Although damaging to modern wheel bearings, the age-old custom of throwing the clay down hard onto the wheel-head may help. Holes in wheel-head bats are a place where pressure can be lost and can be a starting point for an S crack. Most trouble is experienced when throwing many pots from one lump. It is very difficult to compress the base sufficiently. A technique has to be developed whereby pressure downwards inside the pot is met by a pressure upwards from a squeezing action of the other hand. These pots should be turned when fairly soft and the base beaten before turning.

With large flat plates and dishes it may be necessary to beat the inside of the base with a stone, piece of wood or the hand before finishing the throwing. Also running the fingers towards the centre as well as outwards helps. Traditionally the thrown oven dishes were often made oval by cutting a leaf-shaped piece from the base and pushing the joint together. Extra clay was stuck onto the join and beaten into place. The extra compression thus gained improved the strength of the base and overcame the S cracks. Also by cutting across the base, the centripetal base stress was hindered from development in the thermal shocks of use. An oval dish has the stresses connected with only the lesser width but has the stability of the greater width. See also cracks I and K.

CRACK I. The crack is a hairline around the base seen from the underside but probably invisible inside. At its worst it forms a complete circle and the base falls out. However this is more common with crack J which is slightly different and more drastic. Crack I appears on ovenware, both glazed and unglazed, and is often noticed because it has stained. It will be seen to extend itself slowly with further use of the piece of pottery.

Crack I in fairly dense ware both glazed and unglazed.
The crack is caused by thermal shock. There is probably some difference in thickness between base and wall which results in unequal expansion and contraction. Repeated subjection to the stress in daily oven use extends the weakness. See **Thermal shock**.

CRACK J. The crack is circular, or almost, and has an extension at right angles which goes outwards to the edge of the foot and part way, or all the way, up the side of the pot. The crack occurs quickly with a loud noise, or is discovered on opening the kiln. The circular base piece drops out of the pot. This is most common on plates and dishes.

Crack J in glazed ware.
There is stress between body and glaze. The glaze is too large for the body and ruptures the body that is compressing it. See **Dunting: cooling dunts**. It occurs where the glaze is too thick and has collected inside around the base because the base is slightly humped.

CRACK K. There are two hairline cracks seen from underneath. They describe an incomplete oval which would overlap the base. The cracks, or just one of them, appear on ovenware after use.

Crack K in fairly dense ware both glazed and unglazed.
The crack is caused by thermal shock and is similar to crack I. See crack I and **Thermal shock**.

CRACK L. The first illustration (a) shows the underside view of a plate. Haircracks, at first not noticeable, result in rectangular pieces breaking from the rim. In the second illustration (b) the haircracks do not reach the rim but form a set of cracks like brickwork which give that part of the pot a deadness although the rim may still ring when struck.

La

Crack L in biscuit ware:

1. The crack is a dunt caused by cooling the biscuit too quickly or firing it insufficiently to give it strength. See **Dunting: biscuit dunts**. Plates that are piled one inside the other, not rim to rim, will hold their heat around the foot rims when the outer rims cool. A thin plate on a thick kiln shelf is also unable to cool uniformly.

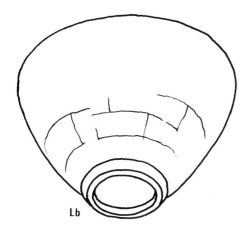

Lb

Crack L in glazed ware:

2. The crack is probably more than a haircrack in a few places and results from a biscuit dunt that was unnoticed at biscuit stage. At biscuit stage some dunts do not penetrate through the pot. A slip coating could dunt separately from the pot body and *vice versa*.

CRACK M. A sharp-edged crack with sideways displacement. This occurs on glazed ware and is discovered on opening the kiln, soon after and on rare occasions up to a year later. The crack is accompanied by a loud noise as it quickly ruptures the pot. It may not reach the rim.

M

Crack M in glazed ware, especially dense stoneware.

There is stress between the body and glaze which cannot be absorbed. The body is compressing the glaze but the glaze is strong and does not flake away as in crack O. The glaze remains as one piece because it is well attached to a dense and finely-grained body. The body therefore ruptures and as it does so there is sideways displacement or strain to accommodate the stress. This displacement ruptures the brittle glaze also. See **Dunting: cooling dunts**. It is likely to happen with stoneware bodies which include cristobalite. See **Silica inversions**.

CRACK N. The cracks are hairlines but, where glazed, are sharp edged and can often be felt before seen because there is a very slight displacement. They appear above, below or along a glaze roll.

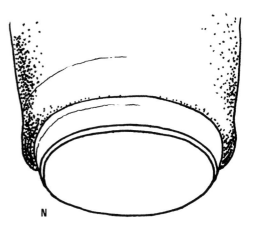

N

Crack N in glazed ware.

The crack is a dunt caused by the difference in expansion/contraction rates of body and glaze. The stress between the body and glaze over most of the pot is satisfactorily absorbed by the body-glaze layer. However at the roll there is an exaggerated stress which is sufficient to cause the dunt. Sometimes part of the glaze roll will shiver also. **See Dunting: cooling dunts, Glaze fit** and **Shivering**.

CRACK O. This is a crack through the glaze whereby a thin flake of glaze leaves the pot. The flake is sharp edged and if

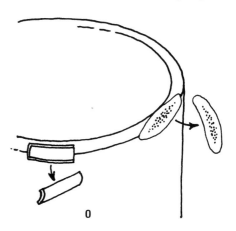

O

there is a strong body-glaze layer it will have carried with it some of the body. It occurs on rims, edges of handles, relief decoration and throwing marks.

Crack O in glazed ware.

There is stress between body and glaze that cannot be absorbed by the body-glaze layer. The flaking is called shivering and shelling and, in the case of shelling, may have started before the glaze was fired. The lack of bond between body and glaze, or the lack of sufficient body-glaze layer is often caused by over-sponging of rims and edges. Over-sponging takes away the fine clay and leaves behind the sand. If this sand is not fused in the body-glaze layer it presents a weak structure with no elasticity to absorb the stress. See **Shivering** and **Shelling**.

CRACK P. A network of cracks forms a lace-like pattern in the glaze. This is called crazing. It usually develops after the pot is taken from the kiln but in extreme cases occurs during cooling. On opaque glazes it is often difficult to see and only shows if the glaze is misted by condensation or becomes stained.

Crazing results when the glaze is under tension and cracks to relieve the stress. See **Crazing** and **Glaze fit**.

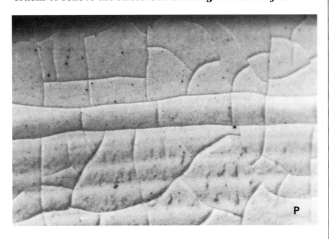

P

CRACK Q. A series of short cracks which divide at the ends into the spaces surrounded by other cracks. They occur in slip coatings and can be seen at dry raw stage but may not be noticed until the biscuit stage or very occasionally through a transparent glaze. They might cause crawling in the covering glaze. Also glazes which contain a high

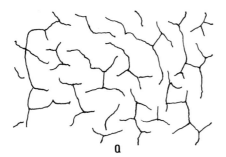

Q

proportion of clay, e.g. slip glazes and some dolomite glazes, may crack in this way and later crawl during the firing. See **Crawling**. In extreme cases, the slip may peel and lift from the body.

Crack Q in raw ware.

The crack is caused by the drying shrinkage of the clay slip. The slip shrinks more than the clay body which it covers because it is too rich (over-plastic and too fine), applied too thickly, applied when the body was too dry, or dried too quickly. Small cracks rarely show through a glaze. The cracks can be overcome by the addition of some non-plastic material to the slip, e.g. sand, flint, feldspar, pitchers, or by the use of a thinner layer and more controlled drying.

Cracks in slip also appear as a result of crazing and dunting of a thick layer of slip and are seen at biscuit stage. The three types of cracks can be identified by their different patterns. Compare crack illustrations P, Lb and Q.

CRACK R. These defects are included for completeness. Defect (i) occurs on both biscuit and glazed ware. Defects (ii) and (iii) occur on glazes.

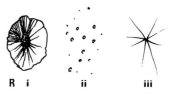

R i   ii   iii

i. This is a spit-out caused by foreign matter in the body. The object is usually a small stone which decomposes in the firing leaving an unfused spot which is porous. The porous spot absorbs moisture from the air, expands and pushes off a flake of glaze and probably part of the body. This occurs after the pot is taken from the kiln. The foreign matter can sometimes be seen at the biscuit stage and if small can be dug out and the hole stopped with ground biscuited body. Such foreign matter exists in most clays as dug, or might be accidentally introduced as broken bits from drying slabs made from plaster. A sea shore sand used as grog introduces specks of shells which are calcium carbonate. This decomposes at 825°C (1517°F) to little pockets of calcium oxide. If the firing continues beyond 1150°C (2012°F) these will become integrated. But if the firing is finished below this, as for a biscuit at 1000°C (1832°F), then the ware is likely to be covered by a host of little flakey spit-outs within a few days, especially in damp weather. This defect is also called chalking. See **Lime blows**.

ii. The spots are called pin-holes. They are small craters left by escaping gases. The glaze is probably stiff and contains a high proportion of aluminium oxide. It therefore requires a slightly longer firing to give sufficient time for the glaze to heal over. Alternatively, a slightly higher firing may be used but this could result in more pin-holes if the higher temperature boils or decomposes one of the glaze constituents. Alteration of the glaze recipe to reduce the aluminium oxide content slightly should be considered as a long-term policy.

iii. The radiating lines on the glaze surface may be quite tiny or may cover an area 6 mm across. The defect is called crow's feet and occurs on fairly stiff glazes which have difficulty in wetting the body which they cover. Stiff glazes with a strong surface tension do not easily soak into the body or flow into hollows or bridge over large particles. Crow's feet often form around specks of grog and sand on the body surface. Over-sponging, which takes away the fine clay and leaves the coarse clay, sand and grog, is one cause of crow's feet. Under-firing of the glaze is also a cause, because it does not allow the glaze to fuse fully and cover the coarse spot. The use of too much binder in the form of a glue or other organic material on the biscuit or in the glaze can also cause crow's feet. Loss of fine surface by sponging or bad fettling is the usual cause. A reduction in grain size of sand or grog, or the introduction of a ball clay into the body, or a slight extra fusion of the glaze may also be required.

CRACK S. The crack is where a handle joins a pot, either at the top or the bottom. It is called 'springing'. All handles, lugs etc are subject to springing. It originates in the making but may not be seen until after the glaze firing.

Crack S in raw ware, biscuit ware and glazed ware.
The handle was incorrectly joined for one or more of the following reasons:

The join was made too wet.
The join was not made wet enough. (Less common than above.)
The join was dried too quickly.
The pot was too dry when the handle was attached.
The handle became too wet during attachment.
The handle clay was too stiff and was subjected to stress during attachment.
The handle was distorted during drying, causing stress.
The handle clay was different from the body clay and was therefore subject to a different shrinkage. A handle which

shrinks less than the body of a pot can usually survive better than one which shrinks more.

CRACK T. The crack is a break through the handle other than at the joint. It often occurs in the lower half of a pulled handle as in the illustration. The latent crack occurs during the making but can remain undetected until it shows as two parted ends after the glaze firing.

Crack T in raw ware, biscuit ware and glazed ware.
There are two possible and related causes. The clay used for the handle was too weak, possibly because it had become tired by being overworked in making the handle. The handle was too thin for the type of clay used.

Crackle

Crackelle. Craquelle. A craze in the glaze used as a decorative feature. On some Chinese porcelains the first long craze lines were filled with a stain before the minor craze lines in between were established. The first cracks are inevitably wide but close as the stress is eased by further minor cracks. It is thus possible to choose the best time to

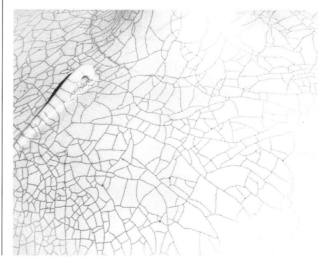

stain the craze to show the network of lines to its best decorative effect as a crackle.

Crackle is often a feature of raku ware. A white glaze shows this to advantage after smoking in sawdust. A detail of this is shown on a large pot by Dave Roberts (page 91).

There is a method known as melt-crackle in which the glaze is first underfired and allowed to craze. Colouring oxides are rubbed into the craze when it achieves a desired pattern, then the pot is refired to fire the glaze to its correct temperature. The craze shows finally as lines which are inlaid stains.

It is possible to produce one crackle network over another by the use of two separate glazes. The two glazes may have completely different patterns of crackle and the effect can be an interesting lacework.

When considered as a technical fault, crackle is called crazing. See ***Crazing***.

Crank

A refractory support for plates, tiles etc in glost and enamel firings. By the use of a crank rather than separate shelves, it is possible to more than double the weight of ware in a given kiln space.

With one type of crank, the plates and tiles rest upon projections (pins) which support the ware close to its edge. Thus this type is not suitable for maturing bodies which would sag. In the other type of crank, the crank is built from a series of separate chairs, tables or thin shelves which support each plate by its base. Pins are usually a refractory body but metal is also used.

CRANK MIXTURE. Fireclay or other refractory clay used for making cranks. It is well grogged and sometimes sanded. It is finer in texture than saggar marl and chamotte clay, and is often used as the basis of raku bodies and coarse stoneware bodies.

Crater glazes

Lava glazes. Glazes deliberately 'frozen' at a stage between bubbling and smoothing out. This is more difficult than it first appears because glazes usually have time to smooth out during cooling. To achieve craters, which must be smooth-edged rather than sharp-edged broken blisters, the bubbling needs to produce large bubbles rather than a general frothing. This is achieved by the use of coarse materials and the employment of gases erupting through stiffish melts.

Crater glazes can be produced at any temperature but are easier to produce in the range 1000°C to 1200°C (1832°F to 2192°F) because the gases used to create the bubbles are liberated in this range. Firing higher eliminates the craters unless the glaze is thick and viscous. A stoneware crater glaze needs to contain a large proportion of clay or feldspar.

Crater glazes can be produced in three ways: by additions to the body; by additions to the glaze; and by the use of a slip and a glaze reacting during firing. There is some advantage in using raw glazing since trapping gases escaping from the body is intentional with crater glazes. The firing and cooling cycles are equally as important as the compositions of body, slip and glaze. The temperature rise and top temperature create the craters and then the drop in temperature freezes the effect. Experiments are needed to determine the favourable cycles as well as the compositions.

Additions to the body can be up to 5% coarse silicon carbide or coarse clays normally unsuitable for potting because of their high sulfur and fluorine content. See also ***Health hazard***. Additions to the glaze can be up to 5%

coarse silicon carbide (50's to 150's mesh) or barium sulfate.

The use of a slip and a glaze, or the use of two glazes, gives a wide range of effects by thickness variations. The slip or first glaze is usually very fusible and concocted from estuarine muds or other clays containing sulfur and fluorine. Some potters add salt, cryolite, calcium fluoride and coarsely ground gypsum. This layer is often a dark colour. The glaze over this is usually an opaque light colour through which the dark erupts. This second glaze needs to be a slow maturing stiff glaze which traps the escaping gases until they burst out as collective large bubbles.

Robert Fournier's recipe uses fluorine contained in lepidolite for his stoneware glaze to be used as a single or first glaze.

talc	43·5
lepidolite	54·4
bentonite	2·0

Aki Moriuchi uses multiple glazes and firing techniques followed by refiring and sandblasting to achieve lava/crater glaze effects as in the photograph.

Crawling

Creeping. Rolling. Ruckling. Beading. The glaze defect characterized by the way the glaze parts and rolls back on itself leaving a bald patch of body. The defect may happen on a part of a pot such as an edge or where a pre-firing crack in the glaze occurred. Or it may happen in small patches all over a pot, or on the part where there is a slip. Sometimes it is very decorative although unwanted. If the glaze rolls itself into separate globules it is called beading. See **Beading**. The photograph shows a semi-opaque glaze which has crawled over a black slip to produce an interesting, if unintentional effect.

Glazes which are prone to crawling are those which have a high surface tension and are viscous when molten. A high aluminium oxide content makes a glaze viscous. Tin oxide and other opacifiers tend to increase surface tension and thus encourage crawling. Crawling might occur on all types of ware. In some cases the glaze recipe can be adjusted to

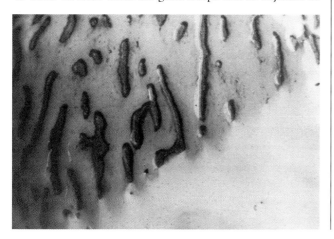

lessen the surface tension in the molten stage without losing the necessary character of the glaze. In addition, the supplementary causes which provide starting points for the areas of crawling must be avoided. See **Surface tension**.

With Bristol glazes it is the zinc oxide content which causes both high surface tension and pre-firing glaze cracks, which provide sites for the parting of the glaze. Glazes crawl away from a pre-firing crack in the glaze layer which occurs at a sharp edge, on a throwing ring, and where slip or other decoration meets plain pot etc. The crack is often caused by the shrinkage of the glaze.

When the glaze dries after application it is liable to shrink slightly, especially if it contains some clay. Over a uniform area the cracks will 'heal' during fusion. But on a variable surface, the shrinkage is liable to concentrate into larger areas pulling open a wide single crack. This can be seen where the glaze is thick, for example around a handle joint. Zinc oxide gives less trouble if it is calcined with some of the china clay before adding both to the glaze batch.

Celadon glazes have a high aluminium oxide content, and are prone to crawling especially where a thick glaze is used to emphasize the translucent character. The aluminium oxide gives high surface tension and, where present as clay, pre-firing cracks are a problem. Chinese Song celadons are often crawled and this may be due to the prolonged grinding the potters are reputed to have given their celadon glazes.

Borocalcite glazes lack sufficient fluxes of the low surface tension type. See **Surface tension**. In addition, colemanite in the recipe introduces a contributory cause of crawling because of its high water content. As this water is released during the early stages of firing it tends to loosen the glaze. See **Colemanite**. Whiting in a glaze recipe may contribute to crawling since it releases carbon dioxide. Wollastonite provides an alternative source of calcium oxide. A compound of calcium oxide and silica, it avoids the disturbance caused by carbon dioxide. The quartz or flint content of the recipe must be adjusted to allow for the extra silica. See **Wollastonite**.

A particularly viscous glaze melt such as a celadon may be provoked into crawling by a calodrop, the drop in temperature occasioned by increased reduction. The glaze surface is cooled causing a contraction crack which later draws apart.

A glaze which contains a high proportion of clay can be altered in a few ways: some of the clay can be replaced by feldspar; some can be calcined to render it non-plastic; and some or all can be replaced by a clay of low shrinkage. Some china clays are available which have a low shrinkage from wet to dry.

The second photograph shows another enlarged detail of crawling. This example was caused by pre-firing shrinkage of a dolomite glaze containing 25% of china clay. The typical lines of crawling due to shrinkage are simplified in the accompanying drawing.

A pre-firing crack is the commonest cause of crawling but another cause is greasy and dusty biscuit which prevents the glaze from adhering properly before firing. Also the over-grinding of a glaze can make it too fluffy to adhere properly to the biscuit. Similarly, the firing of ware which is still wet from glazing causes steam from the body to lift and loosen the glaze. The loosened glaze, like the glaze over dust or grease, crawls when it melts. This crawling is also called lifting. When a viscous glaze melts, it prefers to stick to itself rather than wet the body and stick to that. As a general rule, lead glazes are more wetting in their fusion than leadless glazes and are therefore less likely to crawl.

Sometimes a glaze begins to crawl when it has previously been satisfactory. Firing of wet ware should first be considered as the cause. The second possibility is that a thicker layer of glaze is being used. The glaze slop may have thickened by evaporation or use. Alternatively, the biscuit ware may be slightly underfired. This gives a more absorbent biscuit which not only takes a thicker layer of glaze but dries it too quickly to allow it to become compact. An immediate remedy may be to thin the glaze slop and add a little gum to hold the glaze firmly. A third possible cause is that the biscuit has become dusty or has been overhandled and become greasy.

Crazing

Crackle. Craquelle. The glaze defect characterized by a network of fine cracks. The effect can be decorative and if deliberate is called crackle.

On earthenware, the glaze is intended to be an impervious layer to cover an absorbent body. If the glaze crazes, it no longer fulfils this function. Crazed earthenware which has been in use for a number of years will have absorbed dirt with the moisture so that the craze lines show distinctly. On tableware this is unpleasant and probably unhygienic. On true stoneware the crazing does not present such a hazard. The body itself is impervious and the glaze's function is to present a smooth hygienic and decorative surface.

Crazes are cracks in the glaze. They occur because the glaze contracts more than the body as the pot cools after firing. If the glaze is unable to sustain the tension that thereby comes upon it, it cracks. The first cracks that occur are usually long ones which often spiral upwards on a pot or go straight across a plate. If these cracks were inspected through a lens they would be seen to be wide. Even so, stress still exists between body and glaze which is eased by further crazing of the areas between the first long cracks. The long cracks are called primary crazing.

The filling in of an area with smaller cracks to form a host of little squares and/or triangles is called secondary crazing. When secondary crazing has taken place, close inspection of the primary cracks will show that they have closed considerably. At the time when the primary crazing has taken place, it is possible to rub colouring into the cracks to give a decorative effect. This was done with Chinese crackle celadons.

Crazing may take place during the cooling in the kiln but most glazes come from the kiln craze-free. The stresses which will cause the crazing exist but are contained by the strength and elasticity of the glaze. However these stresses become exaggerated by the expansion and contraction during everyday use until they result in crazing. This may take many years. Earthenware bodies are porous and absorb moisture from the air. As they do so they expand permanently. The glaze does not expand but crazes to accommodate the tension put upon it. This is another reason for the crazing on earthenware and other porous bodies.

To counteract this expansion through moisture it is usual to arrange for the body to be too small for the glaze. The glaze is then under compression and not tension. This allows the body to expand later without causing tension in the glaze. The device employs the cristobalite squeeze and is described under **Cristobalite** and **Silica inversions**. Crazing often occurs on ovenware because of the unequal heating and cooling of glaze and body. This is detailed under **Thermal shock**.

The correction of crazing is theoretically simple but not always so in practice. It is explained in detail under **Glaze fit**. A glaze or a body can be altered in composition thereby altering its rate of expansion and contraction. Harmony of body and glaze can be achieved but only at one temperature. The various temperatures of a day, of a pot's use as tableware and especially of its use as ovenware invariably create stresses. These stresses, if not absorbed by the resilience of body and glaze, result in crazing, or its opposite, shivering. Shivering is the worse because it ruins the pot and is dangerous on table and kitchen ware. Most potters therefore are content if their wares craze occasionally.

A glaze can be made more elastic by the addition of lead oxide and/or boron oxide. Glazes based upon the sodium and potassium oxides, and to a lesser extent calcium oxide, are brittle and likely to contract a large amount. Alkaline glazes are notorious for crazing because their oxides have a high rate of contraction. Boron oxide has an extremely low rate of contraction and amounts of up to 15% in the glaze will have beneficial effect in countering crazing. This is approximate. The amount is different for each glaze. More than 15% may have the opposite effect because the glaze's resilience is lowered by large amounts of boron oxide. The effect has been called boracitis.

Glazes often craze if they are underfired or overfired. In the former case it is because there is insufficient body-glaze layer forming. This layer absorbs the stress between the body and the glaze. Improvements in craze resistance can be achieved by facilitating the growth of a body-glaze layer as described under *Buffer layer*.

Where a glaze is overfired and then crazes it is because the overfiring affected the body more than the glaze. This happens on stoneware where body and glaze mature together. The crystalline silica in the body becomes fused silica and in this form it has a much lower rate of contraction. The glaze still has the same rate of contraction and therefore in proportion it contracts more when overfired than when correctly fired.

This phenomenon explains the apparent paradox in the statement that to cure crazing one adds silica to the glaze, or the body, or both. In the case of the glaze the extra silica fuses in the melt. In this state it has a low contraction rate. Aluminium oxide is also effective in small amounts and therefore china clay is often added to glazes to counteract crazing. In the case of the body the extra silica is intended to remain crystalline, a form in which it has a high rate of contraction. Sand is often used for stonewares but flint is used for earthenwares with the additional possibility of creating cristobalite. Cristobalite squeeze has already been mentioned.

Crazing is a common fault which is simple to understand but difficult to eradicate. In earthenware the answer would lie in the balanced use of lead oxide and boron oxide in the glaze and possibly cristobalite in the body. If the earthenware body is biscuited at a higher temperature than the glaze will be fired, then this temperature greatly affects craze resistance. Underfiring biscuit will cause crazing. Overfiring of non-cristobalite bodies may also cause crazing by fusing the previously crystalline free silica.

In dense stoneware, cristobalite may lead to the worse faults of shivering and dunting, and the temperatures used may be too high for lead which has a practical upper limit of about 1250°C (2282°F). Therefore a pure silica sand in the body, boron oxide in the glaze or an adjustment of the glaze oxides will be necessary. The glaze oxides to be considered first would be boron oxide to replace silica, additional silica possibly with some aluminium oxide, or the replacement of sodium oxide by potassium oxide or potassium oxide by calcium, barium and lithium oxides.

Creamware

Cream-coloured earthenware. The forerunner of today's English white earthenware. It was developed in the early 18th century by the Astburys, and later perfected by Whieldon and Wedgwood. Creamware was possible because of the increasing use of china and ball clays, and cornish stone from south-west England. A typical recipe shows their importance:

china clay	25
ball clay	25
flint	35
cornish stone	15

The photograph shows an example of scratch-blue creamware by W. and T. Taylor, Greenhead Pottery, *c*. 1760.

It was on creamware that the method of using a glaze slop was perfected. This was possibly introduced into southern England with the making of delft in the 17th century and was taken up by the slipware potters of northern England in the early 18th century. At first galena was mixed with water but later flint was added and lead oxide replaced the galena. By 1750 a balanced glaze slop was in use which gave a uniform layer of glaze when fired. At the same time plaster of Paris was replacing gypsum and biscuit as a mould material. When, in 1760, the idea of biscuiting ware before glazing was introduced, the foundations of the mass-production industry had been laid.

Creeping
See **Crawling**.

Crete
The Mediterranean island which had a highly-developed Bronze Age known as the Minoan Civilization. From 2600BC a series of distinctive pottery styles developed with robust forms and decorative painting. The decoration was based upon flowers and sea creatures and was the most exuberant of any Bronze Age pottery. The pottery decoration was contemporary with but not the same as mural painting. The two need to be seen as a whole. The pottery decoration was purely a decorative treatment and owed nothing to a religious significance. The climax of the pottery decoration was about 1900BC; after this, more expression went into mural painting. Eventually the forms and the decoration became rigid and the freedom was lost. This coincided with the Iron Age and this rigidity reflects the stricter qualities of both the material, iron, and the people who worked it.

Cristobalite
Silica. SiO_2. One of the primary phases of silica which are important to the ceramicist. The others are quartz, tridymite and silica glass. See **Silica phases**. These four phases are chemically identical but are physically different in their molecular structures. They therefore exhibit different physical properties. It is for its unique expansion rate that cristobalite is used in ceramics. Cristobalite bodies have anti-craze properties.

Cristobalite does not expand at a constant rate when heated from room temperature. In the first 200°C (360°F) it expands approximately 0·7% volumetrically. Then at 226°C (439°F) it suddenly expands by 3%. Following this, a slow rate of expansion is continued. The expansion curve is shown in the graph.

PHYSICS OF CRISTOBALITE. Cristobalite is a crystalline solid. The sudden expansion is caused by a straightening of the Si-O-Si bonds of the crystal lattice. The silica lattice, while maintaining the valency commitments of its atoms, is capable of some nine regular variations. Of these, quartz, cristobalite and tridymite are important to the potter. They are each capable of a slightly collapsed version and a very straight, extended version. These give the two forms alpha and beta and account for the size change which takes place.

If oxygen atoms are packed together they can be most economically packed in a regular way as in fig. 1. In silica, each oxygen atom is attached to two silicon atoms and this is achieved by placing silicon atoms in the hollows formed by three adjacent oxygen atoms. Such sites are marked with large dots in fig. 2. The sites marked X cannot be occupied because the oxygen atoms drawn in thicker line are already satisfied in their valencies by the silicon atoms already inserted.

However, although the oxygen atoms may be satisfied, the silicon atoms are not. They require four oxygen atoms each to satisfy their valency requirements. These extra oxygens fit one on top of each silicon as in fig. 3. The building brick of silica is therefore a tetrahedron formed by four oxygen atoms surrounding one silicon atom as in fig. 4.

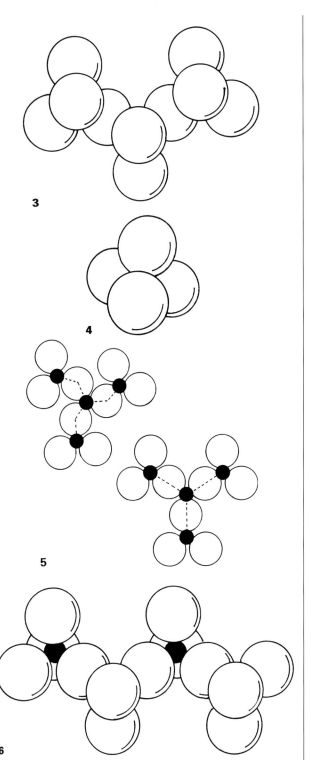

3

4

5

6

See also **Crystal**, which includes drawings of the single tetrahedron.

The silicon atom is slightly too large for the space left inside the four oxygen atoms. The silicon therefore pushes the oxygen atoms slightly apart. This gives space in the lattice for minor adjustments like those of the alpha to beta forms. These occur by a collapsing or straightening of a

line drawn through the silicon-oxygen-silicon bonds as in fig. 5.

This accounts for the inversions but there is also space for larger adjustments as can be seen from fig. 3 which is obviously more open as a lattice than is the tight packing of fig. 1.

If this is visualized as a three-dimensional structure one can imagine how the individual tetrahedra, while retaining their identity and with comparable links with other tetrahedra, can be placed in different relationships to one another. An obvious one is that in which alternate tetrahedra of a chain are inverted as in fig. 6.

Many possibilities apparent in a flat diagram cancel one another out when viewed from other angles. However some nine variations are possible of which fig. 6 represents cristobalite in contrast to fig. 3 which is quartz. The individual way in which each can collapse as an alpha form accounts for its different behaviour at inversion.

CRISTOBALITE IN BODIES. One of the defects of glazed earthenware is crazing. Crazing occurs when the glaze contraction is greater than that of the body. The accompanying graph shows comparative cooling curves for a glaze and two bodies during the last stages of cooling. The temperature is indicated across the graph cooling from left to right. Note that this is the opposite of the previous graph. Contraction is indicated down the graph so that the glaze shown by the heavy line (G) contracts by the amount from A to G (approximately 0·9%) in cooling from 400°C (752°F).

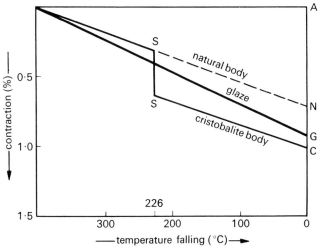

Cristobalite's 3% firing expansion is sudden and it is exactly reversible. That is, during cooling, the cristobalite suddenly contracts by this amount. If cristobalite is present in a pottery body, the whole body will suddenly contract at this temperature in proportion to the amount of cristobalite it contains. This is a valuable characteristic because by giving a body this extra contraction, crazing of the glaze can be overcome.

A natural earthenware body contracts only by the

amount from A to N (approximately 0·7%) and is therefore larger than its covering glaze. The result is crazing of the glaze.

If 10% cristobalite is present in the body, the body will contract by the amount A to C (approximately 1%). This is more than the glaze which is thereby compressed by the body and unable to craze.

The compression, which occurs at 226°C (439°F), is shown at SS on the graph. This is known as the cristobalite squeeze and it is invaluable as an anti-craze measure. It can, however, be over-accentuated, resulting in the opposite of crazing which is shivering. See **Crazing** and **Shivering**. Fortunately, a glaze can withstand about ten times the amount of stress under compression before it shivers than the amount of stress it can withstand under tension before it crazes.

The stress which is created between the body and glaze by the cristobalite squeeze can have a marked effect upon the overall strength of the pottery object. It is possible to double a pot's resistance to physical knocks, as well as to create so much compression that a pot is at a tense point where the slightest knock shatters it. The optimum amount can only be discovered by tests. Such tests are beyond the means of the individual potter who, if he wishes to incorporate cristobalite into his body, should do so by a series of simple tests containing 1%, 2%, 3% etc of cristobalite. The effect can be judged by the crazing of a thick layer of glaze. The maximum addition of cristobalite is unlikely to exceed 10%. Some loss of plasticity and the opening effect of a non-plastic refractory material are to be expected.

The amount of cristobalite required cannot be calculated from the amount of crazing. The experiences of one potter in terms of percentage additions of cristobalite are not directly transferable to another potter's work unless it is identical. The presence of some cristobalite in a body encourages the conversion of other silica to cristobalite phase. The presence of other free silica, of other catalysts, and the temperatures involved, all play a part. Refiring a piece of pottery encourages the conversion of further cristobalite which upsets the balance of glaze compression and makes the ware extremely brittle. Before the mechanics of the cristobalite squeeze were understood, potters introduced talc into the clay. It had been empirically discovered that this addition inhibited crazing. The magnesium oxide in the talc encourages the conversion of quartz to cristobalite. See **Silica conversion**.

Cristobalite, with or without attendant catalysts and compensatory body fluxes, can be purchased in fine-grain and fine-powder forms. It is preferable to add the cristobalite to the clay at the blunging stage but it can be satisfactorily added along with sand, grog etc at the plastic stage, provided that it is thoroughly mixed into the clay. Like all fine powders it tends to cling to itself thus making it difficult to thoroughly disperse it.

The sudden contraction of the cristobalite squeeze creates a stress within a piece of pottery as well as between its body and glaze. Earthenware bodies which are 'open',

and hence resilient, can withstand this stress but dense stoneware cannot. The sudden contraction can be disastrous to stoneware. See **Dunting: cooling dunts**.

The cristobalite squeeze occurring at 226°C (439°F) is within the range of a domestic oven. Cristobalite is therefore undesirable in ovenware. To overcome the sudden contraction and yet exert compression upon the glaze is a problem that has been overcome industrially by the use of tridymite in combination with cristobalite.

The combined cristobalite/tridymite is often referred to as disordered cristobalite. Powders purchased as cristobalite are sometimes of this order and give a smoother contraction of slightly less amount but over a temperature range of some 100°C (180°F). Tridymite is unlikely to form in pottery bodies because it takes longer to convert from quartz than does cristobalite. See also the description of cristobalite and tridymite in **Silica inversions**.

CRISTOBALITE IN GLAZES. There is no advantage whatsoever in using cristobalite rather than quartz, flint or sand in a glaze. All are silica and chemically identical. Their physical differences disappear once their lattice structures are destroyed by the molten state.

Critical moisture content

The water content of a clay, paste or other suspension, where this water fills all the hollows between the particles yet leaves the particles in contact. The critical moisture content is usually considered in relation to clay or suspensions as they dry out. It is the point at which a glaze slop 'sets' on the ware and the point at which plastic clay becomes a solid. In normal usage the point of critical moisture content for a clay is the same as the leatherhard stage.

Crocus martis

Anhydrous iron sulfate. Calcined copperas. $FeSO_4$. A cheap iron salt used for colouring glazes. It is soluble in water and in the glaze, giving soft yellows in lead glazes and greenish colours in boron glazes (3%–6%).

If heated alone it does not fully decompose until approximately 1200°C (2192°F) when it forms red iron oxide, sulfur trioxide and sulfur dioxide:

$$2FeSO_4 \longrightarrow Fe_2O_3 + SO_3 \uparrow + SO_2 \uparrow$$

Partially decomposed crocus martis is often used to obviate the possible problem of solubility in the glaze slop. Its further decomposition only takes place during the later activity of glaze melting and it therefore produces a speckle. The partially decomposed crocus martis is a dark purple-brown and can be obtained by calcining at approximately 900°C (1652°F). It has a theoretical formula of $FeO.Fe_2O_3.FeSO_4$.

Cross draught kiln

Horizontal kiln. A kiln in which the hot gases travel through the ware across the chamber from a pierced bag wall to exit flues in the opposite wall.

Cryolite

Fluoride of aluminium and sodium. Na_3AlF_6. A natural mineral associated with granites. It is used in the preparation of vitreous enamels and occasionally in frits and glazes. Cryolite, albite and nepheline are the only native sodium compounds that are insoluble in water. Cryolite is used to produce crater glazes and crackle effects in alkaline glazes.

Cryptocrystalline

Composed of exceedingly fine crystals which are not detectable with the naked eye or normal magnification. The crystals may be no more than the nuclei of crystals with each structure only a few molecules in size. However, the fact that they are crystals may be important as starting points for crystal growth or, in the case of flint, important because they are subject to inversions.

Crystal

The concentration of many identical molecular units in a regular three-dimensional pattern. See also **Lattice structure**.

The atoms which form simple molecules, and the molecules (radicals) which form complex molecules, group themselves in balanced ways dictated by their electrical charges and their physical sizes. A compact group produces a 'cell' which is the unit of the whole structure. Many units together give a crystal whose form is directly related to the cell.

The illustrations show a quartz crystal whose six-sided column (fig. 1) is composed of units which have triangular sides (fig. 2). The unit 'cell' is a tetrahedron which is a three-sided pyramid standing on a triangular base (fig. 3). This is the silica tetrahedron (SiO_4) (figs. 4 and 5) which becomes SiO_2 when each oxygen is linked to another silicon. See **Silica structure**.

In a crystal, one set of bonds will always be weaker than the rest and this set will form planes through the solid. A crystal splits most readily along these planes of cleavage producing pieces which are smaller versions of the original.

Crystalline solids tend to melt suddenly at a given temperature. Here all the links of one type are released. See **Amorphous** which describes non-crystalline solids.

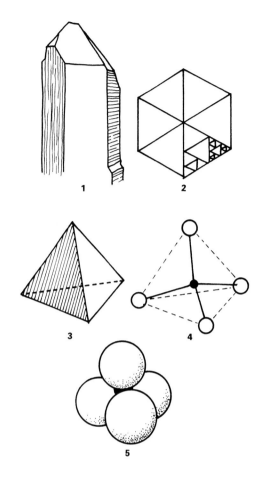

The crystals in crystal glazes are built up from units which separate from the molten glass upon cooling. They are usually complex crystals like calcium silicate, magnesium silicate and zinc silicate.

Crystalline glazes

Glazes which contain crystals within the amorphous (glassy) matrix of the glaze. The glaze itself is not entirely composed of crystals. Crystals give opacity, matt surface and visual effects. The crystals grow mostly during cooling by isolation of the essential oxides from the surrounding fluid glaze. The process is known as devitrification and is given encouragement by seeding and by controlling the rate of cooling.

The three types of crystalline glaze are separately described following a discussion of principles general to all types. The three types are: glazes with separate crystals within the glaze just visible to the naked eye; glazes opacified or made matt by crystals; and glazes with large surface crystals. The first two types are often referred to as microcrystalline and the last type as macrocrystalline.

GENERAL PRINCIPLES. The chemistry of crystalline glazes is interesting. A molten glaze is a completely fluid mixture of theoretically individual molecules. Upon cooling, these molecules link together in random fashion to form chains. This gives the amorphous substance called glass.

There are inevitably some unsatisfied valencies within a glass which, if given the opportunity, are satisfied by orientation of the molecules into more regular chains. If the cooling is done slowly, the molecules seek to establish patterns of bonds which completely satisfy their valency requirements. Such bonding produces a regular structure or lattice which is the framework of a crystal. See **Crystal** and **Lattice structure**.

Crystals grow more readily in glazes which have low viscosity. Such glazes are more thoroughly dispersed and, during the building of the crystal, present little resistance to the growth of a perfect lattice. Aluminium oxide stiffens glazes and is therefore kept to a minimum. The resulting fluid runny glazes are eminently suitable for tiles which are fired horizontally but less suitable for tall pots. The fine-grained aluminium oxide matt is one obvious exception. See **Aluminium oxide in glazes** and **Run (1)**.

During cooling a combination of two or more oxides can solidify by forming the necessary molecular bonds. In coming from a hot to a cooler state they are often said to be precipitated because the melt can no longer hold them in solution (dispersed state). As they are precipitated, time is necessary for the orientation of molecules to take place so that the frozen precipitate has a regular structure—that is, it is crystalline. It is worth remembering that the crystals may or may not include the colouring oxide present in the glaze. Crystallization is a selective process so that white crystals within a coloured matrix are possible as in the photograph of a crystalline glaze by Theo Whalley.

At a given temperature therefore there are crystals which are able to form and also potential crystals awaiting suitable conditions but still in fluid state. Many mixtures will never crystallize. They form the glassy matrix of the glaze.

The isolation within the molten glaze of some of its constituents upsets the balance of the rest. Some of the remaining oxides are no longer able to stay in solution because the oxides whose close presence enabled them to be liquid have been removed by crystallization. These second precipitated oxides combine as larger molecules and opacify the matrix. The removal of the second stage of oxides hastens the isolation of others with the net result that the glaze sets quickly. The setting of the matrix precludes any further development of crystals.

In contrast to the above, plutonic igneous rocks are often completely crystalline and consequently one might academically consider it possible to render a glaze completely crystalline if a comparable cooling time of perhaps twenty years were used. However, plutonic rocks are subjected to extreme pressures and although the last mineral to crystallize in them is often silica it remains sufficiently plastic to allow orientation of its molecules into crystalline state. At atmospheric pressures the isolated silica would set immediately to an amorphous glass.

The setting of the matrix of some crystalline glazes will therefore occur whether the temperature is falling, steady or even rising. It is brought about by the creation of the particular combination of oxides which sets at this temperature. Naturally, this combination is likely to set more quickly if the temperature is falling and more quickly still if the temperature is falling rapidly. Thus both temperature and time do affect the setting of a crystalline glaze and affect the amount of crystallization that is able to take place.

Lastly, the general principle of seeding requires explanation. Crystals start to grow more readily if they have a starting point. Where there is a positive body-glaze layer, as in stoneware and porcelain, the mullite crystals are often starting points for inglaze crystals. Other starting points exist in most glazes and with sufficient time crystals will grow. But the normal cooling of most kilns is too fast for this to happen and deliberate seeding of the glaze becomes necessary. Suitable seed is included as part of the glaze recipe.

The most popular seed is titanium oxide. Titanate crystals grow on the refractory nucleus of titanium oxide during the firing from 820°C (1508°F) upwards even as high as 1300°C (2372°F). An active fluid glaze surrounding these crystals dissolves them even as they grow. When the activity of the glaze decreases during the cooling, the crystals can develop which they do first as titanates and then as crystals of other composition depending upon the oxides available in the melt. Ultimately the crystals could be mainly of non-titanate type like calcium silicate.

Seeds are always refractory material. They are tiny particles, often of colloidal size and possibly consisting of only a small group of identical molecules. Being refractory they do not enter the fusion of the glaze because their own molecular bonds are not broken by the heat. If seeded glazes are seriously overfired they cannot satisfactorily crystallize upon cooling because their seeds have been broken up and dispersed through the melt. Although it is true that crystals grow more easily from a thoroughly dispersed molten glaze, it is necessary to have the seeds in isolated existence. The required dispersed melt is achieved by making the glaze of low viscosity which usually means low in aluminium oxide content.

Seeding of high-temperature glazes can be done with titanium oxide or ilmenite to foster titanate crystals; calcium phosphate and zirconium silicate to foster calcium borate and calcium silicate crystals; and different sources of silica for silicate crystals. One per cent is often sufficient seed but the glaze must contain suitable oxides to form the crystals.

For low-temperature glazes titanium oxide is the usual seed and the crystals are usually titanates. Titanium oxide up to 5% of the recipe gives milkiness, 10% to 12% gives full opacity and 15% gives a matt crystalline surface. Titanium oxide 4% and up to 18% zinc oxide give the fine-grained satin matts. See *Satin matt.*

1. SMALL VISIBLE CRYSTALS. Some crystals, formed within an otherwise transparent and shiny glaze, show as a glittering or sparkle especially against a dark body. As they catch the light, these crystals appear to be needles about a millimetre long. They are not needle crystals but this is the manner in which they catch the light. The crystals are precipitated from the glaze but are often assisted (seeded) by the crystallization of the body-glaze layer. The traditional aventurine glaze has iron oxide crystals but other colouring oxide crystals are possible. See *Aventurine.* Historical examples of galena-glazed wares with dark brown bodies often contain iron sulfate crystals which give a rich gingery sparkle.

2. CRYSTALS GIVING OPACITY AND MATTNESS. Crystals which are too small to be seen individually nevertheless give opacity in bulk. Examples are those of: iron oxide in oxidized tenmokus; zirconium silicate in white opaque glazes; and calcium phosphate and calcium borate in jun glazes. See individual compounds and glaze types. Where crystals spread on the surface they produce mattness. Crystals associated with mattness include those of: calcium silicate; calcium magnesium silicate; magnesium silicate; iron oxide; calcium aluminium silicate; and calcium silicon titanate. For information about the crystalline minerals involved, see *Diopside, Enstatite, Ilmenite, Titanite, Willemite* and *Wollastonite.*

Crystalline glazes of the overall matt type which are usually cooled by allowing the kiln to cool naturally might not have sufficient time to crystallize. Small fast-fire kilns often cool very quickly indeed. An openly set firing will cool more quickly than a firing which has many tightly packed shelves and will give different results. Pots near the door or walls of the kiln will be different from ones in the middle of

the kiln. A single pot may come out with its glaze having crystallized on one side but not on the other. The photograph shows such a pot in which a lime matt has developed on one side but quick cooling has prevented it on the other where, instead, a transparent and shiny glaze has resulted.

If the cooling rate cannot be controlled a refiring of the glaze through the crystallization temperature can be used. The graph in fig. 1 shows how a refire, drawn in solid line, gives more than double the time within the crystallization range. The dotted line shows the normal cooling from the glaze firing. Putting a pot in with a soft biscuit firing often has the result of forming crystals, sometimes with colour, that did not previously exist. Once started, crystals will grow whether the temperature is falling, rising or steady providing the conditions are suitable—that is, the glaze is not too viscous and the necessary oxides are present.

Many glazes respond to a refiring of this type. A reduced black tenmoku, for example, has iron oxide crystals near to the surface where it is starting to break to rust. This iron oxide oxidizes fully to a rich iron red. The black areas might emerge covered with bright yellow crystals as a grainy flecking. Such results, of course, occur naturally the first time in a large kiln which cools very slowly.

Crystals are forming in the body-glaze layer during a firing. See *Mullite* and *Body-glaze layer.* These crystals are small but seed more crystals which grow irregularly on them during cooling. The strong body-glaze layer of stoneware encourages this more than in earthenware. Essentially transparent glazes often have matt streaked patches because of this, especially those glazes slightly overfluxed with wood ash. The crystals are growing throughout the cooling, accelerating in their growth down to 700°C (1292°F).

Out of a fluid mixture of perhaps ten different oxides, a crystalline combination like calcium silicate can isolate itself. But it is impossible to establish an exact temperature for a particular crystal which can be used under all circumstances. Although it is known that isolated calcium silicate has a solidifying point of 1545°C (2813°F) the growth of this crystal in a glaze is dependent upon the composition of the melt from which it is precipitated.

Fortunately it is only necessary to know that most matt forming glaze crystals are isolated in the range between 900°C and 700°C (1652°F and 1292°F). This is well below the melting points of many of the crystalline minerals involved and results in the sudden creation of many small crystals. Lime matts, which rely upon calcium silicate, have small crystals giving a fine grain.

Zinc silicate is precipitated above 1000°C (1832°F). This is nearer to its melting point and also that of the surrounding glaze. Therefore large crystals up to 10 cm across are possible.

3. LARGE SURFACE CRYSTALS. These glazes always attract admiration. They are difficult to produce. They require infinite patience and very accurate weighing, glaze application, firing, cooling and note keeping of recipes and firing/cooling schedules. A change of 1% of any of the constituents gives a different result, hence the need for patience. A borrowed recipe is an essential starting point. See ***Recipe Appendix***.

Potters who produce crystalline glazes recognize three factors which can be considered separately. One is the cooling schedule which establishes how large the crystals will grow and also, with some glazes, the shapes of the crystals. Another factor is the chemical composition of the glaze which establishes how fluid the melt will be. The third factor is the colouration of the crystals and matrix.

Large surface crystals are zinc silicate ($2ZnO.SiO_2$), sometimes coloured by other oxides. A crystal starts where a tiny titanium oxide or a zinc oxide crystal provides a seed or nucleus. To this crystal a free silica molecule and two zinc oxide molecules will attach themselves. Once the combination of zinc silicate is formed, many more zinc oxide and silica molecules attach themselves in specific orientation.

Cooling schedule. The crystal-growing period, from 1140°C down to 1010°C (2084°F to 1850°F) can be divided into three overlapping opportunities for crystal growth. Two are focused around 1140°C and 1100°C (2084°F and 2012°F), and the third is in the range from 1090°C down to 1010°C (1994°F to 1850°F). The 1140°C period is when the crystals formed are of the long needle type. Even when the temperature is passed rapidly, the crystals start their growth on nuclei. If the temperature is held for sufficient time around 1100°C the crystals may grow into shapes known as double axe-heads. Photograph of a bottle by Derek Clarkson. Holding the temperature in the range from 1090°C to 1010°C encourages rounded shapes. A study of

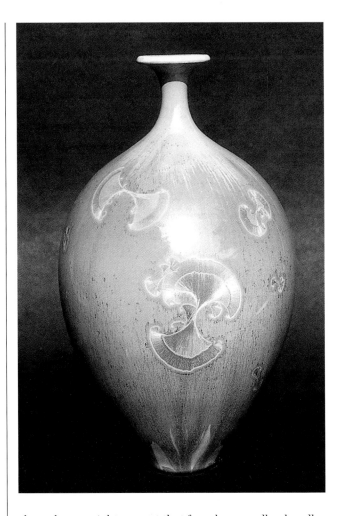

these shapes might suggest that from long needles, bundles of feathery needles fan out to form the axe-head shapes. If these are given a longer time to develop the fans become more complex, link up, and soften into round floral shapes (see fig. 2). The forming of crystals is susceptible to many interlinked conditions so this might not always be the case.

The effects produced are also affected by the chemical composition of the glaze which itself will emphasize one crystal shape at the expense of another, as well as requiring temperature adjustments.

The body type and firing programme are interrelated and critical. Zinc silicate crystals at the surface can be contaminated and even inhibited in growth by the crystals of a body-glaze layer. For this reason most crystal growers use porcelain bodies which are not taken to maturity and therefore the body-glaze layer is negligible. Fast firing up to the top temperature and fast cooling down as far as the critical crystal-growing period precludes the growth of a body-glaze layer.

It follows that to achieve a full melt in a fast fire, the glaze must be taken to a relatively high temperature. To produce the melt quickly the recipe will contain a similar percentage of frit to a recipe designed to melt at a lower temperature which would be given a longer time to mature. In this respect, recipes for crystalline glazes, although fired to

2 Developing crystal shapes

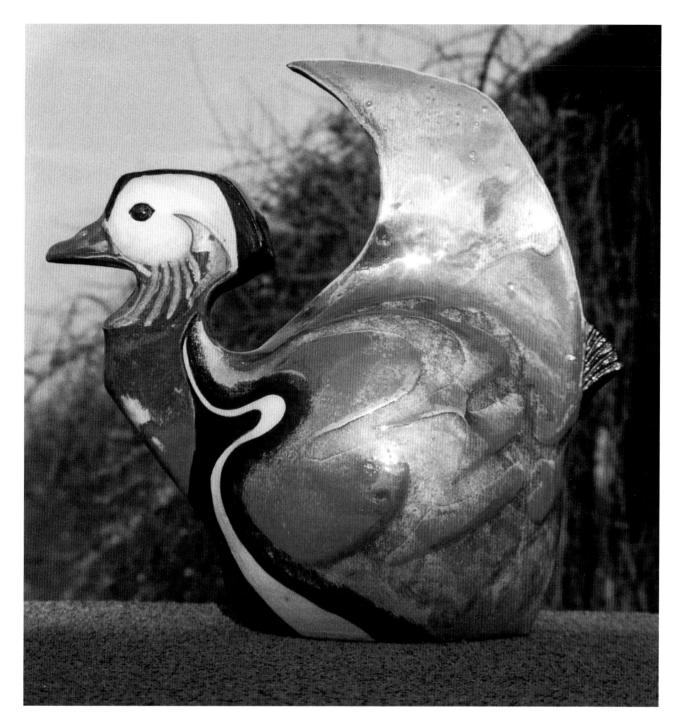

PLATE 1
MANDARIN DRAKE, slab built by Janet Hamer. Height 32 cm.
A 50/50 blend of stoneware clay with 'T' material and extra Molochite is used to
avoid shrinkage cracks on the variably tensioned slabs. The striking copper red and
lustred glaze catches light with gold, purple and pink effects. These colours appear
best where the glaze is thick and beginning to move down the piece. See **Copper
lustre, Lustres** and **Recipe Appendix.**

(photo: *Janet Hamer*)

PLATE 2
High temperature inglaze lustre is developed using a glaze containing up to 4% of copper carbonate. The copper oxide migrates through the glaze as it fuses and matures. Reduction during the cooling cycle changes the oxide to metallic copper. Within the glaze this gives deep red colours. To achieve lustrous effects a layer of minute particles of copper must be caught at the surface and held in reduction there as the glaze cools. This gives iridescent effects of magenta-purple and blue, best seen when reflecting daylight. Size of area shown is 18 cm across.

PLATE 3
A denser accumulation of metal in the surface of the glaze catches the light with colours of pink and gold. A photograph can record these colours seen from one angle. A slight tilt of the surface will make the colours flash through fascinating combinations of the spectrum. Size of area shown is 14 cm across.

PLATE 4
The movement of copper through the glaze is assisted in this case by lead which at a temperature above 1200°C (2192°F) is, like the copper, beginning to volatilize. The timing of this movement and the timing of the reduction is critical. A thickly applied glaze layer gives the potter a greater chance of fixing the metal where it is wanted. Where the fused glaze moves down the side of a ceramic, and accumulates a mass of copper metal, excessive and lurid effects can occur. A concave surface increases the concentration. The result can look fiery and volcanic. Size of area shown is 5 cm across.

Details of glaze on a Ruddy Duck and a Carolina Drake by Janet Hamer. See **Copper lustre, Lustres** and **Recipe Appendix.**

(photos: *Janet Hamer*)

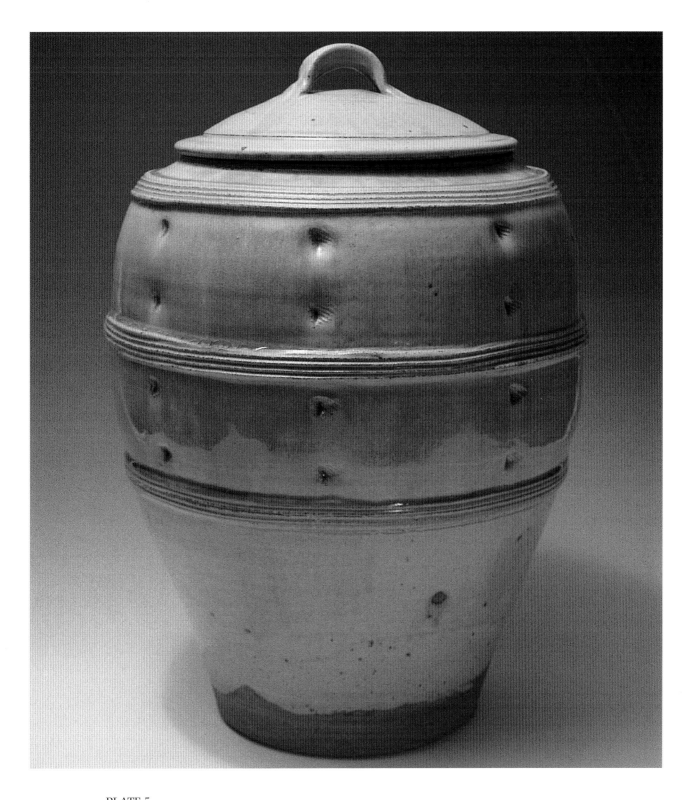

PLATE 5
STONEWARE STORAGE JAR by Phil Rogers. Height 56 cm.
The large but serene jar was thrown in two sections, the second joined as a collar of clay onto
the leatherhard lower section and thrown higher. A white slip, composed of SMD ball clay (2
parts) and 200's mesh Molochite (1 part), creates the ideal intermediate layer for the ash glaze
because it is high in aluminium oxide. The glaze is well-fluxed by a mixture of elm and oak
ashes, thus creating glassy sections where it collects after running, and matt and streaked
areas where the aluminium oxide from beneath encourages crystallization. See **Ashes, Wood
ash** and **Recipe Appendix.**

(photo: *Phil Rogers*)

PLATE 6
SALT-GLAZED BOWL by Rosemary Cochrane. Diameter 28 cm.
Variety of colour and texture is encouraged by areas of slip which are self-coloured or draw colour from the iron-bearing clay. High-silica slips attract a thicker glaze cover while those low in silica attract a thin gloss. Fusible engobes, glazes and rutile are trailed, brushed and sponged on. The overlapped components interact and blend under the attack of the salt firing. See **Salt glaze** and **Recipe Appendix.**
(photo: *Rosemary Cochrane*)

PLATE 7
SALT-GLAZED JUG by Walter Keeler. Height 12 cm.
A thrown cylinder is cut at a slant from its base, coaxed to an oval shape and rejoined to a flat slab base. This gives the piece a sensitive, slight tilt, typical of the 'Keeler' jug. The spout is reserved from a cutaway section of the top. The handle is hollow. See **Salt glaze** and **Jug**.
(photo: *Janet Hamer*)

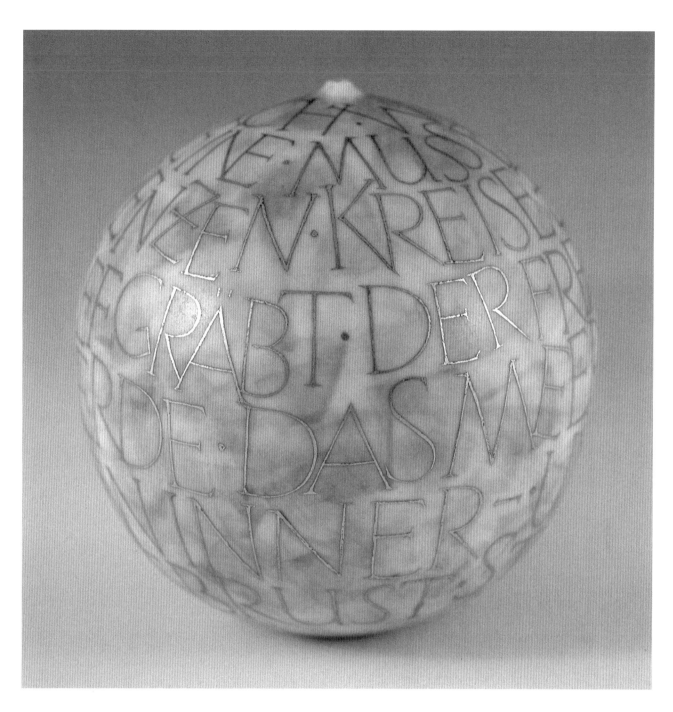

PLATE 8
SPHERICAL PORCELAIN BOTTLE by Mary White. Height 17 cm.
Blue underglaze colours painted under an oxidized barium glaze fired at 1260°C (2300°F).
The gold-lustre painted letters are from a poem by Margot Brust. See **Barium carbonate**
and **Lustres**.

(photo: *Mary White*)

PLATE 9
BOTTLE by Avril Farley. Height 18 cm.
Copper carbonate is used to stain the glaze. Zinc silicate crystals form and copper oxide exhibits its ability to stain both crystals and matrix. See **Crystalline glazes**.

(photo: *Martin Avery*)

PLATES 10 and 11
BOTTLES by Derek Clarkson. Heights 20 cm and 24 cm.
The glaze is applied thickly by brush. The firing is usually to 1285°C (2345°F) and the crystals are grown in a precisely controlled stepped cooling programme.

(photos: *Derek Clarkson*)

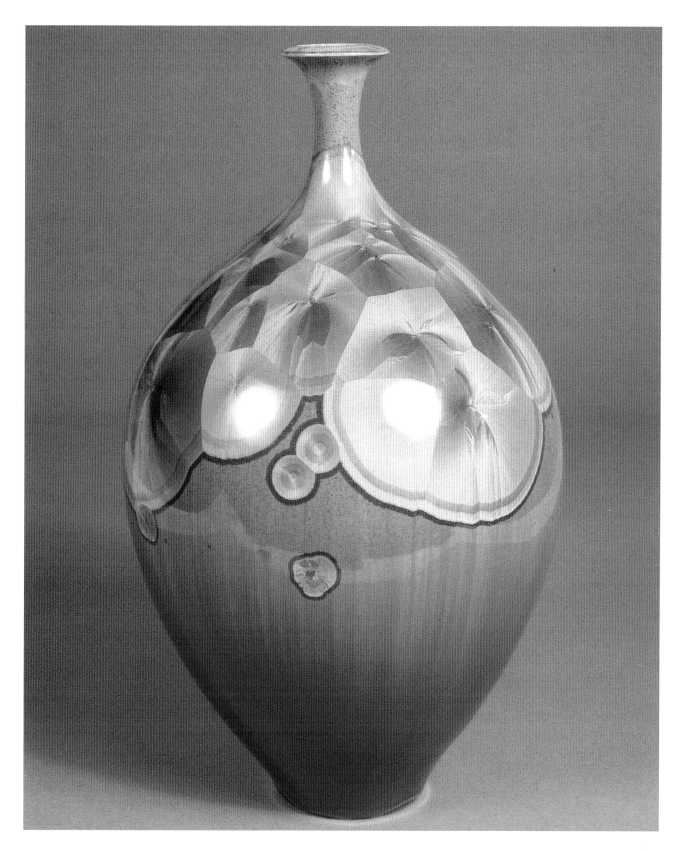

PLATE 12
BOTTLE by Derek Clarkson. Height 19 cm.
Derek used 115 g of Degussa frit plus 2·0 g titanium oxide, 0·15 g cobalt carbonate, 2·0 g copper carbonate and 1·7 g manganese oxide. The crystal-growing period was 5 hours 53 minutes at 1065°C (1949°F). See **Crystalline glazes** in text, **Colour plates 74/75** and **Recipe Appendix.**

(photo: *Derek Clarkson*)

PLATE 13
Cobalt blue lines painted on an opaque white glaze in maiolica style. The gold/silver lustre areas are fired on at a lower temperature. This 15 cm plate with a deep central well is modern but is a close copy of the style of 'Betrothal' plates perfected in Deruta, Italy in the early 16th century. The part shown is 14 cm across. See **Maiolica** and **Lustres**.

(photo: *Janet Hamer*)

PLATE 14
Silver lustre brush painting in the centre of a white tin-glazed bowl by Edgar Campden. Painting onto an already-fired, smooth glaze surface with a precious metal pigment allows extremely fluid and articulate brush painting. The pigment is a mixture of silver carbonate and red clay or ochre (20:80). The piece is then refired to reduce the carbonate to pure silver and to attach the metal to the glaze. In this example the reduction atmosphere has partly sullied the white tin glaze. The painted motif is 8 cm across. See **Transmutation lustre** and **Tin oxide black**.

(photo: *Janet Hamer*)

PLATE 15
'APPLE LUSTRE' SMALL BOWL by Alan Caiger-Smith. Diameter 13 cm.
The bowl is tin-glazed over red earthenware clay. The lustre pigment consists of copper carbonate, silver chloride and red ochre and is fired in a wood kiln to 660°C (1220°F) with reduction. As the copper attaches itself to the glaze, copper chloride is liberated. It vaporizes and causes red flashing. The painted area is less red and more metallic because it contains silver. See **Lustres, Transmutation lustre** and **Flashing**.

(photo: *Ben Johnson*)

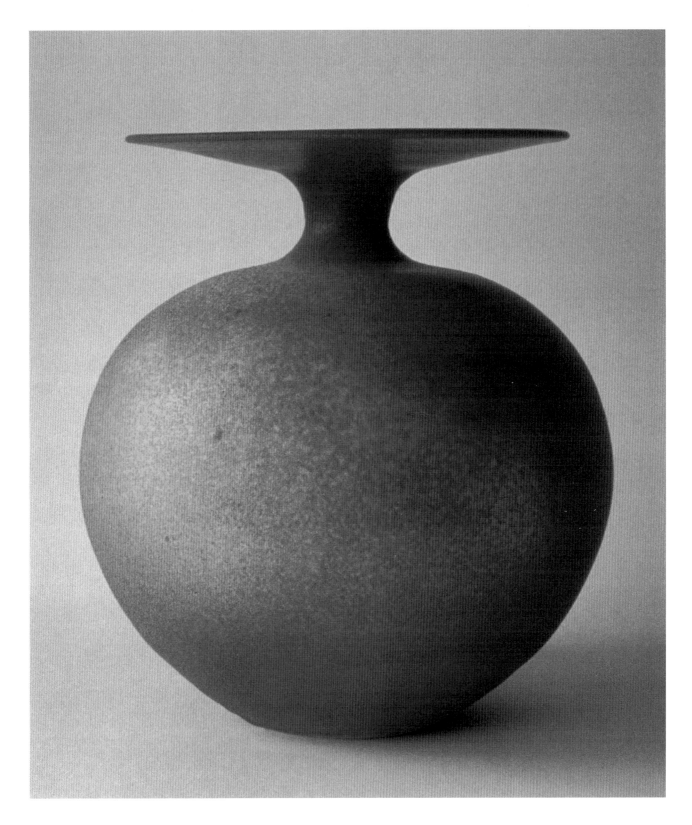

PLATE 16
BLUE-GLAZED BOTTLE by Delan Cookson. Height 22 cm.
The bottle was thrown in porcelain clay and assembled from two sections. The glaze of alkaline nature is a barium matt coloured by copper carbonate with extra dark-blue glaze stain sprayed on the wide top of the bottle. The piece was biscuit fired at 1000°C (1832°F) and glaze fired at 1280°C (2336°F). See **Barium oxide**, **Alkaline glazes**, **Copper oxides**, **Health hazard**, **Poison** and **Recipe Appendix**.

(photo: *Delan Cookson*)

PLATE 17
MAIOLICA CASSEROLE by Rob Bibby. Diameter 22 cm.
Rob cuts shaped sponges with a band saw and prints the shapes with glaze stains onto a tin glaze. This is fired to 1100°C (2012°F). See illustrations of technique under **Printing**.

(photo: *Robert Meadows*)

PLATE 18
LARGE BOWL by Daphne Carnegy. Diameter 35 cm.
Early training with a faience potter in Burgundy influenced Daphne to make maiolica ware. She mixes a buff clay with red earthenware to emulate the warm apricot colour of Mediterranean folk pottery. As a keen gardener she enjoys painting the soft shapes of flowers and fruit with free brushstrokes on the unfired glaze. See also **Recipe Appendix**.

(photo: *Stephen Brayne*)

PLATE 19
'MIDNIGHT FUN I' by Emmanuel Cooper. Height 30 cm.
The jug is thrown and assembled in porcelain clay and fired to 1260°C (2300°F) in an electric kiln. Cobalt and chromium oxides are painted under the glaze. See **Chromium oxide, Cobalt oxide, Tin oxide** and **Recipe Appendix.**

(photo: *A & C Cooper*)

PLATE 20
Detail of a plate by Adas Dworski.
Actual size 8 cm across.
This maioloca glaze contains both tin and titanium oxides. Together they produce this rich curdling effect when the free-flowing pale blue glaze fuses on top of the more stable white glaze. The orange glazes are stiffer than the pale blue and prevent this interruption from underneath. The dark brush-painted lines show the typical texture of maiolica caused by the bubbling of the glaze during melting. See **Maiolica**.

(photo: *Janet Hamer*)

PLATE 21
Detail of 'cipollino' porcelain agate vase by Ron Payne.
A multilayered sandwich of differently coloured clays is compressed by rolling and then wrapped around a core of white clay. The whole is thrown as a vase and later planed to reveal the structure within the pot wall. Actual size of part shown is 10 cm high. See also **Agate, Neriage** and **Rolled inlay**.

(photo: *Frank Hamer*)

PLATE 22
Salt-glaze firing creates a typically orange-peel textured gloss over the surface. The searching effect of the fumes fuses and integrates the body, stained slips, engobes and glazes causing strong interactions. This close-up shows black from combinations of iron and cobalt, orangey tan colours from iron, blue from a cobalt-stained glaze, and green where rutile has been sponged over the blue. The crazing in the blue glaze is typical of a high-soda glaze. This detail of a jug by Rosemary Cochrane is approximately 10 cm across. See **Salt glaze** and **Recipe Appendix**.

(photo: *Janet Hamer*)

PLATE 23
*TULIP CHARGER. Diameter
40 cm.*
Hand-painted maiolica lends
itself to individual
commissions, heraldic and
commemorative ware. When
the obsession with growing
tulips was widespread in the
Netherlands in the 17th
century, many large 'Tulip
Chargers' were made. The
painted rim also defines this
as a 'Blue Dash' charger. This
one is dated 1680.

(photo: *F & J Hamer*)

PLATE 24
*DELFT PLATE. Diameter
40 cm.*
This large Delft plate,
probably from Bristol,
commemorates Siamese
twins. There appears to be
some satire in the depiction
of richly-apparelled persons
possibly making money by
presenting the unfortunate
infants.

(photo: *F & J Hamer*)

PLATE 25
MOSAIC PICTURE by Dee Hardwicke.
30 × 30 cm.
This picture shows a unit from one of
six mural panels each 60 × 120 cm at
Maindee Primary School, Newport,
Gwent. The design uses direct
translations from children's drawings.
Red earthenware clay; white slips
coloured by commercial stains;
transparent glaze; 1145°C (2093°F).
See **Slip** and **Stains**.

(photo: *Janet Hamer*)

PLATE 26
STREET SIGN IN SEVILLE. Width 76 cm.
'Children: Don't deprive the birds of their freedom, don't
torment them and don't destroy their nests. God rewards
the children who protect the birds and the law prohibits
that they are hunted, their nests destroyed or their chicks
removed.'

(photo: *Frank Hamer*)

PLATE 27
MAIOLICA TILED PANEL by Pat Birks. Width 46 cm.

(photo: *Pat Birks*)

PLATE 28
SALMON SERVING PLATE by Frank Hamer. 68 × 40 cm.
The salmon shapes are cut from newspaper and attached to the damp slip which is the colour of the fish. The paper resists the dark blue background slip. Sgraffito and added pigments give details. Transparent glaze. Reduction stoneware. See **Resist** and **Slip**.

(photo: *Frank Hamer*)

PLATE 29
PORCELAIN BOWL WITH CHROME-TIN PINK AND BRONZE EFFECTS by Peter Wills. Diameter 15 cm.
Peter throws and turns his porcelain bowls and brushes glaze onto the raw pots. For this bowl, 0·5% chromium oxide was used in the glaze and fired to over 1280°C (2336°F). Post firing, the bronzed areas were polished to avoid finger marks. See **Recipe Appendix**.

(photo: *Peter Wills*)

PLATE 30
'ELEMENTAL CONCERNS'. A sculptural installation in Leicester Royal Infirmary by Jim Robison. Height 3 metres.
The pieces were made in crank body and glazed with ash and matt glazes over blue and white slips. Reduction fired in a gas kiln to Orton cone 8.

(photo: *Jim Robison*)

PLATE 31
WALL-MOUNTED FOUNTAIN FOR A JUNIOR SCHOOL by Jim Robison. Height 1 metre.
A water pump is built into the interior.

(photo: *Jim Robison*)

temperatures close to 1300°C (2372°F), are unlike those for typical stoneware and porcelain.

Zinc silicate crystals can grow outwards at the rate of 1 mm per 10 minutes. The temperature must be held steady or have a controlled uniform decrease to achieve the simple large crystal. Crystals with concentric rings, halos and different growth textures are achieved by varying the temperature sharply in steps up and down with long periods of hold. Experiment is necessary to establish the best temperature for a particular recipe but a bright light shining into a large spyhole opposite a piece makes direct evidence available of what is happening. But see **Safety**. The crystal growing period can be as long as eight hours. Electric kilns with programmable control are popular but gas kilns can be controlled manually with the help of a digital pyrometer. See **Colour plates 74/75**.

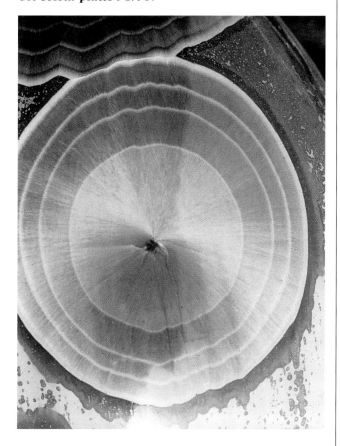

Glaze Composition. The glaze composition affects the fluidity/viscosity of the molten glaze. See **Viscosity**. For crystals to grow, the two main components of crystals, zinc oxide and silica, must be able to move freely, orientate themselves and come together. The glaze fluxes which produce fluid melts are the oxides of lithium, sodium and potassium. Because sodium and potassium compounds are soluble these are included in fritted form. Ferro frit 3110 is popular and accounts for 45% to 60% of most glaze recipes. This frit is composed of 15·5% sodium oxide, 70% silica and below 7% aluminium and boron oxides together. These two are kept below 7% because aluminium oxide by its physical

stiffening effect, and boron oxide by its chemical bonding between the many oxides, both inhibit the growth of zinc silicate crystals. The remaining 40% to 55% of the recipe will be up to 30% zinc oxide and 20% free silica with some titanium oxide. The exact recipe is particular to body and kiln and found only by progressive experiments.

The balance of oxides in the recipe is calculated to provide a melt which can remain fluid at the critical crystal-growing temperature even when the crystal-forming oxides are being isolated and depleting the matrix.

Also present in the glaze could be the oxides of barium, calcium and magnesium which are stabilizers included in the frit. Or these could be in the recipe in small amounts to stabilize the final glaze or to modify a colour. Their presence will have some effect. Some crystal growers have found that magnesium and barium oxides encourage crystals to grow but others comment that these oxides, and also calcium oxide, encourage many small crystals rather than a few large ones. Crystal growers are also divided on the desirability of having potassium oxide in the glaze. Some equate its usefulness with sodium oxide but others declare that it encourages small rather than large crystals. Its action must be dependent upon the other oxides present which fact emphasizes the fine balance of crystalline glazes.

Colour separation. The attractiveness of large crystals in a glaze is increased when the crystals take up a distinctly different colour from the background or matrix from which they have grown. It is predictable that, where both cobalt oxide and manganese oxide are present, the cobalt oxide will stain the crystals blue whereas the manganese oxide remains to colour the matrix yellow. Copper oxide, nickel oxide and iron oxide also colour the crystals in an established order of precedence. In the absence of cobalt oxide, nickel oxide will enter the crystals. Manganese oxide will enter when the former are not present, and copper oxide, if it is the only colourant, will stain both crystals and matrix. This order is established by the crystal-field energy strength of each colouring oxide.

In order to colour the precipitating zinc-silicate crystals the colouring oxides must be able to fit into the lattice structure. To enter the crystal, the metal colouring atom must be able to occupy one of the six sites otherwise held by zinc in the zinc-silicate lattice. Cobalt, nickel, copper, iron and manganese are transition metals and are adjacent to zinc in the periodic table. They are polyvalent and can be divalent to match zinc. Their atom sizes are also similar to that of zinc. Therefore all of these metals can enter and colour the crystals. See fig. 3.

The reason for the order of precedence is that they have different liquid-to-crystal partition co-efficients, or field strengths. Cobalt oxide and nickel oxide have high field strengths. Manganese oxide is intermediate and copper oxide is low. Zinc oxide has a higher field strength than does copper oxide and therefore copper oxide tends not to partition strongly but will stain both the matrix and the crystals at the same time.

Site taken by cobalt oxide

3

growing crystal

Practical points. The glaze has little or no clay content and settles rapidly. It is stirred and painted onto the pot with only a thin layer at the bottom grading to a thick layer (0·5cm) at the top. The firing is fast up to the top temperature between 1250°C and 1300°C (2282°F and 2372°F) and down rapidly to the chosen crystal-growing period. The reason for this rapid rise has already been explained and the rapid fall is to stiffen the glaze slightly before it has time to run off the pot. If the glaze runs beyond the foot of the pot and attaches it to the collecting saucer, they must be separated and the foot ground clean.

The speeds of rise and fall are determined by what are safe and practical for kiln and pot. Between 1140°C and 1010°C (2084°F and 1850°F) the cooling is controlled for crystal growth. See fig. 4. See also **Colour plates 9 to 12** and **42**.

Crystalline silica

Silica in crystalline form in contrast to silica glass. The distinction occurs in consideration of dunting where crystalline silica, whether quartz or cristobalite in crystal structure, is subject to inversion (change of size). Silica glass is not subject to inversion. See **Silica inversions**. In these considerations, the crystalline silica which exists in a body as flint, quartz, sand or cristobalite is referred to as free silica.

Cullet

Broken glass bought as pieces or powder and useful for melting into hollows on decorative plates and tiles. Cullet is cheaper than glaze and enamel but its composition is not guaranteed. It is not intended to be used as a glaze and therefore contains little stiffening or stabilizer.

Culm clay

Clay from the culm measures of the carboniferous system. Culm is a coal which contains too many impurities of clay and limestone to be acceptable as coal for burning. Culm

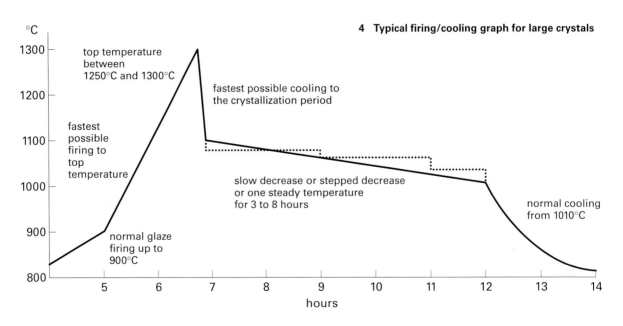

4 Typical firing/cooling graph for large crystals

top temperature between 1250°C and 1300°C

fastest possible cooling to the crystallization period

fastest possible firing to top temperature

slow decrease or stepped decrease or one steady temperature for 3 to 8 hours

normal cooling from 1010°C

normal glaze firing up to 900°C

hours

clay was the seat-earth for the vegetation and can be regarded as a type of fireclay. It is very variable, containing much quartz sand and is often sandwiched between two layers of gritstone showing a progressive change from one grit to the other via soft crumbly grit, shale, a black coal layer, sand and grit.

Occasionally the culm clay has been weathered and washed out of its deposit, naturally levigated and re-deposited nearby in pockets of workable clay.

Cup and saucer

The idea of a handled cup with retaining saucer is said to have been originated by the Marquise de Pompadour. Its fore-runner was the bowl and stand, a favourite ritualized piece in the Far East.

The examples shown are by Madoline Keeler, Sheila Casson and Joanna Howells.

Cup-head

A wheel-head which has a hollow top into which prepared bats, moulds and chucks can be fitted. The advantage of using a cup-head is that the accessory to be inserted is thereby automatically centred. The accessory is often made from plaster and is cast and turned in the cup-head which it thereby fits perfectly. Sometimes a keyway or natch is included in the design. The jigger and jolley system depends upon the use of a cup-head to centre the moulds. There is need only for one cup-head and one profile which remain on the wheel. The moulds are duplicated.

Cupric oxide

Black copper oxide. CuO. See ***Copper oxide***.

Cuprite

Copper sub-oxide ore. Cu_2O. A partially oxidized native copper or copper ore: the result of weathering. It is easily identified by its deep red colour which in samples adulterated by iron might be brownish. It can be crushed and used as a colourant. See ***Copper ores***.

Cuprous oxide

Red copper oxide. Cu_2O. See ***Copper oxide***.

D

Damper

A device for adjusting the cross-sectional area of the exit flue of a kiln. It is placed at the exit from the kiln chamber where the fumes enter the chimney but occasionally it may be part way up the chimney or even at the top of a short chimney. It usually consists of a slab of refractory material held in slots in the brickwork so that it can be slid in or out quite easily from outside the kiln. By closing the damper one cuts down the amount of hot exhaust fumes entering the chimney. Theoretically the speed of the fumes remains the same because their speed is based upon the temperature difference inside and outside the kiln and the effective height of the chimney. When less fumes enter the chimney a pressure is built up within the chamber. This has the effect of baffling or holding the heat within the chamber. It also means that less secondary air is drawn in at the fire-mouth/burner so that operation of the damper is an effective way of controlling the oxidizing/reducing atmosphere in the chamber. At the close of a firing the damper is often completely closed to slow down the rate of cooling.

Dead plaster

Calcined plaster. Plaster which has been overheated during manufacture or accidentally afterwards. If all the water of crystallization is driven off the gypsum, there is no crystalline start for a setting action. Dead plaster will therefore not set. Dead plaster is not synonymous with set plaster because set plaster contains hydrated calcium sulfate crystals.

De-airing

The removal of air from plastic clay. This is achieved by a de-airing pug mill which first shreds the clay and then subjects it to a vacuum. Here the air pockets explode and the air is removed. The clay is then re-united and compressed by a pug mill.

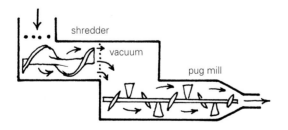

By de-airing it is possible to bring the clay particles into closer contact. In this state they have a greater overall friction although their capacity to slide—that is, their plasticity—is neither impaired nor improved. Contrary to popular belief de-airing does not increase plasticity. It increases the strength of the clay which thereby improves its 'workability'. See **Workability**.

Decal

A transfer used to carry a ceramic pigment shape from an original design to the surface of a ceramic work. The desired image is painted or printed with oil-based ceramic inks onto the gummed side of decal paper. When dry, this is covered with a painted or screenprinted layer of Covercoat (*trade name*). The Covercoat creates a thin plastic film which holds the pigment image. Placed in warm water, the gum will soften enabling the film to slide off the backing paper. The film can then be positioned on the clay or fired surface and carefully smoothed to express any air. The pigment image now has contact with the ceramic and the plastic film burns away in the firing. Good ventilation must be provided during firing.

Pre-covercoated decals can be bought. The ceramicist then prints the image on to the film. The film will burn away from underneath the image without distorting it. Custom-made decals can be obtained giving the freedom to design without the fuss of making. Industrially-produced decals can be bought from stock. The images they carry are often banal so ceramicists try to use them in original ways. The results are often either amusingly irreverent, or merely arbitrary according to your standpoint.

The photograph shows the use of decal transfers forming a collage by Paul Scott. See also **Printing** and **Colour plate 61**.

Decomposition

The breaking down of a chemical compound into simpler parts. In ceramics this means the creation of oxides during the firing out of carbonates, sulfates, and other complex minerals, and might include the taking up of additional oxygen. Decomposition temperatures are given in **Table 30** and in the articles on each compound. However, decomposition actually takes place over a wide range of temperatures starting very slowly as much as 400°C (720°F) below the quoted temperature. The decomposition accelerates as increasing amounts of material change up to the optimum point quoted as the decomposition temperature. After this the action decelerates very quickly to nothing in less than 100°C (180°F).

Deflocculation

The action of dispersing the fine clay particles in a slip so that the slip becomes more fluid. Slips used in casting are deflocculated and can thereby have a high density, that is, they can contain a high proportion of clay, while remaining fluid enough to be poured.

Deflocculation is achieved by adding, to the suspension water, suitable soluble alkalis called deflocculants. These exchange their ions (charged atoms) with those of the clay particles so that the clay particles are all of similar powerful electrostatic charge. See **Zeta potential**. In this state they repel one another and are unable to aggregate. No matter how closely they are packed together they prefer to slide past one another and avoid contact. The repulsion acts as an effective lubricant.

Thus a slip can be created which contains a large proportion of clay and only a small proportion of water. A kilogram of plastic clay can be converted into a fluid slip with only 100 ml of water plus suitable deflocculants. Without the deflocculants it would require 600 ml of water to reach the same fluidity.

The exact amounts of deflocculant can only be established by trials. See **Casting slips**. The type and amount is dependent upon the type of clay. The following recipe for a casting slip is included as a guide to the amounts involved:

plastic red clay	20 kg
water	2 litres
sodium carbonate	50 g
sodium silicate 75°TW	75 ml

Details of deflocculants and their actions are given later. In general terms, deflocculation involves the build-up of electrostatic charges on the clay particles. Each particle has two layers: the inner layer is negative and the outer layer is positive. See **Double layer theory**. When strong enough, the outer layer has the ability to repel identical layers on other particles as in the diagram.

The principle of deflocculation is to replace the small-charge ions, in these layers, with stronger ones and, if possible, increase their number. The whole character of a clay is thereby changed. One possible equation for this action is:

$$\left.\begin{array}{c} Ca \\ \\ Mg \end{array}\right\} \begin{array}{c} \text{ions} \\ \text{on} \\ \text{clay} \end{array} + 2Na_2CO_3 \rightarrow 4Na \begin{array}{c} \text{ions} \\ \text{on} \\ \text{clay} \end{array} \left.\begin{array}{c} CaCO_3 \downarrow \\ + \\ MgCO_3 \downarrow \end{array}\right.$$

Here sodium carbonate, which is soluble, is used to effect an ionic exchange. The calcium and the magnesium ions take the carbonate radical and are precipitated as insoluble compounds of calcium carbonate and magnesium carbonate. Slight deflocculation is produced when cellulose-type binders are used with glaze slops of low clay content. The effect is sometimes only temporary. See **SCMC**.

Deflocculation involves **Deflocculants, Fluidity, Thixotropy, Forces of attraction, Double layer theory** and **Zeta potential** which are separately indexed.

DEFLOCCULANT. Deflocculent. A soluble material which is added to clay suspensions (slips) to increase fluidity. Increased fluidity without loss of bulk is advantageous in the slip-casting process. The deflocculant creates fluidity by increasing the electrostatic forces of repulsion which the clay particles possess so that they repel one another. Thus the particles refuse to aggregate and prefer to slide past one another even though the number of particles suspended in the water is great. The particles are said to be in dispersed state or a state of deflocculation. See also **Fluidity**.

Deflocculants are of two types: the alkali cation type and the polyanion type. It is usual practice to use one of each type in combination because, although their action in creating fluidity is the same, they give different side effects. The most important side effect is that upon thixotropy.

The alkali cation type of deflocculant promotes cation exchange between itself and the clay particle. The new cation increases the zeta potential of the particle. For example, sodium carbonate replaces each calcium cation on

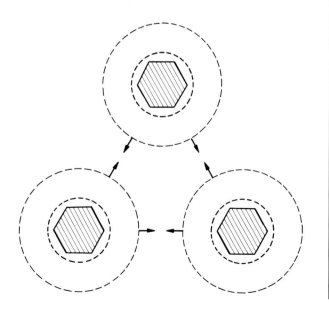

the clay particle with two sodium cations. It similarly replaces magnesium cations. The displaced calcium cation takes up the carbonate radical to become calcium carbonate. This is precipitated because it is insoluble and so it becomes suspended particles of solid matter in the slip.

The clay particle thus realizes an outer layer of sodium cations which have a large 'stand-off distance'. Figs. 1 and 2 show this action in diagrammatic form. The repulsive force is strong and able to repel like particles. See **Zeta potential** and **Double layer theory**. The equation is:

$$Ca\,(clay) + Na_2CO_3 \rightarrow Na\,(clay)\,Na + CaCO_3\downarrow$$

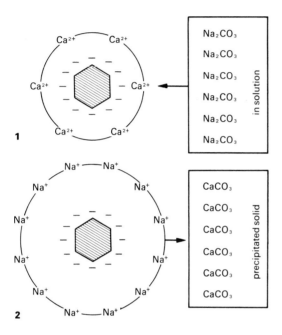

1

2

Examples of the alkali cation type of deflocculant are sodium carbonate, potassium carbonate, sodium hydroxide and sodium oxalate.

There is obviously a limit to the deflocculatory effect which can be achieved by cation exchanges. The full effect is achieved when all the exchangeable cations have been replaced by those of greater 'stand-off distance'. At this state a slip is fully deflocculated because the zeta potential of the clay has reached its greatest possible value. The addition of more alkali cation now has an opposite or flocculatory effect. Additional cations crowd into the double layer system filling the theoretical gap which is the stand-off distance. The zeta potential is therefore reduced. This over-crowding caused by adding too much alkali deflocculant is called salting-out or over-doping.

The polyanion deflocculant achieves similar deflocculatory results but in a slightly different way. The polyanion type provides cations for the outer layer (as does the alkali cation deflocculant) but it also enters the inner layer. Here the polyanion half of the deflocculant replaces the anions on the clay particles. This is an anion exchange

and is effective in deflocculatory terms because polyanions of multiple negative charge replace simple hydroxyl groups of single negative charge. The overall result is that the negative charge is increased and therefore there are additional sites for cations in the outer layer. The charge of the outer layer is thus stronger and the zeta potential value is higher. The exchanges are diagrammatized in figs. 3 and 4.

Examples of the polyanion type of deflocculant are sodium silicate, sodium poly-phosphate, sodium poly-acrylate and sodium tannate.

Again, there must be a limit to the deflocculatory effect which can be achieved. However, the effect of over-doping is not so drastic. Once the optimum effect has been reached, further additions of polyanion deflocculants serve only to crowd the double layer with anions. This crowding does

3

4

little to reduce the effectiveness of the cation outer layer so that the result may be negligible in terms of the zeta potential unless a great excess is added. There is certainly not the drastic effect of over-doping experienced with alkali cation deflocculants. In fact there often appears the additional phenomenon of 'protection' whereby the crowding of the double layer by anions prevents the over-crowding by cations. Crowding by excess anion deflocculant therefore provides some protection against over-doping.

A balance of two deflocculants should therefore give full control of deflocculation. The potter's choice for casting slips is usually sodium carbonate for cation exchange and sodium silicate for cation and anion exchange. Any precipitates from these two are harmless in the suspension and fired ceramic.

Sodium carbonate gives effective progressive de-flocculation but with little effect upon thixotropy. Sodium silicate gives equally progressive deflocculation with attendant decrease in thixotropic effect. Some thixotropy is required in casting slips and therefore a balance of the two deflocculants is required. See **Casting slips** and **Thixotropy**.

Deflocculatory materials can only act when there is sufficient water for them to go into solution and thereby release their ions for exchange. Also, they can only produce a result when the solid in suspension is of colloidal size. Thus clays, especially the fine clays like ball clays and bentonite, give good results, but other minerals like feldspar are hardly affected. Some specially-ground materials intended for fine dispersion give some favourable reaction. An example is prepared zirconium silicate. Coarse materials like flint show no reaction to deflocculants but some to flocculants. Thus the suspension must be a colloidal suspension for deflocculation and the deflocculant a solution, although it may be weighed and calculated as a solid.

Dehydration
The removal of water. The term is usually reserved for the removal of chemically combined water in such minerals as kaolinite, borax and aluminium hydroxide. The manufacture of plaster of Paris involves a semi-dehydration of gypsum.

Dehydroxylation
The process whereby the bound water is removed by heat between 450°C and 600°C (842°F and 1112°F). It is described under **Water: bound**.

Delft
Faience. Maiolica. Tin-enamelled ware. Tin-glazed earthenware produced at Delft in the Netherlands. This ware was first made by Italian potters working in Delft in the mid-16th century. Although incorporating Gothic and Renaissance decoration its greatest influence was from Oriental porcelain which it sometimes copied. Thus delft is often thought of as blue decoration on a white glaze although red-brown, yellow and green were also used.

It is possible that the Italian potters moved on to England soon after settling in Delft but production in England cannot be proven before 1630. English delft never reached the perfection of the Dutch in thinness of potting and quality of glaze. However the English delft had its own qualities. It divorced itself from imitating Oriental and Continental wares and gained a freedom of overall decoration which is artistically equal to any other tin-glazed ware. Only in some of the early Spanish maiolica is there an equivalent freedom and feeling for pattern. English delft was an important artistic expression and a practical ware. The commemorative plate shown here is dated 1680.

In England, delft was made at Lambeth, Bristol and Liverpool. It enjoyed a steady vogue for 150 years until the development of creamware. See also **Galleyware** and **Lambeth**.

Density
See **Slop weight** and **Relative density**.

Devitrification
Phase separation. The crystallization of a glaze upon cooling. Transparent shiny glazes contain no crystals and are referred to as supercooled liquids. However, if glazes are cooled very slowly, crystals begin to form and the resulting glaze is clouded with crystals and the surface often appears matt. This is called devitrification and it may happen that it only occurs on part of a pot. It is avoided for transparent shiny glazes by cooling them as quickly as possible down to their freezing points. Conversely, glazes intended to be crystalline are cooled slowly and also contain oxides which encourage crystal growth such as those of calcium, titanium and zinc. The blue flushes of some jun glazes are partial devitrification. See **Jun**.

It would seem natural to expect crystals of different silicates to grow at different temperatures during cooling. Zinc oxide, having acted as a flux to melt the glaze, combines with the free silica in the glaze to form zinc silicate crystals between 1140°C and 1010°C (2084°F and 1850°F) during cooling. Calcium oxide behaves similarly and forms calcium silicate crystals at approximately 700°C (1292°F). If both are present, one will undoubtedly influence the other so that it would be difficult to isolate the two results. In the complexity of a glaze magma are many fluxes capable of combining with silica to form silicate crystals and with boron oxide to form borates under certain conditions. These conditions may be fulfilled especially when encouraged by other crystals. See *Crystalline glazes*.

The formation of crystals, notably alumino-silicates, encourages other combinations by isolating those combinations and providing edges of crystals upon which the new combinations can grow. This probably encourages combinations to crystallize which would not otherwise have done so. If devitrification is occurring where it is not wanted and a quicker cooling is not possible, the crystallizing agents—oxides of calcium, titanium, magnesium, zinc, manganese and iron—will have to be replaced partly or totally by other oxides.

Once crystals have started to grow they continue to grow as the glaze cools until the glaze becomes too stiff to allow the different silicates and borates to isolate themselves within the glaze. This lowest point is therefore dependent upon the general maturing range of the particular glaze and can be as low as 500°C (932°F) even for glazes that have been melted at 1200°C (2192°F). Because of the complex nature of a glaze, the devitrification can occur anywhere between 1050°C and 500°C (1922°F and 932°F). It is usual to hold the temperature somewhere between 850°C and 700°C (1562°F and 1292°F) or at least to slow down the rate of cooling to encourage crystal growth. Holding the temperature in this range gives most glazes the chance to crystallize. See also *Lag*.

Dewatering

Taking water out of clay or slip. This is done by leaving the clay, slurry etc outside in pits to dry in the sun and wind; by putting the clay on to an absorbent surface such as plaster, wood or bricks sometimes heated from below; or by filter-pressing which is forcing the slurry into pervious cloth bags. See also *Filter-pressing*.

DF stone

See *Cornish stone*.

Di

See *Bi*.

Diaspore

$Al_2O_3.H_2O$. Aluminium hydrate of pure form. It is whiter and harder than the other aluminium ores.

Diatoms

Inshore plankton whose cell walls are silica. In some places their carcases have been deposited as reefs. These rocks are almost pure silica and are composed of empty silica cells. Pieces cut from these rocks make excellent high-temperature insulation bricks. Where impurities of calcium oxide and iron oxide are found with the diatoms this is called diatomaceous earth. This more frequently occurring material is also an excellent insulation because of its cellular structure but is limited to temperatures up to about 900°C (1652°F).

Dinas rock

A pure silica gritstone or quartzite quarried in south Wales and used as a source of silica for making refractory silica bricks.

Diopside

Calcium magnesium silicate. $CaMg(SiO_3)_2$. A non-aluminous pyroxene which occurs in igneous rocks. The crystals grow as long needles and it is possible for this same mineral to precipitate itself from dolomite glazes. See

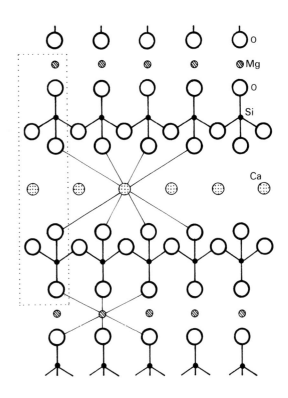

Dolomite matt and **Crystalline glazes**. Chains of SiO_3 molecules form sheets when held together by Ca and Mg ions in eight-fold and six-fold co-ordination.

Dioxide

An oxide combining two atoms of oxygen with one atom of the other element. For example, silica is silicon dioxide in which one molecule is made up of one atom of silicon and two atoms of oxygen. The chemical formula is SiO_2. See also **Oxide**.

Disordered kaolinite

The clay crystal which has been subjected to isomorphous substitution. The composition therefore no longer meets the formula $Al_2O_3.2SiO_2.2H_2O$. Instead, up to one in ten of the aluminium sites have been occupied by iron and possibly titanium; and up to one in fifty of the silicon sites have been occupied by aluminium. The resulting imbalance is adjusted by magnesium and other divalent atoms which fit into the holes of the silica layer.

The disordered kaolinite crystal is therefore distorted and is not able to attach closely to other similar crystals. The net result is a weakness, not only within the crystal itself but in the build-up of particles and grains. Unlike the ordered kaolinite which forms almost perfectly shaped large grains, the disordered kaolinite forms grains of random aggregation. During weathering water can more readily infiltrate the random aggregation and break this down into a very fine and hence very plastic clay.

Disordered kaolinites, when weathered and transported, therefore become the fine and plastic secondary clays, e.g. ball clays, stoneware clays and some low-grade fireclays. Ordered kaolinites, on the other hand, resist break-up of crystal and become low-plasticity secondary kaolins and high-grade fireclays. They also remain refractory unless they have collected impurities. These impurities are external to the clay crystal which remains refractory whereas the disordered kaolinite crystal actually contains some fluxes in its structure and could never be so refractory as pure kaolinite. See **Kaolinite** and also **Clay: origin**.

Distinguishing stain

Organic stain. Burnaway colour. A colour used to stain bodies and glazes for identification before firing. The colour is due to a combination of carbon, hydrogen and oxygen and therefore burns away completely during the firing. Usual colours are pink, blue and blue-green.

Divalent oxides

Divalent fluxes. The oxides of the elements in Group 2 of the Periodic table. They are:

beryllium oxide	BeO
magnesium oxide	MgO
calcium oxide	CaO
strontium oxide	SrO
barium oxide	BaO

They are referred to in this book collectively with the other fluxes as the alkaline oxides.

A characteristic of the group is that the fluxing action must be in collaboration with at least one other oxide. That is, while each is a flux, it cannot give a satisfactory glaze alone with aluminium oxide and silica. Its action is only practical in interaction with other fluxes.

A second characteristic is that each oxide has a minimum temperature at which it acts as a flux. Below this temperature its action is neutral or even anti-flux.

Details are given under each oxide and they are collectively compared under **Viscosity, Surface tension, Glaze fit** and **Periodic table**.

Dod box

Dog box. This operates on the same principle as a wad box but is used for making dods which are strips of clay for handles. The handle section is created by the specially shaped hole or die in the bottom of the box. Dod boxes are also used for making strips for coiled pottery. See also **Extrusion**.

The drawing shows a cut-away view of the box with a dod plate in position. The photographs are of the dod box made by Gosling and Gatensbury Ltd and (overleaf) of a dod handle on a 19th-century Lambeth salt-glazed jug.

and 46% MgCO$_3$. There is usually more calcium carbonate and less magnesium carbonate. There is usually also some iron carbonate which makes it a buff colour and makes glazes cream coloured. Partially dolomitized limestones are often called dolomitic limestones.

Its value in glazes is as a high-temperature flux and crystallizer. It does not reach its full power as a flux until 1170°C (2138°F). If the glaze contains a high percentage of dolomite, the crystalline mineral diopside is formed during cooling, giving the popular crystalline effect. See **Dolomite matt**.

Dolomite matt

A matt-surfaced glaze achieved by the creation of crystals of calcium and magnesium silicates. Dolomite is the double carbonate of calcium and magnesium which decomposes to

Dog ears

Dog's teeth. The torn edge on a slug of clay emerging from a pug mill. The ears are the result of a partial blockage or an insufficiently polished nozzle especially on square sections. If the nozzle is clean, it can be taken as an indication of insufficient plasticity in the clay. Otherwise, dog ears are not an indication of clay condition but of the condition of the pug mill.

Dolomite

Dolomite limestone. Magnesian limestone. CaMg(CO$_3$)$_2$ or CaCO$_3$.MgCO$_3$. The double carbonate of calcium and magnesium which is a single crystal structure and not a mixture of the two carbonate crystals. Dolomite exists as a rock which forms complete strata and it is also present in areas of normal limestone where magnesium has been able to substitute itself for some of the calcium during deposition in the sea. Dolomite is used to introduce calcium and magnesium oxides into glazes.

The dolomitization is not always completed up to the maximum of equal molecules in any sample of rock. The proportions of the ideal dolomite mineral are 54% CaCO$_3$

become calcium oxide (CaO) and magnesium oxide (MgO) in the firing. These act as fluxes creating the silicates which devitrify upon cooling. The examples of dolomite matt glazes are a basket by Frank Hamer and a bowl by Janet Hamer.

Dolomite matts became popular because they give variable effects, taking some colouring from the body where thin and producing oatmeal mottlings in brown and black. Where thick they look buttery and unctuous. They are usually cream but vary from buff to white according to the quality of the dolomite used. They are particularly suitable for reduced stoneware. Reduction has no effect whatever upon the calcium and magnesium oxides but reduces the small iron oxide content giving more fluxing power and turning the colour more grey. The additional breakdown of the body in reduction results in a thicker body-glaze layer and blacker, smoother iron spots.

It is essentially a high-temperature glaze. The fluxing action of dolomite is not effected below $1170°C$ ($2138°F$). In oxidation the glaze fuses best over light-coloured pure bodies. With dark bodies some sulfur remains to be burnt out and this bubbles through the viscous molten glaze creating roughness and pin-holes.

During the firing, the dolomite decomposes. This is a slow process starting at $350°C$ ($662°F$) and completed by $800°C$ ($1472°F$) when the carbon dioxide has been released. There remain calcium and magnesium oxides and a small percentage of black iron oxide, which reoxidizes to red iron oxide if fusion of the glaze has not begun.

$$CaMg(CO_3)_2 + FeCO_3 \xrightarrow{800°C} CaO + MgO + FeO + 3CO_2 \uparrow$$

Dolomite matt glazes are often fairly viscous during fusion because there is more than adequate dolomite to flux the silica present. The extra flux can only inhibit fusion although it is involved in the melt. The glaze is therefore a solution with excess alkali which encourages crystallization upon cooling. The calcium and magnesium oxides seek free silica to form diopside crystals ($CaMg(SiO_3)_2$). See *Diopside*. It is possible that some aluminium oxide is actually isolated which causes separate crystals. Other crystals involved are enstatite, wollastonite and anorthite. See *Crystalline glazes*.

The following recipes are dolomite matt glazes. In the first one, fusion at $1200°C$ ($2192°F$) is made possible by the inclusion of a small amount of lead bisilicate in the recipe. This is suitable for oxidized firing. See also *Recipe Appendix*.

feldspar	48
china clay	23
whiting	6
dolomite	15
lead bisilicate	8

In the second recipe, which is for $1250°C$ ($2282°F$), the amount of whiting is very high. This gives a very viscous glaze which will smooth out on vertical surfaces but not on horizontal ones. For horizontal surfaces the whiting should be decreased to 10 parts and the potassium feldspar increased to 30. Some reduction will help the fusion.

potassium feldspar	20
sodium feldspar	20
china clay	20
whiting	20
dolomite	20

Double dipping

A glazing action whereby the inside and outside of a pot are glazed in one action without glazing the base. A sharp jerk upwards, after dipping the pot, rim first, into the glaze, splashes the inside of the pot provided that the rim does not come out of the glaze.

Double fritting

The process of making two separate frits which are destined for the same glaze. The frits are usually a lead silicate and a boro-silicate. At the glaze slop stage there is usually some additional china clay and feldspar.

The advantage of using two frits over using a single combined frit are:

1. The solubility of the lead content is effectively decreased to a point where it presents little hazard as a poison.
2. Blends between two different frits produce a range of effects equivalent to a large number of single frits. Standardization of these two frits assists the frit manufacturer to establish efficient fritting plants.
3. Two frits can achieve a wider maturing range than one frit. The fusion is also more uniform. Adjustments to the range are easily achieved by adjusting frit amount rather than altering the frit composition.

Double layer theory

Theory which explains the electrostatic charges on colloidal clay particles whereby particles repel one another and do not sediment in a suspension. The theory concerns the ends of the atomic lattice of the clay crystal. See *Clay: crystal structure*.

The clay crystal is a continuous sheet in which atoms satisfy the valency requirements of the adjacent atoms on both sides. It follows that at the edge of the crystal there are unsatisfied valencies. This is called the 'broken bond theory' and it is accepted that the end atoms are oxygens and hydroxyl groups (O^{2-} and OH^-). The unsatisfied charge is therefore negative. This is the inner layer. See diagram.

The outer layer of the double layer has therefore a positive charge. See diagram. It is composed of sodium, potassium, calcium and magnesium cations (Na^+ K^+ Ca^{2+} Mg^{2+}) and also water molecules. This is the anchorage of the bound water layer. See *Adsorption*. The water molecules, although electrically neutral with the two negative charges

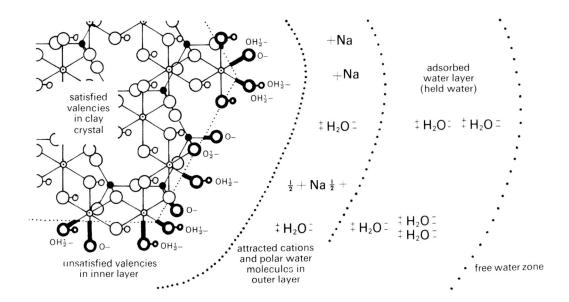

of the oxygen satisfied by the positive charges from two hydrogen atoms, have a polarity like a small magnet. They orientate themselves towards the clay, positive pole inwards.

While the outer layer contains different elements, clays tend to have outer layers which have a dominant element. Most natural clays are calcium dominant. The dominant element gives a character to the clay in terms of plasticity and behaviour in suspension. The reason is that the cations of these different elements have different 'stand-off distances'. Their character is measured as the latent energy they possess for repulsion of like charges. See **Zeta potential**.

However, the cations composing the layers can be quickly replaced by others of different character. This is done by introducing suitable cations into the suspension water. The process is called cation exchange and occurs in the deflocculation of casting slips. See **Fluidity, Deflocculant** and **Casting slips**.

Down-draught kiln

A kiln design in which the flames are deflected downwards throughout the chamber to use the heat fully and evenly before the cooled fumes escape at the flue exit to the chimney stack. From the fire-mouth or burners, entering from opposing directions, the flames are directed upwards by baffles or bag walls, and enter the setting space containing the ware about, or above, half-way. By arrangement of the setting of the ware the heat is then directed downwards as evenly as possible throughout the space before being allowed to reach the exit flue to the chimney. At a point in the exit flue or in the chimney a damper is incorporated to control the air available for oxidation or reduction.

This system produces a much more efficient firing than an up-draught system. The longer distance through which the flame is drawn makes full use of its energy potential and uses the longer flames which can be obtained from wood and oil. This makes it possible for a single firebox source of heat to be satisfactory in a small kiln. A tall chimney is usually required and some kilns have underground flues to an isolated chimney. The draw may be supplemented by forced secondary air.

Draw (1)
To unpack a kiln.

Draw (2)
The energy exerted by a chimney on the kiln gases.

Drift
Mining term for a tunnel which has to be at a steep angle in order to follow the seam. Used in coal, fireclay and ball clay mining. A horizontal tunnel is called a level.

Dry clay

Clay which has dried completely and is therefore as dry as the surrounding air. The workshop test for a dry pot is to put it to the cheek. The dry pot feels as warm as the air but the pot which is still drying feels cold.

Because the atmosphere contains moisture, dry clay will always contain some moisture by virtue of the effects of adsorption and capillary condensation. See **Adsorption**. Therefore the early stages of a firing are taken slowly in what is called the pre-heating or water-smoking period. See also **Drying**, in which the term bone-dry clay is used for clay which has reached 120°C (248°F) in an artificial drying situation.

Drying

The removal of moisture. In pottery this usually means the drying of wet clay or newly-glazed ware. Technically, drying is the establishment of equilibrium moisture content between object and air. Wet clay dries by wetting the air around it. When the air holds as much water as the clay, the drying ceases.

Clay can therefore only dry out up to a point which is determined by the atmosphere. If taken beyond this point by applied heat, which creates its own special localized atmosphere, the clay will take up moisture from the atmosphere when the heat is removed. See **Readsorption**.

Three factors are involved in drying: temperature, which encourages evaporation; humidity of surrounding air, whether this is the general atmosphere or a controlled one; and the movement of the air past the surface, thereby replacing saturated air with drier air. In simple terms, the conditions which are good for drying washing out of doors are good for drying pots, whether these conditions are natural or created in the workshop. When barometric pressure is high, the atmosphere can hold more water than when pressure is low. Warm, dry and breezy weather is more effective than cool, damp and still weather. The most effective conditions, however, could cause unequal drying out at rims and handles. This results in warpage and cracking and must be avoided by sheltering the pots or

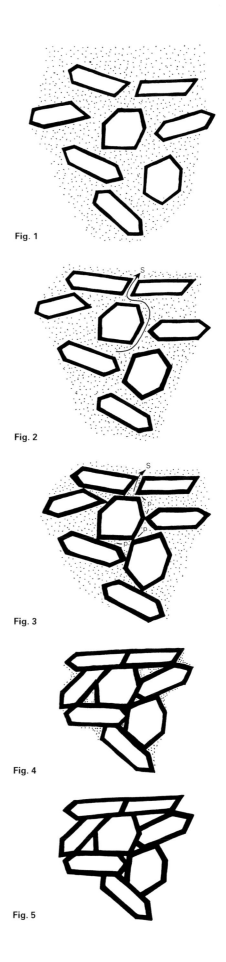

Fig. 1

Fig. 2

Fig. 3

Fig. 4

Fig. 5

slowing down the drying rate. Pots will need to be turned around and over to even out the effects of sun and wind.

The easiest way to understand the theory of drying and to relate this to pot-making is to consider it as two stages. The first stage is the removal of the water of plasticity and the second stage is the removal of the pore water. See ***Water***. The leatherhard state is the dividing point.

The enlarged sections, figs. 1 to 5, show the stages in detail.

Fig. 1 is a clay slip or slurry. The clay particles are suspended in water and can move freely. Fig. 2 is plastic clay. Here, the particles are much closer together and there is therefore some friction caused by the suction seal of water between particles. See ***Plasticity***. However the particles can be moved past one another using the water as lubricant. In contrast, fig. 3 shows leatherhard clay in which the particles have physical contact and friction.

At this point it should be realized that each clay particle has a surrounding layer of water which is firmly attached. In the diagrams, this is shown as a solid thick line. This is part of the bound water content. The water is held there by the hydroxyl groups and unsatisfied valencies of the clay crystal structure. See ***Double layer theory***. In comparison with the clay crystal, it is a very thin layer—a few molecules in thickness. On the finest clay particle this would mean about a hundredth of the diameter. Yet this layer provides a lubricated cushion. In leatherhard clay, as shown in fig. 3, these cushions are touching and thus provide a 'solid' state. The anchorage is by molecular attraction but there is still sufficient 'loose' water on the outside of the layer to act as a lubricant. Leatherhard clay can be reshaped by strong pressure without rupturing the whole piece of clay.

Clay can only dry where the water can evaporate at the surface. The clay surface is shown at the top of the diagrams. Water migrates from the centre of the clay through the pores (P) to the surface (S). See figs. 2 and 3. As the gaps between the particles close, it becomes increasingly difficult for the water to migrate. It can do so only by a system of substitutions along the bound water layers or by circuitous routes via pores that are still linked. The drying process therefore slows down considerably.

The rate of drying can be shown by a graph as fig. 6. Here it is assumed that the drying conditions are constant, i.e. a constant temperature, humidity and air flow. The rate of drying is constant from plastic state to almost leatherhard state, but the escape of the water is hindered as the particles come closer together. The leatherhard stage is a distinct turning point which is reached in about a third of the total drying-out time and at a point when about half the water has evaporated. The dotted lines show the possible variation of drying out dependent upon the humidity of the air around.

Fig. 4 represents air-dried clay. This is the furthest dry state possible in the open air. The tiniest pores are still filled with water but the large pores have drained and contain only a meniscus of water held by capillary action. The

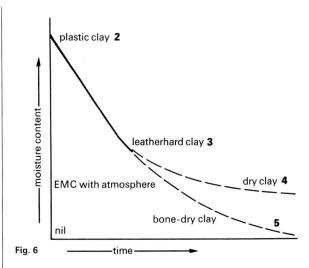

Fig. 6

bound layer of water around each clay particle is theoretically reduced to its minimum. This is seen where two particles 'touch'. The particles now share the same layer and it is only two or three molecules thick. The whole mass of clay is now solid and cannot be reshaped without rupturing the bonds between the particles and thus breaking the clay.

Fig. 5 represents bone-dry clay. This state occurs in the early stages of firing, after the water-smoking period, and is considered as existing from 120°C (248°F) up to the ceramic change at 600°C (1112°F). See ***Firing***. In bone-dry clay, the pore water has gone but the bound water remains to be eventually driven off in the ceramic change. The pore water must be driven off carefully because there are few passages through which it can escape to the surface. See ***Water smoking***. Happenings above 120°C (248°F) are described under ***Firing*** and the diagrams used overlap with, and continue on from, those used here for ***Drying***.

An important effect of drying is shrinkage. Shrinkage, or rather unequal shrinkage, is responsible for drying cracks and warping. See ***Cracks*** and ***Clay: physics***. A clay's behaviour is shown diagrammatically by a drying-shrinkage graph. Fig. 7 is a typical graph related to the figs. 1 to 5. The vertical axis of the graph represents, in cubic centimetres, the volume which 100 grams of dry clay becomes at different water contents. The water contents are represented on the horizontal axis and the numbers here refer, in grams, to a weight of water which is combined with the theoretical 100 grams of dry clay. This is usually described as percentage moisture content but it should be understood that the figures here do not correspond to the description of a plastic clay as 20% water. The 20% water of plastic clay is compared with the weight of the plastic clay as a whole and not the dry clay content only. For an explanation of the two methods of percentage expression see later in connection with fig. 8.

Reading this graph (fig. 7) in relation to the figs. 1 to 5 one finds that fig. 1, which represents slip, relates to a point somewhere in the top right-hand corner of the graph. An

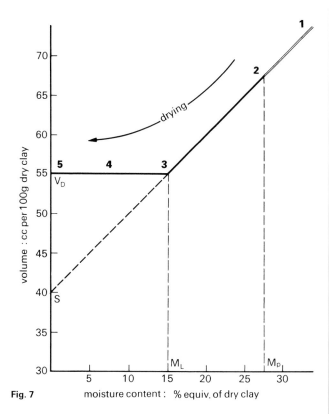

Fig. 7   moisture content : % equiv. of dry clay

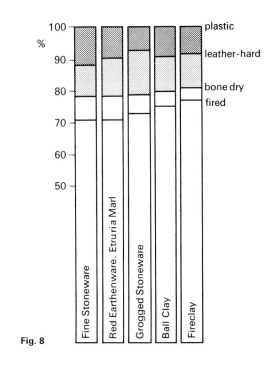

Fig. 8

exact position would be determined by the water content. Fig. 2, which is plastic clay, comes further down the line and fig. 3, which is leatherhard clay, further still. These three points are in a straight line which slopes at 45° since 1 gram of water is 1 cubic centimetre in volume. As the moisture content of the clay decreases in grams, so the volume of the clay decreases by an equal number of cubic centimetres. From these first three points one might expect the final dry solid piece of clay to be point S on the graph, but of course, at leatherhard state the particles are touching and so the overall volume of the clay decreases very little from that point to the bone-dry state (fig. 5).

One finds therefore that most drying-shrinkage graphs have angular 'curves' and that the line from V_P (the dry volume) to the point of moisture content M_L (leatherhard moisture content) is often horizontal or nearly so. The danger period for shrinkage cracks is therefore from plastic state to leatherhard state and not from leatherhard to dry state.

Each clay is individual in physical behaviour so suppliers often quote the figures for points V_D, S, M_L and M_P. To make comparisons one can draw graphs using the information supplied, starting at point S and drawing the 45° line. The leatherhard state is directly above point M_L. The leatherhard point is joined by a straight line to point V_D.

Fig. 8 is a diagrammatic representation of the water content of different clays. The amounts are true only for the actual clays tested but serve as a guide to similar clays. Plastic clay is taken as 100%. For example, plastic ball clay is

approximately 80% dry clay content and 20% water, by weight. The weight of the clay after the ceramic change is included to link with the articles on **Firing, Ceramic change** and **Water**.

Formulae for discovering percentage content of water in clay etc are as follows. If percentage contents are required, it is first necessary to discover the water content of a sample piece of plastic clay by weighing the sample when plastic and when thoroughly dry. Weight of plastic clay minus weight of dry clay = weight of water content.

Dry basis method for percentage:

$$\frac{\text{weight of water}}{\text{weight of dry clay}} \times 100 = \% \text{ moisture content}$$

Plastic basis method for percentage:

$$\frac{\text{weight of water}}{\text{weight of plastic clay}} \times 100 = \% \text{ moisture content}$$

For example, if a piece of plastic clay which weighs 12 kg is composed of 9 kg of dry clay and 3 kg of water, the resulting percentage contents are: 33·3% on the dry basis and 25% on the plastic basis.

The basis chosen is dependent upon the approach one is making. If one is concerned with dry clay and is adding an amount of water to this one would consider the dry clay as 100% and add to this a further percentage of water. For example, a recipe for a slip would be expressed as a percentage recipe of dry ingredients and the water to be added would be expressed as a further percentage weight above the 100% of the recipe. On the other hand, if one were starting with a plastic clay and one wished to know how much of it was water, then one would express the water as a percentage of the whole.

Dunk

Tunk. To dip or plunge into liquid. Raku pots are often dunked into water to seal special effects. Dunking also causes quick crazing. Stained water or tea may be used to colour the first crazed pattern. Dunking is sometimes used as an empirical thermal shock test for ovenware.

Dunting

Cracking of pottery caused by stresses which form during firing and cooling. The resulting crack is called a dunt. See also **Crack**.

The main causes of dunting are the two silica inversions which take place at 573°C and 226°C (1063°F and 439°F). Differential contraction of body and glaze, without the action of a silica inversion, also causes stress which could result in dunting. All pots have stresses within them and most pots are strong enough to contain them. The few pots that crack do so because a number of factors come together: excessive stress; poor design (weak form and wrong material); and perhaps imprudent firing.

Some pots are already cracked when the kiln is opened whilst others crack a month or more later. Both are cases of dunting. If, however, a pot, such as a teacup, cracks in use, there will be other factors involved and such cracks are said to be caused by thermal shock. See **Thermal shock**.

The following dunts can be differentiated: biscuit dunts, firing dunts and cooling dunts. See also **Silica inversions** and **Glaze fit**.

BISCUIT DUNTS. Biscuit ware may dunt during cooling because the quartz and cristobalite inversions cause sudden decreases in body size. A very soft biscuit firing, e.g. 800°C (1472°F), may not sufficiently vitrify the body to give it strength to withstand the sudden change.

Biscuit dunts are hair cracks, almost invisible and easily overlooked. They are concentric with the pot and vertical, often looking like brickwork. The hair cracks show when the pot is being glazed. When the pot is taken out of the glaze

slop and is still wet, the cracks will show lighter in colour because they have taken more glaze. Badly dunted pots disintegrate when being taken from the kiln or sometimes when being glazed, however a mild dunting of a single hair crack could pass unnoticed. Unfortunately, such a dunt usually opens during the glaze firing.

Slips sometimes dunt separately from the body. This happens when the slip and body are not matched in their vitrification range. If the slip is more refractory and more siliceous, the slip will dunt. A common example is the use of a siliceous ball clay as a white slip on a red body. Again a brickwork net of lines will show at the glazing stage. The cure is to add some flux or glaze to the slip.

The dunting cracks in a slip should not be confused with a network of crazing cracks which is the result of poor fit. Crazing cracks are more usual when the slip is over-fluxed. Crazing cracks are irregular squares, pentagons and hexagons whereas dunting cracks are rectangles following the lines of the pot. Dunted slip does little harm, except for the uneven glaze application, but it is an indication that dunting conditions were present and that the slip and body are not fully compatible.

To avoid biscuit dunts, a number of cumulative measures can be employed.

1. A slightly higher biscuit temperature will strengthen the ware by extra vitrification. It will also leave less free crystalline silica in the body.
2. A slower rate of cooling will allow a pot to adjust itself slowly to the change in size. The fastest contemplated rate should be a uniform 100°C/hr from 600°C (180°F/hr from 1112°F).
3. A decrease in the free silica in the body will decrease the amount of sudden contraction. Free silica may be quartz, flint, sand or cristobalite.
4. An increase in the amount of body flux will strengthen the ware by extra vitrification. It will also convert free silica (crystalline silica) into silica glass which is not subject to inversion.
   The problem is similar to that of **Cooling dunts** which should be read in conjunction with the above.

FIRING DUNTS. Cristobalite and quartz inversions may cause dunts during the warming-up period of a glaze firing. Such dunts are rare. The inversions give the body a sudden increase in size, which, if not allowed to happen uniformly throughout a pot, would cause stress between two parts of the pot. This happens if the firing is too rapid.

In practice most biscuit ware, which is what the body is at this stage, is strong enough to withstand the stress over the temporary period until all the pot has had its cristobalite or quartz inverted. Refires suffer if made from bodies which are fine and dense and contain cristobalite as an anticraze. Cracks which occur during firing can be distinguished from those which happen during cooling because the glaze crawls away from the crack or fuses with rounded edges on the crack.

Firing cracks, as opposed to cooling cracks, are usually the result of previous cracks which open further. They could be biscuit dunts but they could equally be other cracks which started before the biscuit and remained undetected after the biscuit firing. They could be the result of unequal structure, drying stress, mishandling, or readsorption at the raw stage. These cracks occur no matter what precautions are taken with the glaze firing although they are often blamed on the glaze firing. They are described simply as firing cracks. See **Crack**.

Firing dunts may be ring cracks concentric with the pot or vertical cracks from the rim, possibly spiralling around the pot. The pot often falls in pieces, the pieces jumping apart. It should be repeated that firing dunts are rare. They can be overcome by the following measures:

1. A slower rate of firing over the dunting points allows a pot to expand as a unit as the silica inverts.
2. A slightly higher biscuit firing will give a stronger biscuit to withstand the stress.
3. A reduction of the free silica in the body will reduce the sudden expansion proportionately.

COOLING DUNTS. The most common time for dunting to take place is during the cooling after a glaze firing or after a high-temperature firing of unglazed stoneware. The immediate period after taking pots from the kiln and before they are put into use is also included.

Cooling dunts are long, clean, body cracks with sharp edges. If the ware is glazed, then the glaze obviously cracks with the body and since the glaze is set when the crack takes place, it too has very sharp edges. There is often some sideways displacement (strain) which makes the dunt detectable by touch although it may not be immediately visible. The cracks are vertical ones, horizontal ones (ring cracks) and spiral ones which may or may not reach the rim. See also **Crack**.

For the purposes of explanation, three types of cooling dunt are discussed: two which occur in the kiln and are discovered upon opening; and one which occurs one or two months after the pots are taken from the kiln. The first two types of dunt occur with glazed and unglazed ware. The third type occurs only with glazed ware. The types are very closely related and look the same.

The first type of cooling dunt is the result of the quartz inversion which occurs at 573°C (1063°F). Here the free silica (quartz phase) undergoes a sudden contraction. See **Silica phases** and **Silica inversions**. At this point, the body contracts proportionally to the amount of free silica (quartz) which it contains. The ideal cooling would allow the whole pot to reach this dunting point at one moment so that it could contract as a whole. In practice it is difficult to arrange this and a pot must undergo the stress of having one part contracting before another. If the body contains much free silica, the contraction will be great. The stress between two parts of a pot will also be great and it is at this stage that dunting may take place. Even the usually safe descent of 200°C/hr (360°F/hr) may not be slow enough for a large pot.

A tall pot on a thick shelf will cool quicker in its upper part than near the base. The thick shelf on which it stands will hold the heat and keep the base of the pot hot while the rest cools. At dunting point, when the free silica changes its size, the upper part of the pot contracts but the base does not. The result is a ring crack around the pot about 2 cm up from the foot.

Similarly, a wide bowl is fortunate if it can contract as a whole. If one side cools before the other, cracks occur at the intermediate points. These cracks run from the rim downwards then curve towards the cooler side. A piece of the bowl may even break away completely. It will be seen that uniform cooling is important and for this reason all draughts are excluded from a kiln during cooling below 600°C (1112°F).

The second type of cooling dunt is the result of the cristobalite inversion which takes place at 226°C (439°F).

This concerns free silica of the cristobalite phase. See **Silica phases** and **Silica inversions**. All the points relevant to quartz inversions are applicable to cristobalite inversions and of the two types of dunt, the cristobalite one is the one to be feared. A potter is unlikely to open a kiln, except a raku kiln, above 573°C (1063°F) but there is a natural eagerness to open a kiln at about 250°C (482°F) when the glazes can be seen. In fact, the drawing of some wares, ovenware for instance, could actually begin at this temperature but it could be disastrous for dense wares containing cristobalite.

Some potters cool their kilns quickly from top temperature to 1000°C (clear red heat, 1832°F), but they then clam up all cracks and vents to provide a slow cooling thereafter. The kilns are not opened until the ware is cool enough to handle with bare hands. An initial quick cooling is important with stoneware because it hinders the formation of cristobalite. The silica conversion of quartz to cristobalite takes place above 1100°C (2012°F) and whilst some cristobalite in the body is useful as an anticraze it is possible to get too much. Dense stonewares are susceptible to cristobalite dunting. Earthenware bodies, which are porous and more elastic, can absorb a larger amount of cristobalite movement.

The third type of cooling dunt is the one which occurs after the pot is taken from the kiln. The pot remains whole, for perhaps six or eight weeks, then suddenly rips apart, possibly with a loud report and probably during a particularly cold night. This type of dunt is caused by stress

between body and glaze, which stress may have originated with a silica inversion but may be the result of unequal body and glaze contractions.

At 573°C (1063°F) by far the majority of glazes are still plastic. This means that any stress set up between body and glaze by the quartz inversion in the body could be absorbed by the plasticity of the glaze. A dunt caused by body-glaze stress arising from quartz inversion is therefore unlikely.

However, at 226°C (439°F) the glaze has set and the cristobalite inversion in the body must create a stress between body and glaze. This phenomenon is known as the cristobalite squeeze and is encouraged as an anticraze measure. See **Cristobalite in bodies**. Excessive stress which cannot be contained results in a dunt known as a cristobalite dunt.

The name cristobalite dunt is often used to describe a dunt which occurs after the pot is removed from the kiln. It should be realized, however, that a similar stress can occur without the assistance of a cristobalite inversion simply by the different contraction rates of body and glaze. See **Contraction**.

The stress which causes these dunts is in the form of a compression on the glaze. That is, the body is squeezing the glaze because it (the body) has contracted more than the glaze during the cooling. Considered another way, the glaze is putting a tension onto the body. That is, the glaze is stretching the body because it (the glaze) has contracted less than the body during the cooling. If the body is stronger than the glaze, it will shed the glaze. See **Shivering**. But if the glaze is strong and the body weaker by being perhaps brittle, the body is torn apart as a dunt. When this occurs, the covering glaze invariably goes with it.

Poor resistance to stress is accentuated by certain construction features. For example:

1. A thick layer of glaze on the inside of a pot, and only a thin layer or no glaze at all on the outside, forces all the stress one way. The dunt is usually a spiral.

2. If the outside glaze stops short of the foot, especially in a thickened roll, the stress produces a ring crack.

3. If the inside glaze has run down and produced a pool inside the pot, the tension on the body creates a split across the base of the pot. This crack may carry on up to the rim of the pot on one side or the pot may crack into halves. Such cracks in bases are often difficult to see and, inside a bowl, a crack may look very similar to a single craze line. However, it can often be felt as a sharp edge by the fingers in a way that a craze cannot. This is because, in releasing the stress, the strain has resulted in a misalignment of the edges.

4. Often in combination with number 3, the unequal thickness of the body accentuates the stress on the thinnest parts. If the pot is thick-walled with a thin base and the glaze has run down into a pool as in number 3, there is a high risk of a dunt occurring.

5. A thin brittle body is not strong enough to exert compression upon a thick glassy glaze. Overfiring often causes the body to be brittle and the glaze to be glassy.

6. A thin, open and weak body like an underfired fireclay, is not strong enough to exert compression upon a glaze. This might happen if the wrong body were used or a porous body normally kept for ovenware were used for thinly-potted tableware with a thick glaze.

Cooling dunts can be overcome by a number of measures, some of which seem contradictory and cannot be used together. It is not easy to decide which preventative action to take and some experimental testing may be necessary.

1. Slowing down the rate of cooling at the dunting points will help large pots to survive the silica inversions, but it will not remove a stress which exists between body and glaze. If the pots dunt after being taken from the kiln, other measures must be taken to remove the stress.

2. If the stress is diagnosed as between body and glaze, the glaze can be altered to make it contract more. See *Glaze fit*. Alternatively the body can be made to contract less.

3. If cristobalite is part of the body recipe, this should be drastically reduced or left out altogether.

4. The firing and cooling cycle can be altered to reduce the amount of time that the pots withstand temperatures above 1100°C (2012°F). The top temperature remains the same and, as far as possible, the glaze fusion remains the same. However, the heat has less time to penetrate the body and therefore less quartz is converted into cristobalite. Time is an important factor in silica conversion. This method is effective with medium and coarse stoneware and ovenware.

5. The amount of sand, quartz and flint should also be lessened. The less free silica that there is in a body, the less proportionately will be the overall contraction. This is important with glazed ware.

6. The addition of more flux to the body will decrease the free silica by incorporating some of it into the molten parts of the vitrification. Feldspar and cornish stone are the usual body fluxes but the usual glaze fluxes are effective, with the exception of calcium and magnesium oxides which act as catalysts. See *Silica conversion*.

7. A slightly higher firing or a slightly extended soaking will involve more of the free silica in glassy vitrification. It will then no longer be crystalline and thus not subject to inversion. This is the method to use with fine stoneware and porcelain. Here the free silica is extremely fine and vitrification helps to give translucency. It is not always effective with coarse sandy stoneware bodies which resist involvement.

8. In contrast with number 7, if the body is too brittle because it is too dense and glassy, a lowering of the top firing temperature will give strength and a capacity to absorb the stress. This method is used with sandy bodies. See *Vitrification* and *Thermal shock*.

Dunting points

Inversion points. The temperatures at which the silica inversions take place. They are 573°C (1063°F) for quartz and 226°C (439°F) for cristobalite. These are given as exact temperatures because this is the way in which the potter thinks of the action as taking place. They are the usually accepted dunting points but the ceramic physicist has proved that under differing circumstances the quartz inversion may vary between 550°C and 575°C (1022°F and 1067°F) and the cristobalite inversion between 220°C and 260°C (428°F and 500°F). Quartz and cristobalite dunting points are also called the upper and lower dunting points, respectively. See *Silica inversions*.

The upper dunting point is the one at which most biscuit dunts occur. The lower dunting point is the one at which most of the dunts to glazed ware occur. A slow cooling past these points is necessary with most pottery.

Dust

Airborne solid particles. The danger to health from airborne concentrations of any fine powder is now accepted. All pottery materials, clay, glaze, pigments, plaster, are potential dust.

When materials are in powder form it is an academic detail to know whether they are toxic or not. Silica is chemically non-toxic but because of its fineness it irritates the capillaries in the lungs eventually diminishing their effectiveness. Many materials which previously were considered non-toxic have been discovered to be or are suspected of being carcinogenic when inhaled and lodged in the lungs.

The only safe way to handle powders is to wear a mask or respirator. Do not create dust by mishandling of powders or sweeping the worktops and floor. Use a vacuum with an absolute filter for powder spillages. Wherever possible work with damp powders and mix materials in suspension with water. Flint and quartz are sold in damp form and should be kept this way. Wipe up wet spillages of clay, slip, glaze, pigment etc with wet cloths or sponges before they can dry and become dust. See **Health hazard** and **Silicosis**.

Dwight

John. The first English potter to experiment systematically on a scientific basis. In 1671 he started to produce salt-glazed stoneware and in 1674 founded his famous Fulham Pottery. He made both brown and white salt glaze, some of which was translucent where thin, but he laid no claim to it as a porcelain. He experimented with soft-paste porcelain and red porcelain or red stoneware.

E

Earthenware

Pottery made of a porous body which is waterproofed, if necessary, by a covering glaze. The simplest division of all pottery is into earthenware and stoneware. A criterion for this division is the porosity of the body. If the fired body has a porosity of more than 5%, then it is earthenware.

Many potters add to this criterion of porosity a consideration of the temperature at which the glaze is fired. The softer temperatures below 1100°C (2012°F), which are associated with earthenware glazes, allow a wider range of colour and a particular quality of visual shine and texture. By considering only the porosity of the body, one ignores the glaze which is probably more important since most earthenware is almost completely glazed. It is also in the glaze that differences between earthenware and stoneware are first apparent. The physical hardness or softness of the glaze is also a possible criterion and so is the presence or otherwise of a well-formed body-glaze layer. See **Hard** and **Stoneware**.

The following are earthenwares:
Raku: porous body and soft glaze.
Slipware: mostly porous body with little integration of body, slip and glaze; soft glaze.
Maiolica, Majolica and Faience: porous body and soft glaze.
Creamware: porous body in spite of possible high bisc temperature; soft glaze.

The following are earthenwares by quality:
Bone and non-bone china: soft glaze although covering a non-porous body.
Soft paste porcelain: soft glaze and use of soft temperatures for firing.
Red stoneware: soft glazes integrating with a dense body at soft or medium temperatures.

The photograph shows a large slipware platter by Josie Walter.

The widest range of working methods is used for earthenware: throwing, hand-building, pressing, slabbing, jigger/jolley and slip-casting. No one clay is sufficiently versatile to be used for them all. Earthenware clays are therefore many and various. They are chosen for their colour and their workability. When buying prepared clays or bodies one should ascertain for what making method they are intended. See **Workability**, **Plasticity** and **Clay: types**.

Egyptian paste

A prepared body which creates its own glaze during drying and firing. It was used from pre-dynastic to Roman times in Egypt and was developed for the production of beads, charms, special models and vessels. Archaeologists gave the objects the misleading name of Egyptian faience. A number of potters use Egyptian paste for making beads and small ornamental pieces. The low-plasticity body is difficult to work but the resulting colours, especially the copper turquoise, make it an attractive material.

The body is prepared from clay and glaze materials. One of these materials is soluble sodium carbonate which migrates through the clay to the outside as the work dries. It crystallizes at the surface and, during the firing, fluxes the body to form a glazed surface layer. The other glaze constituents and colouring are part of the body. In this sense it is similar to salt glaze. An object standing on a board dries out only to the air so that its base does not become glazed. The usual bat wash or whiting on shelves is all that is needed to prevent sticking in the kiln. Beads are threaded for drying and firing on nickel-chromium wire. The ware is fired between 850°C and 950°C (1562°F and 1742°F).

A typical body is composed of:

ball clay	20
sodium feldspar	35
silica	35
sodium carbonate	10

The body must be prepared with sufficient water to make it workable. Different recipes use china clay and bentonite; other feldspars etc; and bicarbonate of soda and lithium carbonate. Colourings are added up to 30%. The most popular is copper carbonate but all colourings, including stains, are effective.

Electric kiln

This is the simplest type of kiln to construct and fire. For oxidized firings this is simply an insulated chamber heated by electric elements, with a closable port to allow water and fumes from clay and glaze to escape.

The chamber may be constructed from high temperature insulation brick (HTI), or low thermal mass brick, or other structure lined with ceramic fibre in the form of blanket, board or paper. See *Kiln building materials*.

There are two common types of element: nickel-chromium alloy or, for temperatures above 1100°C, Kanthal A1. A thinner wire gives faster temperature rise but will burn out more frequently than stouter gauge. A thickness of 15 standard wire gauge is the maximum suitable for manually self-winding. Encased wire elements and silicon carbide rod elements are available for reduction atmospheres.

Electric kilns with normal elements are sometimes adapted for occasional light reduction. Combustible material is introduced through a special port during the firing. This shortens the life of the elements because it removes their protective oxidized coating but subsequent oxidized firings will restore this coating. Reduction during the cooling cycle causes little damage. See *Element (2)*.

Unlike other kilns, electric kilns can be designed to operate efficiently at almost any size. Special wiring such as three-phase supply may be needed for the larger sizes but the choice would depend chiefly on the size of ware to be fired, the quantity and frequency of the making cycle, and whether the kiln, if purchased complete, will go through the workshop door!

Although an electric kiln does not have a chimney emitting fumes from burnt gases and is therefore usually sited indoors, surprising amounts of noxious fumes are emitted, even when firing relatively pure clays. Sulfur dioxide and trioxide, and fluorine gas can fill a room with visible choking fumes and over a period of time will etch window glass. Good ventilation in the room is therefore essential.

When comparing running costs with those of other types of kiln there is more to consider than the cost of electricity per firing. Since maintenance, packing and firing are simpler operations than with fuel kilns this is less costly on time. The clean atmosphere does not have the destructive effect on the structure and furniture which fuel fumes have and therefore the kiln has a long life. An electric kiln is certainly the most convenient for biscuit firing.

The firing of an electric kiln can be partially or fully automated. From a simple low, medium, high switch to give gradual temperature rise, the process can be automatically controlled using a cam operated programmer. An electric kiln controller can give delayed switch on and top temperature soak, and can also supply print-out or read-out information on the firing in progress. See *Instrumentation*.

Element (1)

Chemical element. A substance which is so pure that it contains only atoms of the same atomic number. For example, if all the atoms in a substance are of atomic number 29, then the substance is the element copper. The following list gives elements which the potter is likely to use and includes their chemical symbols, valencies and atomic weights correct to one decimal place. See also *Tables 17* and *34*.

Element	Symbol	AW	Valency
aluminium	Al	27·0	3
antimony	Sb	121·8	3
arsenic	As	74·9	3
barium	Ba	137·3	2
beryllium	Be	9·0	2
bismuth	Bi	209·0	3
boron	B	10·8	3
cadmium	Cd	112·4	2
calcium	Ca	40·1	2
carbon	C	12·0	2 and 4
cerium	Ce	140·1	4
chlorine	Cl	35·5	1
chromium	Cr	52·0	3
cobalt	Co	58·9	2 and 3
copper	Cu	63·5	1 and 2
fluorine	F	19·0	1
germanium	Ge	72·6	4
gold	Au	197·0	—
hydrogen	H	1·0	1
iron	Fe	55·8	2 and 3
lead	Pb	207·2	2 and 4
lithium	Li	6·9	1
magnesium	Mg	24·3	2
manganese	Mn	54·9	2, 3 and 4
nickel	Ni	58·7	2 and 4
nitrogen	N	14·0	3
oxygen	O	16·0	2
phosphorus	P	31·0	3 and 5
platinum	Pt	195·1	—
potassium	K	39·1	1
praseodymium	Pr	140·9	4
selenium	Se	79·0	—
silicon	Si	28·1	4
silver	Ag	107·9	—
sodium	Na	23·0	1
strontium	Sr	87·6	2
sulfur	S	32·1	2 and 4
tin	Sn	118·7	4
titanium	Ti	47·9	4
uranium	U	238·0	3, 4 and 5
vanadium	V	50·9	2, 3, 4 and 5
zinc	Zn	65·4	2
zirconium	Zr	91·2	4

Element (2)

An electric current conductor which has a calculated resistance enabling it to generate continuous heat energy. The radiant heat created is used to heat electric kilns.

Kiln elements are designed to fulfil a wide range of requirements. Simple lengths of wire of suitable alloys are coiled to fit small low-temperature kilns. Thicker wire of higher temperature alloy is used for stoneware and porcelain firing. Silicon carbide resistance heaters are designed to cope with high temperature and reducing atmospheres. Sophisticated devices, using variously molybdenum silicide, carborundum with granular carbon, stabilized zirconium oxide and molten tin have been developed for furnaces requiring the extremely high temperatures of 1500°C to 2000°C (2732°F to 3632°F).

The first photograph shows a supply of element wire being fitted to a dispensing wheel. The wire is fed on to a rotating spindle through a feeder tube to tighten it on to the spindle as it is coiled from right to left. Photographs taken at Potclays Ltd.

These different fittings have in common the requirement to generate sufficient heat without themselves becoming too hot and to have a sufficiently cool connection to the electricity supply. The wire types are coiled spirally

and need the support of horizontal grooves in the kiln wall. The element types of most interest to the potter are listed below.

NICKEL-CHROMIUM. The wire is an alloy of 80% nickel and 20% chromium. These elements can withstand up to 1100°C (2012°F) but are recommended for repeated use at 1000°C (1832°F). A thinner wire gives out heat more quickly but will burn out sooner than a stouter gauge such as 15 s.w.g. Sulfur compounds attack nickel-chromium elements.

KANTHAL. Kanthal A1 elements are the ones most popularly in use in pottery kilns for temperatures up to 1350°C (2462°F). Nickel-chromium wire has better hot strength at temperatures up to 1000°C (1832°F) but higher than this Kanthal elements must be used. More recently Kanthal AF has been introduced for temperatures up to 1350°C (2462°F), although above 1300°C (2372°F) A1 has a longer life. AF has a hot strength equal to nickel-chromium and its life at the same temperature is two to four times as long. With improved strength and less tendency to creep Kanthal AF can be used with less support allowing less weight in kiln construction.

Kanthal alloy is approximately 22% chromium, 5·8% aluminium, 72·2% iron. The elements acquire a coating of oxide which protects them from attack by sulfur but not fluorine or lead vapour. The coating is attacked by reducing conditions and must be restored by subsequent oxidized firings to prevent rapid deterioration.

SILICON CARBIDE. These resistance heaters were developed for temperatures up to 1400°C (2552°F), and destructive kiln atmospheres in industrial conditions. Their use has been extended to smaller kilns to satisfy the individual potter's desire to reduce in electric kilns. In some cases the resistance wire is encased in a tube of silicon carbide to protect it from the kiln fumes, and where it can also be cooled by a passage of air. Sometimes the silicon carbide is itself the heating element. These types of elements tend to be expensive. The design has to provide cooler connections for incoming leads and cope with the gradual change of the silicon carbide to silica and carbon. This change gives increased resistance and also the formation of cristobalite gives increasing mechanical weakness.

Elephant's ear
A close-textured, natural, springy sponge shaped roughly like an elephant's ear. It is flattish and about 12 cm across. It is used in press-moulding where its springy character is useful for forcing the clay against the mould without scratching the surface.

Elers (Ehlers) brothers
John and David. Dutch potters who settled in England in 1688 and produced a red stoneware, first in London, then at Bradwell Wood in Staffordshire. They used the Staffordshire

red clay and washed and levigated it to obtain a fine body. This was thrown and turned to a thin section. It was burnished and had sprigging from engraved brass and copper moulds applied to it. Tableware was popular in Boccaro style, the dense body firing to a rich red brown and being unglazed.

Elutriation

The separation of fine clay from a mass of coarse clay by use of the property of fine clay to remain in suspension in water when larger particles, such as sand and stones, will sink. Elutriation uses a mechanical device to move the slurry, sometimes upwards against gravity. The finest particles can be moved the furthest distance. Proportionately coarser ones fall out on the way. Elutriation differs from levigation which uses gravity to move the slurry slowly past settling riffles. In sedimentation and settling the slurry is not moved at all but is allowed to stand still in bins or tanks.

Enamel

Onglaze enamel. Metal enamel. Glass enamel. Vitreous enamel. Porcelain enamel. A soft-melting glass used to decorate pottery, metal and glass. The material is similar in all cases and like other ceramic glazes is composed of fluxes and alumino-silicates. Sodium, potassium and boron oxides are the main fluxes with some lead oxide in glass and onglaze enamels. The colours are the usual metal oxides.

Potters mostly use the onglaze enamels but some of the other types give interesting results when melted as pools on tiles and into hollowed areas on decorative dishes etc. In using other than onglaze enamels, one should remember that enamels for metal often contain minerals which may volatilize and cause blisters in the longer duration of a pottery firing. See also *Cullet*.

The terms onglaze enamel and onglaze colour are used for pottery enamels. These are abbreviated to O/E and O/G. See *Onglaze*.

Metal enamel is used for decorative metalwork cloisonné mostly on copper. Glass enamel is used for decorating glassware. Vitreous enamel and the rather misleading name porcelain enamel are names for the glaze coatings given to sheet ironware and cast ironware.

Encaustic

A method of decoration whereby coloured clays are inlaid in the body clay. The inlaid pieces are made to fill cut-out lines and shapes or are rolled onto the surface. See *Rolled inlay*. The encaustic method was used by the Cistercian monks to produce paving tiles. It provided a decoration which was permanent even when the covering glaze had worn away.

Engobe

A term of wide meaning often interchangeable with slip but including other materials. An engobe is used to cover a clay, produce a buffer layer and give a different surface, texture and colour. It is applied by brush, dip, spray etc.

Clay slips and glaze slops are essentially fluid forms. An engobe can be in a jelly form or a stiff form. It is often halfway between a clay and a glaze in composition and contains materials which are normally considered glaze materials. It therefore fires to a more vitreous state than the body which it covers. However, since it does not fuse to a glassy state, it cannot be called a glaze. And since it can be composed entirely of non-clay materials, it cannot be called a slip. The term engobe is often the only one that is suitable.

Enstatite

Magnesium silicate. $MgO.SiO_2$. The simplest and purest of the pyroxene minerals. It is a crystalline precipitate in intermediate and basic igneous rocks. The crystal growth is quickly established because in basic rocks there is no lack of suitable alkaline oxides in with the silica melt. This crystal growth occurs in cooling glazes which are similarly high in magnesia. See **Magnesian matts** and **Crystalline glazes**.

For example, if a glaze contains talc for the purpose of a flux, it is likely to recrystallize as enstatite upon cooling, giving an opacity and mattness. The stage equation would be:

$$3MgO.4SiO_2.H_2O \xrightarrow{900°C} \text{decomposes to give:}$$
$$\text{talc}$$

$$\underset{\substack{\text{free magnesium} \\ \text{oxide}}}{3MgO} + \underset{\substack{\text{free} \\ \text{silica}}}{4SiO_2} + \underset{\text{water}}{H_2O\uparrow} \xrightarrow{1180°C}$$

At 1180°C (2156°F) the magnesium oxide and silica are involved in a ceramic fusion During cooling, some of the magnesium oxide and silica devitrify to give:

$$\underset{\text{enstatite}}{3(MgO.SiO_2)} + \underset{\substack{\text{free silica involved} \\ \text{in other fusion}}}{SiO_2}$$

The diagram shows the lattice of enstatite in which continuous SiO_3 silica chains have alternate units inverted. Two silica chains are drawn. The Mg^{2+} ions are in six-fold co-ordination, each regularizing one silica chain and linking it to one other. Thus a sheet type of structure is formed with emphasis upon the long needles of the thereby straightened silica chains.

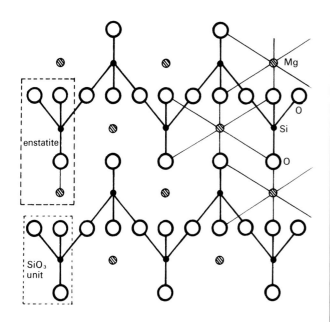

Epsom salt

Epsom salt is sometimes used to thicken a glaze slop that is too thin. This is a rule-of-thumb procedure used when one cannot wait for the glaze to settle and have its water siphoned away. Only a small amount of epsom salt is required. The action is that of flocculation. Other flocculants are plaster of Paris and calcium chloride. See **Magnesium sulfate**.

Equation

Chemical equation which shows in symbol or formula form what is happening in a chemical action. For example:

$$CaMg(CO_3)_2 \longrightarrow CaO + MgO + 2CO_2\uparrow$$

The two sides of an equation should balance in number of atoms represented.

Equivalent

Equivalent number of molecules. The term is used when referring to the substitution of one compound for another when the calculation of amount is done on the basis of the unity formula.

For example, suppose one wished to increase the amount of sodium feldspar in a glaze recipe at the expense of the potassium feldspar. This may be necessary to overcome shivering. A straightforward substitution, weight for weight, is the usual approach of the potter and is sufficiently accurate in most cases. However, if the glaze is carefully balanced, as may happen with a dolomite matt, it may be necessary to do the substitution on the basis of the number of molecules involved. This is called an equivalent substitution. Sodium and potassium feldspars have different molecular weights and therefore a weight for weight substitution would involve a different number of molecules.

For the purpose of this example, the dolomite recipe from the article on dolomite matt will be used. The recipe is:

potassium feldspar	20
sodium feldspar	20
china clay	20
whiting	20
dolomite	20

The unity formula is:

$$\left.\begin{array}{l} 0·073\,K_2O \\ 0·077\,Na_2O \\ 0·222\,MgO \\ 0·628\,CaO \end{array}\right\} 0·309\,Al_2O_3 \quad 1·218\,SiO_2$$

The adjusted unity formula substituting 0·5 equivalents of sodium oxide for potassium oxide is:

$$\left.\begin{array}{l} 0·023\,K_2O \\ 0·127\,Na_2O \\ 0·222\,MgO \\ 0·628\,CaO \end{array}\right\} 0·309\,Al_2O_3 \quad 1·218\,SiO_2$$

And the percentage recipe calculated from this new unity formula is:

potassium feldspar	6·26
sodium feldspar	33·05
china clay	20·23
whiting	20·23
dolomite	20·23

A potassium oxide molecule is heavier than a sodium oxide molecule. In order to get the same number of molecules, the sodium feldspar has only needed to be increased by 13·05% whereas the potassium feldspar has been decreased by 13·74%. To keep the whole recipe in percentage form, the other items have been increased. It must be realized that the overall proportion of molecules $RO:R_2O_3:RO_2$ has remained the same throughout.

Eutectic mixture

The proportioned mixture of two or more substances which melts at the lowest possible temperature. This temperature is called the eutectic point.

For example, lead oxide melts at 880°C (1616°F) and silica at 1710°C (3110°F). It would be reasonable to expect that a 50/50 mixture by weight would melt at the halfway point of 1295°C (2363°F). However, such is the interaction of these two materials that this mixture would probably melt at about 800°C (1472°F). This temperature is lower than the melting points of the constituents and it is by no means the eutectic point or lowest possible melting point for lead oxide and silica combinations. The lowest melting point is achieved by the eutectic mixture approximating 90% lead oxide and 10% silica with a melting point at 510°C (950°F).

Another example is that of aluminium oxide and silica melting at 2050°C and 1710°C respectively (3722°F and 3110°F). Both these substances are considered highly refractory and are often added to glazes to raise the melting point, that is, to stiffen a glaze which melts too much. Yet aluminium oxide and silica have a fluxing power on each other so that a 50/50 mix melts at about 1750°C (3182°F) instead of an expected halfway of about 1880°C (3416°F). The eutectic mixture is 10% aluminium oxide and 90% silica melting at 1545°C (2813°F), which again is lower than the melting point of either constituent.

All alkaline oxides react with silica to produce melting points lower than one could calculate by a straight-line graph. Thus in graph 1, the dotted line shows the straight line between the two melting points of imaginary alkaline oxide RO and silica. Along this straight line one might expect to find the melting points of the mixtures as they range in proportion from 100% RO at the left-hand side to 100% silica at the right-hand side. However, in reality, the melting points lie on the continuous line at the lower temperatures. The point E is the eutectic point and, in this imaginary example, the eutectic mixture is 60% alkaline oxide and 40% silica.

Graph 1 shows that if one starts with 100% silica at the right-hand side of the graph and progressively adds the alkaline oxide, and at the same time decreases the silica, the

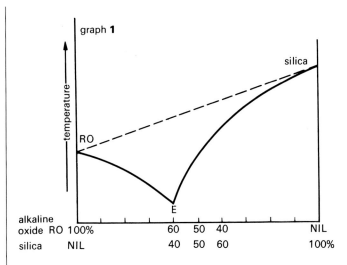

mixtures melt at progressively lower temperatures until point E is reached. After point E the addition of more alkaline oxide, with decreasing percentage of silica, results in mixtures which melt at progressively higher temperatures. Since most glazes are typical of the right-hand side of this graph whereby an increase in alkaline oxide results in more fusion, alkaline oxides are generally termed fluxes. However, if one considers the left-hand side of the graph one will realize that the increasing amounts of silica are having a fluxing action upon the alkaline oxide.

Some alkaline oxides have very low melting points to begin with, so that mixtures with silica cannot melt below the temperature of the pure oxide. Strictly speaking, there is no eutectic mixture and no eutectic point. Graph 2 shows this using the same graph framework as graph 1. There still occurs an optimum point marked E on the graph which most people agree upon calling a eutectic point. Graph 3 shows a more complex line with three eutectic points (E) and two reverse eutectic points (R). Some alkaline oxides, notably lead oxide and copper oxide, give graphs like this. Potassium and sodium oxides give graphs like graph 2, and the high-melting oxides of magnesium, calcium, zinc and manganese give graphs like graph 1.

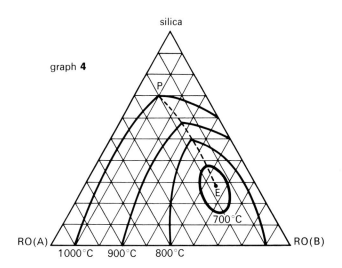

Eutectic mixtures in glazes are not a simple matter of one oxide with silica but a case of each oxide reacting with every other. The most obvious reactions are those of alkali with acid, e.g. sodium oxide with silica. The reaction is usually considered the simple effect of a flux attacking a silica. This is an over-simplification. It is equally true that the silica attacks the flux as was earlier proven. Also, in mixtures of amphoteric oxide and acid there will be a reaction because the amphoteric oxide presents an alkaline property. Similarly, in a mixture of amphoteric oxide and alkali there will be a reaction because the amphoteric oxide presents an acidic property.

All oxides are excited in the presence of heat and in the presence of other oxides the excitement is multiplied. The increased intramolecular vibration results in fluidity, that is, melting. Therefore some effect must result from a mixture of any two oxides, even two acids, e.g. silica and phosphorus oxide, or from a mixture of two alkalis, e.g. potassium and sodium oxides. However, the most significant results will be those with strong alkali and strong acid. Only silica need be considered as the acid but there are many alkaline oxides and each one is different in its effectiveness as a glaze flux.

As a glaze is heated the simplest eutectic combinations will melt first. Once fluid, they will soak into the surrounding material and discover other combinations or oxides with which to produce more complex eutectics. This continues until the whole mass is molten. If the process is stopped before the end point, it will be found that some parts have completely melted producing a glass but within this glass are specks of unmelted material. The effect may be a desirable opaque glaze but the end point, where all the eutectic combinations have occurred, would be a transparent, if coloured, glass.

It is relatively easy to understand the graphs 1, 2 and 3, but, as has just been stated, a glaze is much more complex. In glaze reasoning one would usually be faced with substances which within themselves contain potential eutectic combinations, e.g. cornish stone, feldspar and frits. These eutectic mixtures may combine to form more complex ones involving 3, 4, 5, 6, 7, 8 etc, individual oxides. Involved combinations cannot be represented on graphs like 1, 2 and

3. A diagram for three constituents is plotted as on graph 4. This is called a triaxial diagram, a triaxial blend, or popularly, a triaxial graph. Here point P represents 70% silica, 20% RO(A) and 10% RO(B). This is arrived at by counting across the diagram from a flat side towards an apex. At an apex 100% is represented for the ingredient there named. There is no room on this diagram for a temperature scale, only for the various mixtures. The temperature of the melting points of the various mixtures is therefore plotted as a series of lines linking mixtures with the same melting temperatures.

In this example, the temperatures are 700°C, 800°C, 900°C and 1000°C. The eutectic mixture appears at a point E. However it can happen that no point E exists, because within the enclosed line linking the lowest temperatures, the mixtures melt at higher temperatures. In this case the most practical mixture for glazes is the one containing the most silica. In fact it is usual to find, as on graph 4, that there is a point or angle on each temperature line. Joining these points gives what is known as the eutectic axis.

If four constituents are involved, the diagram becomes three-dimensional. The fourth constituent would be at the apex of a pyramid based on graph 4. The reading of such diagrams is obviously difficult, so most ceramicists would standardize one constituent and plot a series of diagrams like graph 4, or else standardize two constituents and plot a series of graphs like graphs 1, 2 and 3.

Testing for different melting temperatures is done by run and sag tests in a kiln with a good viewing system and an accurate digital pyrometer. Refractory test blocks are used. The test mixtures are packed into A (see drawing on page 129) and seen to run and melt into B, or the mixture is made into a bar, C, which sags when melting.

Rather than consider different temperatures, most potters have a series of test mixtures in the kiln fired to the same temperature. The triaxial diagram can be used to plot areas which have similar results, e.g. matt rough, matt smooth, shiny, bubbled. Such results are obviously the outcome of eutectic fusion, or lack of it, but the diagram could not necessarily be used to position a point E. Triaxial diagrams can be plotted for any three materials such as clay, wood ash and feldspar as well as pure oxides as illustrated here.

Individual potters need not make exhaustive eutectic tests. It is sufficient to understand the theory behind eutectic mixtures and apply this theory to workshop situations. It is possible to draw the graph 5 which is purely theoretical, yet sufficiently typical, to enable one to understand any glaze. The line represents all the possible mixtures of flux and silica. Here flux means all the alkaline oxides present in a glaze. An increase in flux assumes a decrease in silica and vice versa because the graph represents a ratio of the two at a constant total weight.

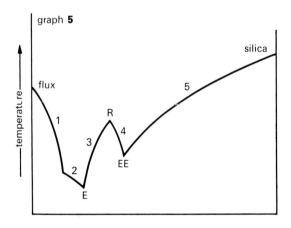

graph **5**

General observations would be that glazes having mixtures between flux and E would tend to be matt-surfaced due to crystallization. Between E and EE glazes would be shiny, and from EE to silica the glazes would get pro-gressively duller.

Normally one would expect that an increase in flux would result in the glaze melting more easily. This is true for most glazes, such as maiolica and transparents, both earthenware and stoneware, and is represented on the graph by Section 5. It takes quite large changes of amounts to make appreciable changes in the glaze. This is shown by the shallow angle of the line of the graph. The difference between 40% and 50% of silica may not be discernible in some glazes.

If minute changes of less than 1% affect the glaze then its position is probably in Section 3. This is a steep part of the

graph and here only slight variations of the flux:silica ratio will result in very different fusion temperatures and hence results at a given temperature.

If the glaze happens to coincide with the point E or EE then any alteration as increase in flux or silica will result in a glaze fusing less at a given temperature. When tests prove this, and one is not satisfied with the glaze, one is in a very bewildering position. One must introduce yet another eutectic mixture, or near eutectic mixture, which is different from all those present. This needs to be very soft: certainly softer than the glaze by 300°C to 400°C (540°F to 720°F), otherwise it may be found not to give sufficient reaction. If the results are still not satisfactory there must exist another eutectic point for the glaze which has not yet been discovered.

If the glaze is at position R, an increase in either flux or silica results in over-fusion. Results tend to be disastrous as well as disappointing. Sometimes increases in flux in Section 3 can be satisfactory. Section 4 is unlikely to be satisfactory because it contains the unstable bright, shiny glazes. The best solution is to attempt to step across into Section 5.

Glazes from Section 5 are more usable and satisfactory, giving practically the same visual result, and with more silica they are composed of more stable silicates. Lastly, Sections 1 & 2 are the matt glazes. Section 1 is too steep a graph to be practical and contains too little silica to be a stable hard glaze when set. Section 2 contains the lime matts, alumina matts and zinc matts, in both earthenware and stoneware, and the stoneware dolomite matts. The point to note is that an increase in flux does not produce an increase in fusibility. If one wants such a glaze to melt more one has to decrease the flux content. This is an unusual approach for a potter who has previously only dealt with the more conventional glazes from Sections 5 and 3.

Expansion
Increase in size due to temperature change. In pottery one is concerned with rates of expansion as a means of calculating the expansion and contraction of bodies and glazes. See *Glaze fit*. Each constituent oxide of a body and glaze has its own rate of expansion.

For comparison, a few examples are given of volumetric expansion resulting from a rise in temperature from room temperature to 600°C (1112°F). They are based upon the observations of Winkelmann and Schott.

silica glass	(SiO_2)	0·5%
lead oxide	(PbO)	1·7%
aluminium oxide	(Al_2O_3)	2·9%
calcium oxide	(CaO)	2·9%
potassium oxide	(K_2O)	4·3%
sodium oxide	(Na_2O)	5·8%

Extrusion
Forcing clay through a die to give a desired cross section. All methods use the same principle whether the equipment is a finger-held barrel activated like a syringe, a hand-held gun

based on a builder's mastic gun, a dod or wad box with screw-down pressure, a vertical extruder using arm pressure to pull down a lever, a vertical or horizontal pug mill with attachment or a specially-constructed extruder using compressed air to power a ram.

The extruded product is a strip, trough or tube of uniform section and any convenient length. The extruded pieces are usually allowed to stiffen slightly before use. John Alliston re-forms the still-soft clay into folded bases for pots, and ends for dishes. John Glick and Paul Stubbs construct their work from leatherhard pieces.

Dies are made from metal, wood and plastic. Complex sections often drag at one place causing the extrusion to curve. If the curve is not wanted, extra drag is put on other parts by adding to the inside of the die until a straight extrusion is achieved. Curved extrusions can be created by hand control during extrusion.

The photographs show John Alliston extruding a triangular tube, a selection of strips with dies, square tubes with die, the re-forming of a soft square tube and the beaten four-leaf-clover base which results, a dish cut from an oblong tube which has been re-formed at the ends, and a wall planter. A square planter is shown in **Colour plate 38**. Paul Stubb's de-airing pug mill is shown with extruded slab from which are cut tailored pieces. See photos under **Salt glaze**. John Glick's 'Trudee' hydraulic-powered extruder has a force nearing 10 tonnes forcing 55 kg of clay through a chamber 40 cm by 15 cm.

F

Fahrenheit

°F. Degrees Fahrenheit. The Fahrenheit scale is a scale of temperature measurement which is an extension of the thermometer scale 32°F to 212°F for the freezing point to boiling point of water. The scale is named after Gabriel Fahrenheit, the early 18th-century physicist.

Faience

Earthenware with colourful decoration or colourful glazes. Faience was the term originally given to wares from Faenza in northern Italy. These were tin glazed wares of the maiolica type. However, as the popularity of tin-glaze earthenware spread through Europe its character changed. Modelled decoration, as used on stoneware, was included with glazes which were more fluid than the maiolica glazes. This is the style that is now considered faience—that is, plain and modelled surfaces covered with shiny and matt glazes often blended together. Tin oxide, titanium oxide and rutile are much used.

The name faience is used by archaeologists to describe tin-glazed wares from Egypt and south-west Asia. Also, any glazed pottery, pottery ornaments and small beads, as yet unclassified, and which were made throughout Europe during the Bronze and Iron Ages, are collectively referred to as faience. The photograph shows a turquoise tin-glazed bottle from Persia.

Fast-fire kiln

A term which came into use in the late 1970s when the use of ceramic fibre and low thermal mass bricks began to revolutionize the construction of kilns. Both these materials provide a mesh of minute air pockets which give excellent insulation. Firing schedule times can be halved and fuel consumption cut by up to 40% compared with older brick kilns. The faster firing cycle produces different results on cones and glazes. Cones fall later but suddenly, and otherwise crystalline glazes cool shiny. See **Insulation**.

Fat clay

Long clay. Highly plastic clay. These clays are often added to other clays to improve workability.

Feather combing

A slipware pattern of feathered shapes produced by combing through a series of trailed lines. One colour, traditionally white, is trailed across a ground slip of contrasting colour which covers a slab of clay. The trailed slip is made to sink into the ground slip by knocking the board on which the clay slab rests. A bristle, bullrush or feather is then combed across the lines to give the feathering.

Feldspar

Fieldspar. Felspar. A group of minerals used in proportions of up to 25% as flux in bodies and up to 100% in glazes. Feldspars contain alkalis plus silica and aluminium oxide and are therefore natural frits or glazes. In fact, they have cooled and crystallized from a molten magma. They contain alkalis, notably potassium and sodium oxides, which if alone are soluble, but when combined with aluminium oxide and silica in feldspars, these alkalis are reasonably insoluble. The value of feldspar is thus seen as an opportunity to introduce alkalis into a body or glaze without recourse to fritting.

Feldspars begin to soften at about 1150°C (2102°F) but because of their high aluminium oxide content do not run, even at 1300°C (2372°F). The photograph shows test blocks of feldspar fused at 1250°C (2282°F). Feldspars make very stiff glasses containing innumerable small bubbles giving a milky opacity. They can be converted to usable glazes by the addition of more flux and silica. For example, a simple glaze for 1250°C (2282°F) is feldspar 70, flint 12, whiting 18.

Some feldspars show signs of plasticity like clay and similarly react to flocculation. This quality is too small however to be of use in getting a feldspathic glaze to grip to ware before firing. A binder should be included in the recipe. Clay is to be preferred because it will help the slop suspension.

Feldspar has a high surface tension during fusion so that too much feldspar in a glaze can result in crawling. The crawling starts because the glaze is reluctant to grip the body before firing.

The commonest feldspar is orthoclase, so that if no other type of feldspar is indicated in recipes it can be assumed that orthoclase is intended. Albite is the second commonest feldspar.

Crystalline rocks can often be approximately identified as feldspars and feldspathoids by their general properties of cleavage into angular pieces with hexagonal tendencies, a grained appearance on the surfaces, polarized reflections at the broken faces and, with orthoclase, a pinkish colour. The accompanying photographs show the comparison between normal pieces of broken feldspar and a selected specimen of a twinned crystal of orthoclase. See also *Albite* and *Orthoclase*.

TYPES OF FELDSPAR. There are twelve types of true feldspar and many other feldspathic materials called feldspathoids. The important feldspars are orthoclase, albite and anorthite, and these are separately indexed in this book. The twelve true feldspars can be separately identified by chemical composition and crystal structure and will correspond to idealized formulae, though this is only possible in carefully selected specimens. Feldspar quarried in bulk cannot be so pure but always contains some admixture of another feldspar and traces of other minerals. Thus orthoclase will contain a small amount of sodium oxide and possibly calcium oxide. Calculations using the theoretical formula will therefore not be so accurate as ones using the percentage analysis. See *Calculations: finding the unity formula*.

The chart (overleaf) shows the relationship of feldspars to one another.

The three across the top are called the alkaline feldspars. At the left-hand side is the most common feldspar called orthoclase. Microcline is chemically identical to orthoclase but its crystal structure is different. Orthoclase and microcline are the potassium feldspars and have the chemical formula $K_2O.Al_2O_3.6SiO_2$. Albite at the right-hand side is the sodium feldspar with the formula $Na_2O.Al_2O_3.6SiO_2$. Between are combinations called, collectively, perthites or potassium sodium feldspars. They are chemically alike but different in crystal structure and have the formula

$$NaKO.Al_2O_3.6SiO_2$$

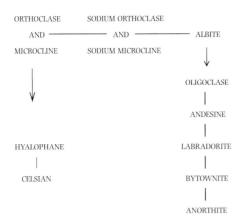

```
ORTHOCLASE      SODIUM ORTHOCLASE
   AND      ———      AND      ———   ALBITE
MICROCLINE      SODIUM MICROCLINE
                                        |
                                        ↓
                                   OLIGOCLASE
                                        |
                                   ANDESINE
   |                                    |
   ↓                                    |
                                   LABRADORITE
HYALOPHANE                              |
   |                               BYTOWNITE
CELSIAN                                 |
                                   ANORTHITE
```

Below albite are listed four feldspars in a chain leading to a fifth one called anorthite. Anorthite has the formula $CaO.Al_2O_3.2SiO_2$ and is therefore called lime feldspar. The feldspars in between albite and anorthite are progressive stages in the replacement of Na and Si by Ca and Al. The whole group of six feldspars from albite to anorthite is known as the plagioclase feldspars.

A similar progression at the left-hand side of the chart has only two stages in which K and Si are replaced by Ba and Al to give celsian with the formula $BaO.Al_2O_3.2SiO_2$. Hyalophane and celsian are called barium feldspars.

Feldspathic glaze

A glaze which contains a high percentage (50–100%) of feldspar. For example, a feldspathic glaze for 1250°C (2282°F) is:

feldspar	66
flint	10
whiting	23

The term is also used for a glaze which, while containing less than 50% feldspar, is compounded of minerals which create an artificial feldspar. Such glazes use one or two fluxes only and have a high proportion of aluminium oxide. The aluminium oxide:silica ratio may be as high as 1:6 as in the common feldspars. For example, another feldspathic glaze for 1250°C (2282°F) is:

feldspar	45
china clay	20
flint	20
whiting	15

Feldspathic glazes are usually stoneware and are stiff glazes with a milkiness due to minute bubbles. They tend to crawl because they have a high surface tension when molten and tend to craze when cool because their alkalis have a high coefficient of expansion and contraction. The photograph shows a globule of feldspathic glaze made opaque by thousands of bubbles.

Feldspathoids

Feldspathic minerals. Feldsparic minerals. Feldspar is such an important mineral to the potter that it has given its name to a whole family of minerals which are not true feldspars at all. These are more correctly called feldspathic minerals or feldspathoids.

Feldspathoids have similar properties to feldspars: they are alumino-silicates with various alkaline oxides and they are crystalline. They melt between 1100°C and 1300°C (2012°F and 2372°F) and are useful in glazes. However, they cannot be considered as true minerals because they do not conform to unified chemical formulae.

Feldspathoids are therefore not single chemical compounds with regular lattice structures. They are mixtures of different compounds whose lattices partially link in random fashion. They are therefore more easily weathered than the true feldspars, often contain soluble substances and are often easier to fuse because of their variety of alkaline oxides. Any formula given for a feldspathoid is necessarily complex and more in the nature of an analysis.

The commonest feldspathic minerals are cornish stone and nepheline syenite. Others are riebeckite, granite, nepheline, leucite, sodalite, petalite, lepidolite and spodumene. The photograph shows a cavity in basalt filled with zeolithic feldspathoids.

Ferreous

Containing iron in any form. This term includes both ferriferous and ferruginous.

Ferric oxide
Red iron oxide. Fe$_2$O$_3$. See ***Iron oxide***.

Ferriferous
Capable of yielding iron or iron oxide. For example, the iron ores contain iron which can be extracted. Red and brown clays also contain iron but it is not possible to isolate the iron and therefore these are called ferruginous.

Ferrosic oxide
Ferroso-ferric oxide. Magnetic iron oxide. Fe$_3$O$_4$. See ***Iron oxide: types***.

Ferrous oxide
Black iron oxide. FeO. See ***Iron oxide***.

Ferruginous
Containing red iron oxide. For example, the red and brown clays are ferruginous clays. The term is often used to signify the colour as well as the origin of the colour.

Fettling
The trimming away of excess clay either at leatherhard or dry state. This may be large amounts turned off by shaving on a wheel or lathe, or small seam marks from casting which are scraped off with a knife held at right angles to the surface. See also ***Turning***.

Fibre
See ***Insulation*** and ***Kiln building materials***.

Filler
A non-plastic addition to a clay or body. Its functions are:

1. To open the clay for texture and/or workability (grog and sand).
2. To control drying shrinkage and firing shrinkage (grog, sand, pitchers and whiting).
3. To change the fired state for reasons of porosity, glaze fit or whiteness (flint, quartz, feldspar, whiting and calcined china clay).

The grain size of a filler is an important consideration if it is to fulfil its function properly. In relation to the three functions above, the following observations can be made:

1. The smallest grain size will usually be 120's mesh for grog and 80's mesh for sand. Some very fine openers kill plasticity without assisting a clay's workability. See ***Preparation of clay: control of grain size***.

2. Drying shrinkage is proportional to the amount and fineness of the clay content. Fillers therefore proportionately reduce shrinkage but different grain sizes give different speeds of drying according to the sealing effect of the clay content. As a general rule, medium grogs etc in the 60's to 100's range tend to give the faster drying when compared weight for weight with coarser or finer material.

Firing shrinkage is dependent upon the chemical nature of the filler as well as its grain size. Whiting and some pitchers are only effective as refractory fillers up to defined temperatures. Quartz and flint fillers are often finely ground (smaller than 200's mesh). As fine grains they do not present a refractory property in bodies but become involved in the molten phases. As such, they could accelerate vitrification and subsequent shrinkage. See ***Grain size***.

3. Similarly, a body's densification, its ultimate porosity and expansion rate for glaze fit purposes are dependent upon whether the filler is involved in the glassy parts of the body. In this context silica needs particular assessment because it can present three different phases each with distinctly different character: quartz phase as a refractory, cristobalite phase giving anti-craze properties and amorphous phase giving glassy and apparently fluxing results. See ***Silica phases and conversion, Cristobalite*** and ***Grain size***.

Filter-pressing
Mechanized dewatering whereby a prepared slip is turned into plastic clay. The slip is pumped at pressure into pervious cloth bags formed from two sheets clamped together at the edges. The cakes of clay are removed by unbolting the frames. The photograph shows the press at Cardiff College of Art, Wales.

Vacuum filtering and centrifugal filtering are also done. See also ***Dewatering***.

Finger combing
Wet combing. The most direct form of sgraffito, whereby freshly applied slip or glaze is removed by the stroking action of the fingertips. The beauty of this method is the feeling of freedom it imparts to the decoration which is enlivened by the thickening of the colour where it is displaced alongside the track of the finger. The plate (overleaf) by Pat Culpin shows finger-combed slipware.

Fireclay
Clay associated with the coal measures of the Carboniferous

System of sedimentary rocks. A few deposits are residual clays similar to china clay. Fireclays are often refractory clays and are used for firebricks. The name gives this impression but there are fireclays which vitrify below 1300°C (2372°F). These are used for drainage pipes, building bricks, sanitary ware and stoneware. Grog is usually fired and ground fireclay.

Fireclays can be divided into the compressed rock fireclays and the underclays. The rock fireclays are both solid rocks and shales. The rock fireclays must be crushed in a mill before they can be wetted and pugged or even blunged. They are often mined rather than quarried and come to the surface as hard lumps which take twenty or thirty years to weather to a plastic clay. In contrast, the underclays have often remained damp. They are more obviously clays when won and can often be blunged without previous milling. They weather quickly, surprisingly quickly for their clay particle size, and produce plastic clays suitable for ovenware.

All fireclays are the seat earths of vegetation which grew during the Carboniferous Period over 280 million years ago. The underclays were the soil for the coal forests and this is why an underclay is found immediately under a coal seam. The coal forest vegetation has taken from the soil much of the potassium and other soluble salts. It may also have taken some silica but it has not taken aluminium oxide. Hence these clays are high in aluminium oxide and are refractory. The rock fireclays tend to be less refractory than the underclays. All contain organic impurities, some as much as 3% carbon and others actual carbonaceous matter as old root hairs etc. They also contain free quartz, which may be large visible grains; mica; iron pyrites; iron carbonate (siderite) and calcium carbonate (calcite).

The presence of impurities which are volatile, e.g. the carbon in the organic impurities, the sulfur in the pyrites, the carbon dioxide in the carbonates, dictates a careful firing of these clays if the impurities are not to be trapped. Trapped carbon and sulfur cause the most trouble. Even a relatively small amount, like 0·5% of the dry clay, is sufficient to cause a black core with attendant problems at higher temperatures. See ***Black core***. The carbon dioxide usually

escapes without difficulty from the carbonates and also the bound water presents no difficulty. With fireclays more than with other clays, the bound water escapes over a long period of the firing starting around 350°C (662°F) and continuing up to 600°C (1112°F). This fact and the general coarseness and quick-drying nature of these clays often lead potters to think that they can withstand any treatment.

The fired colour of fireclays is pale buff. Some are nearly white. All tend to be speckled with iron particles which originally were pyrites. Well-weathered fireclays have often had the pyrites decomposed to carbonate, and fire to a more uniform pink colour. Fireclays associated with iron ore deposits are often red-burning and are used for making bricks.

Fireclays are various in chemical composition. It is usual to quote a fireclay by its aluminium oxide content and to relate this, with some justification, to a point of refractoriness. Whether a clay deforms at a low temperature or a high temperature is dependent equally on the amount of alkali present but it is true to say that a fireclay containing 40% aluminium oxide is unlikely to melt easily. Fireclays contain between 10% and 40% of aluminium oxide, between 40% and 80% of silica. Compare this with china clay, which contains 38% aluminium oxide and 46% silica.

Some fireclays are as refractory as china clay and are able to withstand 1700°C (3092°F) without deformation and probably melt around 1800°C (3272°F). In Britain these are the Scottish fireclays. It has been suggested that nearly all the fireclays originated in the north of the British Isles and were transported southwards. In so doing the impurities were collected. Certainly there seems to be some progression in the amount of impurities from north to south and a resultant drop in refractoriness.

It will be understood that it is impossible to give an accurate chemical formula for fireclay. In calculations one should correctly work from an analysis. However for the small amounts which may be contained in a glaze, and for quick calculations, the formula $Al_2O_3.4SiO_2.2H_2O$ will be found reasonable. The aluminous fireclays of Scotland approximate the formula for china clay: $Al_2O_3.2SiO_2.2H_2O$. With increasing free silica and proportionate decrease of aluminium oxide in the more southerly ones, an acceptable formula for south Wales fireclay is $Al_2O_3.5SiO_2.2H_2O$.

Firing

The process of conversion from clay to pot. It involves heat of at least 600°C (1112°F). Clay disintegrates in water but is changed by firing into a stone-like material, unaffected by water, and in some cases impervious to water. The change is called the ceramic change. Other changes occur during the firing, e.g. organic matter is burned away, the colour changes, a layer of glass is fused onto the surface.

The decorative effects which are used in pottery often require separate firings. The first firing converts the clay to pot. It is called the biscuit firing. Subsequent firings involve colour, perhaps underglaze colour, glaze, onglaze colour, lustre and are named after these purposes. They will vary in temperature, speed of temperature rise and fall, and in atmosphere (oxidation and reduction). However, it is often possible to achieve a number of results from one firing. It is only the sophistication of potting methods, occurring in the last 300 years, that has resulted in the general practice of separate firings for biscuit, glaze and colours. Prior to this, the general practice was a single firing, although the use of subsequent firings for different effects was known to early potters around the Mediterranean. See **Biscuit, Through firing, Onglaze, Lustre, Oxidation** and **Reduction**.

The stages of a biscuit firing are:
Water smoking
Decomposition of vegetable matter
Ceramic change
Burning out or oxidation of carbon and sulfur
Progressive vitrification

This achieves a strong and porous material: strong so that it may be handled, and porous so that it may be glazed. A summarized description is given in the next section and references made to other articles.

The stages of a glaze firing are:
Drying out
Start of glaze fusion
Continuation of vitrification of body
Integration of body and glaze
Completion of glaze fusion

The cooling which follows involves the growth of crystals within the body-glaze layer, in the glassy parts of the body and possibly in the glaze. The individual actions of the different glaze constituents are given under these materials. A summarized general description is given in the section following the summary of the biscuit firing.

BISCUIT FIRING. The progression is described under headings taken from the accompanying chart (fig. 1). The sectional diagrams here, showing clay particles, overlap with, and are a continuation of, those used in the article on **Drying**.

Water smoking. The remainder of the pore water, which has been unable to dry out because of atmospheric humidity and pressure, is now driven out by heat. The action takes place between room temperature (20°C or 68°F) (fig. 2) and boiling point of water (100°C or 212°F). It is usually considered to be completed by 120°C (248°F) (fig. 3). This period of a firing must be taken cautiously. Two hours is usual for general ware up to 2 cm in thickness. Thicker ware will require proportionately longer. Too rapid a rise in temperature will cause steam pressure to build up and possibly shatter the clay. The water-smoking period is over when the kiln vents are dry. During water smoking there will be water vapour escaping from the chamber. This can be seen or, if not visible, can be detected by condensation onto

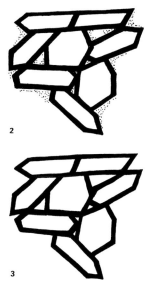

a cold glazed surface held near the vent. This test is effective with electric and wood-fired kilns but, with kilns fired by natural and liquid petroleum gas, the test needs interpretation because these gases produce water as they burn. See **Water smoking, Drying** and **Water**.

Decomposition. Many clays contain vegetable matter which breaks down at approximately 200°C (392°F). This is the same action as the compost heap and with surface clays the effects can very occasionally be detected by smell. This is not a burning process. The burning out of carbon comes later. This part of the firing can be taken quickly because there are no changes to cause trouble.

Even the presence of cristobalite makes no difference at this dry clay stage although the cristobalite dunting point is passed. There is a very slight expansion of the ware over this period. It rarely amounts to more than 1% linear and, since the kiln props and shelves have similar expansion, it is unlikely to cause trouble. However, large pots set close to the kiln arch have been known to break their rims against the roof. In such cases the kiln structure is probably expanding inwards to meet the pots and it is advisable to leave about 2 cm clearance between pot and kiln arch.

Ceramic change. The bound water which is part of the crystal structure of clay is driven off at this stage (fig. 4). The result is a change, from clay to pottery body, known as the ceramic change. This action begins very gently between 350°C and 450°C (662°F and 842°F) and increases to a maximum at 600°C (1112°F), after which the action quickly fades away before 700°C (1292°F). There is little danger from the escaping steam and the firing can be taken quickly. Water vapour will be seen escaping from kiln vents which have been dry during the decomposition stage.

Dunting point (573°C, 1063°F) is passed during this period, but the open texture of the body enables adjustments of size to be made without rupture.

Theoretically, the now thoroughly dried particles are only just touching, as shown in fig. 4. However, the body retains its form and does not collapse as a pile of dust, because the particles are fastened to each other by a process called sintering. This is not fusion in the vitrification sense but a welding of similar particles at points of extremely small contact as shown in fig. 5. It is as if a vibration at these points creates an incandescence of sufficient heat to fuse the tips together.

The strength created by sintering is sufficient to hold a pot in one piece while allowing adjustments of size caused by the silica inversion. Dunting is therefore very unlikely to happen. However, there is insufficient strength to allow a pot to be held for glazing and so it is necessary to take the firing to a higher temperature. A partial vitrification is necessary to give a satisfactory biscuit ware and it is also necessary to burn out the carbon and some of the sulfur content from the body.

There is a very slight shrinkage over the period of ceramic change.

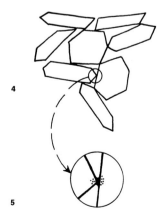

Burning out. Carbon and sulfur are present in clays and remain to be burnt out by the process sometimes called oxidation. They combine with oxygen to form monoxide, dioxide and trioxide gases (CO, CO_2, SO, SO_2, SO_3). This process requires at least the dull red heat of 700°C (1292°F) and reaches its climax around 800°C (1472°F). Most of the carbon has been burnt out by 900°C (1652°F) but some sulfur lingers until 1100°C or 1150°C (2012°F or 2102°F).

It is essential that this process is thoroughly completed. With thick pieces of work this may take a number of hours. Some potters slow down the rate of firing or try to hold the temperature steady at 800°C (1472°F) for a couple of hours. With normal potting clays made into tableware, the thickness is not great and the usual hour taken from 750°C to 850°C (1382°F to 1562°F) is satisfactory. Surface clays and present day estuarine muds require more care because they contain a lot of carbon and sulfur respectively.

These volatiles cause trouble at a later stage if they are not removed from the body. The vitrification of the body begins at 800°C (1472°F) and, from this point, the body progressively loses its pervious nature. A body will bloat if the outer part becomes impervious by the action of heat while there is gas attempting to escape from the inner part. The impervious outer part is soft and glassy by vitrification. Bloating usually occurs at the upper temperatures of a stoneware firing and is often a sign of overfiring of the body. However, the causes of premature bloating lie with a hurried burning-out period in the biscuit firing. At biscuit stage the fault is not visible on the outside of the body, but, in broken section, a black core will be found. See **Black core, Breakdown** and **Bloating**.

Clearly, different clays require different treatments because the amounts of carbon and sulfur vary from clay to clay. The coarser clays, like fireclays and brick shales, often contain a lot of carbon which takes a few hours to burn out in spite of the open texture of these bodies.

A problem arises in the through firing of these clays, that is, when firing these clays with glazes in one firing. The glaze must not melt before the burning out is completed or else the outer pores of the body will be sealed. Some fine slips can cause trouble in this way and it is noticeable that on much of the traditional slipware, which was once-fired with soft lead glazes, the pieces are slipped and glazed on one side only. Plates and dishes were glazed top side only, and jugs etc were glazed inside and just over the rim. Potters with less troublesome clays were able to decorate and glaze all over but this achievement was limited to a few localities.

During the burning-out period there will be no change in body size. Any slight expansion is countered by the sintering and incipient vitrification.

Vitrification. This begins at 800°C (1472°F) when the sodium and potassium oxides within the body start to flux the free silica. Vitrification progresses throughout the firing, filling the pores between the alumino-silicate (original clay) particles and eventually involving these also. The body shrinks during vitrification. See figs. 6, 7 and 8 which show the effects of vitrification but do not show the original fluxes and free silica. For simplicity these have been omitted from all the diagrams overleaf.

Vitrification strengthens the final product by welding the particles together with glass. If the firing were to continue, then the vitrification would be completed to the point where the whole body melted to a glass.

Above 1000°C (1832°F), the fused alumino-silicate is able to form mullite. Mullite crystals are long needles which considerably strengthen the final body. See **Mullite**.

The temperature chosen for a biscuit firing depends upon the balance required of the properties of strength and porosity. See **Biscuit**. Strength is also required to withstand the shock of the silica inversion during cooling. See **Dunting: biscuit dunts**.

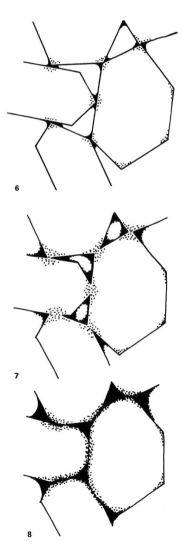

6

7

8

Cooling. During cooling, the biscuit contracts at a regular rate except for the sudden contractions occasioned by the quartz and cristobalite inversions. The glassy parts of the body set solid, possibly with crystals, binding the whole into a strong unit.

GLAZE FIRING. There are two types of glaze firing: the one in which glaze and body mature together; and the one in which the body is already matured and only the glaze is affected. Both types have advantages and disadvantages.

An example of the first type is porcelain. With porcelain, the body matures and becomes translucent during the glaze firing. At the same time the glaze matures and together body and glaze create a thick body-glaze layer which is often thicker, in section, than the pure glaze layer.

An example of the second type is raku. Here the body is already fired to a temperature equal to or higher than the glaze firing. It is therefore unaffected by the heat of the glaze firing but the glaze changes completely. There are obvious advantages in this. The biscuited ware can be inspected with the knowledge that it will retain its biscuit properties of soundness and shape through the glaze firing. Delicate ware is easier to handle. With the English industrial earthenware method, the differences in temperature between biscuit and glaze are marked. The biscuit temperature may be in excess of 1250°C and the glaze below 1080°C (2282°F and 1976°F respectively). The terms bisc and glost are used for these firings to indicate this temperature difference. See **Bisc** and **Glost firing**.

The disadvantage of a glost firing is that there is little body-glaze layer established. Glaze fit must therefore be accurate. Without it, the glaze readily crazes or flakes.

Returning to the first type, in which body and glaze mature together, one can see that the advantage is in the establishment of a sound body-glaze layer. The integrated ware has a soundness which can be related in terms of strength in comparison with unglazed ware. For example, a piece of glazed porcelain can be twice as strong as its unglazed counterpart. The strength lies in the integrated bonding of body and glaze with the slight compression of the glaze by the body. Integration also gives integrated colour, a fact made full use of in reduced stoneware. Earthenware, although not reaching the vitrified state of stoneware, can still make use of this integration if the biscuit firing is around 950°C (1742°F) and the glaze firing around 1100°C (2012°F).

The disadvantage of this combined maturation is that the body or glaze might be affected adversely. Fluid glazes are absorbed by porous bodies and can cause over-fluxing which results in warping, bloating and deformation, although the glaze effects themselves are interesting. Stiff glazes, like lime and dolomite matts, do not integrate well on some buff bodies. The body inhibits the glaze's fusion unless reduction can be used to create fusion with iron oxide at the body-glaze interface. Body and glaze must be matched to achieve maximum benefit from the body-glaze integration.

The combined maturation can occur in a glaze firing which follows a soft biscuit or in the firing of a glaze applied to raw ware. See **Raw glazing**. In the following description, it is assumed that there has been a biscuit firing to 1000°C (1832°F). The glaze firing is a stoneware glaze firing to 1300°C (2372°F). The stages are described under headings taken from the accompanying chart.

Drying. The first 100°C (180°F) of the firing, from room temperature to beyond the boiling point of water, is a drying period. Most glazes are applied as suspensions in water and this water must be driven out of the absorbent biscuit. It must be done slowly. Many potters do it prior to kiln packing by a system of open, slatted shelves and a moving current of warm, dry air. There is an advantage in this when one has to fire the glaze within a tight schedule but a slow warm-up to the glaze firing is acceptable. Too rapid a warm-up will not burst the pots as with raw ware, but it will loosen the glaze from the biscuit. Loose glaze either falls off or crawls when it starts to fuse. The defect is known as wet ware.

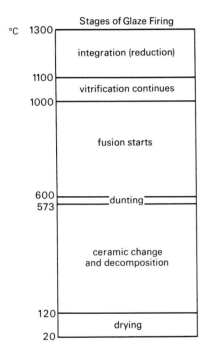

Stages of Glaze Firing

°C 1300

integration (reduction)

1100

vitrification continues

1000

fusion starts

600
573

dunting

ceramic change
and decomposition

120

drying

20

Ceramic change and decomposition. A final glaze requires a number of oxides but these oxides do not necessarily appear in the glaze recipe. The recipe includes raw minerals and prepared materials which are also carbonates, sulfates and clays. This use may be for a special effect, ease of handling before firing or for economic and supply reasons. The firing converts these minerals to oxides. Clay is converted to alumino-silicate by the ceramic change between 350°C and 700°C (662°F and 1292°F). Carbonates and hydrates decompose at various temperatures up to 900°C (1652°F). Each compound has its own decomposition temperature. Sulfates often require the presence of other minerals to assist their decomposition. See **Ceramic change** and the individual mineral concerned. Resist waxes burn out between 200°C and 300°C (392°F and 572°F).

Dunting. The biscuited body is subjected to a sudden expansion because of its crystalline silica content. This occurs at 573°C (1063°F). A temperature rise which is too rapid could create a large temperature difference across a

pot causing a stress which results in a crack. See **Dunting: firing dunts.**

Fusion starts. Some fusion starts at 600°C (1112°F) with sodium and potassium oxides. Also the earthenware glaze fluxes, lead oxide and boron oxide, start their work here. By 1000°C (1832°F) most earthenware glazes are semi-molten but stoneware glazes, although bonded like a biscuited body, are rarely as vitrified as the body at this point.

Vitrification continues. Up to the biscuit temperature, the body is unchanged. But from that temperature upwards, the arrested vitrification continues. It is here that the body fusion actually assists the slow fusion of the glaze. But while the body makes a slow but steady maturation towards the final temperature, the glaze makes an increasingly rapid one. The glaze fluxes start their action at different temperatures and therefore, as the temperature rises, more fluxes become involved in active fusion. The oxides of calcium, magnesium and zinc are notable examples. See **Fluxing action** and **Viscosity of molten glazes.**

Integration. During the later stages of firing, the body and glaze flux each other to produce a body-glaze layer. This is the period of the active glaze fluxes. It is the period over which the glaze truly melts to a glass. Previously the body has been susceptible to reduction. Now the glaze too is affected by reduction. The use of reduction to assist creation of the body-glaze layer in stoneware and porcelain is most effective as the glaze starts its fusion. Once the glaze has fused, the effects of reduction are limited to the surface.

Part of the body-glaze layer begins to crystallize as it forms, encouraged by the formation of mullite. Some glaze crystals, notably wollastonite, also begin to devitrify from the melt during this period.

Cooling. At the top temperature of the firing, there are a number of crystals growing or establishing nuclei for later growth. Upon cooling, growing crystals establish a firm bond between body and glaze, and in some glazes create a crystalline opacity or matt surface for the glaze. Cooling is part of the firing 'cycle' and its rate affects glaze shine, colour and mattness by allowing or hindering reoxidation and the formation of crystals.

Even the relatively refractory stoneware glazes do not set solid until about 500°C (932°F). Crystals are able to grow during cooling down to about 700°C (1292°F), after which, the glaze slowly sets, becoming stiffer and stiffer. The final colour is not reached until below 150°C (302°F).

During cooling from 1300°C (2372°F) to room temperature, a body and a glaze contract about 3% volumetrically. If a glaze contracts more than the body, it is put under tension and might break to accommodate the stress. This is called crazing. If a glaze contracts less than the body, shivering might result. See **Glaze fit.**

Two temperatures at which trouble can occur are the dunting points of 573°C and 226°C (1063°F and 439°F).

Here, the free crystalline silica in the body is subjected to a sudden decrease in size. Wide bowls and thin pots on thick shelves are prone to cracking if the temperature-fall rate is too rapid. The 226°C (439°F) decrease in size is unusual in stoneware but often present in earthenware where it helps to compress the glaze and prevent later crazing. See *Cristobalite* and *Glaze fit*.

Firing cycle
The time and actions of firing and cooling pottery. The term is used in relation to graphs or other information about the rate of temperature rise and fall. The word cycle implies that it is repeated but it is really only a part of the larger kiln cycle which also includes packing, drawing, cleaning up and sorting the ware.

First red
Description of the incandescent glow of the pots in a kiln. The temperature is about 600°C (1112°F) and is an indication that dunting point 573°C (1063°F) has been passed and that the ceramic change is almost complete. Where open flames are concerned or electric elements may be glowing, the first red is about 500°C (932°F).

Fishout
Draw-out test. Trial. Draw ring. Any object taken out of the kiln during firing to determine what is happening within. Buller's rings are fishouts. Loops of clay are often used and glazed appropriately. These are easily withdrawn by a hooked rod. The effects of glaze fusion and reduction can thus be considered during firing and appropriate action taken. They are particularly useful in determining the glaze layer in salt glazing. Note that there is a danger in using a metal rod for fishouts from an electric kiln.

Fit
See *Glaze fit*.

Flaking
See *Shelling*.

Flambé
Rouge flambé. Iridescent red glaze produced by trans-mutation of colloidal copper into a relatively transparent glaze.

Flameproof ware
Fireproof ware. Ware capable of withstanding the extreme thermal shock of direct flame contact. Ovenware withstands a temperature of about 300°C (572°F) all over. To be flameproof a pot must withstand 500°C or 600°C (1112°F) in direct contact at one point only. Another part of the pot may be quite cool. Extremes of heat expansion must take place and very few bodies are capable of absorbing the difference.

Primitive cooking pots are sometimes flameproof. The globular form of these pots is strong and resilient to thermal shock. The extra flameproof quality can be attributed to careful selection of materials, empirically discovered, which contain a high proportion of micaceous sand. Also, an extremely low firing was used which achieved the ceramic change but did not flux any free silica to form a glassy matrix. The body particles are held together by sintering of the particles which leaves the mass extremely elastic. In addition, porous pots are often soaked in oil. The oil assists the heat transference by filling the pores which are otherwise an insulation.

Some high-fired porcelains are also flameproof. They have achieved a state where they contain negligible crystalline silica. Free silica has been fused and so rendered of low expansion rate. See *Table 26*. These porcelains are almost glasses but do not contain any of the oxides of high expansion rate which have low resistance to thermal shock. They are fired at over 1400°C (2552°F) which is necessary to vitrify the extremely pure form of china clay which is used.

Some medieval cooking pots were used on the fire but it is unlikely that they withstood the flames or direct contact with the hottest parts of the fire. For cooking there is sufficient heat if the pot is near to the fire or amongst the hot ashes. Today it is occasionally possible to make a soft-fired redware which is capable of withstanding a gentle flame.

Since the making of the first cordierite body by Felix Singer in 1926, many ceramicists have tried to produce a commercial cordierite body. Cordierite is a magnesium alumino-silicate of low expansion and cordierite bodies withstand flames. The difficulty lies in producing a sufficiently plastic body which is free from catalysts that upset the equilibrium of the cordierite. There are also lithium-based bodies which have extremely low expansions. These are very difficult to match with a suitable glaze.

Flashing
The interesting or annoying colouration and fusion which occurs when volatiles settle on pots and produce unexpected ceramic combinations during the firing. Firing by wood produces fine ash which settles on pots and gives flashing. The reducing action of a flame can also increase the fusion of a pot on one side giving a scorched appearance. Salt-glazing is deliberate flashing. The term flashing is sometimes used to describe the process of alternate short periods of reduction and oxidation, one result of which is the movement of colour from the area where it was applied to surrounding areas of a glaze surface.

The volatiles involved are sodium, lead and boron oxides and to a lesser extent barium, zinc and potassium oxides. These oxides produce shiny glaze surfaces by fluxing un-glazed parts. The effect is often an attractive toasted colour.

Some colouring oxides are also prone to volatilization which thereby distributes colour to other glazes in the same kiln. Small amounts can give surprising results on what was intended to be a pure white ware. The oxides concerned are chromium oxide, copper oxide, cobalt oxide and manganese oxide.

Deliberate colour flashing is sometimes done by placing pots in a saggar. The required volatiles are painted onto the inside walls of the saggar and a lid used to almost seal the atmosphere inside. Alternatively, calcium chloride or common salt (sodium chloride) is placed in a dish with the pots in a completely sealed saggar. The chlorine gas combines with the colouring oxides which have been painted onto the ware. These become volatile chlorides for a brief spell and cause a flashing of the colour around the original decoration. This effect is also termed flowing and is to be seen around painted decorations on salt-glazed ware.

The bowl is by Oldrich Asenbryl.

Flashing is also the name given to discoloration patches which occur on slip-cast ware. See ***Casting slip: adjustment of*** and ***Colour plate 15***.

Flint

SiO_2. Cryptocrystalline native silica. Flint is almost pure silica containing less than 5% impurity in the form of calcium carbonate. It is prepared by washing, calcining and grinding. The calcination turns the flint from its native dark colour to white. Thus flint is purchased as a white powder for introduction into bodies and glazes. In bodies it gives a whiteness, hardness, and a resistance to crazing. In glazes it provides extra silica when needed and is often used to balance the silica amount when adjustments are made for purposes of glaze fit. See also ***Silica***.

Thomas Astbury was the first potter to add flint to his clay to produce a white body. This was in the early 18th century. By the end of the century the addition of some flint was standard practice and flint was also used in glazes. Flint's properties as an anti-craze, when added to both body and glaze, had also been discovered.

Flint occurs as hard nodules in chalk and as chert nodules in limestone. It varies in colour from light to dark brown and black. Its exceedingly fine crystalline grain gives it a glassy character so that it fractures conchoidally. It is related to the semi-precious chalcedonies. See ***Quartz***.

The structure of native flint involves 3% or 4% of water and 3% or 4% of calcium carbonate. The water is locked within the cavities of the irregularly joined micro-crystals. It is likely that some water is involved in the structure as hydroxyl groups and its presence prevents the full crystallization of the silica when it dissolves from its original place in the carcases of diatoms and siliceous sponges and is redeposited in the chalk cavities.

Raw flint is hard and therefore difficult to grind. However calcination renders the flint crumbly and brittle. The water within the flint is removed by calcination at around red heat and sometimes the hot flints are dropped into water to shatter them into smaller pieces preparatory to grinding them in a ball mill. Calcination breaks the existing weak bonds between the micro-crystals enabling grinding to break down the flint into an exceedingly fine powder. The photograph shows a raw and a calcined flint pebble.

Grinding was originally done in open stone mills, sometimes dry. The flint dust was a severe silicosis hazard. Grinding is now undertaken in closed ball mills and the powder is always kept wet. Flint is sold with sufficient water, often 5% to 10%, to prevent its dispersal as dust. Flint powder should preferably be stored wet and allowance made for its moisture content if it is measured by weight. It is the invisible fine particles which cause pneumoconiosis. See ***Silicosis***.

Flint is introduced into bodies to provide a non-plastic and refractory addition; to give whiteness; and to produce anti-craze properties produced by the cristobalite squeeze. See ***Cristobalite***. For earthenware bodies, it is preferred to quartz or sand as the silica addition because it more readily converts to cristobalite during the firing. It does so because of its cryptocrystalline nature and intimate involvement with the catalyst calcia. See ***Silica conversion***. Earthenware bodies can contain up to 50% of flint.

Flint is not used for stoneware because of conversion. For stoneware the coarser grained sand and quartz are used.

Flint is almost interchangeable with quartz in glaze recipes. It is often a matter of personal choice. Theoretically, flint should melt more readily because of its calcium oxide content. However it does not always appear to do so, probably because other factors are involved owing to the presence of the other glaze constituents. The two types of silica, flint and quartz, are sometimes used to deliberately introduce two types of silica nuclei for jun and other crystalline effects. Alternatively a mixture of flint and quartz is often found to provide extra fusion in a glaze when substituted for the single type.

Flocculation

The action of altering the physical properties of fine particles in a suspension so that they no longer repel one another but aggregate into larger particles, called flocs, and settle by gravity. The action is most noticeable with the colloidal particles of clay but other minerals are subject to the effect if the particles are sufficiently fine. Flocculation also improves the strength of clay in storage.

Flocculation is used by the potter:

1. to settle fine suspensions;
2. to make a suspension more permeable so that it dries quickly;
3. to thicken slips for use on clay, and glazes for use on hard biscuit;
4. to thicken glaze slops in a way that keeps the coarser minerals in suspension;
5. to develop strength in stored clay.

All particles, whether fine or coarse, have mutual attraction. See ***Forces of attraction***. The attractive pull increases as the distance between two particles decreases. Exceedingly fine particles in suspension are pulled together and held together by these forces. The flocs thus formed settle under gravity. The deliberate acceleration of this process is called flocculation.

Acting against this tendency to flocculate are the electrostatic charges of the particles. If these are stronger than the forces of attraction, the particles will repel one another. It is then possible for extremely fine particles to overcome the downward pull of gravity completely and suspensions like this will never settle. These are called colloidal suspensions. The deliberate establishment of this state is called deflocculation.

Flocculation is achieved by reducing the overall electrostatic charge of the particles so that the mutual forces of attraction can take over from the forces of repulsion. When the overriding repulsive charge is reduced it is found that extremely fine particles, e.g. those of colloidal size, often exhibit polarity like magnets. They therefore attract one another in a distinct pattern which completes the magnetic field. The most important example of this is the clay particle which is a flat hexagonal crystal. The edges of the crystal have a dominant positive charge and the faces have a dominant negative charge. Clay flocs therefore follow a magnetic pattern which will appear as in fig. 1 if seen edgewise. The structure is known as 'card-house structure'.

For greater scientific detail relating to flocculation see ***Flocculant, Viscosity, Fluidity, Forces of attraction, Double layer theory*** and ***Zeta potential***.

The general details of the potter's use of flocculation are as follows:

1. Colour pigments are often ground in excess water with the intention of settling the slop to a usable paste. If the suspension will not settle, the use of a flocculant may be necessary. Dilute hydrochloric acid is often used but vinegar or calcium chloride work equally well in most cases.

2. Clay suspensions which are slow to settle often produce slippery, dense sediments. The clay particles are tightly packed together in what is called a 'card-stack structure'. Here the plates lie flat upon one another. As the water dries from this structure on the outside of the clay it pulls the plates together thus presenting an impermeable layer through which the remaining water cannot pass. See fig. 2. This occurs against porous surfaces like drying troughs; against pervious surfaces like filter cloths used in filter-pressing; against clay in slip coating; against biscuit in glazing; and against the air in normal drying of slip and glaze coatings. See ***Dewatering***.

The problem presented by this is one of slips and glazes that will not dry on pots and of slurry that cannot be dried to plastic clay. The solution is flocculation by a small amount of vinegar or calcium chloride.

The flocculant encourages polarity in the particles which, as previously explained, are platelike with negative charges on the faces and positive charges on the edges. The structure produced is therefore one of 'card-house' as opposed to 'card-stack'. See figs. 1 and 3. Card-house structure is full of pores through which water can pass.

3. Clay slips and glaze slops are sometimes too fluid to give a coating of sufficient thickness. If the suspension contains a high proportion of clay, as occurs with a slip and a slip-glaze, the trouble often arises from soluble salts in the water. These may be in the water supply as water softeners or, in the case of the glaze, may have dissolved out of a wood ash or other glaze material. The net result is deflocculation and the solution to the problem is flocculation with vinegar or calcium chloride.

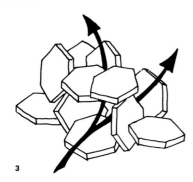

In the case of a glaze, the problem may be one of over-fired biscuit which cannot absorb sufficient water. Flocculation will provide a more viscous and bulkier slop which will give a thicker layer. Magnesium sulfate (epsom salt) and calcium sulfate (plaster of Paris) give satisfactory results with glazes containing some colloidal clay, e.g. ball clay and bentonite. See **Magnesium sulfate**. Glazes which contain very small amounts of colloidal clay, e.g. fritted glazes containing china clay but no ball clay or bentonite, do not respond so well. They can sometimes be temporarily flocculated by the use of gelatine and polymer adhesives. Gelatine should be dissolved in hot water and added until the desired viscosity is reached. The effect will last a few hours. With polymer adhesives, the effect lasts a few days. Over-doping with these organic acids, especially gelatine, may lead to problems of glaze creep in the warming-up stage of the firing.

4. Glazes which contain a high proportion of non-clay materials, like frits and flint, have a tendency to settle rapidly. If the water contains soluble salts there is also the added nuisance of the sediment's setting to a hard layer in the bottom of the tub. To keep the glaze in suspension, a clay is often included in the recipe. Approximately 10% of china clay is popular. A ball clay works even better but may discolour the glaze. A small amount of bentonite, even 1%, gives noticeable results. This clay content is flocculated to make its power more effective.

It may seem strange that clay which will not settle is flocculated to make it do so and yet to keep a glaze in suspension, the clay content is also flocculated. The difference is one of clay amount. Within the glaze slop there

needs to be sufficient flocculated clay structure to hold the heavier particles. The open structure around the particles creates flocs which are of lower density than the particles alone. The flocs of clay and other materials therefore sediment more slowly than the other materials would do without the clay's help. Flocculation does not prevent sedimentation but it slows it down.

The flocculated clay in the glaze increases its bulk in an open card-house structure. Bentonites swell to twenty or thirty times their dry volume and produce a viscous jelly-like structure which is highly effective in the holding of non-clay particles and the slowing down of their sedimentation. Bentonites are usually flocculated with calcium chloride. One per cent of bentonite in a glaze recipe is sufficient to keep the remainder in suspension during glazing operations.

5. Souring clay involves amino acids which improve the thixotropy and strength of clays. The development of the desired acid environment for the clay particles can be encouraged by the addition of an organic flocculant. See **Plasticity**, **Ageing** and **Sour**.

FLOCCULANT. Flocculent. A soluble material which is added to a suspension to increase the viscosity. Flocculants are usually considered as acids.

Increasing amounts of flocculant have progressively more flocculatory effect but an optimum point is reached after which further increases have no effect. There is no reverse effect as there is with the use of deflocculants. The amount of flocculant required is small. The optimum effect is usually achieved by amounts of flocculant in the region of 1% of the amount of colloidal matter involved. In practical terms this means that an eggcupful of concentrated calcium chloride solution is sufficient to flocculate about 20 litres of glaze slop containing about 150 gm of bentonite.

Flocculants are acids or salts which act as acids. They release free, positively-charged ions (cations) into the suspension water. These cations do two things: first they neutralize free anions in the water. These anions are negatively-charged ions which have encouraged cations of large repulsion to exist around the colloidal particles. Second, those not involved in the neutralization replace the cations of large repulsion. The substituting cations have a lower repulsive charge. The replaced cations take up the radical of the flocculant to become new compounds either in solution or in precipitated form.

For example, a deflocculated clay of strong electrostatic charge (Na_2 clay) is suspended in water which is alkaline. The water is alkaline in character because it contains free hydroxyl anions (OH). They are free because they are not combined with cations but serve to create a negative force which balances some of the sodium cations on the clay. To this suspension is added hydrochloric acid (HCl) as a flocculant.

$$Na_2(clay) + OH^- + HCl \rightarrow$$

The hydrochloric acid dissociates in the water to become hydrogen cations and chlorine anions.

$$Na_2(clay) + OH^- + H^+ + Cl^- \rightarrow$$

The hydrogen cation combines with the hydroxyl anion to form water (H_2O). This decreases the pressure on the clay to maintain all its original sodium cations. Some therefore are able to combine with the chlorine anions to form sodium chloride (NaCl).

$$Na_2(clay) + H_2O + NaCl$$

The sodium chloride solution is weak and can do nothing to effect any reversal of the equation. The clay particle is left with a much weaker charge and the suspension is less deflocculated.

A second example shows the action of the flocculant calcium chloride ($CaCl_2$). This effects a cation exchange with the clay to give a clay with calcium cations and sodium chloride in solution.

$$Na_2(clay) + CaCl_2 \rightleftharpoons Ca(clay) + 2NaCl$$

This is a reversible equation but it is weighted in the direction left to right because calcium is of higher valency than sodium. To reverse the equation would require a far higher concentration of sodium chloride than occurs here.

Flocculants are acids or salts which act as acids. The following are flocculants:

Inorganic acids:
hydrochloric acid (HCl)

Salts of divalent cations:
calcium chloride ($CaCl_2$)
calcium hydroxide ($Ca(OH)_2$)
calcium sulfate ($CaSO_4$)
magnesium sulfate ($MgSO_4.7H_2O$)
magnesium chloride ($MgCl_2.6H_2O$)

Organic and amino-acids:
vinegar
gelatine
polymer adhesives

Vinegar is an effective flocculant but its effect is not permanent. The treated suspension will slowly return to its original fluidity over a couple of weeks. Gelatine and polymer adhesives create structures through a glaze slop that encourages the clay particles to adopt similar structures. They act as fillers rather than flocculants. Again the effect does not last. The gelatine structure breaks down in a few hours. The polymer adhesives last a few days. Gelatine and the adhesives also give a binding effect which is useful with friable glazes. Calcium chloride is not effective in glazes containing bone ash.

Flotation

Separation by density. A process whereby two materials, one heavier and one lighter than water, can be separated from a mixture. The mixture of the materials is put into water and stirred. The heavier material sinks, the lighter material floats. Flotation is used in the separation of wood ash from charcoal. The charcoal floats for a while until waterlogged. Industrially, the process of flotation is used to separate very fine particles from coarse particles. The fine particles are floated away in a foam caused by rapid agitation and assisted by suitable chemicals.

Flow

See *Run*.

Fluidity

The property of a liquid to be able to flow or move freely without the hindrance of friction. The friction involved is between adjacent particles or molecules within the liquid. The term is used to describe slips, e.g. deflocculated casting slips that pour freely; and to describe glazes which melt to very runny glasses. The opposite of fluidity is viscosity.

It is normal technical practice to speak of slips and other suspensions in terms of fluidity but to speak of molten glazes in terms of viscosity. Therefore a stiff slip will be described as of low fluidity but a stiff molten glaze will be described as of high viscosity.

Fluidity is measured first as viscosity. That is, the amount of drag which neighbouring particles or molecules impose on one another. The unit of measurement for viscosity is the poise. Values given for viscosity are then recast as values of fluidity and are measured as rhe.

$$rhe = \frac{1}{poise}$$

A freely-flowing suspension like a glaze slop with a viscosity of 2 poise has a rating of $\frac{1}{2}$ rhe or 0·5 rhe. A stiff slip might reach a rating of 0·002 rhe which is very low fluidity. Water has a fluidity of 100 rhe.

FLUIDITY OF SLIP AND GLAZE SUSPENSION. Plastic clay and wet powdered glaze materials have high viscosities because their particles drag upon one another. Their viscosities will be in the order of a million times that of water. Therefore when water is added it provides a lubricant whereby the particles can more effectively slide past one another. Clay which is soft and easy to push into new forms contains more water than stiff clay. Clay with a large amount of water becomes so soft that it cannot withstand the pull of gravity. At this stage it is a slip. Similarly, glaze slops with large amounts of water are 'thin' and easy to stir. Glaze slops made with only a small amount of water are 'thick' and paste-like.

The technician considers all these stages as different fluidities measured in inverse relation to the friction the parts encounter. Thus, a runny suspension which has little friction is considered to have a high fluidity.

A number of factors are involved which influence the fluidity of suspensions. They are: the particle size and, to a lesser extent, the particle shape; the particle reaction to electrostatic forces; the density; and the fluidity of the dispersion medium. Since the medium is usually water there are negligible differences in the use of different waters at different temperatures. The factor of density is directly acceptable. Suspensions of high density, that is, heavy suspensions, are less fluid than suspensions of low density. Particle size and the electrostatic forces require fuller consideration.

Particle size. Considering particle size first, one realizes that if the friction is proportionate to the surface area of the particles, then the finer particles present greater total friction. If a lump of material is broken into two pieces it presents two new surfaces as well as the previous surface, while the total weight and bulk remain the same. The surface area has been increased by approximately 25%. This increase of surface area continues if the two pieces are further broken and ground to a powder. The eventual surface area is of staggering proportions. A teaspoonful of an ultrafine powder could have a total surface area of twice the area of the pages in this book.

A suspension made from fine materials requires more water to gain the same fluidity as a slop made from coarser materials. This difference is noticeable with different minerals that have been milled to different particle sizes. It is also sometimes noticeable with supposedly similar minerals from different suppliers. It is very noticeable where two clays are involved.

A slip made from ball clay requires almost double the amount of water required to make a slip of similar fluidity from china clay. The ball clay particles average only a fifth of the size of the china clay particles and therefore present a larger total surface area.

Electrostatic forces. Considering electrostatic forces, one is presented with another phenomenon which noticeably influences the fluidity. To understand the phenomenon one must consider the way in which clay particles stack together and relate this to the friction existing between the particles.

The clay particles or crystals are flat hexagonal plates. If these plates lie side by side or on top of one another in a flat way it is possible to fit more in a given volume of water than if the plates are determined to come to rest at angles to each other. These two situations are called 'card-stack structure' and 'card-house structure'. See figs. 1 and 2.

Small particles tend to attract one another and create larger particles. This effect is a drag upon the movement of a suspension. If the clay particles can be persuaded to repel one another instead of attracting one another, then a more fluid suspension can be created.

By combining the effect of low friction (repulsion) with that of card-stacking it is possible to create a slip of large

clay content which is, at the same time, of high fluidity. Such a slip is required for the slip-casting process and is achieved by altering the electrostatic forces. The process is called deflocculation.

By giving strong electrostatic charges to the particles they repel one another and overcome the mutual forces of attraction. These charges are concentrated at the edges of the plate-like particles and the zone of repulsion is, in reality, only small. However the effect of the charges is as if the zone were a protective figure-of-eight in section. This is diagrammatized in fig. 3.

The repulsion zones ensure that the particles cannot come into contact and so there is no friction to hinder fluidity. Even in high concentrations of particles—that is, in a slip containing a large amount of clay and a small amount of water—the particles refuse to meet and continue to repel one another. They position themselves in the most economical use of the volume which is the card-stack structure. A slip in this state is said to be deflocculated.

The reverse of the action just described is a combination of high friction (attraction and physical abrasion) and card-house structure. This gives a viscous slip which has an open pore structure. Such a slip is flocculated.

This state is required when it is necessary to dry off the slip to give a plastic clay. The permeability presented by the pores allows the water to be extracted by absorption on a porous surface or by filter pressing. Also, a flocculated glaze suspension which contains clay will dry more quickly than an unflocculated one. It will give a thicker glaze layer on biscuited pieces of low porosity and also hold in suspension the heavy materials like flint and lead bisilicate which would otherwise settle rapidly. The colloidal clay called bentonite is often used for this latter purpose and is flocculated with calcium chloride.

At colloidal size, the friction between particles is mostly electrostatic attraction of unlike charges. However it also includes Van der Waals' force of attraction of like charges, gravitational attraction and physical abrasion.

To achieve a slip of lower fluidity, therefore, one must reduce the strength of the charges which are repelling the particles. The forces of friction named above can then cause drag between neighbouring particles.

When the strength of the electrostatic charge is reduced it is found that the flat faces of the clay particles have a neutral or slightly negative charge while the edges have a positive charge. The edges are, therefore, attracted to the faces of adjacent particles as shown in fig. 4. With this lower charge at the edges, there is insufficient repulsion to give the effect of fig. 3.

4

The decision to have a large or small charge is influenced by electrolytes. These are soluble materials usually referred to as alkalis and acids, although to avoid confusion they are better described as deflocculants and flocculants. Not all alkalis and acids give satisfactory permanent results. The best deflocculants are sodium carbonate and sodium silicate used in combination. The best flocculants are calcium chloride, hydrochloric acid, vinegar, calcium sulfate and magnesium sulfate. The details of cation exchange whereby the charges are altered are given under the articles on **Deflocculation** and **Flocculation**.

Slips of high colloidal content, e.g. ball clays, react dramatically to electrolytes. If fully deflocculated, a slip can be very fluid and it will feel slippery. It will not settle and cannot be dried to a clay because any drying at the surface, whether against an absorbent solid or into the air, forms a compact impermeable layer through which further water cannot escape.

If the same slip is flocculated, the particles attract one another and form flocs. These in turn become aggregates with sufficient weight to sediment under the pull of gravity, providing there is sufficient water in which to settle. The fully flocculated slip will probably be too viscous to move. It will be like a clay but without strength and jelly-like. It will be highly permeable, dry quickly and give a soft and friable dry material. It is important to realize that the process described here is carried out without altering the weight of clay or the amount of water present. The density therefore remains the same.

By the use of some colloidal clays with electrolytes it is possible to adjust the fluidity of slips and glaze suspensions while keeping control of the overall density.

FLUIDITY OF MOLTEN GLAZES. It is normal practice to speak of molten glazes in terms of viscosity. More details are therefore given under **Viscosity**. However, in trying to understand the phenomenon it is sometimes advantageous to consider it from both points of view. It is here considered as fluidity.

All glaze oxides that increase fusion also increase the fluidity of the molten glaze. Obviously fusion and fluidity are linked. However, some glaze fluxes produce more fluid melts than do others. For example, potassium oxide produces very fluid melts which are distinctly more runny than those produced with the aid of magnesium oxide, even at magnesium oxide's most active fluxing temperature above 1250°C (2282°F).

It is possible to put the glaze oxides in the order of their action upon fluidity. This order is based upon an ideal balance of molecules of these oxides with the glass-forming silica. At 1250°C (2282°F) the oxide producing the most fluid melt is potassium oxide, followed by lithium, boron and sodium oxides. Sodium oxide volatilizes at this temperature and therefore its action is difficult to assess in relation to the molecules involved. The list continues with the oxides of barium, calcium, zinc, strontium, magnesium and lead. Again lead oxide cannot be properly assigned a place because its action at this temperature is not constant. A full chart of these oxides and their effects upon fluidity at different temperatures is given under **Viscosity**.

Fluorspar

Fluorite. Calcium fluoride. Blue John. CaF_2. A compound sometimes used in frit preparation. It is not recommended for direct use in glaze recipes. Its main use is as an opacifier in soft enamels for metals where it can be fully involved in the glass structure. The photograph (overleaf) shows a vein of fluorspar through lead ore.

Fluorspar melts at 1330°C (2426°F) but before this temperature it has active fluxing power and yet gives opacity. The fluorine atoms replace oxygen in the silicate chain causing fluid melts at low temperatures. Inevitably however some fluorspar decomposes with the heat of fusion. The calcium atoms then take up oxygen to become calcium oxide and the fluorine is released as a gas.

$$2CaF_2 + O_2 \rightarrow 2CaO + 2F_2 \uparrow$$

Even when fluorspar is incorporated in a silicate frit, it can still decompose, especially if overfired. The escaping fluorine gas causes blistering. This is not easy to clear since the decomposition is a slow and continuous action and not specific to one temperature. The bubbling can however be deliberately controlled to produce novel cratered effects.

Fluorine gas is a health hazard in the pottery workshop. See **Poison** and **Fumes**. Fluorspar is often present in cornish stones and clays up to perhaps 2% of the whole. It gives the purplish flecks in cornish stone and is here referred to as fluorite. The fluorine gas which is released when these fluorite-containing materials are fired is noticeable in the workshop atmosphere and over a period of years will etch the workshop windows until they are opaque frosted glass. Some cornish stones are marketed as defluorinated (DF). They are cleaner to use and cause less blistering. See also **Cornish stone.**

Flux

An oxide which promotes ceramic fusion by interaction with other oxides. The oxides, which are usually referred to as fluxes, are the alkaline oxides because they interact with the glass-forming silica. Fluxes are monoxides with chemical formulae in the R_2O and RO group. The acceptable exceptions are the sesquioxides: boron oxide and bismuth oxide. Fluxes are introduced as monoxides, dioxides, carbonates and other compounds. Silicates using R_2O and R_2O_3 fluxes soften slowly. Silicates involving RO fluxes tend to soften more quickly. See also **Periodic table**. A full list of fluxes follows:

lithium oxide	Li_2O
sodium oxide	Na_2O
potassium oxide	K_2O
beryllium oxide	BeO
magnesium oxide	MgO
calcium oxide	CaO
zinc oxide	ZnO
strontium oxide	SrO
barium oxide	BaO
lead oxide	PbO
boron oxide	B_2O_3

bismuth oxide	Bi_2O_3
manganese oxide	MnO
iron oxide	FeO
cobalt oxide	CoO
nickel oxide	NiO
copper oxide	CuO
copper oxide	Cu_2O

Fluxing action

Fluxes do not act alike. They have individual characteristics although as fluxes they have properties in common. Some are active at low temperatures and volatilize at higher temperatures. These are the earthenware fluxes like sodium and lead oxides. Others do not start their action until a higher temperature and have no upper limit in their use for pottery. These are the stoneware fluxes like calcium and magnesium oxides. Some act only in the presence of other fluxes by a process of interaction. Details are given under each oxide but, assuming some interaction, a chart of activity can be constructed to compare the different useful ranges. See also **Viscosity of molten glazes** and **Surface tension**.

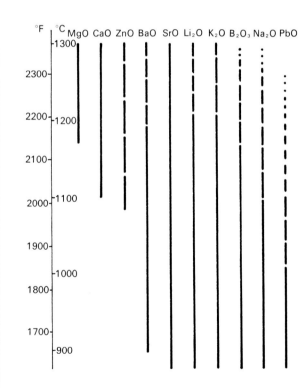

Forces of attraction

Phenomena which cause colloidal clay particles to coagulate. They are referred to collectively in the articles involving fluidity and viscosity as the 'mutual forces of attraction'. They are:

1. The attraction of positive and negative charges which exist as unsatisfied valencies on the broken bonds at the

edges of lattices. Colloidal particles sometimes also exhibit a slight 'apparent polarity' which is sufficient to orientate their positions and increase the attraction.

2. Van der Waals' force of attraction, which is caused by the electron movements within the particles. If the movements have rhythmic sympathy, attraction occurs.

3. Gravitational force of each particle which encourages particles in contact or near contact to stay together rather than drift apart.

The overall result of these forces is that colloidal clay particles in suspension tend to be attractive to one another. They thus form flocs which is the first stage of aggregation, sometimes called coagulation. The next stage is the forming of larger lumps, called aggregates, which are visible to the naked eye. At this stage they come under the pull of gravity and sediment.

The forces of attraction are only small and can be overcome by forces of repulsion. These occur when all the particles possess the same powerful positive charge. Dispersion then takes place instead of coagulation. Suitable electrolytes in the water of suspension will create this condition. See **Double layer theory** and **Zeta potential**.

In consideration of fluidity and viscosity, the friction established between particles in suspension, including those of colloidal size, includes collision of the particles and the consequent loss of energy through abrasion.

Formula

A standardized way of expressing involved principles. The common formulae which the potter will use are here explained under four areas concerned with:

1. converting one measurement into another: conversion formulae;
2. suspensions (slips and glazes): density formulae;
3. chemical symbols: chemical formula;
4. molecules in ceramic fusions: unity formula.

CONVERSION FORMULAE. A simplified framework for calculating a required measurement from known measurements without recourse to the principles involved.

Conversion of dry weights.

To convert from:	into:	multiply by:
ounces	grams	28·35
pounds	kilograms	0·4536
gross cwts (imp)	kilograms	50·803
net cwts (US)	kilograms	45·36
grams	ounces	0·0353
kilograms	pounds	2·2046
kilograms	gross cwts (imp)	0·0196
kilograms	net cwts (US)	0·0221

To convert a batch recipe into a percentage recipe:

$$\% \text{ amount} = \frac{\text{batch item amount} \times 100}{\text{batch recipe total}}$$

For example:

Batch recipe:

	frit	14 kg
	clay	6 kg
batch recipe total		20 kg

$$\% \text{ of frit} = \frac{14 \times 100}{20} = 70$$

$$\% \text{ of clay} = \frac{6 \times 100}{20} = 30$$

Percentage recipe: frit 70
clay 30

See also **Calculations** for conversion of percentage recipe to batch recipe.

Conversion of temperatures.
See also **Celsius, Fahrenheit, Kelvin, Rankine** and **Calculations**.

$$°C = \frac{(°F - 32 \times 5) \times 5}{9}$$

$$°C = °K - 273$$

$$°F = \frac{°C \times 9}{5} + 32$$

$$°F = \frac{9(°K - 273)}{5} + 32$$

$$°K = °C + 273$$

$$°K = \frac{5(°F - 32)}{9} + 273$$

Conversion of capacities.

To convert from:	into:	multiply by:
imp pints	US pints	1.201
imp pints	litres	0·5683
imp fl oz	ml	28·412
US pints	imp pints	0·8327
US pints	litres	0·4732
US fl oz	ml	29·573
litres	imp pints	1·7598
litres	US pints	2·1132

Conversion of densities.

To convert from:	into:	multiply by:
oz pt imp	oz pt US	0·8327
oz pt imp	g/ml	0·0499
oz pt US	oz pt imp	1·201
oz pt US	g/ml	0·0599
g/ml	oz pt imp	20·042
g/ml	oz pt US	16·705

DENSITY FORMULAE. These are many and various but all are concerned with suspensions and solutions and the relationships between their weights and capacities.

Slop weight. In order to record the thickness of a slip or glaze in suspension the potter takes note of the weight of a particular volume.

For example:

> 30 ounces per pint
> 150 grams per 100 ml
> 1·5 grams per ml

Relative density uses these numbers and, by relating the weight of the measured capacity of slip to the weight of the same capacity of water, is expressed as a single number. For example:

$$30 \text{ oz pt imp becomes } \frac{30}{20} = 1 \cdot 5 \text{ r.d.}$$

$$\frac{150 \text{ g slip}}{100 \text{ g water}} = 1 \cdot 5 \text{ r.d.}$$

$$\frac{1 \cdot 5 \text{ g}}{1 \cdot 0 \text{ g}} = 1 \cdot 5 \text{ r.d.}$$

The formulae concerned are:

$$\text{Density} = \frac{\text{Weight}}{\text{Volume}}$$

$$\text{Volume} = \frac{\text{Weight}}{\text{Density}}$$

$$\text{Weight} = \text{Volume} \times \text{Density}$$

Relative density. This is a number which equals grams per cubic centimetre (millilitre). See also the main entry under **Relative density**.

A relative density number can be converted into ounces per imp pint by multiplying by 20, or more precisely by 20·042. For ounces per US pint, by multiplying by 16·705.

The formulae can be stated:

$$\text{r.d} = \frac{\text{oz pt imp}}{20}$$

$$\text{r.d} = \frac{\text{oz pt US}}{16 \cdot 705}$$

$$\text{oz pt imp} = \text{r.d.} \times 20$$
$$\text{oz pt US} = \text{r.d.} \times 16 \cdot 705$$

Twaddell. Most of the potter's suspensions have relative densities between 1·0 and 2·0. This gives a very compressed scale of values which must always be expressed with decimal places. To avoid this, the relative density is converted into degrees Twaddell. This is an expanded scale whereby the relative densities between 1·0 and 2·0 are given values between 0 and 200 thus making comparison easier. See **Twaddell**. The formulae are:

$$^{\circ}\text{TW} = (\text{r.d} - 1) \times 200$$

$$^{\circ}\text{TW} = \left(\frac{\text{oz pt imp}}{20} - 1\right) \times 200$$

$$^{\circ}\text{TW} = \left(\frac{\text{oz pt US}}{16 \cdot 7} - 1\right) \times 200$$

$$\text{r.d.} = \frac{^{\circ}\text{TW}}{200} + 1$$

$$\text{oz pt imp} = \left(\frac{^{\circ}\text{TW}}{200} + 1\right) \times 20$$

$$\text{oz pt US} = \left(\frac{^{\circ}\text{TW}}{200} + 1\right) \times 16 \cdot 7$$

For example: find the degrees Twaddell of a glaze slop weighing 147·5 g per 100 ml.

$$^{\circ}\text{TW} = \left(\frac{147 \cdot 5}{100} - 1\right) \times 200$$

$$= (1 \cdot 475 - 1) \times 200$$

$$= 95 ^{\circ}\text{TW}$$

Brongniart's formula. A formula for discovering the dry weight content of a slip or slop. The formula is expressed:

$$\text{weight of dry content} = \text{apparent dry weight} \times \frac{\text{relative density}}{\text{relative density minus one}}$$

If 100 ml of slip is weighed in grams, the apparent dry weight is this weight less the weight of 100 ml of water. However this is not the true weight of the dry content which is related to the relative density of the dry material in proportion to that of the water with which it is mixed.

For Imperial capacities where one pint of water weighs 20·042 oz, the formula is as follows. It is assumed that one pint of slip has been weighed in ounces and this is called 'oz pt'.

$$\text{dry wt} = (\text{oz pt} - 20) \times \frac{\text{r.d.}}{\text{r.d.} - 1}$$

For US capacities where one pint of water weighs 16·705 oz, the formula is as follows:

$$\text{dry wt} = (\text{oz pt} - 16 \cdot 7) \times \frac{\text{r.d.}}{\text{r.d.} - 1}$$

For example, if one wishes to find the dry weight of materials in 6 litres of stoneware glaze, when 100 ml of glaze weighs 145 g, the calculation will be:

$$(145 - 100) \times \frac{2 \cdot 5}{2 \cdot 5 - 1} = 45 \times \frac{2 \cdot 5}{1 \cdot 5}$$

= 75 g of dry material per 100 ml of glaze slop.

There are 60×100 ml in 6 litres so the 75 g is multiplied by 60 and divided by 1000 to bring it to kilograms.

$$75 \times 60 \div 1000 = 4 \cdot 5 \text{ kg}$$

The amount of water involved is 145 g minus the dry weight of 75 g = 70 ml per 100 ml of slop. The total amount is $70 \times 60 = 4200$ ml = $4 \cdot 2$ litres.

The calculation is based upon the average relative density for stoneware glaze materials which is $2 \cdot 5$. Low sol glazes average about $3 \cdot 0$ and high lead glazes $4 \cdot 0$. Relative densities are listed in **Table 30**. Another example is given under **Calculations** and comparison pint weights for Imperial and US capacities in **Table 19**.

An extension of the relationships between specific gravities of different slips is afforded by the conversion of slips formula. If it is necessary to add water to a thick slip in order to make it more fluid, the ml of water required to be added to each 100 ml of thick slip equals:

$$\frac{\text{existing g/100 ml minus required g/100 ml}}{\text{required g/100 ml minus 100}} \times 100$$

CHEMICAL FORMULA. A method of representing a chemical compound, a molecule or a radical group by the symbols for the elements. See **Chemical symbol**. By a few letters and numbers a chemical formula states the elements involved and the proportionate number of atoms of each element. It is therefore a useful shorthand in scientific information, and in calculations which involve atoms and molecules.

One molecule of the compound called water is made up of two atoms of hydrogen and one atom of oxygen. The chemical formula for water is therefore HHO or HOH or OHH. When more than one atom of an element is involved the convention is to put a figure below and after the symbol for the element to denote the number of atoms. The usual way to write the formula for water is therefore H_2O.

Alphabetical order is used for the symbols but in oxides it is usual to put oxygen last and it is acceptable to put other elements in an order which makes sense as a description. This helps potters.

Formulae are spoken exactly as written. Each letter is pronounced separately. The chemical formula for a molecule of red iron oxide is Fe_2O_3 and this is read as F-E-two-O-three.

When speaking of compounds, a chemical formula represents one molecule of a compound. Thus H_2O stands for one molecule of water and Fe_2O_3 stands for one molecule of red iron oxide. But a formula is also used as a space-saving shorthand in written descriptions and thus H_2O means water, Fe_2O_3 means red iron oxide and MnO_2 is shorthand for manganese oxide.

The figure which appears below and after a symbol indicates the number of atoms of the preceding element only. Two more conventions exist to indicate that groups of elements are present. They are the use of large figures with full stops and the use of brackets.

For example, in lead bisilicate, there are two molecules of silica, SiO_2, to every one of lead oxide, PbO. The formula is therefore expressed as $PbO.2SiO_2$. It would be acceptable to write it as $PbO.Si_2O_4$ or even to total the oxygen atoms and write $PbSi_2O_5$ but neither explains lead bisilicate quite so graphically as $PbO.2SiO_2$. The large figure 2 which appears before the formula for silica refers to the whole molecule of silica, SiO_2, and not just to the first symbol Si. A full stop is included when it is necessary to indicate where the influence of the large figure ends but if this is at the end of the formula it is often omitted.

Examples with large figures are: $Al_2O_3.2SiO_2.2H_2O$ (kaolinite) and $Na_2O.2B_2O_3.10H_2O$ (borax). It will be seen that the figure 1 never appears. The existence of the letter symbol is sufficient to describe the presence of one atom of an element and the letter symbols together describe the presence of one molecule.

Certain groups of elements always appear together but they are not molecules and so cannot be isolated from the rest of the compound by full stops. Nor can they be given a large figure to denote that more than one of the group is present. In such cases brackets are used. For example, copper sulfate is written $CuSO_4$ and the SO_4 group is an important combination, although it is not a molecule that can exist by itself. When this group is combined with trivalent iron in iron sulfate, it becomes necessary to express the conception of two atoms of Fe combined with three groups of SO_4 and this can be done by writing $Fe_2(SO_4)_3$. The brackets enclose the group, in this case the sulfate radical, and the figure 3 below and after the brackets denotes the number of radicals present in the same way that the figure 2 denotes the number of iron atoms present.

Large figures in front of the symbols are reserved for defining a number of molecules. One molecule is separated from another type of molecule in the formula by a full stop. Brackets are used to enclose a radical or other part of a molecule which cannot exist by itself but exists as a convenient expression of a theory.

The chemical formulae as described so far are concerned with the whole numbers of atoms and molecules in strict proportions to one another. All chemical compounds and natural minerals have this property of being combinations of whole atoms and molecules in consistent proportions. It is this fact which enables lattice structures to occur.

When the atoms of two different elements have similar size and valency they sometimes partially replace one another in a mineral. For example, iron can replace calcium in limestone, $CaCO_3$, to produce the mineral siderite, $FeCO_3$. Partial replacements are common and to express this phenomenon the convention of brackets is used around both elements with the elements separated by a comma, e.g. $(Ca,Fe)CO_3$. The comma and brackets therefore mean that both elements are present in an undefined proportion adding up to one atom in relation to the rest of the formula.

A chemical formula which is written on a single line cannot express the three-dimensional lattice structure which is involved in a molecule. For this a structure drawing or a structural formula is used. See **Lattice structure**. However, a specific arrangement of the symbols can often be used to imply attachments which are known to exist. For example, there are certain groups of elements which often come together. These are the radicals previously mentioned and are written after the elements to which they are attached. Three common ones are CO_3 (carbonate), NO_3 (nitrate) and SO_4 (sulfate), which occur in $CaCO_3$ (calcium carbonate), KNO_3 (potassium nitrate) and $BaSO_4$ (barium sulfate).

In a similar way, magnetic iron oxide which has the chemical formula Fe_3O_4 is written as $FeO.Fe_2O_3$ to indicate the theory that one molecule of magnetic iron oxide is a combination of two molecules: FeO and Fe_2O_3. It is true that this division into two oxides, a monoxide and a sesquioxide, makes the whole more easily understood.

Following this practice, it is common amongst potters to divide complex minerals into smaller compounds for convenience. A typical example is that of dolomite which is a single crystal structure created by a double carbonate of calcium and magnesium. The correct chemical formula is $CaMg(CO_3)_2$ which is easier to comprehend if written $CaCO_3.MgCO_3$. Two other examples are kaolinite (pure clay) $Al_2Si_2O_5(OH)_4$ which becomes $Al_2O_3.2SiO_2.2H_2O$ (aluminium oxide, silica and water) and orthoclase (feldspar) $K_2Al_2Si_6O_{16}$ which becomes $K_2O.Al_2O_3.6SiO_2$ (potassium oxide, aluminium oxide and silica).

The expanded formula which the potter uses serves to emphasize the oxides and other compounds involved in bodies and glazes. The scientist's formula is more concise and a more accurate description of the relationships between the atoms present. International recommendations for formulae and names are given in *Nomenclature of Inorganic Chemistry*. See **Bibliography**.

Molecular formula. A chemical formula which describes a molecule. In the description of molecules the two terms, chemical formula and molecular formula, are synonymous. However, chemical formulae have a wider use in the description of radicals and groups of atoms which are not stable molecules.

The term molecular formula has also been used for the ceramicist's method of describing bodies and glazes. This formula is more correctly called the unity formula and is referred to thus throughout this book. While the unity formula describes proportionate amounts of molecules it does not describe a single molecule of a mineral. The term molecular formula should be correctly reserved for chemical formulae which describe molecules involving atoms in whole numbers.

Structural formula. A convenient diagrammatic representation of a molecule using the chemical symbols

joined by the appropriate number of valency bonds. The examples are of aluminium oxide, silica, lead oxide and potassium oxide. See also **Lattice structure, Valency** and **Atom**.

UNITY FORMULA. Seger formula. Empirical formula. Ratio of molecules formula. RO formula. R_2O_3 formula. Also misleadingly referred to as molecular formula. A method of setting out in lists the chemical formulae of a glaze or body's constituent oxides. By this method, the balance of alkaline, amphoteric and acidic oxides is quickly assessed, although the composition may be complex. This assists comparison of one glaze or body with another for the purposes of predicting effects and making adjustments.

Whatever materials are used to produce a body or glaze, the result is a combination of oxides. These oxides can be placed in three groups according to their chemical formulae as monoxides, sesquioxides and dioxides. The unity formula uses this grouping and brings the total of molecules of one group to unity, expressing the other two groups in ratio to it.

The unity formula is usually set out as three columns. These are separated by large brackets or vertical lines to imply that there is no especial relationship horizontally except by a group as a whole. For example:

$$\left.\begin{array}{l} 0{\cdot}5\ CaO \\ 0{\cdot}3\ MgO \\ 0{\cdot}2\ K_2O \\ \hline \text{unity} \end{array}\right\} \begin{array}{l} 0{\cdot}4\ Al_2O_3 \\ 0{\cdot}1\ Fe_2O_3 \end{array} \left\{\begin{array}{l} 2{\cdot}3\ SiO_2 \\ 0{\cdot}2\ TiO_2 \end{array}\right.$$

Alternatively, the oxides are presented as one column divided by horizontal lines:

$$\begin{array}{c} 0{\cdot}5\ CaO \\ 0{\cdot}3\ MgO \\ 0{\cdot}2\ K_2O \\ \hline 0{\cdot}4\ Al_2O_3 \\ 0{\cdot}1\ Fe_2O_3 \\ \hline 2{\cdot}3\ SiO_2 \\ 0{\cdot}2\ TiO_2 \end{array}$$

The unity formula expresses ratios between numbers of molecules. The actual numbers of molecules involved in a glaze are millions of millions. These vast numbers are conveniently scaled down in the unity formula which thereby invariably includes some theoretical decimal fractions of molecules.

The groups are referred to as RO, R_2O_3 and RO_2. R is the symbol which stands for any suitable element capable of fitting the situation. Arising from the actions of the oxides in glazes and bodies, some other names are accorded to the groups in discussion.

RO oxides are monoxides. This group includes R_2O oxides like Na_2O (sodium oxide). This group has many names: the RO group, the monoxides, the fluxes, the bases, the basic oxides, the alkalis and the basic metal oxides.

The second group contains the amphoteric oxides which have both alkaline and acidic properties and are sesqui-oxides. This group has, therefore, the names: the R_2O_3 group, the sesquioxides and the amphoteric oxides.

The third group has the names: the RO_2 group, the dioxides and the acidic oxides.

Two types of unity formulae are used: unity of the monoxide group and unity of the sesquioxide group.

For glazes and frits the monoxide group is brought to unity as in the example above. This formula is therefore called the RO formula. Unity formulae supplied by manufacturers of frits are invariably of the RO type. The RO formula is used in all the examples here.

For bodies, the sesquioxides are unified and the formula is called the R_2O_3 formula. Suppliers of body materials like clay, cornish stone and other feldspathoids issue unity formulae of the R_2O_3 type.

Two glazes may appear to be very different in recipe form but when their unity formulae have been calculated from these recipes it may be found that they are almost identical. It is possible to calculate back to the recipe from the unity formula and, in so doing, one is able to compose the recipe of materials which are available. For example, in the above unity formula the MgO would be obtained more easily and cheaply from dolomite than from magnesium carbonate, and the SiO_2 would probably be supplied in part by feldspar, part clay and part flint. To calculate a unity formula from a recipe and vice versa, see *Calculations*. Alterations to glaze recipes are easier to make at unity formula stage where comparison with other satisfactory glazes can be made on the ratio of the oxide molecules. See *Equivalent*.

Unity formula in use. One unity formula is directly comparable with another unity formula. Once one has established a unity formula for a glaze which behaves well under one's conditions, it is possible to compare other new glazes with it even though the recipe materials are completely different.

For example, supposing the successful glaze has the unity formula:

$$\left.\begin{array}{l} 0\cdot2\ K_2O \\ 0\cdot1\ MgO \\ 0\cdot7\ CaO \\ \hline \text{unity} \end{array}\right\} \ 0\cdot3\ Al_2O_3 \quad 3\cdot6\ SiO_2$$

and a new recipe, provided perhaps by a friend, gives the unity formula:

$$\left.\begin{array}{l} 0\cdot2\ K_2O \\ 0\cdot1\ MgO \\ 0\cdot7\ CaO \\ \hline \text{unity} \end{array}\right\} \ 0\cdot5\ Al_2O_3 \quad 4\cdot5\ SiO_2$$

By a comparison of the two formulae one can see that the new recipe contains a higher proportion of silica (SiO_2) and will therefore be more refractory—that is, it will require more heat to complete its fusion. It also has a higher proportion of aluminium oxide (Al_2O_3) which again is a refractory. In fact, the amount of difference between these two glazes is great. Assuming that the first glaze is fully fused at 1200°C (2192°F), the second glaze will require to be fired in the region of 1280°C (2336°F) to obtain a similar result. The following list relates ratios of fully fused leadless glazes to temperatures. See also *Table 27*.

1000°C° (1832°F) RO: $0\cdot25\ Al_2O_3:2\cdot0\ SiO_2$
1100°C° (2012°F) RO: $0\cdot30\ Al_2O_3:2\cdot5\ SiO_2$
1200°C (2192°F) RO: $0\cdot40\ Al_2O_3:3\cdot5\ SiO_2$
1300°C (2372°F) RO: $0\cdot55\ Al_2O_3:5\cdot0\ SiO_2$

Another important point about the two glazes under consideration is the ratio of Al_2O_3 to SiO_2. In the first glaze the ratio is 1:12 but in the second it is 1:9. Compare these with the typical unity formulae above which gradually raise the ratio from 1:8 at 1000°C to 1:9 at 1300°C.

Clearly the first glaze has a higher ratio than average and it will therefore be a very fluid glaze. The second glaze is clearly more viscous than the first. This property can be expected even when it has been melted at the higher temperature. See *Viscosity of molten glazes*. The most viscous glaze would have a ratio of 1:6. This is the ratio of the alkaline feldspars, e.g. orthoclase is $K_2O.Al_2O_3.6SiO_2$. Note that because the alkali content in the chemical formula is one molecule, the full formula constitutes a unity formula which is comparable with glazes. Orthoclase is fully fused at 1300°C (2372°F) but it provides an extremely viscous glass. In comparison frits have high ratios in the order of 1:12 and higher.

It should be noted that the foregoing is concerned only with the aluminium oxide:silica ratio ($Al_2O_3:SiO_2$). It cannot be broadened to $R_2O_3:RO_2$ because this could include other oxides which do not behave in the same way, most notably boron oxide (B_2O_3).

Boron oxide is a glass-former like silica, yet it is a sesquioxide and by its chemical formula would be listed with aluminium oxide in a unity formula. To make matters even more complicated it acts as a flux. Unity formulae which contain boron oxide can only be partially compared with others which do not.

The understanding of this and a few other phenomena makes the interpretation of unity formulae a personal technique. Exceptions to the usual behaviour pattern occur with the establishment of eutectic mixtures, with the different fluxing actions of different RO oxides, and with the alkali/acid balancing effect of the amphoteric oxides. Each oxide is described separately in this book under its own heading. See also *Periodic table* and *Computer glaze calculations.*

Fosted

Frosted. Underfired in one part only. The fosted area shows as a patch on the side of the pot and often looks lighter than the rest of the pot. It occurs where a slight air intake, through a crack or leaking bung hole, chills the pot and prevents its reaching the desired temperature.

Free silica

Silica existing in a clay or body in a separate crystalline or cryptocrystalline state—that is, neither attached to nor involved in a compound like kaolinite or feldspar. Free silica may exist as a fine quartz sand, coarse sand, flint, cristobalite and tridymite. Free silica influences a body's refractoriness, vitrification range and its susceptibility to dunting.

Freezing point

Solidifying point. The temperature at which a liquid becomes a solid. The freezing point is usually a few degrees below the melting point with crystalline compounds, but with glazes this is not so. Glazes must be considered as supercooled liquids with a softening range. The freezing point will be at the lower limit of the range where the glaze becomes solid. The melting point will be at the top limit of the range. The word freezing is associated with water and ice and therefore the technical term solidifying is perhaps better for glazes.

Frit

Fritt. Part of a glaze recipe that has been melted and reground prior to its inclusion in the glaze slop. For example, in a simple recipe containing litharge, flint and china clay, the litharge and flint could be melted together to form a lead frit. The glaze would chemically remain the same.

First recipe		*Second recipe*	
litharge	50	lead frit	80
flint	30		
china clay	20	china clay	20

The reasons for using the second recipe would be the non-toxicity of the lead content, the absence of silica dust (silicosis hazard) and the probable advantage of a glaze that was easier to fire without blistering.

The purposes of fritting are:

1. To render otherwise soluble minerals insoluble in the glaze slop. For example, the important mineral borax is soluble in water. Soluble minerals cannot be applied to a pot as a homogeneous material. Some will soak into the pot and some will crystallize on the surface. Solubles also upset the fluidity of the glaze slop. See *Alkali.*

2. To render harmless any injurious substance. The main substance is lead but antimony, barium, zinc etc are also poisonous, and silica powders cause silicosis. See *Poison, Lead poisoning* and *Lead frit.*

3. To combine the required minerals and render them less volatile. For example, lead oxide volatilizes less from a molten glaze if it has first been fritted.

4. To give better control over glaze fusion. A frit has a more predictable and uniform rate of fusion than a mixture of minerals. The whole glaze fusion can be accelerated and maturation time decreased. The end result is a shorter glaze firing with less strain on kiln, furniture etc at the top temperature. See also *Grain size.*

5. To prepare the materials which will enter the glaze by ridding them of unwanted volatiles like carbon, sulfur and fluorine. Stiff glazes which are prone to pin-holing can be made smooth by fritting part of the glaze. Special low-temperature coloured glazes and enamel colours need to be free from gases which cause blisters.

6. To prepare special colours in the form of stains, which require controlled conditions in the form of heavy reduction or complete absence of aluminium oxide etc.

7. To prepare colour stains and coloured glazes which would otherwise result in a speckled effect, when a uniform colouring is required.

8. To incorporate materials that in natural state can give rise to troubles before firing. For example: an excess of raw clay causes shrinkage cracks and peeling; zinc oxide also causes shrinkage cracks which later crawl; magnesium oxide and tin oxide are light powders that make friable glazes.

Commercial frits are made under controlled conditions with testing. Frits are therefore more dependable in chemical composition than many raw materials. Using a frit as part of the glaze gives more consistent results. The batch recipe can also be considerably simplified.

The system of using two frits in a recipe increases the permutations of results from standard frits. The system was developed originally to overcome the solubility of the lead content of lead-borosilicate glazes. See *Low sol* and *Double fritting.*

USE OF FRITS. Frits can be used in any glaze and can also be used as fluxes in bodies, slips and engobes.

When originating a recipe which involves a frit, the best way is to consider the frit as a flux only and not as a glass-former. In this way one will not be satisfied with the result simply because it melts. A frit will always melt, but it is not a suitable glaze alone. It requires other alumino-silicates. For general glazes, like transparent and maiolica, the following method is suggested:

China clay is usually necessary in a glaze to provide aluminium oxide and silica and to strengthen the unfired glaze. Start by standardizing the amount at 10%. Flint introduces silica into a glaze. Start by standardizing the amount at 10%, and adjusting this later to balance the glaze. A line blend is created between feldspar and the chosen frit in the proportions of 70:10 and 10:70. The diagram shows such a line blend. One of the blends is likely to be suitable if the frit has been chosen with consideration of the manufacturer's suggestions. The final balance can be made with adjustments to the china clay and flint with possible additions of whiting. See **Glaze fit**.

The advantages of using a frit have been mentioned with the reasons for fritting. The disadvantages are that the composition is not always known and that a frit settles quickly in the glaze slop because it is inert and homogeneous. If the composition is not known, one could get some unexpected colour responses and problems could arise in the balancing of the glaze. However if the previous blending has been used then sufficient information will probably be available to overcome the disadvantage of not having an analysis.

Manufacturers of frits will often quote a unity formula for a frit and sometimes give a percentage composition of its oxides. These can be used in calculating unity formulae from recipes and vice versa only if the molecular weight is also known. If the molecular weight is not supplied it must be proportionately totalled from the unity formula. In calculations involving frits, one must be careful to include only proportional amounts of oxide molecules as they appear in the frit's unity formula.

In requesting information from a frit manufacturer, the relative density should also be sought. It is useful in ascertaining dry weights from slop weights by Brongniart's formula.

FRIT MANUFACTURE. Frits are made by intermittent and continuous processes. In both, measured amounts of raw materials are melted together in large crucibles, which are also called kilns and furnaces. The molten frit is run off into water which achieves initial shattering, after which the frit is ground in water to produce a powder and to wash away the remaining solubles.

The photographs show an intermittent crucible being emptied and a continuous fritting plant for lead bisilicate. Both plants were at the Podmore factory in Stoke-on-Trent, England. The box-like crucible in the background of the continuous process is charged at the far end with raw materials from the floor above. The gas burner can be seen at the near end. A stream of molten frit discharges into a duct and bath of water at the lower end of the dewatering Archimedean screw.

Fritted glaze

A glaze containing frit(s) as its main source of flux. A glaze containing some frit as auxiliary flux would not be called a fritted glaze.

It is rarely necessary to frit a whole glaze except to stabilize a special effect. This occurs with some low-firing coloured glazes, sometimes called enamel glazes, where the glaze must be capable of melting smoothly and quickly.

Generally it would be a disadvantage to frit the whole glaze. To melt and regrind a glaze requires more heat and larger grinding machinery. Also, a glaze is physically harder to grind than a soft frit. Lastly, a homogeneous, inert mineral, like frit, will quickly settle and set hard in the glaze tub. Unfritted china clay and feldspar are valuable materials for keeping a glaze slop in suspension and helping the unfired glaze to adhere to the pot.

Frog mug

A drinking mug with a modelled frog inside at the bottom. This was an 18th- and 19th-century joke mug for tavern drinking. The idea has recently been revived.

Frost

Air temperature below 0°C and 32°F is considered frost. Any water, physically in the form of liquid, will solidify at this temperature. This includes water in glaze slops, slips, plastic clay and the water still in leatherhard clay and in damp biscuit, e.g. glazed biscuit awaiting firing.

The freezing of slop, slip or plastic clay does no harm providing the whole can be thoroughly mixed again when thawed. This in itself is sufficient nuisance. Leatherhard pots and damp biscuit will sometimes survive and can be completed and fired. However, weaknesses and faults sometimes arise in the finished ware which it is difficult to attribute to causes other than the weakening of the ware by frost action.

When the water freezes it expands. This action is important in the weathering of rocks and the ageing of clays. The particles separated only by a thin film of water are forced further apart so that when thawing takes place a thicker film of water enters. This action is obviously not desirable in pots.

Frostproof

Garden pots and outdoor sculpture should always, ideally, be frostproof. Frost is a threat to ceramics where water can lodge and expand as ice thus forcing the ceramic material apart. The material must be completely non-porous itself. Grogs added to control drying and shrinkage, and give texture, also need to be non-porous. Molochite (calcined china clay) and sand are non-porous but fireclay grogs are usually porous. A coarse, textured body used for large sculptures is not ideal in this respect as edges of grog are potential ice holders. A dense, smooth body is more water repellent. Rough, un-processed clay which is not compressed and may contain vegetable matter and stones will produce an open vulnerable body which can get waterlogged. Low-temperature firing may also produce a weak body which has no strength to resist the expansion of ice. This gives rise to the characteristic flaking seen in old plant pots. Well-fired stoneware is less porous and stronger.

Crevices and hollows which can hold water must be avoided. Soft-fired glazes, e.g. raku, enamel and earthenware, are not strongly bonded to the body and may be prized off. Stoneware glazes are integrated with the body and in most cases present no problem.

It is difficult to guarantee completely against severe frost. A silicone weatherproof coating will help. Well-fired plant pots which drain well are not usually a problem as the plants they contain dictate protection from the most severe cold. See ***Grog, Porosity, Stoneware*** and ***Outdoor ceramics***. The photograph is of rhubarb forcers by Brook Street Pottery, Hay-on-Wye, UK.

Fuddling mug

A 16th- to 18th-century ale mug. There were also fuddling cups joined in threes, fours and fives with connecting holes. These were part of the same tavern joking as the puzzle jug.

Fuddling mugs and cups were made in slipware, iron-glazed earthenware and galleyware.

Fuels

The source of energy for the heat needed to fire ceramics.

Those chiefly in use in kilns are oil, gas and wood. Electricity is dealt with separately. See **Electric kiln**. Coal and coke have largely gone out of use but potters achieve creative effects with sawdust and bonfires. Solar energy firing has been attempted but not yet proved viable. For comparative data on the use of fuels see **Table 40**, Energy equivalents and **Table 41**, Pressure equivalents.

Heavy fuel oil is the residue which, with bitumen, is left after crude oil has been distilled to give petrol, paraffin oil (kerosene), gas and diesel oils. The grade of oil most used is 28 second as used in domestic heating systems. The flash point or ignition point is relatively high which is a safety factor regarding the storage or spillage of the fuel but presents the need for a specialized burning system. The liquid oil must be converted into very small droplets, fine mist, or vapour and supplied with air, usually under pressure, to effect burning. The stored oil may be heated to decrease its viscosity. Sump oil is sometimes used by potters. See **Burners**.

Oil gives a very hot, long flame which can be used effectively in a down-draught system. A disadvantage is up to 3% sulfur content which causes fumes detrimental to pots, kilns and potters. See **Fumes**. Burners for oil range from the simple home-made to those which are very complex and expensive. Although the simplest may seem adequate in principle for the potter's needs, there are pitfalls to avoid. If the oil is not atomized and burnt with maximum efficiency a great deal of black smoke is created in the early stages of firing and excess fumes have a destructive effect especially around the entry ports. There is some variation in quality of oil which may affect its burning rate.

Coal gas or Town gas is distilled from coal and has the advantage of neat on-tap supply where it is available. The flame is not so hot as that from liquid petroleum gas or natural gas but, like petroleum gas, it can burn without forced air. It has a sulfur content of 0·04% which can be reasonably cleared from the kiln atmosphere.

Natural gas is a mixture of several paraffin hydrocarbons diluted with nitrogen and oxygen and occurs in sedimentary rocks with mineral oil deposits. It has a high calorific value, and a low sulfur and moisture content. It requires ten times its own volume of air in order to burn but is supplied at relatively low pressure. It follows that the normal flame is weak and to achieve the heat needed for firing, forced air is usually employed. Where available this provides arguably the most convenient, clean and adaptable fuel for potters.

Fuel oil, paraffin, propane (C_3H_8) and butane (C_4H_{10}) are pure hydrocarbons obtained from petroleum by fractional distillation. Liquid Petroleum Gas (LPG) is the alternative to natural gas where there is no mains supply. It is transported and stored in the liquid state under pressure. On the release of pressure, from storage tank or bottle via pipes to the burners, the liquid vaporizes to a burnable gas. These gases have a low ignition point which means that there is unlikely to be any difficulty in lighting burners at the start of a firing. It also means that strict safety regulations must be observed. Propane must be stored outdoors but small amounts of butane may be kept indoors. The gas is heavy so that precautions must be taken to prevent the build-up of leaked gas in low areas or cellars.

Methane gas can be produced from a combination of farm manure and vegetable matter or sewage. An aerobic fermentation takes place producing nitrogen from the manure and carbon from the vegetable waste or sewage. Then an anaerobic digestion takes place. This requires heat in a closed space but the energy required to run the whole plant is only a quarter of the production.

LPG can be supplied under high pressure. There is no need for forced air so the kiln can be independent of electricity. The fuel is very clean and contains no sulfur. Propane burns with a shorter flame than oil or natural gas and this must be taken into account when siting burners or planning flame tracking paths. See **Burners**.

Using wood for firing demands a great deal of skilled application of knowledge on the part of the potter. It is a very variable fuel so that until the kiln, the supply, and the firing programme have been settled into a reliable pattern these things will demand more attention than the finer details of the pots. When the art of manipulating all these variables, including the weather, has been mastered by the potter the reward is a wide range of subtle effects not achieved in any other way.

As a solid fuel, wood can only burn on its surface area, so it must be cut into small pieces to produce adequate temperature rise. It must be very dry. Resin contributes to gas given off in the first stages of burning. When the matter becomes charcoal—hydrogen and oxygen having been burnt off—this has a high calorific value given a good draught of air. Hardwoods, such as oak, have a higher potential in heat per kilogram but this is given off slowly so that hardwoods can be useful in starting a firing slowly. Chiefly, however, softwoods such as pine, fir, hemlock or spruce are preferred. They have an open grain structure which releases heat at a faster rate.

Fugitive

Description of colours which are easily lost by incorrect firing. Selenium reds are called fugitive because they quickly volatilize. They require both a quick firing and cooling.

Fumes

The fumes released during the firing of pottery involve water vapour, microscopic carbon in smoke, carbon monoxide and dioxide, sulfur dioxide and trioxide, fluorine and from salt-glazing, chlorine and hydrochloric acid. Some of the glaze oxides also volatilize. They are the oxides of antimony, barium, boron, chromium, copper, lead, potassium, sodium and zinc. Cadmium selenide used for red colours also volatilizes.

The fumes which present problems and the greatest hazards are carbon monoxide, chlorine, sulfur trioxide, fluorine and lead oxide, especially when these fumes emerge from kiln bung holes directly into the studio or workshop. Carbon monoxide is colourless, without smell and deadly. It is deliberately created for reduction, and kilns for reduction should be efficiently sealed and vented to outdoors. When firing by oil, the sulfur content puts a noticeable smell in with any carbon monoxide leaking from the kiln, but when firing by gas any leaking carbon monoxide is not detectable by smell. Chlorine is released from salt glazing and with water vapour becomes hydrochloric acid. Sulfur trioxide combines with water vapour to produce sulfuric acid which can be smelt and tasted in the atmosphere. It also corrodes the metal framework of the kiln. Fluorine can also be detected in the atmosphere as a choking gas. It attacks window glass, etching this to a frosted opacity. Lead oxide is not easily detectable but its effect on the human system is cumulative. See **Poison, Carbon monoxide, Salt glaze** and **Volatiles**.

Fuming

A term which is used for a variety of processes involving post-firing treatment. Wood is introduced into the kiln during cooling or the pots are smoked in a container of combustible materials after firing. This can produce a carbonized body where exposed, and reduced lustrous colours. The photograph shows a Tim Andrews' Humbug coming out of the smoking bin with the resist glaze peeling off. For details see **Colour plates 55** and **56**. See **Raku, Sawdust, Smoking** and **Colour plates 32, 35, 36** and **37**.

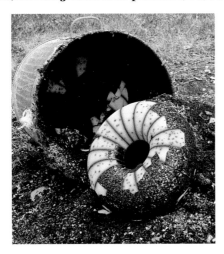

Furniture

Moveable kiln fittings which include shelves, shelf supports and the supports for the ware. Furniture is made from refractory materials. See **Refractory**. Saggars and muffles are not furniture. The upper temperature limits, given by manufacturers, to which shelves and props can be used assume an oxidized firing. Heavy reduction lowers the temperature limit and shortens the life of the furniture. Cast props are more vulnerable than pressed or extruded types. Heavier props and shelves may be necessary. Silicon carbide shelves are recommended for heavy reduction.

It is generally accepted that the weight of the furniture often exceeds that of the ware. This means that over half the heat inside the kiln is being used to heat the furniture. There is also the question of weight handling. Consideration should be given to these points although individual potters are not able to incorporate all the specialized furniture which is used by industrial firms. For example, thick shelves bend less and therefore last longer than thin shelves. They can also be used for more varied ware and therefore fewer are needed. Thin shelves however are easier to handle in and out of the kiln and cost less in terms of firing fuel. The saving in fuel and energy may more than offset the cost of frequent replacement.

Shelves may be solid or pierced. Pierced shelves are used in through-flame kilns, especially up-draught, where they act as heat baffles. They are often specially shaped to fit the kiln. See illustration. They are less strong than solid shelves but are more economical because they absorb less heat.

The materials from which shelves are made determine their life and the weight which they will support. Naturally, a large shelf which spans a wide space and carries a heavy

weight of ware needs to be stronger than a small shelf carrying light ware. Normally a thick shelf is stronger than a thin one and will withstand a higher temperature and greater load. Shelves are also called bats.

The material is usually high in aluminium oxide. Sillimanite is over 60% Al_2O_3; mullite is over 70% Al_2O_3; and fluxed aluminium oxide is over 90% Al_2O_3. All these materials are strong and have good thermal shock resistance which is especially important for use in fast-fire kilns.

For heavy reduction and high temperatures, silicon carbide is recommended. It is stronger still but more expensive. However, it is weakened by oxidation and also increases in size as the carbon burns out allowing the silicon to oxidize. A wash of aluminium oxide helps to seal the silicon carbide and inhibit oxidation.

Cordieritic bodies are formed from mixtures of talc and mullite. They have exceptional resistance to thermal shock and improve with use as further cordierite is formed. However they are limited to temperatures under 1260°C (2300°F).

Shelf supports are called variously props, pillars and castles. Like shelves they have a life dependent upon material and thickness. Cast props are popular and are available in different heights which can be further adjusted by adding castellated tube props on top. Cast props, being thinner, are much weaker than tube props and if used in reduction firings can become very brittle and liable to collapse.

cast prop

castellated props

bits

tube props

pip

stilt

thimbles

spur

saddle

table or chair

Ware supports are used to hold the ware clear of shelves or itself in the firing, thus obtaining uniform heating and cooling, and preventing glazed ware from sticking together. Ware supports have many names. Some are industrial and trade names while others are colloquial ones used at a single pottery. Table, stool, chair, collar, ring and frogs are fairly self-explanatory descriptions. Each gives support over an area especially where it is needed to keep a pot in shape. They are used for dense earthenware, porcelain and sometimes for stoneware. Stilts, pips, pins, thimbles, spurs and saddles give support at a single point and are used for earthenware glaze firing. They set into the glaze and are ground off flush with the glaze surface. Star stilts have metal points.

Cranks are frames into which are fitted the expendable pips and pins which support the ware. They are used for flatware, plates and tiles. The pips and pins are easier and cheaper to manufacture than the saddles and thimbles which they have replaced. See ***Crank***.

A further part of setting is the use of placing sand, biscuit (pads) and bat wash.

Fusion

Ceramic fusion. The melting of different materials into a homogeneous liquid mass. Fusion requires heat (tem-perature absorbed over a period of time) and depends upon the interaction of the different materials present.

The factors which affect fusion can be classified as those which hasten the final stage and those which hinder its evolution. The factors which promote fusion are:

1. The material present classified in pottery terms as glass-formers and fluxes. See ***Interaction***.
2. The ratio of these materials. See ***Eutectic mixture***.
3. A low viscosity in the melt allowing movement of parti cles and a thorough stirring effect created by escaping bubbles. The low viscosity also allows gases to escape. See ***Viscosity of molten glazes***.
4. Opportunity for the melt to move under gravity which allows the different particles to meet one another.
5. Fine particle size which presents a larger surface area to attack by heat and interaction. See ***Grain size***.
6. Previous fritting of some or all of the materials. See ***Frit***.
7. Prolonged firing which gives more opportunity for matu ration. See ***Vitrification***.

The factors which hinder fusion are:

1. The materials present as refractories and anti-fluxes. See ***Anti-flux***.
2. The ratio of these materials to the other more fusible materials.
3. A high viscosity in the melt which inhibits particle move ment and traps escaping gases. See ***Viscosity of molten glazes***.
4. Large grain size of the materials. See ***Grain size***.
5. A firing of short duration. See ***Heat*** and ***Firing***.

The photograph of a porcelain wall plate by Frank Hamer shows how colouring oxides, painted under the glaze have fused and softened into the glaze and moved slightly down.

G

Galena

Lead ore. Lead sulfide. Smithum. Blue lead. PbS. The most important ore of lead from which lead is extracted by first roasting to the oxide and then reducing to the metal. Galena was used as a source of lead oxide in glazes.

From about the 10th century to the mid-17th century, galena was dusted on to pottery ware through a coarse rag. The dust stuck to the newly thrown wet ware or to a fresh slip coating and fused the upper layer of clay into a glaze during the firing. See also **Lead oxide**.

Galleyware

Gallyware. Galliware. The earlier name for tin-glazed ware of the 16th to 18th centuries. The first exports from Faenza arrived in western Europe by ship (galley) from Venice and became known as galleyware. The name was then transferred to similar pots made in Antwerp, Bristol, Liverpool

and Lambeth. After the successful productions at Delft, these wares became known as delftware in the 18th century and it is by this name that we know the ware today. See also **Delft** and **Lambeth** for photographs.

Garden ceramics

See **Outdoor ceramics**.

Gault clay

A true marl of the Upper Cretaceous System of sedimentary rocks. It contains a high percentage, as much as 30% in some cases, of calcium carbonate (chalk) in fine particles. This tends to make the clay 'short' for working and it is possible to remove only the larger impurities. However pockets exist of finely divided gault clay which are plastic and can be used for potting. The coarser clays are used for bricks and extruded insulation blocks.

The interesting yellows and buffs associated with gault clay and the fired body are a result of the bleaching of the iron by the calcium oxide. In the soft-fired body, the calcium oxide is not fully involved in silicate fusions and the excess is able to involve itself with the iron oxide.

The high chalk content precludes the use of gault clay as a pottery body for use over 1060°C (1940°F). Gault clay deforms at approximately 1150°C (2120°F) and melts by 1250°C (2282°F). This property makes it a useful constituent in a slip glaze. Usually the iron content makes such a slip very dark. The calcium oxide content which has previously kept the iron light in colour, has become involved in silica fusions. See **Marl** and **Calcium oxide**.

Germanium oxide

GeO_2. A glass-forming oxide which is present as a trace in many glazes but is not deliberately introduced.

Gerstley borate

A variety of colemanite which includes sodium oxide. It is named after a man who operated a colemanite mine in California. The mine has now been worked out.

Gibbsite

$Al_2O_3.3H_2O$. Aluminium hydrate of pure white form. It is one of the three hydrates of aluminium which are a source of the metal aluminium and of its oxide for abrasives. It is softer than the other two (bauxite and diaspore) and therefore more easily ground. It is used by potters as a refractory bat wash when it is mixed with some china clay which acts as a binder.

The name gibbsite is used for the aluminium and hydroxyl group layer which occurs in the kaolinite crystal.

In this layer, the ultimate composition, also called the average formula, is nearer to $Al_2O_3.2H_2O$ than $Al_2O_3.3H_2O$. However, individual parts (fig. 1) can be seen as $Al_2O_3.3H_2O$ which is also written $Al(OH)_3$ a method which better describes the arrangement of the hydroxyl groups.

In kaolinite, the layer (fig. 2) is gibbsite in character being weak in structure and inhibited from stronger bonding by the occupancy of the oxygen atoms by the silicon layer. See *Clay: physics*.

The two lattice diagrams (figs. 1 and 2) show the isolation of $Al_2O_3.3H_2O$ and the gibbsite layer with hexagonal structure averaging $3(Al_2O_3.2H_2O)$.

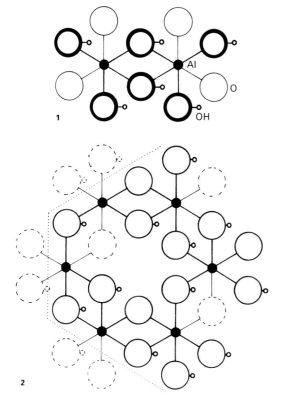

Glass-former

An oxide which is able to retain the amorphous property of its molten state when setting to a solid. Other minerals return to crystalline state as they set or soon afterwards.

Glass-formers are indispensable in pottery. They form the bulk of a glaze and provide the glassy cement which gives strength to the body. The glass-formers, in order of importance are: silica, boron oxide, phosphorus oxide, antimony oxide, arsenic oxide, germanium oxide and selenium oxide. See *Periodic table*.

Each glass-former is capable of existing in a crystalline state and it is in this state that it usually occurs in nature. It appears to be white because light is reflected from the crystal facets but it is transparent. If it is heated sufficiently it loses its crystalline nature by melting to a transparent liquid. If cooled very slowly over a period of weeks or even years it returns to crystals, but if cooled quickly over a period of only hours or at most a few days there is insufficient time for the crystals to grow. The liquid state sets as a transparent solid, technically known as a supercooled liquid.

The most important glass-forming oxide is silicon oxide normally called silica (SiO_2). It is always present in a glaze and is usually by far the largest constituent. It is also the commonest natural oxide constituting 60% of the earth's crust. It occurs naturally as sand, quartz and flint, and as the semi-precious stones rose quartz, cairngorm and amethyst. All these look glassy when inspected and can be imagined as glazes. See *Quartz* and *Silica*.

The second most important glass-forming oxide is boron oxide (B_2O_3). When used in glazes, it is always in combination with silica. It cannot be used without silica because it is soluble in water. Glazes and glasses produced with boron oxide as the main constituent would be soft and soluble.

Native boron oxide is rare. Boron oxide is found combined with other elements in borates of which borax is the most important. See *Boron oxide*, *Borax* and *Borates*.

The other glass-formers are used in small amounts for special effects. Phosphorus oxide retains its individual structure within a glaze and thereby deflects the light giving rise to jun effects. See *Jun*. Antimony oxide does not dissolve in the glaze unless lead oxide is present. It gives opacity in leadless glazes and yellow colours with lead oxide. See *Antimony oxide*. Arsenic oxide is used in the glass industry for clarification of discoloured glass. Germanium oxide and selenium oxide are too rare and unstable to be used on any large scale.

Glaze

A layer of glass which is fused into place on a pottery body. The glaze provides a hygienic covering on pottery because it is smoother than the body it covers and it is non-porous. It is also decorative, providing colour, shine and textural contrast with the body; and it increases the strength of the ware by the creation of a body-glaze layer.

The glaze is first attached to the pottery body in the form of a layer of powder. This powder is composed of glass-forming materials, fluxes and stabilizers. During the firing they all fuse together to form a compact layer of molten material. On cooling, this layer does not separate into its former constituents but remains as the new material, glass.

In order to produce a glaze, there must be present sufficient glass-forming oxides. See *Glass-former*. By far the most important of these is silica and it is introduced into glazes by the minerals quartz (100% silica), flint (95% silica), feldspar (65% silica) and china clay (47% silica).

The glass-forming oxides are fused into a practical glaze by the presence of fluxes and stabilizers. The fluxes are alkaline oxides of which sodium, potassium, calcium, magnesium and lead oxides are the most important. The most important stabilizer is aluminium oxide.

These three groups of oxides—fluxes, stabilizers and glass-formers—are also called the alkaline, amphoteric and acidic oxides. Their relative proportions and the composition of each group give a great variety of possible glazes.

The photographs show David and Margaret Frith pouring glaze.

See also *Frit, Firing: glaze* and *Stoneware*.

THE ORIGIN OF GLAZES. Some authorities claim dates as early as 12,000BC for the first glazes. These were on the glazed paste beads which were made in Egypt. The Egyptians discovered glass where sand and sandstones, impregnated with salt, had been fused by a fire. Certainly by 3000BC the Egyptians were using glazes on some of their pottery. These glazes were alkaline copper glazes which were used effectively as decorative coverings. Later, in south-west Asia, glazes were used to give extra strength and durability to bricks, wall tiles and pottery. Around 1500BC glazes were used as practical and hygienic waterproof layers on pottery. See *Egyptian paste*.

The first Egyptian glaze was a surface fusion of the body which occurred where the soluble salts from the body had crystallized on the surface during drying. In Egypt and south-west Asia, the knowledge of this was used to develop glazes applied as slips. Lead glazes were used to avoid the difficulties which arose with the use of soluble salts but by the 13th century, the solubility of the alkaline fluxes had been successfully overcome by fritting.

Lead glazes were also used in China as early as 200BC. Their development ran parallel to the better-known stoneware and porcelain glazes. The high-temperature glazes followed the realization that fine ash from the wood fire had fluxed the pottery surface. The stoneware glazes were composed of wood ashes, clay and feldspathoids. With improvements in kiln construction, higher temperatures were reached and refined porcelains were perfected by the 10th century.

In Europe, lead glazes developed separately from stoneware glazes which were salt-glazes. Lead oxide was used from the 12th to 17th centuries and was applied as a powdered ore which was dusted onto the wet ware or onto a wet clay slip. The method of mixing a glaze and applying it as a liquid coating did not become standard practice in Britain until the 18th century. The practice spread slowly across Europe from the Islamic countries.

Today, glazes are applied by dipping, pouring, spraying and painting depending upon the convenience and desired effect. Salt glazing has increased in popularity with individual potters since the demise of industrial salt glaze. Economic considerations have also furthered interest in raw glazing.

CHEMISTRY OF GLAZES. A glaze is the result of interaction between alkali and acid. When heated, these two are in active opposition and the excitement engendered gives rise to a fluid state—the molten glaze.

The alkalis and acids in glazes are oxides and these are originally solids. The individual oxides would not necessarily create liquids at the temperatures involved in pottery. It is only by interaction that this occurs. Yet the alkalis and acids involved are not violent. Many of the oxides involved one would not associate with the household idea of alkali and

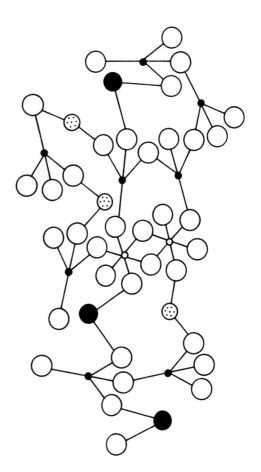

acid. It is difficult, for example, to think of silica as an acid, but its reactive properties must be so described in terms of glazes. In the presence of heat, the molecular structure of the oxides vibrates, loosens or even breaks, and under these conditions interaction can take place.

The amount of heat required depends upon the type and amount of the alkalis present. For example, lead oxide, which is an alkali in terms of glaze balance, interacts with silica at temperatures above 500°C (932°F). Lithium oxide, a stronger alkali in some respects, starts its action at 800°C (1472°F), and magnesium oxide is inert until 1170°C (2138°F) is reached. Details of the other alkaline oxides are given under *Fluxing action*. See also *Periodic table*.

The interaction which is necessary for the creation of a glaze can only take place at or above the minimum temperature for the alkali concerned. Time is also required. A higher temperature gives more molecular vibration and is equal to a longer time at a lower temperature.

The temperature at which action begins is often described as the melting point of a glaze. However, with the necessity of a time consideration and the obvious advantages in the use of a higher temperature to accomplish a full fusion, it is more usual to refer to a range of temperatures rather than a single melting point.

The range often extends upwards to the point where the glaze is spoilt by being overfired. This is caused by gassing as some of the oxides become volatile. Thus a glaze is described as maturing rather than melting and is given a lower and upper limit for its use. The difference between these two may be only 10°C (18°F) or it may be 100°C (180°F), depending upon the oxides involved.

Below the maturing temperature range there is no action. Thus, the action is checked by cooling and the final glaze is no longer liquid but begins to set. It does not usually set completely at the lower end of the range but tarries in a soft state until approximately 500°C (932°F).

The interaction between alkali and acid in the presence of heat produces fluidity. The degree of fluidity involved depends upon the particular oxides and is referred to in terms of viscosity when discussing glazes. Glazes are made more viscous by the presence of aluminium oxide, the most important amphoteric oxide. An amphoteric oxide is half-way between an alkali and an acid, and therefore acts as both. In very small amounts, aluminium oxide will re-balance the alkali-acid interaction towards an optimum fusion but in large amounts it has a distinctly stiffening effect. A large amount would be only one-twentieth or one-thirtieth of the glaze.

See also *Anti-flux* and *Eutectic mixture*.

PHYSICS OF GLAZES. Glazes are composed of the molecules of different oxides which are linked together in random chains. Before the firing, these same molecules are linked to identical molecules in a lattice structure. The lattice structure forms a crystal of the oxide concerned and the different oxides which will compose the final glaze are therefore present as different crystals, particles or grains of powdered material.

During the firing, the bonds which hold the molecules together are broken and a fluid state exists in which it is convenient to assume that each molecule is an isolated particle. This is the molten state of the glaze and the action which brings it about is called the fusion. Part of this fusion is a liberation of gases. These effectively stir the mixture of unattached molecules so that upon cooling they are unlikely to re-establish their original bonds.

If sufficient time is available during cooling, many of the molecules establish bonds with identical molecules. A preferential selection exists whereby one molecule has affinity with an identical molecule in terms of size and molecular vibration. To some extent this occurs in crystalline glazes, but for most of the molecules an immediate link-up is established with any molecule which offers suitable valency. The atoms which flank an isolated molecule have unsatisfied valencies which can remain so in the excited state of a molten glaze but cannot remain unsatisfied as the glaze cools. The comparatively rapid satisfaction of these valencies gives a series of random chains. The drawings show the constituent oxides and the type of random chain which they produce.

The final glaze partially combines the physical properties of the constituent oxides and partially displays new properties. New properties are those belonging to its amorphous state and include its physical hardness, resistance to chemical attack and to abrasion, its colour, transparency, opacity, and its surface texture. The combined properties from the oxides which are displayed by the new state are those of hardness and the overall rate of expansion. The rate of expansion is important if the glaze is to sit harmoniously on a pottery body without defect. See *Glaze fit*.

See also *Devitrification* and *Viscosity of molten glazes*.

GLAZE DEFECTS. Most glaze defects have self-explanatory names. The common defects are separately itemized in this book as: *Blistering*, *Crawling*, *Crazing*, *Devitrification*, *Flashing*, *Overfiring*, *Pin-holing*, *Shivering*, *Spluttering* and *Underfiring*.

Glaze calculations
See *Calculations*.

Glaze fit
In glaze fit one is concerned with achieving a harmony of glaze and pottery body with regard to their thermal expansions and contractions. The suitability of the glaze in terms of colour, texture and thickness is not considered.

A finished pot expands and contracts with the warmth of the day and the cool of the night in common with nearly all other materials, solid, liquid and gas. Pots used as ovenware and food containers are subjected to still more heat and will expand and contract more. The expansion is often sudden so that they are subjected to what is called thermal shock. The body and glaze need to expand and contract together with reasonable harmony. An exact match is impossible and fortunately not necessary. There is a degree of latitude in the harmony of body and glaze expansion and contraction before a defect occurs which spoils the pottery. A defect could show as crazing when the glaze cracks, or as shivering and shelling when the glaze flakes off the body, or as dunting when the body cracks. Glaze fitting is concerned with the adjustment of glaze, and possibly body, composition to achieve the necessary harmony.

The potter is usually concerned with contraction. When the potter opens the kiln and inspects the ware it is after a period of cooling during which the pots have contracted. If they come safely through this period of large contraction one not unreasonably assumes that future small amounts of expansion and contraction will do no harm. In physics it is common practice to talk in terms of expansion and consider contraction as the logical corollary. This practice is followed here.

Nearly all substances expand with heat and contract by the same amount on cooling. Each substance expands and contracts at a different rate but each substance is predictable in that it keeps to its own rate. The glaze is therefore very likely to expand and contract at a different rate from the body. The rate of expansion is a direct result of the composition of a body or a glaze. Each component, usually considered as an oxide, gives to the body or glaze its own expansion rate in direct proportion to the amount present.

For example, if a glaze contains 50% of oxide A which expands a large amount and 50% of oxide B which expands only a little, then the resulting expansion rate is theoretically half-way between these two rates. In practice other factors, e.g. interaction, affect the result so that this statement is only approximately true. By adjusting the percentage composition of a glaze one will undoubtedly influence its expansion rate in a known direction. Alternatively, one may substitute another oxide of different expansion rate but very similar glaze behaviour for one of the original oxides. In this way one is able to make substantial alteration to the expansion rate of the glaze with minimum change in the other glaze properties.

Since 1850 research has been carried out to discover the different rates of expansion for different substances including glaze oxides. Published tables give a rate measured as a percentage increase over a rise in temperature of 1°C. The rate is usually a factor relating to 1% of the oxide in a glaze. Different tables are available which vary according to the way in which the coefficients of expansion were obtained and the tables are named after their originators as English and Turner, Mayer and Havas, Winkelmann and Schott. The table given here is a simplification from various sources and shows the common glaze oxides listed with the greatest expansion rate at the top, the least at the bottom.

Fluxes	Amphoteric and acidic oxides	Crystallizers and opacifiers
Na_2O		
K_2O		
CaO		CaO
BaO		BaO
PbO		
		TiO_2
Li_2O		
ZnO		ZnO
MgO		MgO
		ZrO_2
		SnO_2
	Al_2O_3	
	SiO_2	
B_2O_3	B_2O_3	

(left axis, vertical: *increasing rate of expansion*)

A more detailed list is given in **Table 26**. The actual coefficient numbers rarely concern the individual potter who is more interested in the relationship of one glaze constituent to another. The actual amount measured as a percentage increase is not likely to be of much value unless one is trying to compare the expansion rates of two glazes. A potter wishing to make use of these tables of coefficients should ascertain whether they are linear or volumetric, coefficients or factors for calculating coefficients, and whether they refer to the temperature range under consideration. Some computer glaze programmes calculate an expansion figure for each recipe entered. See **Computer glaze calculations**.

The problem facing the potter is often one of adjusting an existing glaze to make it fit the standard body. Presumably some defect leads to this adjustment and the first action is the analysis of the defect. Either the glaze has contracted too much which has resulted in crazing or it has not contracted sufficiently and has resulted in shelling or shivering. A decision can now be made to replace some of the flux for an oxide of different expansion rate.

If the defect is crazing then the new flux must be one which expands less, and hence contracts less, than the previous one. From the table it will be seen that boron oxide (B_2O_3) has the smallest expansion rate. When boron oxide replaces one of the other fluxes, the resulting glaze will contract less and the crazing defect may be cured. Substitution of one oxide for another is usually done on a molecular equivalent basis although the amount to substitute is a matter for judgement and experiment. See **Equivalent**. Such are the different effects of the oxides that the approach is empirical in any case and even the addition of small amounts of a new oxide may have the desired effect. Boron oxide, especially, is so low in expansion that it has a great reputation as an anti-craze. Additions of small amounts of borax frit to a glaze often cure the crazing and even improve glaze shine and colouring.

In the opposite case, of shivering, one looks for a flux with a high expansion rate. Lead oxide, introduced via lead frit, is popular and has the additional advantage of creating an elastic glaze capable of adapting itself under stress. Alternatively most potters will have noticed how much a sodium-based glaze contracts. Alkaline copper blue glazes are notorious for crazing. The introduction of sodium feldspar (albite) in place of some or all of the potassium feldspar (orthoclase) may be sufficient to cure shivering. Decreasing the silica content by 5% or 10% is another first step.

It should be noted there is always some stress between body and glaze. The two cannot lie absolutely side by side without stress. If no stress exists at one temperature there is sufficient difference in their two expansion rates to cause some slight stress in the variations of air temperature. A glaze can successfully contain about ten times the amount of stress when under compression as in tension. It is better therefore that a glaze should be under slight compression.

Glaze fit is a complex subject involving more than is discussed here. The reader is referred to other factors under the headings of **Crazing, Shivering, Thermal shock, Dunting, Body-glaze layer, Buffer layer** and **Interaction**.

The achievement of a good glaze fit is generally considered a matter of glaze adjustment. But where body and glaze are matured together, it may happen that body adjustment is easier. The addition or subtraction of flint, sand or grog may be a simple remedy to a glaze fit problem. If a glaze matures over a shorter range than does its body it is more easily spoilt, than is the body, by under- or over-firing. Alterations to composition often have the effect of moving the range up or down the scale. With a short glaze-range there is little room for this but it may happen that in the body-range there is room for considerable change. See graph.

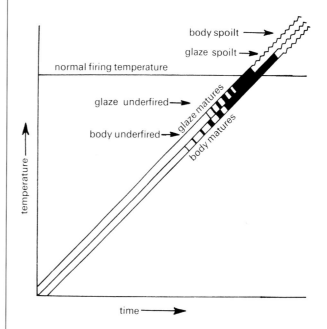

Glaze-body

The combination layer resulting from the interaction of glaze and body. See **Body-glaze layer** and **Buffer layer**.

Glost firing

Glaze firing. The term has come to us from the industry where a glaze firing at a lower temperature than the biscuit is common practice. Glost implies firing of glaze at a lower temperature than the biscuit which is then called bisque or bisc. See **Bisc**.

Goblet

Two examples by Frank Hamer have dolomite and lime-matt glazes. The decoration was brushed on the unfired glaze. One example by Pauline Paterson with applied decoration.

Gowen

Another name for **Cornish stone**.

Grain size

Particle size. A term used when referring to the fineness or coarseness of materials. The term 'grain size' is usually used for sizes larger than 200's or 300's mesh. This involves the grogs, sands and glaze materials which are handled in dry grain and powder form. The alternative term 'particle size' is more often used when referring to near-colloidal sizes. These involve groups of disordered crystals packed together as in clay suspensions and glaze melts.

Grain sizes are measured in mesh size numbers for the larger sizes from 1 down to 200's or 300's mesh, from which size micrometres are generally used. A 200's mesh will pass grains of 76 micrometres (BS 410).

Grain size is relevant in both bodies and glazes.

In glazes, the grain size affects the time required for a complete fusion to take place.

In bodies, the grain size of grogs and other fillers affects the results obtained. Coarse grains give visible and tactile textures but they do not necessarily affect the drying and firing behaviour of the body. Medium grains often alter the drying character of a body by giving a more uniform drying shrinkage over the whole drying period. See **Drying**. Refractory fillers added to bodies as fine grains can give apparently fluxing results.

Specific consideration is given here to the grain sizes of glaze materials and to silica additions to bodies. For a discussion of the difference between china clay and ball clay, see **Particle size**. See also **Filler** and **Preparation of clay** (control of grain size).

Glaze minerals melt by combining two or more oxides to produce a new mineral which is in liquid state. The oxides concerned are usually contained in two different materials, e.g. whiting and china clay. The chemical interaction is only possible where two grains of different minerals can physically touch. The centres of large grains can only melt when the surrounding grain has been removed by melting. Thus large grains are slow to melt because they present a proportionately smaller surface area for contact than do small grains.

If a glaze is to mature quickly, the glaze materials must be finely ground and thoroughly dispersed. Suppliers of glaze materials often mill their products to pass a 200's mesh.

Most potters are content if their prepared glaze slops will pass through a 120's mesh. Glazes which use coarse materials like sands and wood ashes require a longer time to mature.

Refractory materials are often fritted with soft materials. The new material thus formed is ground to a fine state in which it melts quickly and smoothly producing immediate homogeneity. In contrast to the original materials, a grain of frit melts when it reaches a determined temperature. At this temperature the bonds between the oxide molecules are weakened and the solid state collapses as a liquid state. The temperature has only to penetrate the grain for this to occur.

A frit can be said to 'melt' but glazes composed of different materials are advisedly described as 'maturing'. The grain size in both cases affects the time required.

There is a general test for ground sands and quartz to be added to stoneware bodies. It consists of the feel when rubbed between finger and thumb. There should be sufficient bite for the sand to be felt as granules rather than powder. The dividing line approximates 100's mesh in grain size. For stoneware, especially reduced stoneware involving bodies containing some iron, it is necessary to use a quartz sand of about 80's grade and coarser. Sand which is finer can be completely fused during firing resulting in over-vitrification of the body with consequential deformation of the ware. Quartz sand of coarse grain is regarded as a refractory grog but quartz ground to a fine grain size acts as a body flux.

The effect is not quite so noticeable in oxidized stoneware. It is necessary to use a very fine grain size approaching 300's mesh before the 'fluxing' effect is observed.

There is also a desirable grain size for flint which is added to earthenware bodies. Assuming that the flint is being added to increase the cristobalite content as an anti-craze measure, it must convert to cristobalite and not melt to amorphous phase. The usually quoted optimum size is around 200's mesh. Larger than this can cause internal stresses in the body. The flint is also not so ready to convert. Flint of finer grain size is readily involved in the glassy phases of the body and its crystalline property is lost. See **Cristobalite** and **Silica conversion**.

Granite

A feldspathoid occasionally used in glazes. It originated as molten magma which cooled slowly within the earth and is therefore of large crystalline grain. It is hard, resists weathering and is therefore a difficult material to grind, but dust is sometimes available from quarries. It is more refractory in use than pure feldspars and approximates a mixture of feldspar and quartz or one of the more refractory cornish stones. It always contains some iron which gives a greenish tinge when fired. See also **Feldspathoids**.

Granite is related to cornish stone and china clay. These two originated as granite but, before setting from molten state, the magma was subjected to pneumatolysis, a process of composition alteration by the action of liquids and gases. When cool and solid, the resulting rock was not so resistant to weathering as pure granite. The cornish stones are similar in chemical composition to granite but are much more easily crushed.

Not less than 45% and often as much as 70% of granite is feldspar. Orthoclase accounts for about three-quarters of this with the rest made up of albite or albite and oligoclase. Feldspar gives granite its white sparkle sometimes tinged pink with traces of iron.

Between 20% and 50% of granite is quartz which gives whiteness but also a greyness when the quartz is clear.

Up to 15% of granite is mica, usually black biotite seen as sparkling black specks. There is sometimes a mafic mineral like hornblende also present. The iron in the mica and hornblende gives a grey or greenish colour to the granite and, upon melting, the iron is usually involved in reduced state giving a greenish tinge.

Granite is more refractory than pure feldspars and most cornish stones. It requires over $1300°C$ $(2372°F)$ to produce fusion. A molecular formula is not possible for such a complex material but a simplified unity formula would be:

$$\left.\begin{array}{ll} 0{\cdot}7 & K_2O \\ 0{\cdot}2 & Na_2O \\ 0{\cdot}05 & MgO \\ 0{\cdot}05 & CaO \end{array}\right\} \left.\begin{array}{l} 1 \text{ to } 1{\cdot}5\ Al_2O_3 \\ 0{\cdot}1\ Fe_2O_3 \end{array}\right\} 6 \text{ to } 12\ SiO_2$$

In the enlarged photograph of a section of granite, the three minerals are clearly visible. The white crystals are feldspar, the mid-tone areas are quartz and the small black pieces are mica.

Graven

Another name for **Cornish stone**.

Green

Greens are produced in ceramics by silicate solutions. If the colouring is not fully fused in a silicate, the tendency is towards grey colours. Glazes can therefore be green but bodies, especially porous bodies, tend to be greyish greens from the same colouring. Copper oxide is the most dependable green stain for the softer temperatures but volatilizes from glazes above $1200°C$ $(2192°F)$. Chromium oxide produces greyish greens. Both oxides are modified by additions of iron, nickel, vanadium and zinc oxides to produce a wide range of greens. Iron oxide of from 0·5% to 6% in glazes fired in reduction gives greens known as celadon. See **Copper oxides, Chromium oxide, Iron oxide in glazes** and **Celadon**.

Green issues

Potters are well aware of the precious nature of their earth and environment. They make art and artifacts from mud and minerals and rarely squander materials. Consideration must be given, however, to the way in which these mineral resources are won. Large-scale open-cast mining can ruin tracts of land, and destroy valuable plant communities and heathlands which have taken centuries to develop. Coastal sand extraction can cause erosion and dangerously alter tidal effects. The refining of minerals can cause serious pollution. Potters can sometimes avoid using problem products to help bring about change.

There are measures which potters can take within their own working spheres to conserve and keep clean their surroundings. Whatever the choice of fuel for firing there is a conservation problem. Potters defend their use of wood as it is a renewable resource which returns to the atmosphere only the CO_2 which it absorbed in growing. They usually find a source of off-cuts and otherwise wasted pieces. But the production of oil, gas and electricity, with their side effects, causes destruction of the environment, and pollution. Energy can be conserved by using better kiln insulation, lower temperatures and by burning fuel efficiently. The strong shift from the emphasis on stoneware to earthenware also gives direct recompense to earthenware potters in lower firing costs. But they in turn use more refined colours and glaze minerals.

Firing itself causes air pollution by smoke, carbon, carbon dioxide, fluorine, chlorine and sulfur. Careful study of each kiln and firing schedule can help to reduce polluting emissions. Even biscuit firing relatively pure clays in an electric kiln produces enough fluorine to etch workshop windows and attack the potter's throat. Much of the chlorine produced during salt glazing can be 'washed out'

by forcing the fumes to pass through a water jet spray. See **Salt glaze**.

Swimmers in an unpolluted environment are depicted on a large salt-glazed jar by Michael Casson.

Green ware

Ware which is complete from the making but has not yet dried sufficiently to be ready for firing.

Grog

Chamotte. Ground fired body added to clays to provide a proportion of already fired and often refractory material. Grog provides texture, both tactile and visual, along with bite for better control in forming. Grog is an opener which helps the clay to dry uniformly and because it is already fired it proportionately cuts down the overall shrinkage and hence any tendency to crack or warp. It is usual to consider grog as a body that is more refractory than the clay to which it is added and most grogs are fireclay fired to at least 1300°C (2372°F). The word grog is sometimes used in a less specific way to mean any opener—thus embracing sand, quartz etc. See also **Filler**.

Grogs can be considered as either hard or soft. Hard grogs are those which have been previously fired to a temperature above that to which the body is to be fired. The advantage of this is that this grog will not shrink in the firing and hence will work against any tendency to warp. It is useful in the making of tiles and large slab pots. Soft grogs are those which have been fired to temperatures lower than the temperature to which the body will be fired. If a soft biscuit firing is used, a soft grog may even be softer-fired than the biscuit temperature. The advantage of this is that a very porous grog is obtained which can be useful in the tempering of very sticky clays and in quick drying.

If the soft grog is the same body as that to which it is added it is called pitchers. The advantage of using pitchers is that the working character of the body can be altered for various sizes and types of ware, but the fired result is the same. The same glazes and firing schedules can therefore be used.

Grogs are graded by screening. Two numbers such as 40/60 mean that all will pass through a 40's mesh but not a 60's mesh. 60/Dust means that all will pass through a 60's mesh and some particles may be exceedingly small. See also **Analysis: mechanical**.

For large-scale slabbing a large size grog 40/60 may be appropriate to counter shrinkage and also to add texture. For throwing tableware 120/Dust gives fine clay a useful 'bite'. A grog addition which includes a wide range of size is often best. It avoids the loss of wet strength occasioned by too much large grog, and the shortness given by too much fine grog, thus allowing more to be packed into the clay without loss of workability.

There are some dark-coloured clays which are still sufficiently refractory for the potter to use for all the purposes of a hard grog and with the advantage of giving a dark speckle. Coloured pitchers made from dried and ground slips can be added to slips to give colour speckle. This is especially attractive with vitrified slips which burn into matt or other stable glazes.

Growan

Another name for **Cornish stone**.

Gypsum

Hydrated calcium sulfate. Alabaster. $CaSO_4.2H_2O$. The crystalline mineral from which plaster of Paris is prepared. It varies from white to an orange-pink colour. It can be ground and used in glazes as a source of calcium oxide (CaO). The sulfur trioxide is liberated during the firing combining with the atmosphere to form sulfuric acid. See *Acid*.

The decomposition sequence of gypsum is:

$$2(CaSO_4.2H_2O) \xrightarrow{120°-200°C} 2CaSO_4.H_2O + 3H_2O\uparrow$$

$$2CaSO_4.H_2O \xrightarrow{500°C} 2CaSO_4 + H_2O\uparrow$$

$$2CaSO_4 \xrightarrow{1000°-1100°C} 2CaO+2SO_3\uparrow$$

A large amount of sulfur trioxide is dangerous to health if released into the atmosphere of the workshop. Its passage through an already fusing glaze causes bubbling which may not settle before about 1250°C (2282°F). Small amounts of

gypsum, however, can be used in under slips, engobes or the first glaze of a double layer. Here it will cause bubbling through the covering glaze. If the covering glaze is sufficiently fluid, an oilspot effect can be achieved.

The following is a recipe which uses gypsum to introduce calcium oxide. It is a grey lime matt when fired to 1250°C (2282°F). A slow and fully oxidized firing in an open draught kiln is essential to take away the sulfurous fumes.

cornish stone	35
china clay	10
siliceous fireclay	5
gypsum	50

H

Haematite

Hematite. Martite. Specular iron. Kidney ore. Raddle. General name for a variety of iron ores which are almost pure red iron oxide (Fe_2O_3). The ore is usually black or grey on the outside but red inside giving a red brown powder when ground. Haematite is the source of iron metal and iron oxide for ceramics. The ore is sufficiently pure to be considered 99% Fe_2O_3.

Red iron oxide also exists naturally in hydrated forms, that is, in combination with water. The ores are called limonite and laterite. Haematite was probably of this origin and was subjected to pressure and heat (metamorphism). The precipitate was able to form crystals and in so doing became denser and purer. The hardness varies from H1 to H7.

The softest stones are the raddles and red ochres used by early people for self-decoration. The ore was considered the blood of the mother earth and the same consideration is held in the name haematite—the blood-like stone. These are easy to grind and use as pottery colours. See **Iron oxide**.

The hardest stones are distinctly crystalline and are called itabirite and specular iron. These are too hard to grind for pottery but are purer forms of red iron oxide.

Handle

The handle is the first part of a pot to be touched by the user. It is therefore a focal point of the pot and is both functional and decorative.

There are two types of handle: loop and lug. A loop is formed from a strip or roll of clay which gives a closed space itself or with the pot wall. A lug is a piece of clay attached to the pot and usually modelled in place. Both types perform the same functions of assisting lifting, carrying and directionally controlling the pot.

Lugs are used on small pots or where space around the pot is restricted, as with a casserole. They may provide only the merest grip or cluster as a friction surface. They are sometimes pierced for decorative effect, practical reasons of firing or use with thongs etc.

The lug handle is the simplest extension of the pot itself. It arises from the need for a better finger and thumb grip at the rim or for better side friction. The four examples are by Walter Keeler, Rosemary Cochrane, Josie Walter and Christine McCole.

A loop handle is intended to take the hand or at least a finger, otherwise a lug is sufficient. The loop makes a rhythm or continuous movement for the eye to follow taking in the weight of the pot in aesthetic appraisal and functional appearance. The theoretically completed loop of the handle should extend inside the pot and encompass the centre of gravity for control.

It is possible to slip-cast a pot with handles attached or create lugs from thrown flanges but for most pots the handles are additions. They are created at a later stage than the bulk of the pot but are a completion of the form. This is so, even when the handle is a cane one added after the pot's final firing.

Clay handles are usually added as soon as is practical. Some potters add handles to thrown casseroles, jugs and mugs before cutting them from the wheel. This urgency gives greater unity to the conception. Most potters add clay handles when the pot has stiffened slightly and use a special clay saved for the purpose. This clay has the same composition as the pot clay but has been specially soured and for a longer period. The handle clay is therefore more plastic, capable of greater flexibility in forming and results in a stronger handle.

The strength of a handle is the clay itself. A handle which

is weak at the join has not been correctly attached. See **Crack**. The defect can usually be traced to attachment of too soft a handle to too dry a pot or the use of too much water or slip in the process in the mistaken idea that this will effect an automatic weld. Slow drying for the first few hours following attachment is necessary for most clays. This gives the two parts of the join time to adjust their moisture contents, and accommodate the stress they have in relation to one another caused by shrinkage.

Handles are produced by pulling, extrusion, rolling, throwing and cutting. The examples are two by Michael Casson and two lid handles by Peter Starkey and Peter Dick. The rolled, indented and twisted basket handle is by Rosie Farr.

Hard (1)

Physically hard and difficult to scratch or cut. The hardness of a mineral is classified according to Mohs' scale of hardness. See **Table 28**.

Hard (2)

Hard, medium and soft are relative terms describing firing temperatures. Hard means at a high temperature, e.g. hard earthenware, hard-paste porcelain. The term harder is relative and when used against an example could mean merely 10° or 20° higher in temperature.

In describing glazes, soft means 600°C to 1050°C (1112°F to 1922°F), medium 1050°C to 1200°C (1922°F to 2192°F) and hard 1200°C to 1400°C (2192°F to 2552°F). Hard glazes therefore melt at temperatures above 1200°C (2192°F). They are also physically hard and are not easily abraded. Soft glazes are physically soft and scratch easily.

Hard fluxes are those which work at the higher temperatures but not at the lower ones. Magnesium oxide, for example, does not start its action as a flux until 1170°C (2138°F) and therefore is useful in glazes only above this temperature. Wood ashes are often classified as hard, medium or soft according to the temperatures at which they will act as fluxes. Ashes which contain more silica than flux are classed as hard. Paradoxically, hard ashes often come from soft woods.

Cornish stone is also classified as hard or soft but this refers to its physical property. The hard cornish stone is the softer flux.

Hardening on

The fixing of underglaze decoration prior to glazing by a firing in the region of 700°C to 800°C (1292°F to 1472°F). The firing burns out oils and varnishes used as carrying media and fuses the colour slightly by means of soft fluxes so that it adheres to the biscuit surface. See also **Burning out**.

Hare's fur

A variety of tenmoku glaze which has visual qualities resembling a hare's fur. There are two types: one has fine, light-coloured flecks against a dark ground, reminiscent of the hair tips against the fur; the other has the smoky appearance of the soft under-fur.

The hare's fur effect first appeared on Jian bowls during the Song Dynasty. These glazes were of the smoky grey type in which a lustrous swathe of bluey grey flows down the glaze following the line of gravity. The effect could be due to magnesium sulfate which decomposes after the glaze has melted. The gases disturb the surface and carry with them the magnesium oxide which gives the silky flecks. The bluish colour could be due to manganese oxide in the body or in the clay of the glaze. Occasionally the lustre breaks to a rust colour. The background glaze is a very dark brown. See **Tenmoku**.

Later hare's furs in Northern China had the rust flecks developed into yellow flecks. The flecks are about 0·5 cm long and run down the glaze in the gravity line. They show the length of movement of the glaze during firing. This is a difficult glaze to reproduce scientifically but the effect sometimes occurs in otherwise black and rust glazes. It could be due to spots of local reduction which encourage the movement to the surface of particles of iron oxide. The effect often appears on slip-glazes made from heterogeneous muds noted for their volatile content. See ***Albany slip***.

Health hazard

A threat to the health of the potter from the materials in use and the working conditions of a pottery workshop. There are obvious dangers from toxic materials used in glazes and colours. These are listed and explained under ***Poison, Lead poisoning*** and ***Low sol***. But there are hidden and less obvious dangers from dust and fumes. It must be remembered that the level of danger is considerably higher for children, pregnant women, the old and the ill.

Regulations govern the use of all materials by employers, employees and the self-employed. In the UK, no-one is exempt from following the prescribed precautions and routines concerning use, storage and disposal. Notifications are listed in the ***Bibliography***.

Poisons enter the body via the lungs as gases and fine dusts; via the digestion system as dusts breathed into the mouth or taken in on food or cigarettes; via cuts or wounds and occasionally through the skin. They enter the blood stream and affect the brain, liver, kidneys, heart, glands, bones and muscles. The possibilities are frightening. Fortunately a clean, careful and intelligent routine overcomes the risks and the healthy body can cope with small accidental intrusions. A filter mask or half-face respirator should be worn if in any doubt about the situation. After using glazes, glaze materials and especially colouring pigments, the work surfaces and floor should be washed clean and hands and nails scrubbed. Protective clothing should be of the non-porous type which can be wiped clean of splashes and quickly washed and dried. Smoking should be forbidden and food should not be consumed in the workshop, not even the morning cup of coffee!

The danger from dust particles in the workshop atmosphere as the cause of pneumoconiosis is now fully recognized. Any dust is a potential hazard but the substances of particular concern to the potter are silica, in the form of clay dust, feldspar, quartz and flint; ceramic fibre products; and asbestos. It is recommended that worktops are of impervious material rather than bare wood which can hold dust. In any case, all surfaces should be wet-wiped clean as frequently as possible, sweeping avoided, and vacuum cleaners fitted with a recommended absolute filter to retain particles down to 1 micrometre. A mask should be worn when dealing with powders and ceramic fibre, and when spraying glaze. Glaze should only be sprayed inside a booth with filtered extraction. See ***Silicosis*** and ***Dust***.

The threat from fumes ranges from irritation to eyes and nose from the vapour from metal lustre painting medium to sudden death from carbon monoxide. Kilns must be ventilated, so that fumes go outdoors and away from neighbours. This includes electric kilns even when firing only biscuit. The firing of resin lustres gives off acrid fumes of chlorine and sulfur products. Reduction firings make use of carbon monoxide which, if created in excess and allowed to permeate the workshop, could quickly cause fatalities. Note that there is no respirator which filters out carbon monoxide. See ***Carbon monoxide, Electric kiln*** and ***Lustres***.

Clay and glaze materials are not usually harmful to the skin except where it is broken by cut or abrasion. However, some people have especially sensitive skins which are affected by the acid and alkali of flocculants and deflocculants. Most people detect the caustic character when stirring by hand a glaze containing unwashed wood ashes.

A few prepared pigments contain an oil medium with dissolved colourant. This gives a fine dispersion of colour. It also means that, dependent upon the medium, the colourant chemical can enter the body through the skin. Such pigments are not intended to be applied by the fingers.

In addition to the hazardous substances which all potters are obliged to take care with, the materials used by ceramicists using printing techniques pose particular threats. They work with photographic acids and emulsions, varnishes and solvents. Most of their materials can be classified as either toxic, carcinogenic, irritant, corrosive, flammable or even explosive. Ultra-violet light, used to expose screen emulsions, is carcinogenic. Correct procedures must be observed in the use, storage and disposal of such materials.

A danger to the users of pottery wares arises if poisonous metals, such as lead and copper, are not fully involved in the ceramic fusion. Poisonous metals can be leached out from a fired glaze by acids in foodstuffs. Beware especially underfired ware and low-fired ware such as raku. See **Metal release**.

Lastly, one should not forget that a healthy work space is created by the physical and psychological comforts of a warm, light and airy situation with pleasing visual stimuli.

See also **Safety**, and the **Bibliography** for legislation on health and safety at work.

Heat

Energy used by the potter to achieve the necessary chemical and physical changes which convert clay into pot and minerals into glaze. It takes time for the heat of the kiln to transfer energy to clay and glaze minerals and affect their changes. Potters talk about achieving 'heat' and 'work done'. The term 'heat-work' is often used, the factors for which are temperature and time. These are recorded on a firing graph along with essential information on the amount of energy used as electricity input via alternating switchgear, as gas pressure, or as oil or gas flow.

Heat is the sun's energy which is stored in wood, coal and oil and liberated by fire (oxidation) to be transferred directly or indirectly to the pots in the kiln. The energy can be transferred directly by means of flames composed of excited particles which excite and vibrate the molecules of the pot. Indirectly the energy is transferred possibly first as electricity then as radiant heat from glowing elements or a red-hot saggar wall. The energy is used by the pots in chemical changes and rearrangements of molecules.

Most of these changes are endothermic processes, that is, they absorb more energy than they liberate which is the opposite of the change for example, from wood to wood ash which liberates energy (is exothermic). Thus energy is transferred from fuel to pot effecting a change of state in both.

During the period when a pot is absorbing energy and using it to effect a change of state, the temperature of the pot is theoretically constant. For example, a melting glaze remains at its melting point until all the solid parts become liquid. Then its temperature is able to rise. This is irrespective of the temperature of the surrounding atmosphere in the kiln. The temperature difference between kiln atmosphere and pot serves only to alter the time factor.

The energy absorbed by pots must affect the rate at which the temperature of the kiln can rise. Fluctuations can be discerned on the firing graphs of brick kilns where the ceramic change is endothermic causing a slowing down in the rate of temperature rise. Another cause of fluctuation is the oxidation process which burns out unwanted carbon etc in the body. This is exothermic and if not counteracted would cause an increase in the rate of temperature rise. A similar exothermic process occurs during cooling when glazes crystallize. The temperature of the glaze remains constant or may even increase a little at this point. The release of energy causes what is known as a 'lag' in the cooling curve as drawn on a graph.

The foregoing fluctuations of a firing and cooling curve would be difficult to discern with pottery kilns because the proportion of ware to already-fired kiln furniture and kiln structure is too small. However, they are interesting facts necessary to an understanding of the nature of firing.

Hemimorphite

Hydrated zinc silicate. $2ZnO.SiO_2.H_2O$. A variable zinc mineral.

High-temperature glaze

One which matures above 1200°C (2192°F). High-temperature glazes are also called stoneware and porcelain glazes. They make use of the alkaline earth oxides for fluxes and since these can be obtained in insoluble form a glaze can be produced without recourse to fritting. The fluxes are magnesium, calcium, barium and zinc oxides.

Hispano-Moresque ware

Lustred pottery produced during the Moorish occupation of Spain. The occupation lasted from the 8th to the 15th century and during this time a great civilization was established, based upon the philosophy of Islam.

One tradition was the making of lustred pottery. According to the teachings of Mohammed the use of precious silver and gold utensils would be a reward in paradise for those who did not seek such things in this life. Lustred pottery was the substitute for the precious metals and was always called gold lustre. The lustre was not gold however, but a combination of silver and copper. It was painted on to an already-fired tin glaze and fired at a low temperature with reduction. The brush-drawn motifs in lustre were often combined with the maiolica painting in metal oxides giving blue, green and purple. See **Transmutation lustre**.

The Moorish occupation never completely overtook the whole of Spain and there was a fluctuating uneasiness about the situation. Where the two civilizations of Islamic east and Christian west met there was an interchange of decorative motifs. The heraldic symbols of Gothic Europe, including some Christian ornaments, were integrated with the angular patterning and the flowing foliage of Islamic decoration. This evidence of the meeting of two cultures is the true Hispano-Moresque ware.

The potters were both Moors and Spaniards in both the Christian part and the Islamic part of the country, and many Moors undoubtedly stayed after Christianity was re-established by the rule of Ferdinand and Isabella in 1492. But without the Islamic influence of the Nasrid court the pottery lost its richness. The lustre became coppery in colour and the decoration became ungainly. This ware can be seen as a separate tradition slowly declining into the 18th century.

Hispano-Moresque ware is important because it brought a new idea into European decoration at the time when it could be incorporated in the Renaissance. See ***Maiolica: history***.

Historical identification

Close observation of a piece of pottery will reveal the nature of the glaze and body, the making methods, and the type and temperature of firing. Colour, texture, shine, crazing, movement of glaze during firing, bubbles, crystallization, interaction of materials, thickness of glaze, and ring when struck are evidence of how it was made and may be sufficient to place it accurately in its historical period, even its factory provenance.

Where a sizeable sherd is available for destructive examination, chemical testing can provide analysis for the comparative study of glaze and body constituents. The material is finely ground and dissolved in acids from which are precipitated chemical compounds.

When the sherds are too small for chemical testing, or the item is a precious antique which cannot be used, microscopy can provide information. A very thin slice is removed with a diamond-wheel wafer saw. This is polished and mounted for a study with optical and electron microscopes. Each element emits energy causing vibrations which can be read as waves. The measurement of the wavelength, from crest to crest, and its frequency identify the element by revealing its atomic number. The amplitude, the depth of the wave, indicates the amount of the element present. Ceramic scientists can identify the constituents of a glaze and compare, for example, the content and structure of a Ming copper red with a later Qing copper red. It is even possible to deduce the firing temperature and oxidation or reduction levels. Combining this with a study of known kilns of the periods, an accurate picture of techniques is built up.

The electron microscope uses a beam of electrons where the optical microscope uses light. High energy electrons accelerated to an energy of 105 electronvolts make it possible to measure very small wavelengths and thus identify the different elements. The transmission electron microscope focuses an electron beam, via an electron lens, through a very thin specimen on to a fluorescent screen. A visual image is formed and this can be photographed. The scanning electron microscope can be used with thicker specimens and forms a perspective image. An X-ray spectrometer measures fluorescence. Further techniques involve the binocular microscope, the petromicroscope and electron probe microanalysis.

Hovel kiln

A term used in Stoke-on-Trent, England, for the type of bottle kiln in which the chimney is an upward extension of the outer wall. The inner oven or beehive chamber is a separate structure.

Humper

A plate which has distorted, allowing the flat part to rise in unwanted fashion. It is the opposite of a whirler. Humping is accentuated in stoneware and dense earthenware and is usually found on pressed plates and plates which are glazed on the top side only. See also ***Whirler***.

Hyalophane

$K_2O.BaO.2Al_2O_3.8SiO_2$. One of the two barium feldspars and half-way between celsian and orthoclase in the group of true feldspars. It is only available as hand-picked specimens but occurs as small percentages of, or traces within, orthoclase. See ***Feldspar: types of***.

Hydrate

A compound involving water. Clay is a hydrate because there is water chemically combined in its crystals. This water is called the water of crystallization. Other common hydrates are borax, borocalcite, mica and gypsum. They are called hydrated substances. The opposites are anhydrous substances which are without water or, more commonly, the term implies that water of crystallization has been removed.

When hydrates are used in a glaze, the water of crystallization is driven off during the first part of the firing. This action starts at 100°C (212°F) and although rapid firings cause exceptions it is usually finished by 600°C (1112°F). If the glaze contains a large proportion of one of these substances then there is a large amount of water to escape as steam. If this occurs suddenly, the pressure may lift the glaze free from the pot. Later fusion of the glaze could then result in crawling or in spots of glaze falling from the pot. These are found as small beads of glaze on the kiln shelf and their bald patches are left on the pot. Colemanite, which is nearly 25% water, is especially prone to lifting. It liberates its water at 800°C (1472°F).

To cure this problem, fire the kiln slowly over the first 600°C (or more in the case of colemanite) or avoid hydrated substances by introducing fritted ones.

I

Illites

Hydrous micas. Sericites. A general name for the variable micaceous minerals found in clays. The group differs from true micas in having more combined water. The name is taken from Illinois, USA, where they were first identified. Their presence is responsible for the vitrification of the clay and some of its colour.

Ilmenite

Iron and titanium oxide. Iron titanate. $FeTiO_3$ or $FeO.TiO_2$. The ore of titanium and iron. It varies in proportion of iron to titanium. It is difficult to grind and though black in the raw state it gives brown speckles in glazes. It is used in small amounts (up to 1%) to 'seed' crystalline glazes. See *Crystalline glazes*.

The proportion of iron to titanium varies as their atoms occupy, in random fashion, two-thirds of the possible sites within a three-dimensional lattice. Titanium and iron complement one another and present a combined valency of 6 (4 + 2) which allows each to combine with oxygen in six-fold co-ordination. The oxygen is in four-fold co-ordination with titanium and iron in a three-dimensional lattice. One layer only of the lattice is shown in the drawing. There is no

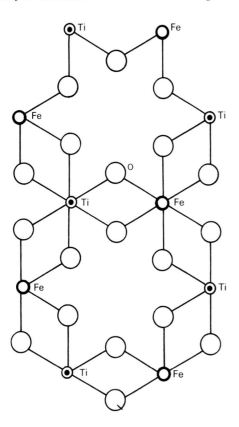

TiO_3 unit in the structure and therefore it is more correct to call ilmenite a double oxide rather than a titanate.

Impressed decoration

Decorative motifs stamped directly into the clay by a metal, wooden or biscuit device.

Incandescence

The emission of energy as light and heat. The intensity and colour of the light is an indication of the temperature.

As the temperature rises, the first indication of incandescence is called first red and appears at about 600°C (1112°F). With electric kilns there is some illumination of the ware by unshielded glowing elements which at this point are about 250°C (450°F) hotter than the ware. First red in electric kilns therefore appears at about 500°C (932°F). Further temperature rise results in brighter colour passing from red through orange, to yellow and white.

Incandescence	Muffle kilns, etc		Electric kilns	
	°C	°F	°C	°F
blue white	1400	2552		
white	1300	2372	1300	2372
yellow	1250	2282	1200	2192
bright orange	1200	2192	1100	2012
orange	1100	2012	1050	1922
bright red	1050	1922	1000	1832
deep red	900	1652	800	1472
dull red	700	1292	600	1112
first red	600	1112	500	932
black heat	up to 550	1022	up to 450	842

Inglaze

I/G. Inglaze colour. Sink-in decoration. Ceramic colours applied on top of an unfired glaze which sink into the glaze and stain it during firing. The colours are pure oxides, prepared stains and strongly coloured glazes.

Inglaze colours are usually applied by brush and the method is described as maiolica painting. But see also *Sink-in decoration*.

Inglaze lustre

See *Colour plate 1*.

Inlay

A method of decoration where lines are scored in a cheesehard clay surface and filled with thick, coloured slip. When the slip is dry, the surplus is scraped away to show the clean lines. Glaze can be similarly inlaid into biscuit or glaze. The photographs show a demonstration by Janet Hamer and a finished bowl by Peter Wills. See also *Rolled inlay*.

A broader inlay technique is to press strips of stained clay on the partly thrown form. These coloured pieces are integrated into the body clay by beating with a wooden mallet and the pot is thrown further to the final shape. Using a sponge helps to prevent tearing the surface. Excess slip is removed with a blade or rib. The photographs 1–4 show Jack Doherty throwing with inlay. See *Agate ware*.

1

2

3

4

Instrumentation

Kiln gadgetometry. The development and use of mechanical, electrical and electronic aids to kiln firing. Instruments and kiln accessories can be categorized as Indicators, Controllers and Safety Devices.

Indicators. Information on temperature is necessary when firing any kiln. Information on the amount of energy or fuel used is also valuable. Other information is more specialized and covers whether circuits are switched on and the amount of current flowing for electric kilns; and for gas kilns the pressure of the gas in main and burner supplies, the pressure of the atmosphere within the chamber and the type of atmosphere whether oxidizing or reducing. Indicators can be linked to recording instruments to give reference information.

Controllers. These instruments take over the repetitious adjustments to kiln control. The more sophisticated ones, which are known as programmers, control the whole firing from start to finish. This is most easily achieved on electric kilns but is possible on gas kilns. Studio potters who choose to fire with wood, coal and oil rarely wish to automate their kilns but prefer the direct involvement with the flame and develop the skills of assessing firing behaviour. Most accept the assistance of thermocouple and pyrometer but not as controls. However, in spite of the fact that coal hoppers sometimes become jammed and oil burners need to be cleaned during a firing, coal and oil fired kilns can be automated and have been so industrially.

THE PYROMETER gives information on temperature and is the most commonly used of all the available kiln accessories. It measures the self-generated electric current of a thermocouple and translates this into a temperature. The current increases proportionately to the increase in temperature.

A thermocouple comprises the outward and return wires of a circuit made from two dissimilar metals. For high temperatures these are platinum and platinum with 10% rhodium. The thermocouple is protected from the kiln fumes by at least one refractory sheath which is the probe through the kiln wall into the chamber. The circuit is extended by a compensating cable in which less expensive dissimilar metals are used. This cable enables the pyrometer to be in a safer, cooler position away from the kiln. It also ensures that one junction of the circuit remains cold at or near its original temperature while the other junction becomes hot. In this way, the temperature difference between hot and cold junctions, which creates the current, relates directly to the chamber temperature. If the cold junction becomes hot, the difference lessens and the temperature indicated is below reality.

The self-generated current is small but sufficient to drive a swinging needle (analogue) type of pyrometer. This is thus independent of any other electrical supply.

A digital pyrometer measures the same self-generated current from the thermocouple but requires additional current, either mains or battery, to drive the digital display. The readout can be light emitting or a non-illuminated crystal display. The advantage of a digital over an analogue pyrometer is that variations of temperature up or down are instantly displayed and rates of change quickly calculated. This is essential with the sensitive fast-fire kilns where reduction can cause a temperature drop. The balance of burners and damper is a fine one needing the help of a digital pyrometer to achieve it.

The pyrometer as controller. The simplest control is one which sets an upper limit to temperature rise. A temperature is pre-selected on the pyrometer and upon reaching that temperature an electric kiln is switched off or a gas kiln is shut down. Soaking at that temperature can also be achieved by remaking the circuit with electric kilns as the temperature falls and with gas kilns by re-establishing gas flow which is ignited by a pilot light. However with gas kilns it is more usual to simulate soaking by a slow climb to top temperature at which the firing is terminated.

By linking the pyrometer with a clock it is possible to control a firing throughout so that it follows a predetermined programme involving slow or fast temperature rises and soaks. Swing-needle type pyrometers can be linked mechanically to a slowly rotating cam. This cam continually changes the upper temperature limit of a soak thereby controlling the kiln. This method is particularly suitable for electric kilns.

An electronic programmer memorizes the cycle of firing and cooling instructions in terms of rates of temperature rise and fall with end temperatures at which different rates become operative. It has its own built-in clock and does not need to provide any form of display although digital readout and even printout are possible. The electronic programmer most easily controls an electric kiln but ones are available to control the valves and dampers of gas kilns.

Full automation is obviously an advantage in personal time saved and the use of 'off-peak' cheaper electricity, but the potter loses involvement with the product during a most important process which could lead to insufficient consideration of this area through lack of understanding. Another disadvantage is the price. Automation for an electric kiln can cost half as much as the kiln itself. With a gas kiln the cost is higher. Full automation involving sensors of the chamber atmosphere could cost more than the kiln.

The illustrations are: a digital pyrometer with facilities for controlling a firing to slow warm-up, followed by more rapid increase to a soak at top temperature by use of 'Limitstat' switch; and a sectional diagram of a thermocouple. Illustrations supplied by The Industrial Pyrometer Co. Ltd, Birmingham.

The accessories available for electric kilns are:

Indicators
1. An Indicator Light to show that the main is switched on or that a particular circuit is switched on.
2. An Ammeter to show how much current is flowing. It is often used on a kiln which employs elements in series and parallel for low and high energy input. It also indicates that the circuit is complete and that an element has not burnt out.
3. An Indicator Light placed in parallel with a resistance in a circuit to indicate that the circuit is complete.
4. An Electricity Meter to measure the units of electricity used.
5. A Thermocouple and Indicating Pyrometer, either analogue or digital, to give chamber temperature.

Controllers
6. An Energy Regulator which switches on and off to give the required percentage input as indicated on the selector dial. Except on very small test kilns the regulator energizes the primary circuit which controls the relay switches to the elements. There are often three relay switches but there may be more. They carry a heavy load which could not possibly be carried by the energy regulator, hence the need for the lightly loaded primary circuit.
7. A Controlling Pyrometer, also called a limiting pyrometer, to switch off the kiln when it reaches its top temperature. The pyrometer can be indicating or non-indicating (blind). The required top temperature is preset by dial, a needle on a dial or by push buttons, and there is usually a choice of switch-off or soak. The pyrometer operates one switch in the primary circuit controlling the relay switches.
8. A Timer or Clock with switch in the primary circuit to delay starting time so that finishing time is within a potter's day or to control the duration of the soak before switching off.
9. A Dawson Kiln-Sitter (*trade name*) to switch off the kiln at top temperature. This device uses a mini-bar, which is like a small pyrometric cone, to support a rod passing through the kiln wall. Outside the kiln the rod holds up a gravity operated lever switch in the 'on' position but, as the mini-bar bends with the heat, the switch falls and the kiln is switched off. This device therefore operates on heat-work like a pyrometric cone rather than on temperature alone as does the controlling pyrometer. See **Cones**.

10. A Mechanical Programmer to control the complete firing. This instrument is an extension of the swing needle controlling pyrometer which has a microswitch to soak at a preset temperature. Instead of setting a single top temperature manually, the upper limit is continually changed by a slowly rotating cam. A change of cam gives a different firing and cams can be cut to suit any firing and cooling cycle within the possibilities of the kiln.

11. An Electronic Programmer to control the complete firing. This instrument memorizes a cycle of firing and cooling instructions in terms of rates of temperature rise and fall with end temperatures at which different rates become operative. A thermocouple and non-indicating pyrometer linked to the primary circuit is an essential part of the control.

Safety Devices

12. A Heat Fuse to protect the kiln from serious overheating. The fuse is made from a metal of known melting point and included in the primary circuit. The fuse part is inserted through the kiln wall in a protective sheath like a pyrometer. It is not intended as a means of controlling a firing but is chosen for a temperature well above the normal operating temperature.

13. Kiln Door Locks can be arranged to complete the primary circuit so that the kiln cannot be switched on with the door open. Alternatively a single master key operates either the door lock or the mains switch and cannot be removed with the door open or the switch on.

14. Audible and visual alarms can be fitted to any circuit.

The accessories available for gas kilns are:

Indicators

1. A Meter to measure the volume of gas used.

2. A Thermocouple and Indicating Pyrometer, analogue or digital to give chamber temperature.

3. A Gauge, usually a dial or a liquid-filled tube, sometimes digital, to indicate the pressure of the gas, and hence the flow, in the main supply and also at each burner. The high pressure of LPG is measured in pounds per square inch (p.s.i.), kilograms per square centimetre (kg/cm²) or pascals (Pa). The low pressure of natural and town gas is measured in inches or centimetres of water greater than atmospheric pressure. See ***Table 41***.

4. A Gauge to indicate positive or negative pressure within the chamber or of the draw of secondary air at the port. This pressure is measured in relation to atmospheric pressure outside the kiln and is given as fractions of inches or centimetres of water in a U-shaped tube or by a sensitive diaphragm. The information is an indication of efficient or wasteful burning of gas and of oxidation and reduction atmospheres.

5. An Atmosphere Sensor to indicate the proportion of oxygen, carbon dioxide or carbon monoxide in the chamber or flue. One sensor is required for each gas analysed. This information is used to achieve settings of gas and air which give efficient burning and oxidation or reduction atmospheres.

6. An Indicator Light to show that the mains current is switched on for the electric and electronic instruments.

Controllers

7. A Solenoid Valve to give on-off control of main gas supply or supply to an individual burner. A solenoid is a powerful electromagnet which can lift and hold a shut-off valve against the pressure of a spring or gravity. While current flows the valve remains open. The current is usually mains electricity. Solenoids can be used to bring extra burners into use. Each burner needs ignition either by proximity to another burner or a pilot light with its own flame-failure protection or by a spark plug. Solenoids are used in a similar way to the primary circuit relays of an electric kiln.

8. A Controlling Pyrometer, either indicating or non-indicating (blind), to shut off the gas supply when the kiln reaches its top temperature. The required temperature is preset by dial, dial needle or push buttons and at that temperature the current which holds a solenoid valve open is switched off. Facilities for soak are less common, the equivalent being achieved by a slow climb to top temperature.

9. A Dawson Kiln-Sitter (*trade name*) to shut off the gas supply at the end of the firing. The device maintains an electric circuit which holds open a solenoid valve until the heat-work is achieved.

10. A Timer or Clock with switch included in a burner solenoid circuit to delay start or to control duration of a soak or slow fall in temperature.

11. An Electrically Controlled Gas Tap or Valve to adjust the gas supply. Short-traverse valves are adjusted by cranks and screw-down valves directly linked to reversible, low-geared electric motors.

12. An Electrically Controlled Damper to adjust the flow of exhaust gases. Slide dampers are adjusted by cranks and counter-balanced vertical dampers by their supporting pulleys, both using reversible, low-geared electric motors.

13. A Variable Speed Fan to adjust the amount of air force-fed as primary and/or secondary air to the burner.

14. An Electronic Programmer to control the complete firing. It memorizes a cycle of firing and cooling instructions and, taking information from pyrometer, gauges and sensors, adjusts the burners, air and damper through motors and solenoids.

Safety Devices

15. A Thermoelectric Flame Failure Valve and Thermocouple to shut off the gas supply if the flame goes out for any reason. The thermocouple, which is usually in a pilot light, generates sufficient current to operate an electromagnet. This holds a shut-off valve in the open position against the pressure of a spring. It differs from a solenoid in that the valve must first be held open by finger pressure while lighting the pilot light.

16. An Ultra-violet Flame Scanner and Flame Failure Valve to watch the flame and shut off the gas supply if the flame goes out. The scanner distinguishes between the ultra-violet colour of the flame and the glow of the hot kiln. This information, through electronic control, holds open the valve by electromagnet.

17. A Heat Fuse to protect the kiln from serious over-heating. The fuse is part of the electrical circuit which operates the main solenoid valve. The valve cuts off all gas supply if the fuse melts.

18. Kiln Door Locks can be arranged to complete the electric circuit to the main solenoid valve.

19. Spark Plugs can be fitted to most burners. They are especially useful where burners are sealed into the kiln structure and secondary air ports are separate.

20. Audible and visual alarms can be fitted to any circuit.

Insulation

Materials for conserving heat within the chamber of a kiln.

The ability of a material to resist the passage of heat through its substance depends upon the air within its structure. Heat travels through solids by means of conduction, and through gases or air by convection and radiation. The most effective barrier to heat transfer is a pattern of very fine pores. When the pores are small and closed there is less convection of air through them so heat is not moved in that way. Radiation depends upon the difference in temperature between two opposing faces. Across a small pore there is less difference to attract heat exchange. Many of the insulating materials that are available are similar in their chemical content but the structure, giving patterns of air-containing pores, determines their relative insulating properties.

Progressively efficient insulating bricks have an increasing number of smaller pores. This also makes them lighter, an advantage in construction, especially of arches, and of better mechanical strength than bricks with large holes. These light bricks are known as low thermal mass bricks.

Firebricks, insulating bricks, bricks of low thermal mass, and ceramic fibre are described under **Kiln building materials.** The diagrams show some hot face to cold face differentials. Some typical chemical analyses are given in **Table 39**.

Three main types of ceramic fibre are available. One ceramic fibre is the alumino-silicate refractory first developed for use in jet engines. It is known as RCF (refractory ceramic fibre) and is usually given a maximum working temperature of 1260°C (2300°F). It is approximately equal parts of aluminium oxide and silica but it is suspected of being, though not yet proven to be, carcinogenic. The high-temperature fibre with up to 96% aluminium oxide content has a working top temperature of 1600°C (2912°F) but it is at present rather expensive. As far as the studio potter is concerned, both fibres are being superseded progressively by a combination of approximately 25% magnesium oxide and 75% silica. This fibre is referred to as a body-soluble low-bio-persistance material. That is, it does not remain in the lungs

Diagrammatic comparison of the different thicknesses of materials required to give a similar insulating effect from a hot face of 870°C (1598°F) down to a cold face of 80°C (176°F)

if inhaled but is very slowly dissolved and removed by the lung fluids because of its composition and very short fibres. Infrequent exposure to this fibre is therefore less dangerous, but all dust prevention measures should be taken and a mask worn by users. Trade names for the magnesium silicate material are: Isofrax; Superwool; and Ultralite.

The ceramic fibres are made by high-temperature fusion of the raw materials and the pouring of the molten product in a thin stream. This stream is air-blown into droplets which are then attenuated in the air current into fine fibres. These collect as a mat on a mesh screen. This material is marketed in a variety of forms which all exploit the principle

Ceramic fibre products are available in thicknesses from 0.5 cm to 15 cm. The diagram compares effectiveness when used as a hot-face lining or as infilling.

of a mass of minute air pockets giving excellent insulation. The tiny fibres interlock in a way which does not produce a brittle structure, thus avoiding stresses during heating and cooling. Ceramic fibre products provide non-structural insulation almost equal in effectiveness to diatomaceous or moler bricks but which can be used at much higher temperatures. Blanket can be cut by knife and cemented or pinned to existing brick structures. Blanket pieces, pre-cut to size and packeted in bags, can be purchased for fitting as interlining thus avoiding the newly cut edges of blanket which create dust. In fact, all ceramic fibre products can shed dust which might be inhaled and can also irritate the skin, eyes and nose. Precautions and protection must be taken. A mask is a must.

The photograph shows a fast-fire propane gas kiln built from dense firebricks with a 2·5 cm lining of ceramic fibre blanket cemented to the inside. A temperature of 1300°C (2372°F) can be reached easily in five hours.

The fibres have a diameter of less than 3 micrometres. This is extremely fine if compared with an average human hair at 100 micrometres. Fibre lengths vary up to 10 cm. The alumino-silicate fibre and the magnesium silicate fibre have melting points near to 1800°C (3272°F) but their continuous-use limits are usually quoted as 1260°C (2300°F). The high-aluminium-oxide fibre melts at 1930°C (3500°F) and has a continuous-use limit of 1420°C (2600°F).

Blanket is sold in various thicknesses and densities. Blankets, felts, mixes, boards and special shapes are designed to fulfil almost any insulating requirement. Their lightweight, low-mass nature means that they do not store heat and so cut the cost of heating kiln structure dramatically. Other favourable points are good thermal shock resistance and resistance to corrosion, except for concentrated alkalis as in salt kilns.

Used as lining or back-up to other structure or insulation, fibre can cut firing costs by as much as 40% and furnace noise by 70% to 90%. Statistics from manufacturers are often limited to a working range up to 870°C (1600°F) or 1000°C (1832°F) suggesting that performance is best at these temperatures, lower than most potters wish to fire glaze. Shrinkage is a potential problem.

Blanket can be attached to an existing kiln wall using high temperature cement. For lower temperatures stainless steel anchor pins and ceramic cup locks are used. Shrinkage must be allowed for. It is recommended that blanket is cut into strips which are then stacked edgeways and applied to the wall. Modules prepared this way or folded can be bought from some manufacturers. A thicker layer of blanket used as chamber lining may decrease the burning space and setting space more than is convenient so this point must be included in calculations. Flames and fumes under pressure would eventually penetrate a blanket used in flues if not backed by more solid brick. Board shrinks at high temperatures by as much as 5%.

Mineral wool blocks and diatomaceous earth are used as back-up—that is, as non-hot-face insulation. Diatomaceous earth is a naturally occurring material with a high insulation value but will not withstand more than 900°C (1652°F). It can be used as a loose infilling or purchased ready bonded as bricks. See **Diatoms**.

Vermiculite is produced from hydrated biotite mica by exfoliation which increases its original volume on heating by sixteen to twenty times. It can be used as loose grains as infilling or piled on to the roof to cut down heat loss. Vermiculite bricks can be used up to 1100°C (2012°F).

Aluminium foil reflects heat and can be used on the outside of kilns or as an interface.

For potters and students experimenting with temporary

Diagrammatic comparison of ceramic insulating materials showing approximate Thermal Conductivity ratings as Btu inch ft² h °F and indicating upper safe use temperatures.

R — Restricted construction
N — Non-structural
S — Structural

1 Btu inch ft² h °F = 124 cal m/m² h °C
1 kcal m/m² h °C = 8.0645 Btu inch ft² h °F

and primitive kilns, earth and clay mixed with leaves and straw assist heat retention effectively.

Interaction

Reaction. The influence which two substances have on each other during melting. It is sometimes referred to as breakdown.

It is commonly assumed that there are fluxes and silicas and that the fluxes attack the silicas causing them to melt. This is an over-simplification but is useful in general groupings and differentiation. However it is true to say that the silicas also attack the fluxes and cause them to melt, and that different fluxes attack one another. This is proved by a study of eutectics where it is seen that a small amount of silica helps lead oxide to melt at a lower temperature just as lead oxide helps silica to melt at a lower temperature than it would alone.

Interaction is an embracing term covering all these immeasurable complexities which occur in a body or glaze during firing. It is also used to describe the fluxing action which a glaze and a body have on each other resulting in a body-glaze layer.

Interface

See **Body-glaze layer** and **Buffer layer**.

Intermediate

Has the normal meaning of being between two different things and in pottery is used for glaze temperatures and for chemical properties.

INTERMEDIATE GLAZE. One which matures in the middle temperature range 1000°C to 1200°C (1832°F to 2192°F). This is a wide range. At the lower end the main fluxes are lead oxide and boric oxide. At the upper end the lead oxide can hardly be used because, unless by that temperature it is held in a strong silicate structure, it will volatilize. However, at the upper temperature calcium oxide, zinc oxide and barium oxide can be effectively used.

Intermediate refers therefore to a whole range of glazes of very different structure and there must be no assumption that any one intermediate glaze could be used at all temperatures in the range. As a range it serves to separate those glazes which rely upon the so-called stoneware and porcelain fluxes (but have no use for the soft fluxes) and those glazes which can only use the soft fluxes.

INTERMEDIATE OXIDE. An oxide of the amphoteric group or one which is so calculated in consideration of a glaze by unity formula. An intermediate oxide is neither acid nor alkali but acts as both and provides a link between these two extremes. Its chemical formula is usually R_2O_3 but some oxides of RO and RO_2 formula exhibit amphoteric properties and may be referred to as intermediate. See **Periodic table**.

INTERMEDIATE ROCK. Igneous rocks are classified according to chemical composition and occurrence.

Chemical classification is by the silica content as Acid, Intermediate, Basic and Ultrabasic. Intermediate rocks contain between 55% and 65% silica. Little or none of this silica is present as quartz, i.e. free silica, because it is combined in minerals such as the feldspars and ferromagnesian silicates.

Intermittent kiln

A kiln which is packed with ware, fired and allowed to cool again to withdraw the ware. This is the commonest type of kiln for a small pottery. The other type of kiln is the continuous kiln which requires a continuous flow of standardized production to be efficient and economical.

The disadvantage of the intermittent kiln is seen when one realizes that nearly all the energy put into the kiln must eventually leave the kiln again as heat before the ware can be withdrawn. In a small studio kiln between one fifth and one half of the energy, whether electricity, oil or gas, will be used to heat the kiln structure. Good insulation in the structure, lightweight kiln furniture and a quick firing cycle will help to keep down this waste of heat energy.

The larger the kiln, the more efficient it will be per cubic metre because pot space increases three-dimensionally, while the wall increases only two-dimensionally. Cylindrical kilns have an advantage over cubic kilns of equivalent pot space because they have less wall area. Good insulation, particularly a system using ceramic fibre, cuts down the amount of wasteful heat storage in kiln walls and speeds the firing cycle. These advantages are proportionately more effective in smaller kilns.

Internet

Access via electronic mail to the Ceramic Art Discussion Group (Clayart) centred at Kentucky University and the Ceramic Gopher information system at San Diego University provides archive information, glaze recipes with commentary, and discussion correspondence with other potters. International access is cheapest via an Internet Server with a local telephone number.

Intrusive

A geological term describing igneous rocks which have

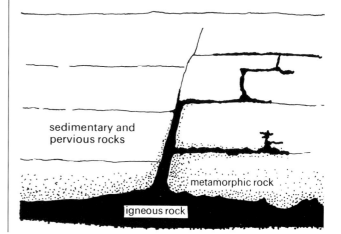
sedimentary and pervious rocks

metamorphic rock

igneous rock

entered other rocks along a line of weakness. The intrusive rock is liquid or plastic at the time of the intrusion and is probably hot, molten and under great pressure. Quartz veins are intrusions.

Inversion
See **Silica inversions**.

Iridescence
The characteristic of thin transparent films seen as colours even though the material itself has no colour. Common examples are oil on water and soap bubbles. In ceramics, iridescence is usually associated with thin layers of lustres and especially with the bismuth lustre known as mother-of-pearl. See **Lustres**.

Iridescence occurs where light is reflected equally from the top and bottom surfaces of a thin film of between 0·1 and 1 micrometre in thickness. The light passing through the film and reflected from the bottom surface rejoins the other half of the light which has been reflected from the top surface. The two halves blend to be seen by the eye.

Light travels in waves and where it happens that the crest of one wave passing out of the film coincides with the trough of another wave reflected from the top surface they are said to be out of phase. If the coincidence is exact in wavelength their energies cancel out one another and that particular wavelength or colour is not seen. The energy of a lost colour is not itself lost but strengthens other colours which have coincided in phase so that these colours appear strikingly luminous.

Iridescence is usually associated with thin metallic lustres, the best effects being obtained with bismuth and silver. Bismuth creates a layered structure of thin films, and silver is capable of being deposited in a thin uniform layer. Both allow light to enter and be reflected from the surface in about equal amounts ensuring a good possibility of totally cancelling part of the spectrum. Copper gives iridescent effects but because it is less transparent and because of its self-colour the colour range of the iridescence is limited.

Iridescence can also occur on darkly stained glazes at all temperatures where some reduction has created a thin metal or metal oxide layer at the glaze surface. This type is usually formed by iron, cobalt, manganese or lead but it never approaches the quality of bismuth or silver iridescence.

Iridescence is seen most effectively in multi-directional light as from the sky or an illuminated ceiling. Natural light is always preferable because it contains the full spectrum of colours whereas artificial light is limited and therefore some possibilities of colour display are missed.

The diagram shows in much simplified form how an orange iridescence occurs. Red, green and blue light waves are equally reflected and allowed to pass through the iridescent layer to be reflected at the glaze. Upon emerging, the half intensity red waves coincide exactly in phase with the reflected other half and a strong red is seen. The two halves of green are out of step so that a reduced intensity of

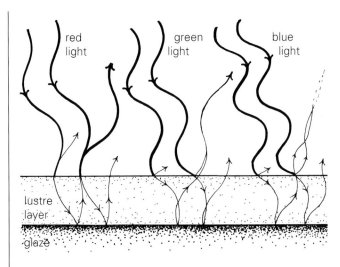

green is seen which modifies the red to an orange. The two halves of blue light combine exactly out of phase so that blue is not seen. See also **Colours**.

Iron Age pottery
Pottery made during the period when people were first able to fashion iron articles. The pottery was unglazed. The acceptance of the idea of glazed ware could be considered the end of the period of Iron Age pottery. The term can therefore only be used in relation to Europe and western Asia. In Egypt and the Far East the Bronze Age extended into the period when glazes were used. Around the eastern Mediterranean the period can be considered to extend from 1100BC to AD300 and in western Europe from 500BC to AD600.

Most Iron Age pottery was dense and provided a practical ware for domestic use. Ritual pottery, which had earlier been important, declined as an artistic expression and was superseded by metal artifacts as important objects in burials. This change of attitude released pottery from its ritual role and enabled it to find importance as domestic ware. A faster production of domestic ware was made possible by an increasing use of the potter's wheel, a fact which characterizes this period.

The Iron Age overlapped and was contemporary with the Roman Empire. The angularity and precision of Roman pottery influenced Iron Age products in many places.

Iron chromate
$Fe_2O_3.Cr_2O_3$ or $FeCrO_3$. A dense compound of iron and chromium oxides obtained from chromium iron ore ($FeCr_2O_4$). It gives opacity and a grey colour in glazes (1–6%) and is also used to give blacks with cobalt and manganese oxides (1–2% of each). It can also be used for underglaze brushwork where the edges can variously bleed with differing colours.

Iron foot
On reduced stonewares, especially celadons, the unglazed foot often reoxidizes during cooling. The iron oxide in the

body, with the help of some flashing from the glaze, produces a marked warmth of red brown at this point which is known as iron foot.

Iron ores

The natural mineral in the form of hard rock or soft earth, from which iron can be extracted. Iron very rarely occurs in pure state except in meteorites. Ores are combinations of iron with oxygen, carbon, sulfur and hydrogen. They are of igneous, sedimentary and precipitated origins and like many metal ores have descriptive names. Each has its own character. Some are almost pure iron compounds and therefore are remunerative to win.

Some ore names are: haematite, magnetite, limonite, laterite, marcasite, pyrrhotite, pyrite, siderite, ironstone, kidney ore and bog ore. The more important ores are separately listed in this book. Iron ores are common throughout the world. Some pockets are too small to win commercially while others are vast and still untapped. Large deposits occur in Norway, Sweden, Morocco, Brazil, USA and Canada. Small pockets and nodules can often be found which are of the oxide type of ore. These can easily be crushed, especially after weathering, and provide excellent pigments for brushwork and colourants for glazes. See ***Iron oxide***.

Iron oxide

FeO or Fe_2O_3 or Fe_3O_4. The general name for compounds of iron and oxygen. They are the commonest colourants in individual pottery usually giving yellows, browns, blacks and greys. The oxides are black iron oxide (FeO), red iron oxide (Fe_2O_3) and magnetic iron oxide (Fe_3O_4). These types are explained later and listed in ***Table 30***. Iron oxide is popular because it can give many colour variations. The oxide responds differently to different glaze recipes and kiln atmospheres. Iron oxide is responsible for the brown colour in red-burning clays. See ***Colour plate 67***.

Iron is a metal that is rarely found in a pure natural state. Instead it is combined with oxygen, carbon, sulfur and hydrogen in a variety of ores which constitute the commonest group of ores found throughout the world. The ores are of igneous, sedimentary and precipitated origins, and have various descriptive names like haematite (the blood-like stone) and pyrrhotite (the sceptic's stone). Small pockets of ores can be found in sandstones and limestones, and nodules occur in fire-clays. Many ores are soft and can be crushed by hand. They can be used without difficulty as colourants for glazes and as pigments for brushwork. A full list is given under ***Iron ores.***

Iron and iron oxides occur as important constituents, as impurities and as traces in many substances. There is iron in the human body. Iron oxide stains many minerals including feldspars and clays making them pink and brown. Iron oxide is used as a paint pigment giving yellows and browns in different combinations with other oxides. Some of these combinations are possible in the colouring of glazes.

When iron oxide is present in raw materials it is responsible for a range of colours from yellow through orange and brown to almost black. However, upon heating, the commonest crystal of red iron oxide is formed and this is a red-brown colour. Therefore clays which contain iron oxide become a reddish or pinkish colour after firing to a soft biscuit; even though they may start as yellow ochre, brown or grey clays. When iron oxide enters a fusion it usually becomes brown, sometimes a very dark brown, which is almost black. This is seen in the colour of clays which are fired to densification and in transparent glazes.

IRON OXIDE IN CLAYS. The use of iron oxide in a body or slip is straightforward. The darkest-burning natural clays contain approximately 6% of iron oxide. This gives a rich orange colour after firing to 900°C (1652°F). The orange colour is improved by small additions of china clay, especially those containing titanium oxide. Higher temperatures, up to 1100°C (2012°F), give a progressively deeper red turning to brown. The richest colours occur in clays with high silica content. Some clays can withstand 1200°C (2192°F) and form a red stoneware. Iron oxide can be added to any clay and will give similar results. To be sure of a uniform colouring it is better to use a red iron oxide and to add this to a clay which is in slip state. The whole should be thoroughly blunged. In slips and bodies to be fired oxidized, with or without a glaze, 5% to 15% of iron oxide will give a range of browns. For reduction, the limit of iron oxide is 10% and this gives a black, unglazed and under suitable glazes.

Speckling of clays can be achieved by the use of coarse iron spangles (magnetic iron oxide). Slips can be speckled with iron filings but these are dangerous in clays because they are sharp. Fireclays contain particles of iron pyrites which are often visible as dark specks in the clay or as light specks in some very dark clays. Finely ground fireclays are added to potting clays to give speckle, amongst other things. Some coarse fireclays contain large pieces (1–3 mm diameter) of iron pyrites which form hard cinders at 1000°C (1832°F) and trouble spots above 1200°C (2192°F) when they melt.

Natural clays which contain iron oxide vary in colour from yellow through orange to brown, grey and almost black. The colour is the iron oxide in different forms and combinations. Occasionally manganese compounds are present giving greys and, when fired, browns. Carbon is present in the blacker clays. Three examples of colour change from clay to oxidized body are given:

1. Some shale clays contain iron as a carbonate which gives a grey colour burning to red.

$$4FeCO_3 \ + \ O_2 \ \xrightarrow[900°C]{450°C\ to} \ 2Fe_2O_3 \ + \ 4CO_2\uparrow$$
$$\text{iron carbonate} \qquad\qquad \text{red iron oxide}$$

2. The hydrated form of iron oxide often gives the brightest reds when fired below 1000°C (1832°F). The iron oxide content is already fully oxidized and therefore gives a pure

red iron oxide (Fe_2O_3) when the water of combination is driven off. In some clays the hydrated iron oxide probably exists as a substitution for some of the aluminium oxide in the gibbsite layer. Such iron oxide has more protection from local accidental reduction than introduced iron oxide and therefore gives cleaner reds.

$$2Fe_2O_3.3H_2O \xrightarrow{500°C} 2Fe_2O_3 + 3H_2O\uparrow$$
hydrated iron oxide   red iron oxide

Hydrated iron oxide gives a yellow colour in clays containing lime. This changes to a bright orange and red with temperatures up to 1050°C. Clays which are high in lime (calcium oxide) content sometimes remain yellow or turn yellow during firing in the 1050°C to 1150°C (1922°F to 2102°F) range. The red iron oxide becomes involved in calcium iron silicate which is yellow.

$CaO.Fe_2O_3.SiO_2$ + increasing amounts
cream colour   of SiO_2
                    $\longrightarrow$ yellow colour progressively
                    becoming dirtier and darker
                    to black

The colour occurs at and near the surface of the body where there is the greatest heat and free oxygen. The effect is known as bleached iron. Overfiring causes such clays to deform quickly. Calcium oxide is a strong flux over 1100°C (2012°F) and these clays melt to black glasses at 1250°C (2282°F).

3. Clays which have contained organic matter have often been affected by decomposition. Some of the required oxygen for this decomposition was taken from the iron oxide leaving this in the black iron state (FeO). These clays look black before firing but burn red.

$$4FeO + O_2 \xrightarrow{900°C} 2Fe_2O_3$$
black iron oxide   red iron oxide

Theoretically it should be possible to achieve the same red colouring whatever the original form of iron oxide. In practice it takes a slow and very deliberate oxidation to achieve full oxidation. The especially difficult case of iron pyrites has already been mentioned but it should also be realized that during the oxidation of the clay between 700°C and 900°C (1292°F and 1652°F) it is difficult to keep the iron oxide fully oxidized. Over 900°C the reduced iron oxide as FeO acts as a flux and is involved in fusion with silicates. Once this occurs it is very difficult to reoxidize it.

The same clays which give reds, oranges and yellows in oxidizing conditions, give greys when fired in reducing atmospheres. These greys can be very decorative, variable and lustrous as used in blue bricks. It is necessary to employ a careful firing which incorporates some oxidation during the early stages. See **Breakdown** and **Black core**. The red iron oxide is easily reduced to black iron oxide around 900°C

(1652°F). The exact temperature and cycle are dependent upon the condition of the body. Carbon, which is inside the clay, must first be burnt out so that a black core is not formed. Following this the reduction of the iron oxide can begin before the native fluxes of the clay begin to form silicates with the free silica. Once this fluxing action has started then some of the iron oxide will be involved in the melts. Other iron oxide will be locked in pores which are sealed by molten glass. Both will be difficult to reach with the carbon monoxide. The equation of reduction is:

$$Fe_2O_3 + CO \longrightarrow 2FeO + CO_2\uparrow$$
red   carbon   black   carbon
iron oxide   monoxide   iron oxide   dioxide

Immediately after the black iron oxide is formed it will become involved in the melts and there will be little difficulty in keeping it reduced.

IRON OXIDE IN GLAZES. Iron oxide is a fascinating variable; variable, that is, in response to the situation. It can be used to produce a wide range of effects which are the responses to different glaze compositions and firing schedules. Many of these effects are known by descriptive names, e.g. celadon, tenmoku, tessha, kaki, oilspot, tea-dust, hare's fur, partridge feather and mirror black. Results are broadly predictable but some effects are narrowly balanced so that surprises occur. The surprise element is part of the charm of iron oxide. The properties can be summarized as follows:

1. oxidation gives red iron oxide;
2. reduction gives black iron oxide;
3. neutral atmospheres give a brown iron oxide;
4. the role of iron oxide in the glaze changes with its oxide state;
5. the amount of iron oxide influences the colour;
6. saturated glazes give special effects;
7. over-saturation gives dull glazes;
8. different glazes give different colours from the same oxide;
9. modifiers alter the colour;
10. other colouring oxides can be added.

1. *Oxidation.* The normal state of iron oxide is red iron oxide (Fe_2O_3). In this state the iron has combined with the maximum amount of oxygen and the resulting crystal is red. Pure crystals are scarlet but most red iron oxides contain impurity traces and iron oxides in lesser state of oxidation. They therefore appear red-brown.

Red iron oxide in glazes gives yellows and browns, modified as described later. Average proportions are: up to 4% for yellows; 4% to 6% for tan; 6% to 10% for browns; 10% to 25% for matt dark brown. The richest colours occur in glazes high in silica and low in aluminium oxide.

The particle size of red iron oxide affects the colour obtained in oxidized glazes. The colour depends upon the amount of integration which takes place with the other glaze oxides. In oxidized stoneware another factor comes into play if relatively large particles still exist above 1220°C (2228°F). At this temperature red iron oxide begins to decompose slowly and a self-reduction takes place resulting in a colour change. The equation is:

$$2Fe_2O_3 \longrightarrow FeO.Fe_2O_3 + FeO + O \uparrow$$

A light reduction would benefit glazes at this point by assisting the removal of the oxygen which otherwise pin-holes the surface of all but the most fluid glazes.

Very finely divided red iron oxide particles are involved in fusion by this temperature and will not decompose. They maintain the clean red-brown colour.

2. *Reduction.* Iron oxide is easy to reduce. It responds immediately to carbon monoxide and is willing to release oxygen and become black iron oxide (FeO).

The equation is:

$$\begin{array}{ccccccc} Fe_2O_3 & + & CO & \longrightarrow & 2FeO & + & CO_2 \\ red & & carbon & & black & & carbon \\ iron\ oxide & & monoxide & & iron\ oxide & & dioxide \end{array}$$

Proportions of black iron oxide and resultant colours are: 1% to 3% for pale to dark grey-green (celadon); 8% for black; 8% to 12% for tenmoku, tessha and kaki.

Once the iron oxide, red and black, is locked in a molten glaze, its oxygen atoms also become involved with other elements, e.g. silicon, aluminium, potassium. These are not so willing to release the oxygen atoms and reshuffle their structures. Oxidation or reduction of iron oxide is therefore more effectively undertaken during the period before and during which the glaze melts. Once a glaze has melted, the reduction or oxidizing atmosphere is only able to affect oxides at the surface of the glaze.

The spinel structure of $FeO.Fe_2O_3$ resulting from the self-reduction of red iron oxide is not so dark a colour as black iron oxide (FeO) nor is it so strong a flux. It also resists further reduction. Therefore to achieve total reduction of red iron oxide to black iron oxide it is necessary to complete the deliberate reduction before this self-reduction begins at 1220°C (2228°F).

The following recipe is for a lightly reduced celadon for 1250°C (2282°F):

potassium feldspar	48
china clay	14
flint	18
whiting	18
black iron oxide	2

3. *Neutral brown iron oxide.* Half-way between red and black iron oxide occurs a mixture which has the formula Fe_3O_4. This is simply a mixture and gives a mixed colour of dark brown. This is not a particularly desirable colour and in no way rivals the fully oxidized tans and browns or the reduced greens and blacks. The mixed oxide occurs in neutral atmospheres and also when oxidation or reduction begins too late to convert all the iron oxide present. Iron oxide in combination with other oxides in fusions is resistant to change.

4. *The two roles of iron oxide.* Black iron oxide is always a flux. Red iron oxide is sometimes a flux but mostly an anti-flux. As iron oxide changes its state of oxidation it also changes its role and since this may happen incidentally as well as deliberately, the results are sometimes unpredictable.

Black iron oxide becomes a glaze flux at temperatures over 900°C (1652°F). Its inclusion in a glaze recipe should ideally be as a substitute for part of another flux. More easily it can be added to existing glazes along with its own weight of silica (quartz or flint). In leadless or low-lead glazes for 1100°C to 1200°C (2012°F to 2192°F) it can be substituted for calcium carbonate, weight by weight, or added with its own weight of silica. Above 1200°C the balance becomes unpredictable. Weight for weight with whiting plus about half its weight in silica is necessary. Alternatively iron oxide can be added along with double its weight in silica. The amounts given are necessarily empirical and in no way intended to be definitive.

In soft glazes it is better to use black iron oxide in the recipe but with hard glazes which begin fusion over 1000°C (1832°F) it is possible to use black or red and reduce to black between 900°C and 1100°C (1652°F and 2012°F).

Red iron oxide should act as an anti-flux in glazes which are kept fully oxidized. The difficulty lies in keeping a glaze fully oxidized. Using a hard biscuit cuts out reduction from the body but the glaze itself contains minerals which decompose and liberate gases. Some of these gases can cause reduction in passing the red iron oxide. The notable example is partial sulfur dioxide liberated between 1100°C and 1200°C (2012°F and 2192°F). Immediately the iron oxide becomes black it will act as a flux and enter fusion. Kiln gases, even in electric kilns, can never be considered exclusively oxidizing.

Different bodies, different kilns and variations of firing cycle, inclusion of various other glazes in the kiln, and even differences of weather and atmospheric pressure will affect the role of the iron oxide. A glaze which is a soft matt tan colour in one firing can become a shiny muddy brown colour in another.

5. *Iron oxide amounts.* Iron oxide is a uniform stain in small amounts and a mottling stain in large amounts when some is undissolved. One per cent will give a slight stain. Approximately 12% is a usual maximum but as much as 25% can be used. Glazes which contain such a high proportion of iron oxide are dark matt glazes in which the surface is dulled by iron oxide crystals.

There is a percentage of iron oxide at which further increases do not serve to stain the glaze by solution but remain as undissolved crystals. These give a mottled effect.

The following table gives the range of iron oxide content

for different glazes and suggests the popular percentage which can be taken as a suitable starting point.

Reduction		
celadon	1% to 6%	(2%)
black tenmoku	4% to 15%	(8%)
kaki	10% to 20%	(12%)

Oxidation		
amber (lead)	1% to 6%	(4%)
tan (lead)	4% to 10%	(8%)
brown tenmoku	6% to 25%	(12%)
yellow (lime matt)	1% to 4%	(2%)
tan (lime matt)	4% to 8%	(7%)

6. *Saturation with iron oxide.* During firing, iron oxide is dissolved in the glaze. During cooling, some of this iron oxide is precipitated.

The molten glass can absorb more iron oxide in active state—that is, involved in fusion—than can be eventually incorporated in combined state in the cooled glaze. The difference between these two amounts is isolated during cooling and forms its own crystals. This precipitation starts at the surface, which is the first part to cool, and spreads into the glaze partially to embrace other iron oxide as it is isolated.

It is this saturation amount that is responsible for some very beautiful colourings from iron. The best known is the stoneware kaki (rust), which is indexed separately. Also at lower temperatures a metallic rust surface is possible with boron oxide and is used in onglaze colours. With lead glazes, the iron oxide gives a bright brick red and variations towards maroon.

It is impossible to predict exactly what the two amounts of oxide will be: the amount that will be absorbed when hot and the amount when cold. Each glaze is different and the factors affecting the two saturation amounts are:

(a) the alkali:acid ratio of the glaze;
(b) the iron oxide state; and
(c) the top temperature linked with the type of body.

The diagram shows these three factors in comparable form. Saturation point has been divided into a point for the hot molten glaze (right) and a point for the glaze when set on cooling (left). There is also a point for the metallic surface described in the next section (7) on over-saturation. The diagram rationalizes many different glazes to give five examples and does not try to show limits.

In oxidizing conditions, the red iron oxide is combining with the alkali and therefore if the glaze is high in alkali it will be capable of absorbing a larger amount of iron oxide than a glaze with less alkali. It follows from this that low-temperature glazes, which naturally have a large amount

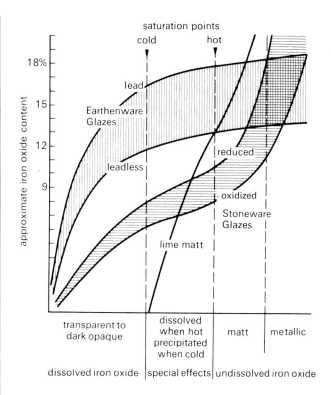

of flux (alkali), are capable of absorbing more iron oxide than high-temperature glazes. The diagram shows this.

It also shows an interesting comparison between the earthenware glazes and the stoneware lime matt glaze which is also high alkaline. In the latter, amounts of iron oxide up to 8% or 12% give precipitated effects of buffs and oranges whilst more only matts the surface and makes the glaze dark. In some earthenware glazes it is possible to dissolve completely as much as 17% of iron oxide. A slight amount more is dissolved when hot and precipitated on cooling. Too much matts the glaze in an undesirable way. This shows the difficulty of achieving these special effects with earthenware glazes. The aventurine effect is a particular type of precipitated iron oxide which occurs within a very soft lead glaze. Some of these glazes contain as much as 30% red iron oxide.

Reduced and oxidized iron oxides are compared as stoneware glazes of the transparent type. The oxidized iron oxide (Fe_2O_3) is an amphoteric oxide. This means that it can behave as an acid or an alkali. In glazes which are high in alkali it will act as an acid and go into solution with unattached alkaline oxides. In highly-acidic glazes the red iron oxide will act partly as an alkali and form combinations of iron oxide with silica also. Contrasting with this is the reduced iron oxide (FeO). This is always alkaline in character and therefore always combines with the acid part of the glaze. A general rule is that more iron oxide can be dissolved in a reduced glaze than an oxidized one. See also **Colour Plate 69**.

White bodies help the development of rust colours by reflection and concentration of heat in the glaze. Buffer layers are often used to assist these effects.

The photograph is of a jar by Mike Bailey which shows three glaze effects from iron colouring and saturation. See also **Colour plates 44** and **67**.

The following recipe is for a rust glaze on white stoneware at 1280°C (2336°F) oxidized:

feldspar	40
china clay	20
flint	10
whiting	15
red iron oxide	15

The following recipe is for a lime matt orange-brown for 1250°C (2282°F) oxidized:

cornish stone	46
china clay	14
tin oxide	5
whiting	28
red iron oxide	7

7. *Over-saturation with iron oxide.* The undissolved iron oxide gives opacity and a matt surface. This iron oxide does not enter the fusion but remains as unattached crystals throughout the firing. It moves through the molten glaze towards the surface where it forms a crystalline skin or matt surface. This surface is dull compared with the precipitated crystals which are cleaner in colour and presumably purer. Its normal colour is a dark and rather dull brown though in lime matt glazes a smoky green-black is possible.

There is a point in over-saturation when the iron oxide gives a metallic surface. Further additions of iron oxide produce a scum and rough surface. The metallic surface is easiest to obtain in reduced stoneware where some lustrous effects are possible. In oxidized stoneware and earthenware there are too many variables to achieve the effect except in small patches.

8. *The effect of the other constituents.* The other glaze oxides might be colourless in the glaze but they present different properties and hence different colours in combination with the iron oxide. The extreme variations are rare but tendencies are discernible.

In oxidized glazes the red iron oxide turns bluish in combination with sodium oxide. Small amounts with boron oxide are also blue. Calcium oxide combinations are yellow. Earthenware glazes high in lead oxide, potassium oxide and sodium oxide encourage the reddish colour in iron-saturated glazes.

In reduced glazes a saturation of black iron oxide is likely to give black with modifications towards brown if the aluminium oxide content is high. Low aluminium oxide content, almost amounting to absence, encourages a blue colour in part saturation. The presence of phosphorus oxide as a glass-former also encourages the blue.

The other fluxes which are assisting the black iron oxide also modify the colour. Lithium oxide and sodium oxide encourage a blue colour. Calcium oxide, barium oxide and potassium oxide encourage a green and are useful in celadons to counteract the duller colours given by traces of other modifiers.

9. *Other modifiers.* There are a number of oxides which are colourless and are used to give opacity, or in traces to modify colours. They are the oxides of zinc, tin, zirconium and titanium.

Zinc oxide modifies iron oxide to a series of unpleasant greenish mud colours. Zirconium oxide is a little better. Tin oxide gives some pleasant coffee browns but the best range of yellows and oranges is to be had with titanium oxide.

10. *Other colouring oxides.* All colours give what could be described as a visual mix of colour: cobalt oxide adds blue; copper oxide adds green; manganese oxide adds the purplish brown and gives interesting speckles in equal amount with iron oxide.

It is more usual to use iron oxide as a modifier to tone down colours which are too strong like cobalt and copper, or to intensify colours like the nickel and chromium orange.

TYPES OF IRON OXIDE. There are three different compounds of iron and oxygen used by the potter. They are red iron oxide, black iron oxide and magnetic iron oxide. They are derived from ores, are precipitated from other iron compounds (before or during calcination or firing) or are altered from other compounds by oxidation and reduction.

Red iron oxide gives yellows, oranges, reds and browns. Black iron oxide gives blacks and greens. Magnetic iron oxide gives black speckles edged with colours derived from the other two oxides. It can exist as separate particles of iron oxide under conditions where the red and black iron oxides would dissolve.

The oxides are described below and their uses are given under **Iron oxide in clays** and **Iron oxide in glazes**.

1. *Red iron oxide.* Iron sesquioxide. Fe_2O_3 (previously called ferric oxide). The pure form is a bright red colour. It is crystalline but the crystals are easily broken. Red iron oxide is therefore a fine powder whether ground from ore or precipitated from one of the salts, e.g. iron sulfate. This finely divided state enables it to spread uniformly through a slip or glaze as colouring. In glazes 2% gives a yellow and 8% a brown. The fine powder is used as a polishing abrasive by jewellers and is known as rouge. Its fineness also enables it to spread easily in the pottery with the result that it is picked up by fingers and transferred annoyingly to pots and book pages!

Red iron oxide is the stable form of iron oxide and is arrived at in various ways, all of which would be called oxidation by the potter. Oxidation is equivalent to burning and some heat is generated although the amount is not likely to have a noticeable effect.

The equations are:

$$FeSO_4.7H_2O \xrightarrow{400°C} FeSO_4 + 7H_2O$$
iron sulfate   crocus martis   water

$$2FeSO_4 \xrightarrow{1200°C} Fe_2O_3 + SO_3\uparrow + SO_2\uparrow$$
crocus   red iron   sulfur   sulfur
martis   oxide   trioxide   dioxide

$$2Fe_2(SO_4)_3 \xrightarrow{1200°C} Fe_2O_3 + 3SO_3\uparrow$$
iron sulfate   red iron oxide   sulfur trioxide

$$2Fe(OH)_3 \xrightarrow{500°C} Fe_2O_3 + 3H_2O\uparrow$$
iron   red iron   water
hydroxide   oxide

The photograph shows reoxidation to red iron oxide crystals on the light trailed lines. The background glaze is a black iron oxide tenmoku. The middle-tone lines are without iron oxide. Detail of a platter by David Lloyd Jones.

2. *Black iron oxide.* Iron monoxide. FeO (previously called ferrous oxide). The simplest compound of iron and oxygen. It is stable at room temperatures but becomes excited at red heat. This excitement is a loosening of the molecular bonds thereby allowing the black iron oxide to combine with silicates. It will therefore act as an alkaline flux in bodies and glazes. In glazes 1% will give a pale green (celadon); 3% a green-grey (celadon); and 8% a black.

The loosening of the bonds also allows the lattice structure to incorporate more oxygen so that the oxide reaches a higher state of oxidation:

$$4FeO + O_2 \longrightarrow 2Fe_2O_3$$
black iron oxide   oxygen   red iron oxide

The process is accelerated by applied heat and although time is a factor, the process of oxidation is inevitable if oxygen is present.

The oxide must therefore be deprived of oxygen if one wishes to keep the black colour of oxide for clays and glazes. Deprivation is achieved by introducing carbon monoxide to give a reducing atmosphere. Iron oxides in any state below full oxidation (Fe_2O_3) are greedy for oxygen but carbon monoxide is even more so! Black iron oxide can be obtained from red by the use of carbon monoxide.

$$Fe_2O_3 + CO \longrightarrow 2FeO + CO_2\uparrow$$
red iron   carbon   black   carbon
oxide   monoxide   iron oxide   dioxide

Further reduction to pure metal requires very heavy reduction and is unlikely to happen in a kiln.

The above equations show complete changes. In practice, partial changes occur because time is a factor in the change. Also, there may be insufficient oxygen or carbon monoxide to effect a total conversion before the result is sealed by a molten glaze or a temperature fall. The result is the half-way oxide Fe_3O_4 which is dark brown in colour.

$$6FeO + O_2 \longrightarrow 2Fe_3O_4$$
$$6Fe_2O_3 + 2CO \longrightarrow 4Fe_3O_4 + 2CO_2\uparrow$$

This dark brown iron oxide (Fe_3O_4) is only a theoretical convenience. It is not the same as magnetic iron oxide (Fe_3O_4) because it has not the same crystal structure. It is simply a mixture of the two oxides black and red.

$$FeO + Fe_2O_3 = Fe_3O_4$$

3. *Magnetic iron oxide.* Proto-sesquioxide of iron. Iron scale. Iron spangles. Fe_3O_4 (previously called ferroso-ferric oxide and ferrosic oxide). This is a separate crystalline form of iron oxide which is different from the other two although at first sight its chemical formula is a simple addition of one molecule of each. The crystal is black and metallic, hard, dense, and resistant to chemical breakdown. The structure is an inverse spinel.

Its action in bodies and glazes is zero until some disassociation has taken place. This occurs above 1100°C (2012°F) in contact with ceramic fusions.

$$Fe_3O_4 + \text{ceramic fusions} \xrightarrow{1100°C} FeO + Fe_2O_3 + \text{ceramic fusions}$$

The action is slow and as it takes place the liberated black and red oxides dissolve into the surrounding melt producing bleeding.

The advantage of magnetic iron oxide is its capacity to remain as speckles in a body or glaze. Being hard, it is never in so fine a powder form as red iron oxide and therefore cannot spread itself uniformly. When purchasing magnetic iron oxide it is better to buy the coarse spangles which look like iron filings with a bluish lustre. Here the individual grains are visible. The fine powder which looks like a greyish graphite gives too fine a speckle to be effective.

It is possible to convert magnetic iron oxide into one of the other forms by oxidation or reduction. The conversion requires at least orange heat, time and a distinctly oxidizing or reducing atmosphere:

$$4Fe_3O_4 + O_2 \xrightarrow{oxidation} 6Fe_2O_3$$

$$Fe_3O_4 + CO \xrightarrow{reduction} 3FeO + CO_2\uparrow$$

The conversions are possible in ceramics at temperatures over 1100°C (2012°F) before glass melts have taken place and the process may be advantageous in producing speckling. There is no other advantage in its use as a substitute for red or black iron oxide.

Magnetic iron oxide is found as the ore magnetite and is produced when hot iron is beaten as in wrought iron (iron scales). It should not be confused with the partial reduction of red iron oxide (or the partial oxidation of black iron oxide) which is given the same theoretical formula: Fe_3O_4.

Iron pyrites
An ore of iron and sulfur found as an impurity in some clays. See **Pyrite**.

Iron spangles
Iron scale. Blacksmith's scale. Magnetic iron oxide. Fe_3O_4. See **Iron oxide: types**.

Iron spot
Rust spot. Small areas of iron oxide crystallization which occur on the surface of reduced glazes. The reduction draws black iron oxide from the small nodules of limonite and pyrite in the clay, through the glaze to the surface.

Under reduction the concentration of iron oxide is finely divided producing a smooth surface although its concentration inhibits its complete solution in the glaze. At the surface a small portion of the iron oxide takes up oxygen in a crystallization which gives a sparkle.

The vase by Michael Casson shows iron spots through a dolomite stoneware glaze. The details are of iron spots through a lime matt in a platter by Leighton Clark and iron spots through an ash celadon inside a bowl by Phil Rogers.

J

Jack

Case. Model from which working moulds are made.

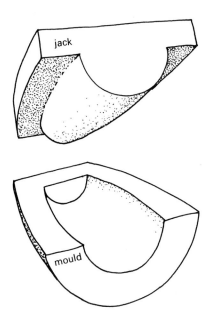

Jar mill

Pot mill. Ball mill. A grinding mill for glazes and colours. The glaze materials are sealed in a porcelain jar with water, grinding medium and space. The medium is pebbles or specially prepared ceramics, often called balls but not necessarily spherical. Jars are of sizes up to 9 litres. The jar rotates by resting on driven spindles. The speed of rotation is such that the medium falls onto the material continuously, the water providing dispersion of the particles.

The photograph is of the jar mill manufactured by Gosling and Gatensbury Ltd. See also **Ball mill**.

Jiggering

Forming a pot by using a spinning mould, usually of plaster, which gives the inside form. Jiggering is used for plates. The outside of the plate is formed by a plastic profile which is fastened to a pivoted arm. This arm is brought down onto the mould and is so adjusted that it leaves the correct clay section.

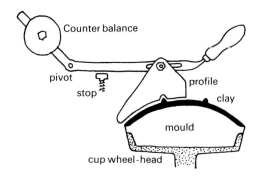

Joggle

Natch. The hollow and corresponding protrusion used in and on adjacent parts of a plaster mould to ensure correct alignment. The joggle is either cast in the plaster by cutting the hollow in one piece when casting a second up to it or bought as a two-piece plastic attachment which is set into the mould.

Jolleying

Forming a pot by using a spinning mould, usually of plaster, which shapes the outside of the pot. First the fingers and then a plastic profile are used to shape the inside of the pot. The plastic profile is on a pivoted arm which brings it into action against the clay but is adjusted so that the correct section of clay is given. Jolleying is used for cups and deep bowls.

Jug

A container for storing and pouring liquid. Until the 17th century, jugs and mugs were synonymous terms. Both were used for storing, pouring and drinking. The refinement of manners and the development of the pouring spout created the division into two specialized containers. The examples illustrated are by: Pauline Paterson, Sheila Casson, Ruthanne Tudball, Trevor Chaplin, Blandine Anderson and Anthony Theakston. See also **Pitcher**.

Jun

A pale blue, opalescent stoneware glaze named after a town in northern China where it was first made in the 11th century. The jun glaze is related to the celadon glaze, being a feldspathic glaze on a buff body and fired in a reducing atmosphere.

The beauty of the jun glaze lies in its fine visual texture and opalescent colour. It looks its best on simple forms. It sometimes incorporates patches of purple as on the illustrated bowl by Derek Emms.

The blue opalescence is a Tyndall effect and is caused by scattered light. White light entering the glaze is diffused by suspended particles of colloidal size. The violet to blue light is scattered back to the observer but the other light waves (green, yellow, orange, red) pass through the glaze and are absorbed by the dark-coloured body. For maximum effect,

the glaze must be applied thickly. Where the glaze is thinner, on rims for example, the colour seen is that of the body beneath and the glaze is virtually transparent because insufficient blue light is scattered.

The particles which scatter the short-wave violet to blue light are smaller than can be seen with the naked eye. See **Colloid**.

In jun glazes, these particles are nuclei of crystals and have been attributed, by different researchers, to phosphorus oxide, black iron oxide, calcium borate, titanium oxide, silica, and devitrification of alumino-silicate from the body-glaze layer. Reduction helps to keep the phosphorus oxide isolated. It is also essential to incorporate the iron oxide in iron silicate nuclei which remain separate from the surrounding glass. The low aluminium oxide content of many jun glazes preserves these nuclei. Many wood ashes contain phosphorus and iron, and jun glazes are associated with wood ash and feldspar glazes. The calcium borate and titanium oxide nuclei usually produce long streaked flushes rather than the short-grained flushes. These occur with or without reduction. See **Clair-de-lune flush**.

Juns are obviously obtainable in various ways. Any form of incipient devitrification which remains within a transparent and colourless glaze will give scattering of light and look bluish. The difficulty is in controlling the situation and producing the correct amount of devitrification to give a jun. An underfired jun is usually semi-matt, dull and not blue because there is too much crystallization. An overfired jun is transparent and glassy because the isolated particles become fully involved in the melt. See **Crystalline glazes**.

The red splashes are due to heavily reduced copper of colloidal size. The amount of copper required is very small and can be successfully added as a thin wash of slip on the raw ware. Three per cent of copper carbonate in the slip is adequate.

One of the jun glaze recipes used by Derek Emms is:

feldspar	43
china clay	1
quartz	30
whiting	20
talc	4
colemanite	1
black iron oxide	1

The enlarged detail of this glaze shows that its opacity is partially caused by minute bubbles as well as the flush streaks. The lower half of the photograph is part of a red-purple splash. See *Colour plate 39*.

Jutland ware

Peat-fired unglazed pottery which originated in Neolithic times, was perfected early and continued to be made until the mid-20th century. The pots were burnished with a flint pebble and, after firing, soaked in buttermilk to make them non-porous. The pots shown are by Ellen Marie.

PLATE 32
BOTTLE by Christine Gittins.
Height 34 cm.

'Using porcelain clay, my pots are all thrown on the wheel, turned and burnished when leatherhard. After an initial bisque firing to 1000°C (1832°F), some pieces have lustre applied to parts and are refired to 750°C (1382°F).

The final firing takes place in a saggar in the kiln when the pots are carefully packed in sawdust together with a mixture of salt and copper carbonate. This is distributed amongst the ware taking care to keep it from touching as direct contact with the salt could eventually erode the clay surface. The kiln is fired to 800°C (1472°F). As some fumes still escape from the saggar an efficient air extractor is essential. Care should be taken not to breathe in any fumes.

I use an electric kiln, taking care to do an oxidation firing in between each saggar firing.

After firing, the pots are gently brushed clean and polished with a wax polish whilst still warm.' See **Burnishing, Fuming** and **Smoking**.

(photo: *Christine Gittins*)

PLATE 33
'THRONE BOWLS' by David Jones. Height 23 cm.
The pots have glaze layers with additions of cobalt oxide, copper oxide, silver nitrate or gold chloride. Resist areas made with tape separate the glazes. The pots are raku fired in a top-hat kiln and smoked in a bin of sawdust. See **Raku**.

(photo: *Rod Dorling*)

PLATE 34
LUSTRED BOWLS by Anne James. Diameters 22 cm to 24 cm.
Anne James uses a finely-grogged porcelain body for these bowls which are sprayed with patterns of stained slips before burnishing and bisque firing. Further patterns of resin lustres are then superimposed by painting, printing and use of latex resist. The lustres are fired at 750°C to 800°C (1382°F to 1472°F) then taken out and treated as raku. Anne finds that beech sawdust is the best for smoking.

(photo: *Rodney Forss*)

PLATE 35
FUMED RAKU POT by John Wheeldon. Height 20 cm.
These pots are thrown using a 50/50 blend of 'T' material and Superwhite stoneware. After biscuit they are decorated with trailed latex and glazed with a mixture of copper oxide 90% with high alkali frit 10%. They are then raku fired to 900°C (1652°F), taken from the kiln and placed on a thin bed of sawdust. This burns creating an envelope of smoke and flame around the pot. After two or three minutes the pot is covered, sealed and allowed to cool. See **Fuming**.

(photo: *John Wheeldon*)

PLATES 36 and 37
SMOKED POTS by Ashraf Hanna. Tall pot height 45 cm.

'All forms are made from smooth white stoneware clay. They are normally started as pinch pots then developed with slabs. After refining using metal and rubber kidneys, the forms are burnished with pebbles.

After bisque firing to 1000°C (1832°F) a piece is covered with a resist slip and a design of simple lines or a pattern which enhances the form is drawn through the slip with a wooden tool. Once dried the piece is placed in an oil drum, surrounded by wood shavings and paper, and set alight. The smoke penetrates the areas not covered by resist.

The shell of resist slip is finally removed revealing the design and a coating of beeswax is applied to enhance the depth of the marking.' See **Fuming** and **Resist**.

(photos: *Ashraf Hanna*)

PLATE 38
BRONZE EFFECT POT by John Alliston. Height 16 cm.
See **Recipe Appendix.** (photo: *F & J Hamer*)

PLATE 39
Jun effect on a porcelain celadon.

(photo: *Janet Hamer*)

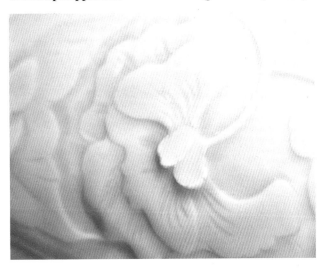

PLATE 40
Yingqing glaze on porcelain. See **Recipe Appendix.**
(photo: *Janet Hamer*)

PLATE 41
Salt glaze forming tiger-skin texture. (photo: *Janet Hamer*)

PLATE 42
DOUBLE AXE-HEAD CRYSTALS ON POT by Avril Farley.
See **Crystalline glazes**. (photo: *Avril Farley*)

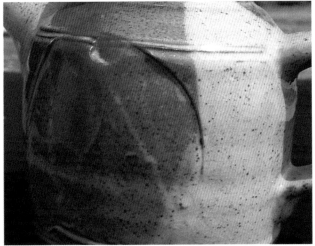

PLATE 43
Shino glaze over dark body and white slip.

(photo: *F & J Hamer*)

PLATE 44
DECORATED PLATTER by David Frith. 40 cm square.
The press-moulded platter is glazed in celadon, then decorated with a panel of vine leaves in wax resist. A kaki overglaze is poured over and further pigments trailed on. The work is fired with reduction to 1280°C (2336°F).

(photo: *David Frith*)

PLATE 45
TEAPOT *in Micki Schloessingk's salt kiln.*
The firing in this cross-draught wood-burning kiln takes more than 24 hours and reaches around 1300°C (2372°F). The salt and wood ash create a wide range of surface effects and autumnal colours. The kiln was built with three linked packing areas which extend the temperature range, ash and salting effects from heavy to light flashing.

(photo: *Micki Schloessingk*)

PLATE 46
SALT-GLAZED CHALICE by Michael Casson. 23 cm wide × 16 cm high.

(photo: *Petra Reynolds*)

PLATE 47
TRANSLUCENT PORCELAIN AGATEWARE BOWL by Linda Caswell. Diam 20 cm.

(photo: *Linda Caswell*)

PLATE 48
JUG FORM by Peter Beard. Height 41 cm.
The form is built in 'T' material. When creating colour patterns of glaze on his pots Peter Beard applies layers of glaze on glaze. The glazes have different maturing temperatures but are fired together in one oxidized firing at 1280°C (2336°F). Each glaze therefore has a different degree of fusion as well as a different colour. His finished surfaces often have a dry and crusty character.
The first glaze goes over all the piece. It is a barium oxide glaze which gives a light-coloured matt crystalline surface. Peter then brushes on a water-based wax emulsion stained with a fire-away food colour so that he can see the resist patterns. Subsequent glazes are low-firing of alkaline type but overloaded with oxides and stains so that, rather than fusing, they effervesce and remain matt. The colours, in this case copper oxide and chromium oxide, volatilize and stain the crystalline surface of the base glaze so that it acquires a bright green or blue.

(photo: *Peter Beard*)

PLATE 49
SMOKED BOWL by Sheila Casson. Width 22 cm.
The biscuited pieces are placed in sawdust, sometimes in saggars, within a kiln for smoking. The kiln is brick-built and circular, corbelled in five courses with a dust-bin lid on top. See **Smoking**.
(photo: *Petra Reynolds*)

PLATE 50
SMOKED BOWL WITH LIP by Sheila Casson. Width 28 cm.
(photo: *Sheila Casson*)

PLATE 51
SALT-GLAZED TEAPOT by Sheila Casson. Height 17 cm.
(photo: *Sheila Casson*)

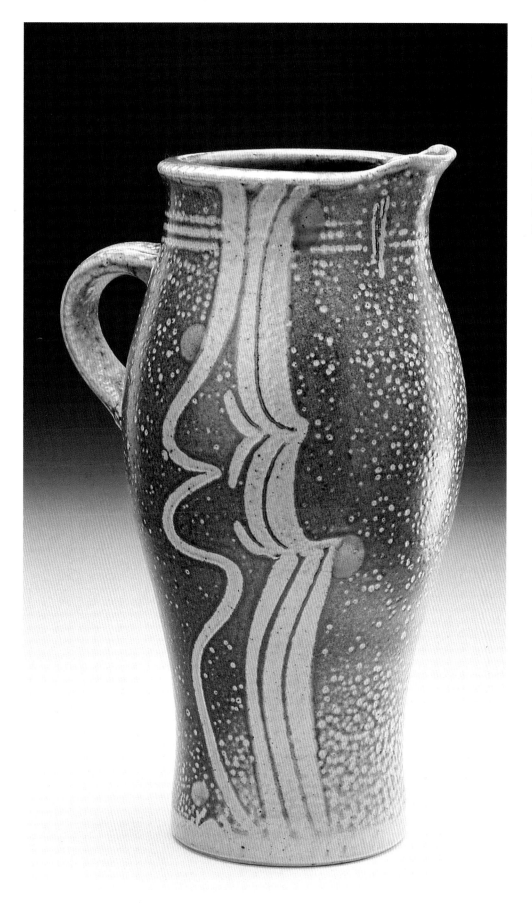

PLATE 52
TALL PITCHER by Michael Casson. Height approx. 40 cm.
The pot was wood fired with salt to 1300°C (2372°F). The decoration was scored through a tan slip using a cut rubber kidney. The salting produces a characteristic orange-peel texture.

(photo: *Peter Harper*)

PLATE 53
SALT-GLAZED JUGS and LIDDED POT by Suzi Atkins. Height of jug 22 cm.
Suzi Atkins works in France with her husband Nigel and three assistants. She has developed a rich palette of slips which work well with the La Borne clay in salt firings. The pots are single fired to 1320°C (2408°F). These pieces are further elaborated with gold-lustred lines.

(photo: *Janet Hamer*)

PLATE 54
SALT-GLAZED BOWL by Michael Casson. Height 20 cm.
In this wood-fired bowl Michael Casson contrasts a reduced iron-glazed interior with tiger-skin texture on the exterior made by tan slip and heavy salt glazing. His shapes are influenced by the crisp lines of early and classical Greek pots. Simple scored lines on the handles and a few spots of glaze add a confident gesture. See **Salt glaze** and **Tiger skin**.

(photo: *Peter Harper*)

PLATES 55 and 56
HUMBUGS by Tim Andrews.
Diameters 35 cm and 50 cm
approx.
The pieces are made in
porcelain body and 'T'
material using throwing and
some handbuilding methods.
The larger humbug forms are
constructed in two sections
and re-thrown as one piece.
Each piece is burnished and
many have a coloured slip
applied which is also
burnished two or three times.
After a high bisque firing
some of the pieces have a
resist slip applied which is
later overlaid by a low-
temperature glaze. Lines or
patterns may then be drawn
through the unfired glaze.
Each piece is fired on its own
in a top-hat gas raku kiln. At
red heat the pieces are
removed and various post-
firing treatments are carried
out, usually involving
smoking in some way.
When cool the pieces are
cleaned off (any resist slip
and glaze has to be peeled off
and the partially smoked
surface thoroughly washed).
After drying, a coat of wax is
applied to seal the surface.
(photos: *Studio 4*)

PLATE 57
'BID BEN BID BONT'
BRICK SCULPTURE by
Gwen Heeney.
Gwen Heeney works
with extruded clay
blocks produced by
brick factories. Oil from
the extruder helps their
eventual separation. A
mound of blocks is first
carved with a sharp
spade progressing to
looped tools. As the
carved sculpture dries,
the blocks separate and
can be numbered for
firing and re-assembly.
These architectural
sculptures are designed
for specific sites where
they are assembled and
the blocks mortared
into place.
(photo: *Cordelia Weedon*)

PLATE 58
THE COMPLETED SEAT by Gwen Heeney.
(photo: *Gwen Heeney*)

PLATE 59
TALL URN by Simon Hulbert. Height 140 cm. The clay is Simon's own blend of terracotta which fires with oxidation to 1160°C (2120°F) in an electric kiln. The piece is assembled from coiled, thrown and press-moulded pieces. Some colour is inlaid at leatherhard stage and some areas are raw glazed. The pot is once-fired.

(photo: *Simon Hulbert*)

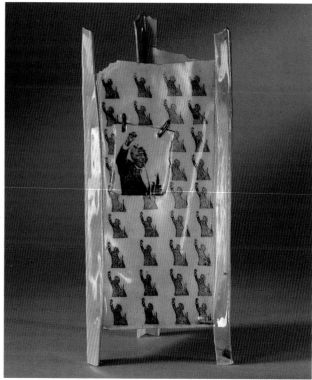

PLATE 60
*PRINTED LUSTRE BOWL by John Wheeldon. Diameter
37 cm.*
The bowl is thrown in John's own black basalt body,
biscuited and glazed in a transparent glaze and oxidized
fired at cone 7. The lustres are applied on the fired glaze.
The liquid lustre pigments are allowed to thicken to a sticky
consistency, mixed on a tile palette and applied with stamps
cut from fine, dense foam rubber. Areas of the bowl are
masked with tape which is removed in sequence so that the
lines of printed shapes fill a geometric pattern. The lustres
are fired in oxidation to 720°C (1328°F) cone 018. See also
Plate 63 and **Recipe Appendix**.

(photo: *John Wheeldon*)

PLATE 61
'FREE AT LAST' by Paul Scott. Height 25 cm.
'I paint, draw and print using paper and ink, porcelain and
paper porcelain, underglaze colours, metal oxides and
glazes. I use porcelain because its whiteness, unlike other
clay bodies, does not muddy ceramic pigments but brings
out their bright and sometimes very intense colours.' Paul
uses Harry Fraser porcelain. The slabs are first printed with
a repeat pattern. The pattern is made up with screen-
printed decals or transfers which are applied to the slab so
that an image made in underglaze colour is transferred to
the clay surface. The piece is then constructed with the
slabs, biscuited and glazed with a transparent 1200°C
(2192°F) glaze. Mother-of-pearl lustre is fired on to
complete the process. See **Printing** and **Decal**.

(photo: *Andrew Morris*)

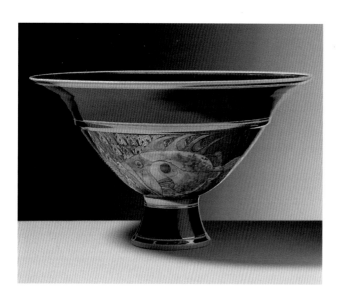

PLATE 62
*'JOHN DORY' BOWL by Michael and Barbara Hawkins.
Diameter 30 cm.*
The bowl was thrown using the Hawkins' own blend of
white porcellaneous stoneware mixed in a dough mixer and
de-aired in a pug mill. After biscuit firing at 1000°C
(1832°F) it was glazed in a shiny white glaze and colours
applied. The work is fired to 1300°C (2372°F) cone 10 to
11, with reduction from 980°C (1796°F) in a natural-gas
kiln. Dark blue, mother-of-pearl and bright gold lustres are
then painted on and refired at 820°C (1508°F). Clay and
glaze recipes and lustre suppliers are in the **Recipe
Appendix**.

(photo: *Steve Teague*)

PLATE 63
BLACK URN WITH LUSTRES by John Wheeldon. Height 20 cm.
The pot is thrown and turned in a black basalt body which John developed. It is biscuited and glazed in a transparent-glaze firing at cone 7. The third firing for the lustres is 720°C (1328°F) or cone 018. The pattern was created using latex masking and brushed lustre. See also **Plate 60** and **Recipe Appendix**.

(Photo: *John Wheeldon*)

PLATE 64
SODA-GLAZED OVAL BOWL by Trevor Chaplin. Maximum width 41 cm.

(photo: *Trevor Chaplin*)

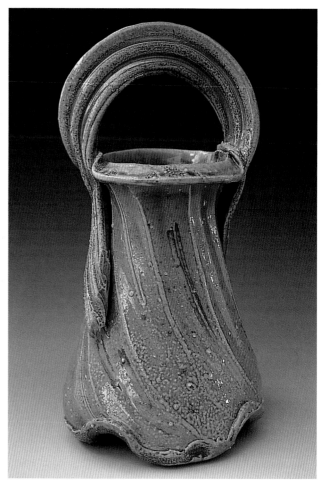

PLATE 65
BASKET by Ruthanne Tudball. Height 40 cm.
Ruthanne Tudball throws, manipulates and assembles her pieces wet while still on the wheel. Continuing the immediacy of this production, she dries and packs them raw into the kiln and soda fires them.

(photo: *Ruthanne Tudball*)

PLATE 66
Ruthanne Tudball sprays a super-saturated solution of sodium bicarbonate into the kiln using a garden pump sprayer. Spraying is repeated every fifteen minutes from 1260°C (2300°F) using approximately 1·0 kg to 1·3 kg of sodium bicarbonate in a 1 m³ gas kiln.

(photo: *David Tudball*)

K

Kaki

The Japanese for persimmon fruit and following this, the name for the rust colour which results when iron oxide crystals spread as a layer on the surface of stoneware glazes. Further detail is given under *Rust*.

Kalium oxide

K_2O. See *Potassium oxide*.

Kalium soda

Natrium potassa. NaKO. The theoretical combination of potassium oxide and sodium oxide. $K_2O + Na_2O \rightarrow 2NaKO$. Its use is in calculations involving feldspathoids where separation of potassium oxide and sodium oxide is undesirable or impossible.

Kaolin

China clay. $Al_2O_3.2SiO_2.2H_2O$. Synonymous with China clay in North America. The purest clay, approximating closely the idealized clay mineral kaolinite. It contains very little iron impurity and is therefore white. It is a primary clay or a secondary clay moved only a short distance. It has therefore little plasticity but it is popular as a body constituent because of its whiteness. It is high in aluminium oxide content and with few alkaline impurities. It is therefore refractory with an assessed melting point over 1770°C (3218°F). It is used in glazes to introduce aluminium oxide and silica and to provide bulk in the slop suspension. It is also used as a paper filler and in cosmetics. See *China clay*. The ultimate analysis of a typical specimen is:

SiO_2	46·6
Al_2O_3	38·3
TiO_2	0·1
Fe_2O_3	0·4
CaO	0·3
MgO	0·3
Na_2O	0·3
K_2O	0·7
Loss	13·0

The name 'kaolin' is said to be Chinese for 'High Ridge', which was the district from which the early supplies were obtained. It is now spelt Gaolin. Kaolins are world-wide in distribution but few seem to have a plasticity to equal Chinese kaolins. British kaolins from Cornwall are called china clays; the name kaolin being frowned upon by potters as one used by the uninitiated. In North America, the word kaolin is correct.

Zettlitz kaolin is the Bohemian kaolin used by Dr Hermann Seger in his study of refractoriness. Kaolins are also mined in France and in the USA in Georgia, Florida and Carolina. The origins of these deposits are various but their ultimate analyses are very similar to that already given.

Kaolinite

$Al_2O_3.2SiO_2.2H_2O$. The idealized clay mineral. Kaolinite is the correct term for the particular crystal structure which is best represented in the material, china clay. However, all clays, with the exception of bentonite, contain kaolinite as their clay constituent. They also, of course, contain many other minerals, e.g. quartz, feldspar and iron oxide.

The term 'kaolinite' is reserved for the description of the pure mineral. The less specific term 'kaolin' is used to describe the material clay. Less pure clays are called simply clays, marls and shales.

The potter uses the formula $Al_2O_3.2SiO_2.2H_2O$ for kaolinite but this should correctly be written $Al_2Si_2O_5(OH)_4$. This second way is a better description of the structure of the crystal which involves hydroxyl bonds (OH) lacing together an aluminium:silicon:oxygen structure.

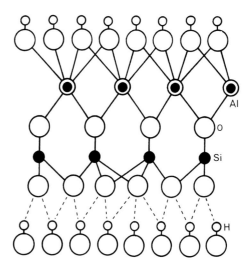

The kaolinite crystal has two layers. These are the gibbsite layer of aluminium oxide with hydroxyl groups; and the silica layer. These two layers share oxygen atoms and are therefore firmly bonded together. However, the combined gibbsite-silica layer is loosely attached to the next gibbsite-silica layer by alternating hydroxyl bonds. The diagram (overleaf) shows a side-view section through the layers. A sheet structure is developed which is strong in one direction but weak in the others. Kaolinite crystals are therefore flat. They are also hexagonal seen from above. See **Clay: physics of**, and also **Disordered kaolinite**.

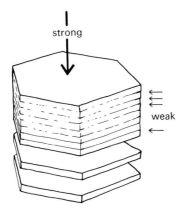

Kaolinization

The process of decomposition whereby igneous and metamorphic rocks are changed. The important new mineral which emerges is kaolinite, the pure clay crystal. The term is sometimes broadly used to include any weathering, leaching or chemical change in rocks if it includes the creation of laminar silicates like kaolinite, mica and montmorillonite.

Kelp

The ash from burnt seaweed, especially wracks. It is rich in sodium oxide and was used during the 18th and 19th centuries as the flux in glass-making. This source was rendered obsolete by the LeBlanc and Solvay processes of the late 18th and mid-19th century which enabled sodium compounds to be manufactured from brine. See **Sodium carbonate**.

Kelvin

°K. Degrees Kelvin are centigrade measurements of temperature. The Kelvin scale was introduced in 1848 by William Thomson, later Lord Kelvin, professor at Glasgow University. It is an extension of the Celsius thermometer scale which has 100 degrees between the freezing and boiling points of water. However, the Kelvin scale starts at 'absolute zero' and therefore 0°K equals −273°C and the boiling point of water (100°C) is 373°K. Degrees Kelvin are also called degrees Absolute (°Abs). The temperatures throughout this book are referred to as degrees Celsius with their Fahrenheit equivalents in brackets.

Keuper marl

A superior mudstone of the Triassic Period. It originated as a desert dust. See **Loess clay**. It is not consolidated and so can be reconstituted as a clay for potting. It has a high clay content, a high lime content and a high iron content. It is brown and grey when raw and brown-burning. Low-grade Keuper marls are called foulstones.

Kidney

Press-moulder's kidney. Rubber kidney. A flat kidney-shaped piece of rubber for pressing slabs of clay into or onto moulds. The rubber is about 6 mm thick tapering to a thin edge. There are various shapes and degrees of hardness. As a general rule the larger the work being pressed the harder should be the kidney. Long, very soft kidneys are excellent for small dishes.

Kidney ore

A type of haematite iron ore which looks like a collection of lustrous black bubbles. Although black on the surface it crushes to a brown powder (Fe_2O_3).

Kiln

A structure built to conserve heat. The word kiln is derived from the Latin *culina*, a kitchen, as in culinary. It is pronounced with or without the n.

The potters' kiln developed from the open trench system of firing by the addition of a dome of sherds to baffle back the heat. Today's structures are more sophisticated but the principle remains the same. Heat is introduced into the chamber where the pots have been placed. The temperature is raised and the amount of oxygen in the atmosphere is controlled according to the needs of the pots and their glazes.

The design, construction materials and insulation used depend upon the fuel to be used and the temperature and atmosphere required by the pots.

Electricity is popular—as a simple to operate, clean fuel—but is usually suitable only for oxidized firing. Reduction atmospheres can be controlled in kilns using oil, gas, wood or coal. The design of flues, tracking of flames, size and height of chimney are determined by the fuel system. See **Cross-draught, Down-draught** and **Up-draught.**

The materials used in the construction are a combination of structurally supporting elements and insulating materials. Traditionally, firebricks have performed both functions within a strong metal framework with special grades used in particular areas. With low thermal mass bricks and ceramic fibre blanket, paper and board available for insulation, there is more specialization of function. These are often used as linings or back-up to brick structures.

Many types of kiln are known by the name of the ware they fire and further information is given under these processes. See **Salt glaze** and **Raku**.

HISTORICAL KILNS. Having developed from a simple bonfire to produce low-fired cooking pots, kilns were improved over the centuries with the purpose of raising the temperature in the pot firing area. Heat was conserved more efficiently around the pots by building baffles or a firing chamber, by creating stoking holes to increase fuel input, and by providing a chimney stack to improve the draw. See **Romano-British kiln**.

A natural draught is sometimes achieved by building the kiln as a long chamber, or series of chambers, rising up a sloping bank. Such kilns were, and sometimes still are, used in China, Korea and Japan, for the production of the high-temperature classic porcelain wares.

Simple up-draught structures were used in Stoke-on-Trent for the production of Staffordshire slipware and in the 18th century for creamware and industrial earthenwares. These brick structures evolved the typical bottle shape. See **Bottle kiln** and **Hovel kiln**.

Since in traditional kilns the bulk of kiln structure and furniture is likely to use at least half of the energy input, kilns have been designed which can be fired continuously to avoid wasteful reheating. They also use heat from cooling for pre-heating. See **Continuous kiln**.

FUEL KILNS. Kilns fired by oil, wood, gas, coal or coke have in common in their construction the need for entry ports for the fuel, controlled air intakes, baffles or bag walls to deflect and spread the initial heat from its source, tracking systems for flames through the pots in the chamber, exit flues, dampers to control the draw and chimney to give draw and/or take off waste fumes. See **Cross-draught, Down-draught** and **Up-draught**. Reduction atmospheres can be controlled at the air intakes or by dampers in the exit flue.

Oil kilns use domestic fuel oil or sump oil which is introduced by burners or drip-feed systems, and the most efficient use forced air from a powered fan or compressor to achieve burning. A supply of oil can usually be obtained where sufficient electric power or mains gas is not available. The burning of oil is noisier and dirtier than the use of gas or electricity, and kiln linings are gradually attacked by the fumes, particularly if the oil is not atomized efficiently. Space must be found for a gravity tank and the storage tank. The fire hazard from the stored fuel is no greater than that of other fuels. Oil firing is suitable for most kinds of reduced stoneware and earthenware. There can be up to 3% sulfur contained in the oil which could be detrimental to the finest of porcelain glazes necessitating the use of saggars.

Gas provides a quieter, cleaner, easily controllable fuel. Where mains gas, coal gas or natural gas is available this is often the ideal. If not, bottled liquid petroleum gas (LPG), propane or butane, may be used for kilns up to 425 litres (15 cub ft) in size, or a larger 1 tonne tank, may be installed. LPG may be twice the cost of mains supply gas. Strict safety regulations govern the siting of tanks and piped supply. Natural gas has a soft flame and usually uses either a forced draught at the fuel entry or a chimney to create the draw. The draught can then be controlled or dampered to regulate efficient burning or reduction atmospheres. Propane gas, on the other hand, burns with a strong flame even at the lowest pressure setting. This has the advantage of obviating the need for forced draught or tall chimney but gives less possibility of extending or re-directing the flame. The strategic placing of burners is therefore more critical. The firing can be independent of electricity and not at risk from power cuts. Reduction can be controlled by narrowing air intakes, dampers or simply by partly blocking the top of the exit flue with ceramic board.

Gas kilns can be viable at small sizes, even down to 57 litres (2 cub ft) internal dimensions. There is no sulfur in this clean fuel and very little abrasion of kiln structure and furniture. White stoneware and porcelain do not need the protection of saggars against contamination.

Wood firing gives a particular quality to the pots as ash and variable flames toast the surfaces. In the pursuit of this exclusive character the convenience of oil or gas kilns is sacrificed and a much more labour-intensive firing programme is undertaken. This programme includes the whole process of maintaining an adequate store of the correct woods, dry and cut to size. For a given firing chamber size the kiln takes up more space with large fire-boxes and chimney, and more space is needed around them for stoking activities. The surrounding air suffers pollution from smoke and fumes and so wood kilns must be sited well away from neighbours. The flames cause considerable structural deterioration and kilns must be rebuilt at intervals. The rewards are: freedom from mechanical kiln gadgetry; a close identification with the whole dramatic metamorphosis; and wood fired pots.

The use of coal and coke has largely been discontinued in preference to electricity, oil or gas due to the storage and stoking involved and problems of sulfurous fumes in the chamber and smoke from the stack.

For further assessments of the use of fuels see **Fuels, Burners** and **Table 40**.

AUTOMATED KILNS. The firing schedule can be completely automated on any kiln where the operation of the necessary controls can be mechanically or electronically effected. There are many controls which can be used in a complete system or used singly to perform part of the operation.

Increasingly sophisticated instruments can take over the task of judging temperature and atmosphere from the experienced potter's eye watching colour, character of flame and smoke, pyrometric cones, bars or fishout tests. Instruments translate these measurements into numbers which can be recorded and more easily transferred for comparison with other kilns and taught to new firing technicians. The choice depends on the situation. Creative potters can fire their well-known kilns with skill and efficiency. A firing technician in a factory must be more accountable to others in the system.

Further instruments monitor the measuring instruments and act upon them, operating the controls to switch on, increase input, move dampers to balance oxidation and reduction, soak at a given temperature, and shut down the firing. See ***Instrumentation***.

Kiln building materials

When contemplating the building of a kiln the choice of materials is governed by:

1. The type of ware—high or low temperature, and whether the atmosphere would cause rapid breakdown of some materials as in, for example, salt or soda glaze firing.
2. The fuel to be used.
3. The size of the kiln.
4. The design of the kiln.
5. The availability and cost of the materials.
6. The siting of the kiln. Few kilns are left completely open to the elements but some materials would be too porous to be suitable outdoors.
7. The skill of the workman. Bricklaying and casting should be within the ability of a skilled potter but can be heavy work. Welding metal frames is another special skill.

If buying a kiln from a potters' supplier it is helpful to be able to compare the materials with more knowledge than catalogue specifications give.

For centuries the main building component for kilns has been the brick. 'Heavies' or firebricks form the main structural and insulating material. Since 1970 spin-off from space age technology has produced ceramic fibre, which, in various forms, now provides often dramatically improved insulation when attached in some way to a load-bearing structure.

Common house bricks (ceramic) can be used for temperatures up to 1000°C (1832°F) which includes enamel, raku, lustre or biscuit firing, but fuel economy would demand some further insulation.

Firebricks come in many grades according to composition and purpose. They are made from fireclay and grog fired to cone 10. The lower grades are more porous and have a shorter working life but are cheaper. Higher grades are denser, stronger and have higher working temperatures. These will remain in a good state throughout many firings as they are refractory, do not spall with repeated reheating, and have good resistance to abrasion from gases and general usage. They give reasonably good thermal insulation and do not suffer from high expansion/contraction. Being made from naturally occurring fireclay or modified with fireclay grog these bricks have been readily available and traditionally used as the main constructional and insulating material.

More specialized bricks are used where there is a particular need. Bricks with a high proportion of silica have high resistance to acid attack but suffer from poor resistance to thermal shock at lower temperatures. They are useful for high temperatures in continuous kilns where this temperature is maintained indefinitely.

For intermittent pottery kilns the high-alumina bricks are preferable. These contain 38% to 45% aluminium oxide. A higher proportion of aluminium oxide is particularly necessary in fire-boxes, and in salt or soda kilns where there is fierce attack from salt fumes.

One disadvantage of using only firebricks in the construction lies in the heaviness of the structure leading to the need for extra support for arches. The structure can be lightened and the insulation improved, giving better fuel economy, by partly using special insulating bricks.

Hot-face insulating bricks are used for the interior of the firing chamber and can withstand high temperature and flame tracking abrasion. High temperature insulation bricks (HTI or K-bricks) have slightly less resistance to maximum furnace atmosphere but are suitable for most potters' requirements. They are not load bearing but are used to line the chamber. They are clean, without fluxes that might affect pot surfaces, and are light in weight. Their insulating property is achieved by the structure of air-filled pores. The best rating is given when the pores are small and closed.

Diatomaceous bricks, made from naturally occurring open-pore silica formations (see ***Diatoms***), give good insulation when used as outer back-up to firebrick or hot-face bricks. They do not withstand temperatures above 900°C (1652°F).

Insulating bricks are lighter in weight and more easily cut to special shapes than firebricks. But they are not suitable for fire-boxes or salt or soda firing where they would be attacked by the fluxes.

The subject of insulation has largely been revolutionized by the introduction of ceramic fibre. This dramatically cuts firing costs especially in lower temperatures and where a simple rise to temperature is all that is required. It is claimed to cut fuel consumption by up to 40% when compared with traditional materials.

The fibre can be bought in many forms, e.g. blankets and felts, paper, ropes, shaped cloths, boards and blocks, formed shapes, bonded sheets, mixes for casting, coating cements, and even a sprayable mix. The practical working temperatures of these products varies from a maximum of 1040°C (1904°F) for cements, to 1420°C (2588°F) for special blankets, with 1260°C (2300°F) being the most common limit. All these forms have high insulating ratings, excellent corrosion resistance and are unaffected by oxidation, reduction, water, steam and oil.

Ceramic fibre therefore can be valuable in many kiln situations, either as an additional lining cemented onto a conventional brick kiln or as a blanket, simply shaped and pinned to a chicken-wire frame to make a 'top hat' or 'tea-cosy' raku kiln. The photograph shows a 'tea-cosy' raku kiln made and used by Barbara Ineson.

Special high-temperature cements are available for bonding blanket to brick. Ceramic fibre paper is sometimes used as a bond between brick courses and as an interface.

The corrosion action of fumes in salt or soda firing, wood firing, and oil firing would damage ceramic fibre if in direct contact. It can be used, in these cases, within the walls, as an interface, or on the exterior. Great care must be taken when working with or close to ceramic fibre, especially the soft blanket. There is always an amount of loose fibrous dust. A mask must be worn. Spraying the surface of the blanket with gum arabic can help to bind the fibres. See also **Insulation**.

Kneading

An action of clay preparation involving the rolling of plastic clay upon itself with stretching and spreading. By kneading, a lump of clay is thoroughly mixed and air bubbles expelled. In this homogeneous condition it is ready for a plastic forming process which immediately follows. In this way, kneading is a specific preparation and possibly involves a carefully weighed amount of clay. A more general preparation is wedging which often precedes kneading.

Kneading is done on the wedging bench. The desired

amount of clay is taken with hands close together and a part of it is pressed against the rest. The action is repeated with a slight progression. Two styles are known. They are ram's head or bull's head kneading, which is the European method, and spiral or shell kneading, which is Oriental. The reasons for the names should be obvious by reference to the illustrations.

Kneading is often used to incorporate grog into the clay and to blend two clays to produce a required texture. Occasionally, as the clays combine, within the structure of particles, an ionic exchange occurs. This results in weaker repulsions which necessitate more water for lubrication. Thus two soft clays can produce a blend which is stiffer.

Kochi

Japanese raku ware using a hard-fired biscuit. The hard biscuit has the effect of overcoming some of the disadvantages of soft biscuit such as general softness of finished ware and crazing of glazes. These advantages are at the expense of the control which a soft biscuit gives of the more subtle colourings.

Kyanite
See **Sillimanite**.

L

Labradorite

One of the plagioclase feldspars. It is mostly lime feldspar but contains up to 49% sodium feldspar.

Lag

Temperature lag. The slowing down in the rate of cooling of a glaze caused by crystal growth. During the cooling of a glaze, there are temperatures at which different crystalline solids are precipitated from the molten glass. Crystals appear as new compounds are formed and the creation of new compounds releases new energy in the form of heat. At this point, the temperature of the glaze is maintained or may even increase although the temperature of the surrounding kiln atmosphere continues to fall.

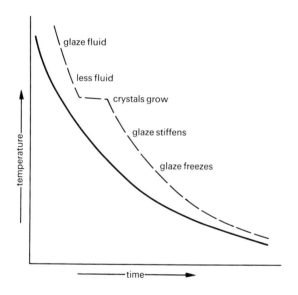

In the graph, the rate of kiln cooling is shown by the continuous line. The dotted line shows the rate for the glaze. The lag shows as a maintained temperature for the glaze. It is obviously too small to be noticeable as an influence upon the temperature curve for the whole kiln, but it is important to realize that by artificially holding this temperature in the kiln then more and larger crystals will grow. See also *Crystalline glazes* and *Devitrification*.

Lambeth

The area of London famous for delftware and salt-glazed ware. Delft was introduced by Italian potters in 1630, having previously worked in Antwerp. Production lasted for about 130 years until creamware became more popular. The salt-glazed ware was made from the late 17th century into the 20th century.

The photograph shows a delftware charger made *c.* 1680. The tulip-type motifs set as a spray are typical of the ware and the blue dashes around the rim gave this type of serving plate the name of blue dash charger.

Nineteenth-century Doulton Lambeth ware is famous for beer mugs and jugs with sprigged country scenes which were made in Lambeth for 200 years. The pieces were thrown and some were turned. The handles were either dod-box type or modelled greyhounds. Before firing, the pieces were traditionally dipped into Thames mud which gave the characteristic dark brown upper half. See also *Dod-box* and *Sprigging*.

Lamination

The combination of thin layers of coloured clay cut into decorative shapes and images. Coloured porcelain clays work well and the result is often finished by rubbing down to a smooth surface which allows the detail to be seen.

See also **Neriage** and **Rolled inlay**. The porcelain bowl with wrapped rim is by Anne Lightwood. See **Recipe Appendix**.

Laterite

Brickstone. A general name given to iron-manganese-aluminium ores in hydrated form. If used without qualification the term laterite is understood to refer to the hydrated iron oxide form with the variable formula: $Fe_2O_3.1$ to $3H_2O$. It was formed from an iron substitution into an alumino-silicate followed by the slow leaching of the silica. It could therefore contain up to 50% aluminium oxide with a formula of $Fe_2O_3.Al_2O_3.3H_2O$. More than 50% aluminium oxide results in the laterite being classified by the more specific term of bauxite. Laterite is found in small deposits around the tropical zone and in parts of western Europe and has been used as a glaze colourant. See **Iron oxide**.

Lattice structure

Lattice. Regular network. The three-dimensional pattern of fixed points on which atoms or molecules are positioned in a crystal. The word lattice signifies that the structure is regular as a repeating pattern and therefore the substance has crystalline character. The word random is used to signify an irregular structure.

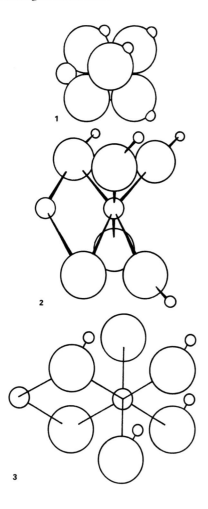

Lattices are often drawn as complex scaffoldings with atoms at the intersections. Diagrams showing these open-work structures are deliberately enlarged to make the structure of the lattice more easily understood. It is assumed that in reality the atoms are touching, even conjoined, so that the open structure is only a diagrammatic convenience.

The drawings show three ways of visually explaining the lattice of the gibbsite molecule (here shown as $Al_2O_2(OH)_4$) which is part of the clay crystal. Fig. 1 shows the molecule as it is theoretically imagined but it is impossible to read the structure. Fig. 2 is a slightly expanded version often used for three-dimensional effects and fig. 3 shows the flattened arrangement which enables some, but not all, crystal structures to be diagrammatized two-dimensionally. See also **Network structure**.

Single molecules are often described by what is known as a structural formula. This uses the chemical symbols for the atoms and lines representing valency bonds between them. Fig. 4 shows sodium chloride (NaCl), sodium oxide (Na_2O), calcium oxide (CaO), silica (SiO_2), aluminium oxide (Al_2O_3), barium sulfate ($BaSO_4$) and magnetic iron oxide (Fe_3O_4) which involves one divalent iron atom and two trivalent iron atoms.

Lava glazes

See **Crater glazes**.

Lawn

A fine mesh of wire, natural or man-made fibre. It is used for separating the fine grains of material from coarse grains, the coarse being retained by the lawn. It is usual to lawn materials in a wet state. Unless materials are soluble, it is easier to lawn them in suspension and also this method creates no dust. In practice the word lawn is synonymously used for sieve which is a lawn fastened to a frame or rim. See also **Mesh**.

Lawn prover

A powerful magnifying lens mounted at its focal point over a metal foot. The foot has a hole in it of known measurement so that the number of threads of a lawn can be counted and inspected. Lawn provers are usually foldable and are useful for inspecting glazes and bodies.

Leach

Bernard (1887–1979). He lived in Japan and first studied pottery in traditional workshops there before starting St Ives Pottery, Cornwall, England, in 1920. His work is the vital link between East and West which gave impetus to the European potters of the early 20th century. He is responsible for bringing to Europe a genuine understanding of the Oriental expression.

European pottery has been influenced by Oriental pottery in a series of impulses since the 17th century. Prior to the arrival of Bernard Leach, the influence had only inspired technical refinements and superficial copying of decorative motifs. Leach was able to subordinate technique to creative

inspirational potting which introduced a better understanding of the Oriental idiom to Europe.

Lead antimonate
See **Antimonate of lead**.

Lead bisilicate
Double silicate of lead. $PbO.2SiO_2$. A prepared compound in which, theoretically, one molecule of lead oxide combines with two molecules of silica. The theoretical proportional weights are lead oxide 65%, silica 35%.

Lead bisilicate is the popular lead frit. It can be introduced into almost any glaze in the range 900°C to 1200°C (1652°F to 2192°F) where it will assist with fusion by lengthening the fusion range and smoothing out the glaze surface. Fusion starts at approximately 700°C (1292°F) and is complete by 900°C (1652°F). This long range of maturation is important and gives the bisilicate its versatility. For use see **Lead frit**.

In the simplest lead bisilicate, the solubility of the lead content could be as high as 8%. However the use of a slight reduction of the silica to 1·9 equivalents produces a eutectic into which 0·1 equivalents of aluminium oxide can easily be introduced as a stabilizer. This has the effect of reducing the soluble lead content to below 0·02%. This is the method generally adopted in the manufacture of commercial lead bisilicate. See **Low sol frits** and **Frit manufacture**.

Lead-borosilicate glazes
The major type of low lead solubility glaze. Prepared low sol glazes are often of the type where the bought powder is a mixture of lead silicate (lead oxide, silica and stabilizers), borosilicate (boron oxide, silica and stabilizers) and other glaze minerals such as china clay and feldspar. The whole fuses to produce a lead oxide/boron oxide/alumino-silica glass with stabilizers. This is shortened to lead-borosilicate.

The use of two frits, lead silicate and borosilicate at the powder stage reduces the solubility of the lead content. A combined frit would have too high a solubility of lead but once the whole glaze has been fused there is no danger. The china clay and feldspar in the glaze enable the same frits to be balanced for different glazes. They also provide valuable bulk in the glaze slop to keep the glaze in suspension. See *Lead poisoning, Low sol, Lead frit* and *Double fritting*.

Lead frit

Lead silicate. Any prepared mineral that contains lead oxide and silica as the main constituents in fused form. It can be used as up to 95% of an earthenware glaze with china clay. Although lead products of any kind are now banned in some countries, lead frit is still popular with certain potters where it is available. Its wide fusion range makes it the most tolerant flux for raku and earthenware glazes. Its elastic property when cooling allows it to fit most bodies without crazing. For potters continuing a historical tradition such as slipware, its soft shine and its interaction with colours are almost essential.

Lead frits were developed during the first half of the 20th century to combat lead poisoning in pottery industries. Strict controls on the solubility of the lead in frit, i.e. its susceptibility to leaching by acids, are in operation. Safety regulations govern the procedures for making frit. Lead frits, correctly handled, are considered to be safe for adult males but should not be used by children or pregnant women. The users of lead-glazed wares are protected by the obligatory testing of all table and kitchenware. See *Double fritting, Low sol* and *Lead poisoning*.

Lead frits are not crystalline minerals. Their structure is a random one composed of silica chains interlinked with lead oxide. Obviously the composition of lead frits can vary enormously. The amount of lead oxide could be 10% or 90%. In recent years, potters have favoured those with published formulae approximating whole numbers. These are:

lead sesquisilicate $2PbO.3SiO_2$
                       $(PbO.1 \cdot 5SiO_2)$
lead bisilicate $PbO.2SiO_2$

These frits usually contain some stabilizers as trace amounts of aluminium oxide and titanium oxide which considerably decrease the lead solubility. Precision potters can consider these and the other variations in calculations but for most purposes the formulae can be taken in their whole number form. Frit manufacturers have welcomed the simplification of supply because they are now using more continuous fritting processes. Trade specifications for frits are established to indicate the limits of composition for these standard lead frits. The frit most popular with individual potters is lead bisilicate.

Below 1200°C (2192°F) there is little difficulty experienced with lead frit. One should consider it as a flux. Consider the glaze as china clay, feldspar or other silicate and add increasing amounts of lead frit as flux until a satisfactory glaze is found. This gives more reliable results than starting with the lead frit, because lead frit alone will give a glaze and comparison of this with other tests is difficult. The whole area can be explored by the use of a blend. See *Line blend*.

For glazes melting over 900°C (1652°F) the better frit is the bisilicate. For glazes below 900°C the sesquisilicate will be needed because it has a lower melting range in glazes. The higher temperature glazes obviously require less flux here considered as lead frit. The higher temperature makes the same amount of flux more active. It also gives a longer time for the action to take place. Above 1200°C (2192°F) lead frit will partially volatilize.

The following glazes are given for comparison:

Transparent raku glaze 800°C (1472°F)
    lead sesquisilicate   85
    china clay   15

Transparent raku glaze 900°C (1652°F)
    lead bisilicate   90
    china clay   5
    flint   5

Maiolica glaze 1000°C (1832°F)
    lead bisilicate   80
    china clay   10
    tin oxide   10

Matt maiolica glaze 1100°C (2012°F)
    lead bisilicate   60
    feldspar   20
    china clay   5
    flint   5
    tin oxide   4
    zirconium oxide   3
    titanium oxide   3

Transparent earthenware glaze 1100°C (2012°F)
    lead bisilicate   65
    feldspar   15
    china clay   10
    flint   5
    whiting   5

Lead monosilicate

$PbO.SiO_2$. Although solubility of the lead content can be kept below the official limit, lead monosilicate is not recommended as a low sol frit.

Lead ore

Lead occurs in many ores and is associated with copper, tin, zinc and iron. The commonest lead ore is the sulfide ore called galena. It is dark blue-grey and occurs as cubic crystals. It is easy to roast and reduce to metal, and for this reason was one of the first metals to be worked. The Ancient Egyptians passed on their skills to the Romans who made full use of lead for pipes, drains etc but they made little use of the Egyptian lead glaze. See *Lead oxide*.

Lead oxide

PbO. (Previously called plumbous oxide.) All raw lead compounds are highly poisonous and their use is now prohibited in factories, individual potteries, studios, schools and colleges in most countries. See **Lead poisoning**.

Lead oxide was one of the most useful and versatile glaze fluxes and was early recognized as such. Its value was further improved when included in fritted form because its effective range was extended.

Glazes containing lead oxide mature gently and are therefore easy to use. They smooth over after gassing and yet are not necessarily over-fluid. They stain readily to a range of rich colours and have a soft deep shine.

Lead glazes were probably first used in the Middle East 3000 years ago. Their use spread to the Far East by 500BC and to western Europe by AD100. The Romans, who knew of the method, used lead glazes rarely and the method almost died out in Europe. However, the medieval potters revived them and made expressive use of them and so did the slipware potters up to the 18th century. After this the Mediterranean influences and Oriental porcelain changed European ideas about glazes, and towards the end of the 19th century northern Europe became concerned about the poisonous nature of the raw lead oxide.

The most important development in lead glazes has been the manufacture of fritted lead to render the lead oxide non-toxic. See **Lead poisoning**, **Low sol** and **Lead frit**. Part of this development has been the introduction of lead-borosilicate glazes for all purposes where raw lead glazes were previously used. See **Lead-borosilicate glazes** and **Double fritting**.

Lead poisoning

Plumbism. Lead and compounds of lead are poisonous in the bloodstream, lungs and digestive system. Symptoms of lead poisoning are lethargy and drowsiness, general abdominal upsets, muscle and joint pains, anaemia and loss of weight. Lead is a cumulative poison. It builds up in the human system until its presence can no longer be accepted.

In most countries the use of raw lead glazes is banned. Instead, the lead compounds must be in fritted form and conform to a specification. See **Low sol**. In Britain, the number of reported cases of lead poisoning in potteries dropped from 432 in 1897 to nil by 1944 as a result of regulations for safe practice and the use of lead frits.

The same restrictions on the use of raw lead and poisonous colours operate in schools and colleges. Individual self-employed potters also are obliged to protect themselves and visitors in the same way.

The amount of poison which can be dissolved from the surface of a fired glaze is usually small but it should be remembered that lead is cumulative and, for a person already sick, even a small dose can be injurious. The poisons are dissolved by strong acids like vinegar and fruit juices and, to a lesser extent, by tea, coffee and other drinks. Potters in doubt about their glazes should consult the suppliers of the materials or the local health authority's analyst. The British Standard Specification 6748 states the permissible limits of metal release from glazed ceramic ware. In Britain, potters making domestic ware using lead glazes or cadmium colours are obliged to have their work tested. Similar specifications and restrictions exist in most countries. See **Metal release**.

Lead sesquisilicate

$2PbO.3SiO_2$ or $PbO.1 \cdot 5SiO_2$. A prepared compound in which, theoretically, every two molecules of lead oxide combine with three molecules of silica. The theoretical proportional weights are lead oxide 71·25%, silica 28·75%.

The solubility of the lead content is about 12% in the straightforward sesquisilicate. This can be reduced to around 1% by the use of stabilizers, e.g. titanium oxide and aluminium oxide. It is difficult to get the solubility much lower chemically, but, by using an acid-proof coating on the frit particles, the solubility can be minimalized to below 0·02%. The frit is first ground to 200's mesh and dried. It is then given a silica shell by immersion in hydrolysed ethyl silicate. The resulting coating is hard and will withstand some further grinding as part of a glaze batch. This process was developed and patented by Henry L. Podmore in the 1950s. See **Low sol**.

Lead sesquisilicate is slightly softer and contains more lead oxide than lead bisilicate. Fusion begins at approximately 700°C (1292°F) and is complete by 850°C (1562°F). Lead sesquisilicate can be used in glazes for the 850°C to 1200°C range (1562°F to 2192°F) and many potters prefer it to the bisilicate. However, the sesquisilicate is more volatile at the higher temperatures. Indeed, large amounts are likely to cause over-fluxing and bubbling above 1100°C (2012°F). Its advantage over the bisilicate is seen in the production of bright yellows and brick reds with antimony and iron oxides at temperatures below 1000°C (1832°F). For the use of lead sesquisilicates see **Lead frit**.

Lead titanate

$PbO.TiO_2$. A crystalline mineral which is precipitated from cooling glazes below 1050°C (1922°F). It crystallizes upon titanium oxide nuclei and also forms large composite crystals with zinc titanate and zinc silicate. See **Crystalline glazes**.

Leadless glaze

Self-explanatory description with the exception that in Britain a leadless glaze may contain up to 1% lead oxide. It is often used as a synonym for borosilicate glaze because these glazes were developed to replace the poisonous lead glazes. Leadless glazes can also be based upon fritted sodium oxide, potassium oxide and zinc oxide for the lower temperatures and upon calcium oxide, magnesium oxide and barium oxide for the higher temperatures. If one wishes to imply the absolute absence of lead one should use the term 'lead-free'.

Lean clay

Clay of low plasticity and strength. See **Short clay**.

Leatherhard

The stage, which plastic clay reaches during drying, when the clay particles are just touching and are thereby giving a stability to the clay. The clay is stiff enough to be picked up without distortion yet soft enough to respond to pressure for burnishing. See ***Drying***.

Leatherhard state is the ideal state for pots to be turned and have handles attached, although there may be some aesthetic advantages in working at an earlier (softer) stage.

Drying from leatherhard to bone-dry state causes little stress within the clay. Nearly all of the drying shrinkage has taken place by the leatherhard stage. Most clays decrease in volume by less than 0·5% between leatherhard and bone-dry. A few extremely fine ball clays shrink as much as 2% in volume but they are exceptional. These figures are to be compared with a range of from 10% to 30% volumetric shrinkage from plastic to leatherhard stage.

Lepidolite

Lithium feldspathoid. Lithium mica. Lithium-potassium mica. A natural material used in glazes to introduce lithium oxide, aluminium oxide and silica. It is also mined for its 5% lithium content, some of which is prepared as a carbonate for glass and glazes.

Lepidolite is an alumino-silicate with a variable base where lithium replaces potassium and involves variable amounts of fluorine and hydroxyl grouping. Various

molecular formulae are acceptable from $(LiKNa)_2(FOH)_2.Al_2O_3.3SiO_2$ to $Li_2F_2.Al_2O_3.3SiO_2$.

Lepidolite has no fixed melting point but matures over a range approximating 1150°C to 1300°C (2012°F to 2372°F). Small amounts of lepidolite can be substituted for other feldspars in glaze recipes with advantageous results for earlier fusion, increased shine and more stable finished glaze. The fluorine content, however, can cause bubbling and can leave a pitted surface if too much lepidolite is used. It will be noticed that the aluminium oxide content is high (over 25%) which results in stiff melts.

The photographs show native lepidolite in fibrous crystal form and lepidolite melted at 1200°C (2192°F) on a test tile.

Levigation

The process of passing a thin slurry through a series of traps where the heavier particles settle and finer particles over-flow. The process is used for clays which contain unwanted material like sand which is too fine to be caught in a mesh.

For example, a clay which has been screened through 100's mesh is used for a potting clay. It is desired that the same clay is used in a slip glaze with wood ash, but it is found that the clay contains a fine sand which causes unwanted specking. The first recourse is a finer mesh sieve for the clay to go into the glaze. But if the glaze has already been made up, a finer mesh would probably take out the wood ash also. Levigation and sedimentation are two practical methods. Of the two, levigation gives easier control for small amounts.

A levigation trough is a channel of any convenient length with one open end. Across this channel are placed riffles to act as barriers. The whole can be made of wood or a piece of guttering can be used with riffles made from plastic clay. The suspension must be very fluid with perhaps three or four times the eventual water content. It is run down the trough into a collecting tub. The angle of the trough is adjusted to give the required sedimentation in the traps.

The advantage of this method is that the deposits can be inspected at any time. By gently steepening the angle of the trough the traps can be emptied of the suspension without losing the sediment. The trough can be sluiced out and the process repeated, usually at a shallower angle, until the unwanted sand etc is removed.

Lid

A hygienic cover which provides a visual focal point and a stimulus for tactile appreciation. A number of appreciation reflexes respond to the way in which a lid sits upon or in its pot.

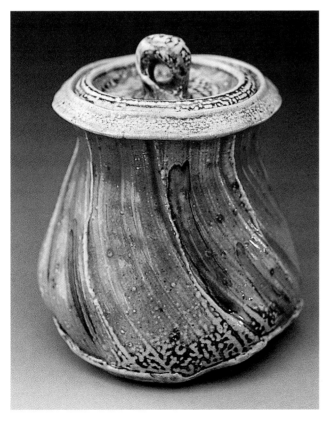

A few sections of thrown lids are drawn for comparison. The sunken lid is useful on casseroles and storage jars where height is limited. It is a stable lid for pots which are to be moved. It allows a large serviceable knob which does not protrude inconveniently. The sunken lid which has galleries on both lid and pot is used for teapots and coffee pots to keep the centre of gravity low and thus overcome the problem of the insecure lid during pouring. Locking devices are possible in a number of ways but rarely seem to be both completely efficient and aesthetically interesting. Most potters rely upon a simple design.

The photographs are of storage jars by Ruthanne Tudball and Peter Dick.

Lifting

A slip and glaze defect in which there is loss of adhesion before firing. Lifting is obvious when pieces of slip or glaze flake off as the raw work is handled. But lifting can occur in the early stages of the firing if the body water is too quickly driven off. The steam pressure lifts the slip or glaze, breaking what adhesion there was. Lifting gives the slip defect of flaking and the glaze defect of crawling and butterfly.

If a slip or glaze has previously been successful but begins to lift, the fault could be that the body was too dry for slip, or too wet for glaze when application was made. The presence of grease or dust on the body, or a different speed of drying effected before or during the firing could cause a previously successful glaze to lift. The photograph shows a stiff glaze which has lifted during firing from a powdery underglaze surface.

The term is sometimes used to describe glazes which leave the pot after firing. However, there are sufficient other words for the various types of this defect described as peeling, shelling, shivering and flaking.

Lime

Calcium oxide. CaO. Lime is a term which has wide use to mean different calcium compounds, e.g. gardeners' lime is calcium carbonate and builders' lime is calcium hydroxide. Quicklime is freshly calcined calcium oxide.

Calcium oxide is an alkaline oxide. It is used as a flux in glazes and is very active above 1100°C (2012°F). Below this temperature it has the opposite effect of inhibiting fusion. Large amounts of calcium oxide have the effect of combining with the silica to produce crystals. These opacify the glaze and give a matt surface. These glazes are called lime matts. See **Lime matt** and **Calcium oxide**.

Lime blows

Small craters which appear on biscuit and once-fired ware. They might occur singly or cover the whole piece like measles. At the base of each crater is a speck of white powder. This is slaked lime. The clay contained limestone (calcium carbonate) as tiny fragments, sometimes too small to be seen or felt. Some estuarine muds contain fragments of seashells, and reclaim clays sometimes contain bits of plaster from moulds or dewatering blocks. These also act like limestone. During firing these become pockets of quicklime (calcium oxide). Once out of the kiln the quicklime absorbs moisture from the air to become slaked lime (calcium hydroxide). It expands in so doing and pushes off the piece of

ceramic above it. The only cure is to prepare the clay as slip and pass it through a sufficiently fine mesh to remove the limestone fragments.

Lime feldspar

Calcium feldspar. CaO.Al$_2$O$_3$.2SiO$_2$. See **Anorthite**.

Lime matt

A matt glaze in which the matt surface is produced by calcium silicate crystals. Lime is calcium oxide.

Calcium oxide is introduced into a glaze by means of whiting, chalk or limestone, which are all calcium carbonate. The carbonate decomposes on heating to 825°C (1517°F) giving calcium oxide and carbon dioxide, which escapes as a gas. To get a matt surface, calcium carbonate is added to a glaze in the proportion of 20% to 30%. Simple transparent glazes and other shiny glazes can be successfully matted. In an earthenware glaze melting below 1100°C (2012°F) the calcium oxide tends to stiffen the glaze and inhibits fusion, and during cooling it combines with the aluminium oxide and silica to form anorthite crystals. Although it is an alkaline oxide it does not act as a flux. Above 1100°C however, calcium oxide becomes active as a flux. Therefore in glazes which melt above 1100°C, whether earthenware or stoneware, the calcium oxide added will perform an action as a flux during firing and as a crystal-former during cooling. A typical oxidized lime-matt recipe for 1250°C (2282°F) is:

cornish stone	50
china clay	15
tin oxide	5
whiting	30

For temperatures in the range of 1200°C (2192°F) and over it is possible to use the calcium oxide as the main flux and the matting agent. In the example recipe, calcium oxide is the main flux, subsidiary fluxes existing in the cornish stone. A little tin oxide has been added to improve whiteness and opacity. This glaze can give alkaline colour responses if a suitably alkaline cornish stone is used.

In glazes fired up to 1200°C (2192°F) the predominating crystal is that of anorthite (CaO.Al$_2$O$_3$.2SiO$_2$) with some wollastonite (CaO.SiO$_2$). Above 1200°C, the wollastonite crystals begin to form during the firing and continue to grow during the cooling. Stoneware lime matts therefore contain more wollastonite crystals than anorthite ones.

The correct balance of calcium oxide is sometimes difficult to discover. Up to 15% of calcium carbonate may be correct for a stable semi-transparent glaze. Here the calcium oxide forms nuclei of crystals which give a milky opacity, but the crystals do not extend to the surface. About 20% of calcium carbonate may make the glaze over-fluxed, very runny and transparent. Here the melt is so liquid that the calcium silicate crystals do not have time to grow before a glaze quickly sets. A prolonged cooling could give successful results. About 25%–30% may be the best amount of calcium carbonate and gives a crystal growth that spreads from within outwards to cover the whole surface of the glaze. About 35% may make the glaze very dry-looking and unpleasant. It will look as if it has not fused and is also likely to have lost its adhesion with the pot. It will have peeled back as flakes of loose skin. For a description of crystallization see *Crystalline glazes*.

At the correct amount, there are sufficient crystals to cover the whole surface of the glaze without making it appear too dry. These crystals sparkle with the light as it is reflected from the different crystal facets. The appearance is that of frost and is very attractive. Lime matt glazes are popular for this reason.

It is possible to get a lime matt that is fickle in firing but generally they are very dependable glazes. Careful firing as well as cooling is necessary; they are slow to mature. Too rapid a firing will result in pin-holes because the glaze is a stiff one and has not the capacity to flow into craters. If a lime matt which is successful begins to misbehave one should look for a change in firing cycle. Both firing and cooling should be compared with previous firings. The final temperature may also be critical. Overfiring can cause loss of crystals. Similarly extra fusion caused by interaction with a different body, a different slip, or extra reduction could result in loss of crystal growth.

Lime matts are alkaline glazes. They therefore give bright colours with cobalt and copper oxides. The calcium oxide has the effect of bleaching iron oxides so that a range of yellow and green glazes is possible. All these colours are better in oxidation using a white clay. See *Calcium oxide.*

On tableware a lime matt has limited application. The crystals form what must be regarded as a rough surface. While attractive, it is not the most practical. Spoons and cutlery scrape the surface with an unpleasant sound. The surface is easily marked by the metal and also stains, because of the gaps between the crystals.

Dolomite limestone is a combination of calcium carbonate and magnesium carbonate. Dolomite matt glazes are similar to, and are related to, lime matts.

Limestone

Stone which is essentially calcium carbonate ($CaCO_3$). It is used by potters to introduce calcium oxide into glazes. It is often more appropriate to use whiting for this purpose. In any case many whitings are crushed limestone.

Limestone occurs widely as a sedimentary rock sometimes of great thickness. The sediments occurred as crystalline precipitates and as shells of sea creatures. Limestones are therefore often highly fossiliferous and while mostly grey or buff can be very decorative.

Limestones have many uses. They are used for building stone, road metal, iron ore smelting and for making cement. The potter uses limestone as a source of calcium oxide for glazes.

Although some limestone shales exist which are useful in glazes, most limestone is difficult to grind. Limestone is hard. It stands out in the landscape as cliffs and mountains and this is why it is a good building material and road metal. Where these materials are crushed there is often a surplus of dust which is a possible source for the potter. The dust has been referred to as calcareous rock flour. However, from the potter's point of view, limestone introduces little more than does whiting.

There are many local names like Portland and Bath Stones but the physical types of limestone are:

1. Crystalline limestone which is extremely hard and sometimes called mountain limestone.

2. Fossiliferous limestone which is built up from the shells of sea creatures. The shells vary from a few centimetres across to ones indistinguishable without a magnifying glass. These limestones often form part of the strata called mountain limestone and are also called shelly limestones.

3. Oolitic limestone is usually softer than the two above and contains some iron giving it a pleasant buff colour. On close inspection it is seen to be composed of spherical particles.

4. Chalk is usually softer than other limestones but it varies enormously. It was deposited as a calcareous mud and therefore the particles are extremely fine. It varies in colour, the purest being white.

5. Marble is crystalline limestone that has had the opportunity to reform its crystals under pressure and heat. It is metamorphic limestone. It is the hardest of the limestones. Some finely textured crystalline limestones are called marbles when they are cut and polished for decorative use.

6. Tufa is crystalline limestone which has been deposited recently. It forms concretions in waterfalls, stalagmites and stalactites. It is not too difficult to grind. Travertine and calc-sinter are similar deposits associated with hot springs.

7. Calcite and aragonite are the pure crystal forms of calcium carbonate. Tufa is composed of tiny calcite crystals. Nailhead spar, dog-tooth spar and Iceland spar are varieties of large calcite crystals. These crystals are softer than the stones and can be ground by hand.

8. Ferruginous limestone is any limestone that is stained by iron. The colourings are often very decorative. The iron is in the form of a carbonate ($FeCO_3$), the iron having replaced some of the calcium. See *Siderite*.

9. Dolomite limestone is a combination of calcium carbonate and magnesium carbonate. It occurs where magnesium has partially replaced calcium in ordinary limestone and where the limestone was deposited under water rich in magnesium salts. See *Dolomite*.

Limonite

$2Fe_2O_3.3H_2O$. The natural hydrated form of iron oxide. The ore is a loose structure which does not form large crystals. It is therefore usually soft and easily crumbled. It varies in colour from a yellow through orange to a dark red-brown. It was originally a bog ore which was precipitated by bacterial action from solution in lakes and therefore is usually relatively pure.

There are large deposits in Scandinavia and North America but small pockets may often be found associated with Carboniferous series rocks. The yellow form, called yellow ochre, is soft and crumbly. The red form contains less water and is called red ochre and raddle. It is harder but can be crushed easily. Hard dark nodules which must be pounded are found associated with fireclays. All forms are useful clay and glaze colourants and the softer forms are often already closely associated and uniformly spread throughout a clay bed. For iron colouring of clay and glazes see *Iron oxide*.

Line blend

A method of determining requirements in practical tests of materials. For example, if one has a black clay and a white clay which are to be blended to produce a predetermined grey, the proportionate blend can be found by a line blend. In this case the obvious way is to start with the white and add increasing amounts of black. A whole series of tests would go into one firing and from them the correct one would be selected. Any convenient number of tests can be decided upon.

It is usual to run a second line blend between two of the tests from the first blend if a fine degree of choice is required. This avoids making the first series unnecessarily long. It is also usual, especially with glazes, to decrease one test ingredient as the other increases. In this way the total bulk remains constant and calculations in percentages are more easily composed. The following two examples should make these points clear:

	A	B	C	D	E	F	G
black clay	0	1	2	3	4	5	6 parts
white clay	6	5	4	3	2	1	0 parts

If the required colour lies between tests C and D a further series might be:

	H(D)	I	J	K	L	M(C)
black clay 2 parts / white clay 4 parts	0	1	2	3	4	5 parts
black clay 3 parts / white clay 3 parts	5	4	3	2	1	0 parts

This gives four further possible blends to choose from which are known to be in the desired area.

It is important to make line blends from two carefully-selected originals. With glazes, particularly, one has a very wide choice. The two originals should be chosen in order that an estimated best blend based on common sense or pure guess work would lie approximately half-way between the two. Thus the two originals may not be glazes at all. One might be nearly all flux and the other nearly all silica. Neither of these would melt to a satisfactory glaze. If one is line-blending two glazes in an attempt to get one that melts at $1200°C$ ($2192°F$), the obvious originals would be two glazes melting one below and one above this temperature. These glazes would need to be similar in character for a beginning, e.g. both transparents, or both lime matts. This is the normal approach.

Alternatively, one may make a series of empirical tests across areas of glaze types in the hope of a chance winner. Such blends have their uses. They may not give any valuable information on a specific problem but they give the potter experience in fluxing and colouring phenomena which can be used in later choice of originals. Line blends are particularly useful for determining colouring amounts.

Line blends are useful in composing glaze recipes when one is using raw materials for which no easy chemical fomulae exist, e.g. wood ash, local clay, local rock, coloured sand. In such cases it is impossible to start with a molecular formula and calculate from this to a suitable recipe. One must work empirically with the materials. One can do this simply by classifying each material as either flux, refractory clay, fusible clay, feldspathic rock, or silica, and consider them as known types for the first test. Alternatively, one may wish to discover more about each material first. This may be necessary to discover if any material has a particular colouring value or annoying property. To do this, a small specimen of each material is fired on a test tile. This gives some indication of properties and enables a first choice to be made.

It is well to start a series of line blends with only two materials if these are completely unknown. From the first blend, which should contain at least seven tests, another starting point may be found. From here it may happen that a side blend, as it were at right angles to the first blend, is made. This may be towards a third material or towards another selected blend. By this stage enough information has usually been gained from which to make prediction of further blends.

In the end one usually arrives at two or three possible solutions with very different recipes and one is tempted to try line blends using these recipes but these rarely give conclusive results. It is more profitable to make a series of line blends which cover the area around a predicted best recipe. By doing this one has covered all the possibilities. To decide upon the originals of such a final blend, make the predicted recipe the middle test of the line and increase one ingredient one way and another ingredient the other way. A few blends will be required to fully cover all the possibilities in the area around the predicted recipe.

Lastly, in making glaze tests it is not necessary to weigh out and make each test separately. One only needs to make two originals. These should be made of equal density. It is then sufficiently accurate to make the blends between in spoonfuls of glaze slop. In this way the percentage recipes for each test do not need to be worked out.

Lithium carbonate

Li_2CO_3. A white crystalline powder, source of the flux lithium oxide for glazes. The carbonate decomposes to become the oxide and carbon dioxide during the glaze firing. Only 40% of the carbonate is lithium oxide. Carbon dioxide accounts for 60%. The equation is:

$$Li_2CO_3 \xrightarrow{650°C} Li_2O + CO_2\uparrow$$

lithium   lithium   carbon
carbonate   oxide   dioxide

Lithium carbonate is only slightly soluble in water and is therefore used in preference to lithium oxide which is highly soluble. Lithium oxide's fluxing properties are similar to those of potassium oxide and sodium oxide, but the much cheaper equivalent compounds of potassium and sodium are still soluble in water. Hence there is an advantage in using lithium carbonate.

Lithium carbonate does not occur as a natural material but is prepared from the lithium ores called lepidolite, petalite, spodumene and amblygonite.

Lithium feldspathoids

These are the three alumino-silicates based upon lithium: lepidolite, petalite and spodumene. They are separately itemized in this book. The lithium feldspathoids occur where lithium has been able to replace sodium and potassium in a residual mica-feldspar. They are mined as low-yield ores for the lithium metal and for the production of lithium carbonate for glass-making. They can also be introduced as feldspathoids into glazes. They are not true minerals because they have variable analyses and chemical formulae. Hence they have no definable melting points but have maturing ranges starting at 1150°C (2102°F) for lepidolite, 1200°C (2192°F) for petalite and 1250°C (2282°F) for spodumene. They are slow to mature.

Lithium oxide

Li_2O. One of the strong alkaline oxides. It is used as a flux in glazes where it gives similar results to sodium oxide. The oxide is soluble in water and is therefore introduced into glaze batches by lithium carbonate or lithium feldspathoids. Lithium compounds are poisonous.

There are four natural sources of lithium oxide. They are the three feldspathoids and the fluophosphate: lepidolite, petalite, spodumene and amblygonite. They are all low-yield ores, below 10% yield, which makes lithium oxide an expensive flux. The commercial lithium carbonate is produced from these ores and, of course, these materials can be introduced into glazes. See individual items.

Lithium oxide is an asset to a glaze as an additional flux. Additional, that is, to the number of fluxes; its presence replacing some, but not all, of another alkaline oxide. A diversity of fluxes gives greater interaction with resulting increases in fluidity and gloss. A number of fluxes also usually provides a more stable glaze structure thus giving a more durable glaze.

Lithium oxide is an active flux resembling sodium oxide and starts its fluxing action at approximately 800°C (1472°F). It is less volatile than sodium oxide above 1200°C (2192°F) and remains an effective flux over the full range of glazes. However, at the higher temperatures, the amount of lithium oxide would normally be decreased in favour of cheaper, but equally effective, fluxes like calcium oxide and magnesium oxide.

The effect that lithium oxide can give, which is different from other stoneware fluxes, is colour response. In oxidation it gives blues with copper oxide and pinks with cobalt oxide. It is a useful auxiliary flux in the production of the more alkaline lime and barium matts.

Lithium glazes are also characterized by the so-called halo effect which occurs around modelled decoration, throwing marks and edges. This is a combination of two effects. First, lithium oxide produces a glaze of low viscosity which runs away from edges into hollows. Second, because it is such an active flux it erodes the adjacent body as well as being involved in the glaze fusion. In this way it produces an effect similar to salt glaze. Interesting colour variation occurs because two different environments are produced: the areas of strongly alkaline, thick glaze and the areas of thinner, less alkaline glaze in proximity to the acidic body.

Lithium is the lightest metal element with an atomic weight of 6·94. See ***Periodic table***. Lithium oxide has a molecular weight of only 29·87 compared with sodium oxide 61·97, potassium oxide 94·19 and calcium oxide 66·07. This means that in equal weights of these four oxides there is a greater number of molecules of lithium oxide than

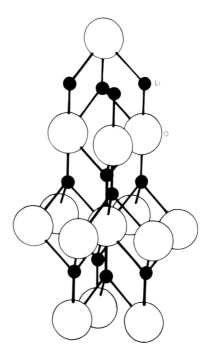

of sodium oxide, potassium oxide or calcium oxide. The smaller atom size of lithium gives a compact oxide. See drawing on page 215.

Thus a smaller weight of lithium oxide, than other flux, will be required to give an equal number of molecules. Lithium oxide is therefore an economical and effective flux in a glaze on a weight for weight basis.

Expansion and contraction rates for glazes are calculated on the percentage weights of the oxides in the recipe. An oxide like lithium oxide therefore accounts for only a small proportion of this rate compared with sodium oxide and potassium oxide. When this fact is coupled with the fact that lithium oxide has a lower expansion rate itself than has sodium oxide or potassium oxide, it will be seen why the inclusion of lithium oxide has such a marked effect upon the expansion and contraction rates of glazes. Lithium oxide is often substituted for some of the sodium oxide in order to inhibit crazing. See *Glaze fit*.

The qualities of lithium oxide have long been recognized and it has been used to balance lead-free glazes and produce special bodies and glazes with high resistances to thermal shock. After taking into consideration its economic dispersal in a glaze, it is still more expensive than the other fluxes: about ten times the cost of calcium oxide and four times the cost of barium oxide.

Lithomarge

A compressed clay which has not yet reached the stage of a shale or slate. The term is sometimes used to describe discoloured china clays.

Litre weight

Slop weight. The weight of one litre of a clay or glaze suspension in water. Litre weights are noted in order to reproduce successive batches of slips and glazes. Litre weight is a description of density expressed as kilos per litre. The figure is the same as grams per ml and relative density. Thus 1·5 kilos per litre is the same density description as 1·5 grams per ml.

To convert to pint weight, multiply by 20·042 for imperial pints and 16·705 for US pints. Thus 1·5 kilos per litre = 30 oz pt imp = 25 oz pt US. See *Slop weight* and *Table 19*.

Livering

A slip-casting fault showing as a rippled or uneven surface on the slip side of a cast. See *Casting slip: adjustment of*.

Liverpool

England. Famous for its production of delft in the late 17th and early 18th century and also for the later production of creamware. It was here, in 1755, that John Sadler invented transfer printing after seeing children sticking waste prints onto broken earthenware to make dolls' teasets. The photograph shows a Sadler tile of 1760. Outstanding amongst Liverpool pottery are the large jugs with very pointed spouts, and large punch bowls decorated with ships.

Lizard skin

Snake skin. A mottled glaze effect resembling scales. The effect is often composed of matt and shiny parts as well as parts of different colour and tone. It is a thick glaze and therefore suitable for horizontal surfaces but sometimes the effect can be achieved with stiffish glazes on vertical surfaces.

The effect is achieved by using two glazes of different composition and melting character. These are applied one over the other, the second being applied as soon as convenient upon the first, and the two are fired together.

The first glaze should sit firmly upon the body without any tendency to flake off. The second glaze tends to pull at the first so the first must not be friable nor yet contain too

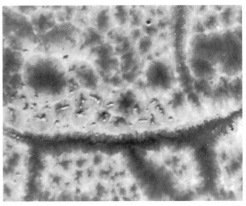

much clay as binder. A gum or polymer resin binder is useful. Some potters have used a soft firing to bond the first glaze to the body without destroying its absorbency.

The second glaze contains a high proportion of clay. With most glazes 20% to 30% is necessary. This causes the glaze layer to shrink during drying. The second glaze layer thus becomes a series of isolated pieces of glaze. See drawing.

It does not matter which glaze fuses first. It is usually the under one because the second glaze contains more clay. If this is china clay it will be slow to melt and produce a stiff molten state. It is usual also for it to be matt. As the first glaze melts, the pieces of the second glaze sink into it to produce an almost level glaze surface.

Local reduction
See *Autoreduction*.

Loess clay
Aeolian clay. A yellowish calcareous clay of central Europe and Asia. It is a sedimentary clay originally transported by wind across the drier parts of the world during the glacial periods.

Long clay
Clay of high plasticity. See *Fat clay*.

Loving cup
A two-handled cup usually commemorating a wedding and having suitable individual inscriptions with names and a date. The photograph (right) shows a plum tenmoku one by Frank Hamer.

Low sol
Low solubility. Description of frits and glazes containing lead oxide where the solubility of the lead oxide is below 5% (British specification). Low sol frits and glazes were developed to overcome the problem of lead poisoning in the pottery industry and to protect users of pottery. See *Lead poisoning.*

Low sol is a general description: it is not specific to one recipe. However, it is often used to imply a glaze which is composed of two frits: a lead frit of low solubility and a borosilicate frit. The method of making a glaze in this way is known as 'double fritting'. For the use of low solubility frits see *Lead frit*.

The acids which break down and absorb ingested lead compounds in the human body are the gastric juices. These approximate a 0·17% hydrochloric acid solution. Tests on

frits and powdered glazes therefore use this acid but at the increased strength of 0·25% and at room temperature (20°C or 68°F) for convenience. The lead dissolved is precipitated as lead sulfate, washed, dried and weighed. The soluble content is usually expressed as a percentage of the metal lead or the lead oxide present in the original frit or glaze.

The greatest danger is from finely-ground lead compounds and lead frit powders. A fine glaze powder presents a vastly greater surface area than it does when it is a fused glaze on ware. Fine dust in the atmosphere enters the lungs and the stomach where its soluble lead content is almost completely absorbed. The soluble lead content of a finished glaze is mostly protected within the glaze although the surface is subject to attack by food acids. See *Metal release*.

Workers in industry are protected by Factory Acts. In Britain the final one forbidding the use of raw lead glazes came into effect in 1949. Similar restrictions on the use of raw lead in British schools etc were made by the Ministry of Education in 1955 with memorandum 517. The Health and Safety at Work Act 1974 amalgamated previous regulations and included individual potters for the first time. The highest acceptable level of soluble lead in a glaze powder is 5% oxide content. All the lead oxides, lead carbonate and lead sulfide have solubility above 5%. Lead monosilicate also has too high a soluble lead content to be considered safe, but the other standard lead silicates (sesquisilicate and bisilicate) are considered low sol frits.

To protect the user of glazed pottery, British Standard Specification 6748, part 1: tableware, part 2: cooking ware, covers the testing of glazed ware and specifies limits for lead and cadmium released by the glazes from different types of vessels. The tests use a 4% solution of acetic acid. Similar specifications exist in Commonwealth countries, in some European countries and in North America. See *Metal release.*

HISTORY OF LOW SOL. The investigation of lead poisoning and an attempt to discover ways of overcoming it were started in Britain in the late 19th century by Sir Thomas Thorpe. He concentrated upon the frits and glazes. Meanwhile, Sir Wilfred Garrett concentrated upon the hygienic conditions in the factories. On the European continent, regulations sought to protect the user of the pottery rather than the potter and Dr J. Koerner investigated the possibilities of low solubility.

The three researches overlapped and much information was published which was successfully integrated in the work of John Mellor. The German attempt to protect the customer led to the use of lead frits which gave safer glazes even when underfired. This, indirectly, also protected the glazers. In Britain the development of safer glazes produced frits also. Better milling and storing of glazes cut down on lead dust.

Lead poisoning was a very worrying fact but the problem of producing lead-free glazes seemed insurmountable. The advantages of lead glazes were their viscosity during firing and their accommodating behaviour on finished ware, known as elasticity. Until the mid-1930s, all lead-free glazes tended to run immediately they had melted, and were prone to crazing. The general shine and finish was also unsatisfactory.

The system of double fritting was discovered before 1900 but it seems not to have been commercially viable until the 1920s. It involves the preparation of two frits: one a lead silicate and the other a borosilicate. These are only brought together when mixed with the remainder of the glaze batch for use. In this way the lead frit can be separately controlled for solubility and a variety of glazes can be compounded from varying proportions of the two frits and other minerals like china clay and feldspar. This method is used in the production of commercial low sol glazes. To ensure further safety in the handling of the glaze or powder before firing, the lead frit is sometimes coated. The coating is an impervious acid-proof layer of silica and the process of coating was pioneered and developed by Podmore and Sons of Stoke-on-Trent, England.

The general principles established were that the solubility of lead decreases when fritted with silica, aluminium oxide, titanium oxide and calcium oxide, and increases with the oxides of sodium, potassium, lithium and boron.

Boron oxide and borax (which contains sodium oxide) were important fluxes and glass-formers in the development of lead-free glazes but their undesirable effect upon the solubility of lead in frits and glazes hindered the development of low sol glazes. The problem was solved by double fritting. See **Double fritting**.

LOW SOL FRITS. In the search for suitable lead frits it was found that lead bisilicate ($PbO.2SiO_2$) was the most immediately practical. While lead orthosilicate, monosilicate and sesquisilicate had generally lower melting ranges and were therefore attractive propositions, their lead solubility was too high. Since that time the use of coated frits has enabled the solubility of the sesquisilicate to be lowered appreciably. Trisilicate ($PbO.3SiO_2$) and tetrasilicate ($PbO.4SiO_2$) were also investigated but were found too viscous to pour satisfactorily from the fritting crucible.

Modifications to the lead silicate pivoted round the introduction of aluminium oxide which dramatically reduced the lead solubility. It was even found that aluminium oxide assisted the melting of the frit. Further tests showed the existence of a eutectic in the region of $PbO.1.9SiO_2$ in which as much as 0.25 molecular equivalents of aluminium oxide could be dissolved without affecting the melting range of the frit and with less effect on the fluidity than could normally be expected. Today's lead bisilicates are mostly of this type. They are high in lead oxide content: nearly 65% PbO. They have a smooth melting range, due to the introduction of aluminium oxide, and the solubility of the lead content is extremely low. The aluminium oxide content is usually below 0.1 equivalents in order to keep viscosity to a minimum. It is also around this point that its optimum power is achieved in its effects upon solubility.

The number of possible lead frits is legion. To simplify the field, the frit manufacturers have concentrated upon the production of a few standard frits. This has been necessary with the building of continuous fritting plants. Lead bisilicate was an obvious choice because there is only a limited application for the use of softer frits, i.e. in the production of special colours. The frits chosen approximate closely to the whole number formulae. They are lead bisilicate ($PbO.2SiO_2$), lead monosilicate ($PbO.SiO_2$) and lead sesquisilicate ($2PbO.3SiO_2$). Trade specifications for these frits are established to indicate the limits of composition, grain size and solubility. Stabilizers are used in the form of aluminium oxide and titanium oxide, and many frits are silica-coated. However, lead monosilicate is rarely considered a low sol frit although some approximations to this formula have solubility below 5%.

The use of low sol frits and glazes, and the controlled manufacture of them has completely eradicated the incidence of lead poisoning in potteries and glaze works.

Low-temperature glaze

One which matures in the range up to 1050°C (1922°F). Low-temperature glazes make use of the soft fluxes: lead oxide, boron oxide, sodium oxide and potassium oxide. With the exception of raw lead glazes it is necessary to employ frits in low-temperature glazes because the fluxing oxides are soluble in water.

Low thermal mass

The property of a material which has low heat conductivity across its structure. Such materials are: low thermal mass or K-bricks; diatomaceous bricks; boards; and ceramic fibre used in kiln building. They have a structure which contains a high proportion of fine air pockets across which heat travels slowly.

This structure also makes these items very lightweight which is a big advantage in kiln construction. See **Kiln building** and **Insulation**.

Lustres

Metallic surfaces on glazes. The pure metal is deposited on the glaze surface by many different methods but all involve reduction from a compound to the pure metal. The metals used are gold, silver, platinum, copper, titanium, bismuth and tin, with some experimental work involving ruthenium, rhodium, palladium, osmium and iridium.

Compounds of the precious metals gold, silver and platinum are readily reduced to pure metal. Precious metal lustre compounds carry their own reducing agent which, in burning off in an oxidized firing, achieves complete reduction. These are called resin lustres. The temperature required is 750°C (1382°F) and good ventilation of kiln and kiln room is essential. See **Health hazard**. The pigment is also poisonous. See **Poison**.

A precious metal is dissolved in hydrochloric acid to produce a chloride. The chloride is added to sodium resinate to produce a precipitate which is suspended in oil. The oil medium carries the metal for ease of application. This and the resin burn out in the firing and provide the necessary reduction. A thin layer of almost pure metal between 1 and 20 micrometres thick is thereby deposited on the glaze. The metal does not readily oxidize. Silver sometimes tarnishes and is polished. Commercially prepared lustres are of this type. See **Colour plates 13** and **60 to 63**.

Most other commercial lustres make use of the iridescent sheen created by an extremely thin layer, between 0·1 and 1 micrometre, of bismuth. This is the mother-of-pearl effect. To this are added other colouring metals and compounds which lie under or are layered with the bismuth. These lustres are prepared as resinates and fired in an oxidized firing. The theory of iridescence is separately explained under **Iridescence**.

Copper gives a deep golden lustre varying to a rich red. The Hispano-Moresque lustres were copper lustres often with some silver. The rich lustre was often mistaken for gold. It was achieved by transferring colloidal copper from a refractory coating to the glaze surface during a special low temperature reduction firing. See **Transmutation lustre**. and **Colour plates 14, 15** and **33 to 35**.

A copper compound can also be introduced into the glaze mixture or applied to the unfired surface. In both cases the lustre would be called an inglaze lustre as opposed to the surface lustre of the transmutation method. See **Copper lustre, Ruby lustre**, and **Colour plates 1, 2, 3** and **4**.

All lustres involving copper require reduction. This is usually done with carbon monoxide. See **Reduction** and **Copper oxide in reduction**.

Tin lustre is produced in raku. See **Tin lustre**.

The contemporary gadrooned bowl is in traditional

Gubbio style using ruby and silver lustre. The Carolina drake by Janet Hamer uses a high-temperature inglaze copper lustre. See **Recipe Appendix**.

Lute

To join together two pieces of clay in leatherhard condition by wetting the seam. The theory is that the two pieces are softened to plastic or softer state so that they produce one piece when brought together with suitable pressure. Slip or slurry is used for fine clays but coarse clays are often more effectively softened with water.

M

Mafic minerals

Ferromagnesian minerals. A complex group of silicates in which iron, magnesium and calcium play important parts. They are mostly dark in colour and alkaline in character. They can sometimes be isolated when they occur as fibrous stars of crystals in small pockets, but mostly they occur as small indistinguishable crystals within basic igneous rocks, e.g. basalt. The remainder of the rock will be a feldspar. Apart from the fibrous pockets they are difficult to grind. Some melt to a black glass at 1250°C (2282°F) but the colour is strong and to make a practical glaze more feldspar and free silica is required. Mafic minerals are sub-divided into: pyroxenes, amphiboles, micas and olivine. A few are marketed in powder form as feldspar variants. See also **Basalt**.

Magnesian matts

Matt glazes created by surfeits of magnesium oxide. These glazes are of two types: low-temperature and high-temperature.

The low-temperature matts employ magnesium oxide as an opacifier and surface modifier. The magnesium oxide is usually introduced as magnesium carbonate in amounts up to 15% of the glaze. This is extra to the normal fluxes. The magnesium carbonate decomposes upon heating to become the highly refractory magnesium oxide. Some of the magnesium oxide is dissolved by the action of the melt but most remains in suspension. The result is a white, opaque and matt glaze, but it is often discoloured and is not so dependable as glazes produced with tin, titanium and zirconium oxides.

The high-temperature matts employ magnesium oxide as a flux, opacifier and surface modifier. More magnesium oxide is present than is necessary for a full fluxing of the silica. Exact amounts can only be established by line blends and will lie between 20% and 30% magnesium carbonate in the batch recipe. The excess, in becoming involved in the molten glaze, creates simple silicates with low amounts of silica. Because there is an excess of alkaline oxides, there is likely to be only from one to three molecules of silica per unit of alkali. Half of these will be involved in the alumino-silicate melt and remain as liquid phase but the simple silicates readily crystallize upon cooling to give opacity and a matt surface. The magnesium silicate crystals, which are of enstatite ($MgO.SiO_2$), possibly stretching to $MgO.2SiO_2$, are often assisted by calcium silicate crystals of wollastonite ($CaO.SiO_2$). There may also be some compounded diopside ($CaO.MgO.2SiO_2$) and isolated aluminium oxide (Al_2O_3). See **Enstatite**.

High-temperature magnesian matts are related to alumina matts, lime matts and dolomite glazes. They are capable of giving some interesting colour responses with cobalt and manganese oxides.

Magnesite

$MgCO_3$. A stone, similar to limestone, which is a source of magnesium oxide for glazes. See **Magnesium carbonate**.

Magnesium carbonate

Magnesite. $MgCO_3$. Crushed-ore source of magnesium oxide for glazes. It is obtained from the mineral magnesite and some is prepared by precipitation although the light basic carbonate, described later, is easier to prepare.

The carbonate decomposes at 350°C (662°F) to provide magnesium oxide and carbon dioxide.

$$MgCO_3 \xrightarrow{350°C} MgO + CO_2\uparrow$$

The magnesium oxide is highly refractory and is an opacifier in glazes up to 1170°C (2138°F) when it becomes an active flux. It is then involved in creating silicates which, if sufficiently simple, will crystallize out upon cooling to give a matt opacity. See **Magnesian matts**.

Light magnesium carbonate is the basic carbonate ($3MgCO_3.Mg(OH)_2.3H_2O$). It is slowly soluble in water if there is acid content with which to react. Otherwise it is less soluble than the pure carbonate. It is more convenient than the heavier pure carbonate in that it also mixes better in the glaze slop.

Magnesium carbonate is less soluble than magnesium oxide but it must be accepted as slightly soluble. For this reason it cannot be used in clays as a catalyst because it upsets workability. Talc is used instead for this purpose.

The following glaze recipe for a magnesian matt at 1250°C (2282°F) uses light magnesium carbonate. It is typical of the type of glaze that cannot be stored because of the solubility of the magnesium carbonate and the high clay content. The high clay content makes the glaze behave as a slip so that it can be so used on raw clay. Alternatively, it gives high pre-fire contraction so that it can be used over shiny dark glazes to give lizard skin effects.

Siliceous ball clay	50
Feldspar	15
Whiting	25
Light magnesium carbonate	10

Magnesium oxide

MgO. A constituent of bodies and glazes. At low temperatures it acts as a catalyst in bodies and as an opacifier in glazes. At high temperatures it acts as a flux giving viscous melts which as glazes are opaque and matt. Its action is similar to those of calcium, barium, zinc and strontium oxides but it is not interchangeable for any one of them. For example, it gives unique and interesting mauve colours with cobalt oxide.

Magnesium oxide's fluxing action begins at 1170°C (2138°F) from which temperature it is active for all temperatures upwards: it does not volatilize. Prior to 1170°C it is a refractory anti-flux and can be used as an opacifier in earthenware glazes. Its melting point alone is 2800°C (5072°F). However, in the presence of other fusions created by sodium and potassium oxides it can be encouraged at least to enter the fusions although it takes no active part. A small amount will dissolve but most will remain as suspended white refractory particles. See **Magnesian matts**.

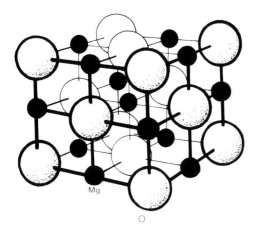

The effect of magnesium oxide as a flux is often most marked in the period from 1190°C to 1230°C (2174°F to 2246°F). When magnesium oxide is included in a glaze as an auxiliary flux it often produces a late fluidity which gives flecks of movement. This is similar to the hare's fur effects. The late fusion is also valuable in producing a mottled and oil-spot effect. In this case the magnesium oxide is included in an underlayer of glaze. The upper layer of glaze fuses first and seals the surface. The under layer begins to melt and boil at a later stage which erupts the lower colouring into the upper surface. The upper layer must be a fluid glaze which quickly heals over. See **Reactive slip**.

In stoneware glazes therefore, a small amount of magnesium oxide can be a great help. By virtue of interaction it brings increased fluidity in the later stages of firing but it always brings an increase in surface tension.

The surface tension, however, gives excellent rounded edges to glazes covering modelled surfaces and the finished glaze has a fatty or buttery appearance. It is also valuable in creating a lizard skin effect. Here the tendency to crawl created by the surface tension is used to create pieces of isolated glaze which float in another more fluid glaze.

As a flux alone, magnesium oxide gives viscous melts of high surface tension. These are rarely satisfactory glazes but

when magnesium oxide is an auxiliary flux of not more than 0·25 molecular equivalents, it can give a startling amount of increased fluidity. It is also used in very small amounts as an anti-craze. It is substituted for calcium, barium and zinc oxides. See **Glaze fit**.

The surface tension is less noticeable in glazes fired in reduction atmospheres. Reduction also encourages more iron oxide from the body to enter the glaze. The iron oxide stain is a pleasant dark grey and occurs decoratively on edges of throwing rings, handles and modelling. A slightly thinner glaze for oxidized firings will allow the body colouring to burn through and will also overcome some of the problems associated with the high surface tension.

Magnesium oxide is slowly soluble in water, forming the slaked hydroxide (Mg(OH)$_2$). It is therefore introduced into glazes by magnesium carbonate (MgCO$_3$), which is less soluble, and by dolomite (CaCO$_3$.MgCO$_3$) and talc (3MgO.4SiO$_2$.H$_2$O), which are insoluble.

Magnesium is a lightweight metal used in alloys. It is essential to life and its compounds occur in plant growth and are used in medicines. It is a common element occurring in many compounds from which it is extracted, e.g. carnallite (KCl.MgCl$_2$.6H$_2$O), magnesite (MgCO$_3$), dolomite (MgCO$_3$.CaCO$_3$) and sea water. It also forms the silicates: talc (3MgO.4SiO$_2$.H$_2$O), serpentine (3MgO.2SiO$_2$.2H$_2$O), meerschaum (2MgO.3SiO$_2$.2H$_2$O), olivine (MgFeO$_2$.SiO$_2$) and asbestos (3MgO.CaO.4SiO$_2$).

Magnesium oxide is introduced into earthenware bodies as a so-called secondary flux. The term flux is here misleading because the desired action is that of a catalyst. At temperatures over 1000°C (1832°F) it assists the conversion of silica from its quartz phase to its cristobalite phase without becoming involved in fusion: the silica remains free and micro-crystalline. Magnesium oxide is therefore an effective measure against crazing of the glaze on earthenware and was discovered empirically long before its scientific signification was explained. It is introduced by talc (magnesium silicate) which is insoluble.

Magnesium oxide is introduced into stoneware bodies to provide a viscous flux. The desired action here is the involvement of free silica in a stiff liquid phase to decrease the amount of crystalline silica, both quartz and cristobalite. Magnesium oxide has a low rate of thermal expansion and by using it to change silica to the non-crystalline phase, bodies can be created which have high resistance to thermal shock. See **Talc**.

Magnesium sulfate

MgSO$_4$. Is used in its hydrated form as a glaze flocculant. It is also a stoneware glaze flux. It occurs in many clays and is one source of the scums which occur on unglazed red-burning clays.

Magnesium sulfate occurs naturally in the hydrated form from MgSO$_4$.H$_2$O (kieserite) to the more common heptahydrate MgSO$_4$.7H$_2$O called epsomite (Epsom salt). The chief deposits are in Germany and the United States.

Magnesium sulfate is soluble. In solution with water it

creates an acidic (sulfuric acid) reaction with electrolytes. One per cent of a recipe is usually ample magnesium sulfate to keep a glaze flocculated. It is thus used as a substitute for calcium chloride. The effect of the magnesium sulfate is unlikely to be seen in the finished glaze because the magnesium oxide content of the fully hydrated sulfate (Epsom salt) is only 16%.

Sometimes up to 5% of magnesium sulfate is added to an already-prepared glaze slop. In this case the effect is that of extreme flocculation, whereby the clay particles in the glaze slop refuse to lie near to one another. Instead they will only rest at angles. The two extremes, deflocculation and flocculation, are shown diagrammatically in figs. 1 and 2. The result is a stiff or thick glaze slop because the clay particles produce a bulky structure with a high degree of internal friction.

This thickening of the glaze slop is useful when the biscuit has been overfired or one wishes to reglaze previously fired ware. The amount added is usually judged as a couple of teaspoonsful dissolved in warm water and added to the slop until the desired effect is obtained. Other rule of thumb methods use calcium sulfate (plaster of Paris), vinegar and gelatine. See also *Flocculation*.

In glaze or body, the magnesium sulfate begins to decompose at 150°C (302°F) when all but one molecular equivalent of water escapes. The remaining water is driven off at approximately 210°C (410°F) to leave the anhydrous magnesium sulfate:

$$MgSO_4.7H_2O \xrightarrow{150°C} MgSO_4.H_2O + 6H_2O\uparrow$$

$$MgSO_4.H_2O \xrightarrow{210°C} MgSO_4 + H_2O\uparrow$$

In bodies and glazes fired below 1150°C (2102°F) the magnesium sulfate will act as an anti-flux. In glazes it may cause a discolouration resembling smudged pencil marks. Above 1150°C (2102°F) the magnesium sulfate melts and becomes a flux. In both bodies and glazes, amounts greater than 3% of the batch may cause blistering. To overcome these disadvantages it is necessary to decompose the sulfate and obtain thereby the oxide. The sulfate is very stable and

will not decompose by heat alone but requires an agent. Agents occur in vitreous bodies and molten glazes above 1150°C (2102°F) but here the decomposition causes blistering with the escaping sulfurous gases. Paradoxically, the oxidizing process can be achieved in two stages of which the first is reduction. Reduction in the 500°C to 800°C range (932°F to 1472°F) deprives the stable sulfate of its oxygen, leaving it in an unstable state. The unstable state is then oxidized and liberates the sulfur as sulfur trioxide. The equations are:

$$\underset{\substack{\text{stable} \\ \text{sulfate}}}{MgSO_4} + \underset{\substack{\text{carbon} \\ \text{monoxide}}}{2CO} \xrightarrow{500° \text{ to } 800°C} \underset{\substack{\text{unstable} \\ \text{metasulfate}}}{MgSO_2} + \underset{\substack{\text{carbon} \\ \text{dioxide gas}}}{2CO_2\uparrow}$$

$$\underset{\substack{\text{unstable} \\ \text{metasulfate}}}{MgSO_2} + \underset{\substack{\text{oxygen}}}{O_2} \xrightarrow{800° \text{ to } 1000°C} \underset{\substack{\text{stable} \\ \text{oxide}}}{MgO} + \underset{\substack{\text{sulfur} \\ \text{trioxide gas}}}{SO_3\uparrow}$$

Magnesium compounds are present in many clays, especially those originating as marine deposits or associated with salt water or marine rocks like limestones. Clays with magnesium sulfate are often red-burning clays which contain iron oxide. They originally contained iron pyrites which, by weathering, was able to give a sulfate radical to the magnesium and calcium compounds, or exchange it for their carbonate radicals. The sulfur is thus still present in the clay in soluble sulfates. These migrate to the surface of the clay to form crystals as the clay dries. The crystals form a whitish scum which shows as white edges or fingermarks on the fired ware if it is unglazed. See *Scum*.

Magnetite

Loadstone. Lodestone. Magnetic ore. (Fe_3O_4). It is a heavy black ore and one of the few that respond to a magnet. It is in crystal or micro-crystalline form and difficult to grind. Hardness on Mohs' Scale: 6. It probably originated as limonite from bog ore. With pressure and/or heat it became metamorphosed and was able to crystallize. It is found in metamorphic and igneous rocks.

Magnetite is an excellent ceramic colourant. Ground magnetite tends to be in large particles when compared with limonite. It therefore produces a speckled effect in bodies and glazes. It is sold under various names such as black magnetic oxide, magnetic iron oxide etc. See *Iron oxide: types of*.

Maiolica

Decorated tin-glazed earthenware. Maiolica was traditionally soft-fired with a lead glaze made opaque by tin oxide.

The low temperature, originally dictated by the type of clay and some of the colours used, was responsible for a delicate suffusion of colours which allowed strong colours to be used in a sensitive way.

Maiolicas originated in the Mediterranean where the warmer and drier climate made it possible to accept the porous body as practical. Good maiolica, wherever made, retains this relaxed spirit of the Mediterranean with its combination of richness and sensitivity, even though it may need to be harder fired to be accepted as a practical ware. The picture shows present-day Deruta painting in traditional style.

HISTORY OF MAIOLICA. Tin-glazed wares had been made in many places around the Mediterranean long before the potters on the island of Maiorca (Mallorca) established a good trade in tiles and vases. Tin glazes were probably indigenous to Italy and Spain as a development from the lead glazes, but the Moorish conquest of Spain in the 8th century gave a boost to decoration. Lustred ware was introduced as a means of producing an alternative to precious metalware. See **Hispano-Moresque**. In the 15th century, Italy imported Spanish pottery and especially the work from Maiorca. The name maiolica was given to these wares and at first referred only to the lustred ware but later embraced all tin-glazed wares. It is in this broad sense that we use the term now.

It is interesting to note that exports from Italy tended to be called faience after Faenza. Later, when Italian potters established tin-glazed production in Delft in the mid-16th century, the exports were called delft. The methods employed were similar throughout but the feeling for colour

and decorative rhythms of the Spanish wares were changed in Italy and the rest of Europe. The Classical Renaissance and Chinese influences led potters away from the Hispano-Moresque expression which had successfully blended mid-eastern decoration with gothic.

The large plates and vases made in Spain retained the fluency of the production pieces in their decoration. The brushstrokes themselves had decorative meaning irrespective of what they portrayed. In Italy the technique was subordinated to the subject depicted, as the decorative method of Spain met the visual narrative of the Renaissance. The first fusions of these ideas were responsible for some fine productions, of which the lustred work from Deruta in the early 16th century is the best. A large Deruta blue and gold plate is illustrated.

The over-emphasis on pictorial representation and the use of crude colour resulted in a loss of the decorative balance of the earlier wares. Only in the smaller and humbler productions did a sensitivity continue, as with the small flask which is illustrated. This sensitivity fortunately continued and was extended into Europe and can be seen in the galleyware of Britain. See **Lambeth**.

MAIOLICA METHODS. The maiolica method is open to many variations since its essential element is simply that colouring given a soft biscuit firing to enable the friable tin-opacified glaze to adhere. The unfired glaze surface is painted with metal oxides which sink into and stain the glaze during firing and produce an inglaze decoration. A subsequent lustre firing may be used. The temperatures involved approximate 900°C, 1000°C and 700°C (1652°F, 1832°F and 1292°F).

Variations have involved the use of red-burning clays which encourage the integration of iron from the body into the glaze on edges like rims and throwing rings; the use of slips and colours painted underneath the glaze; the use of extra transparent glazes sometimes fired with the tin glaze and sometimes fired subsequently along with some softer enamel-type colours; and the use of higher temperatures to give a stronger finished ware.

The historical maiolica, delft and galleyware used a clay of the true marl or malm type. These calcareous clays have a high coefficient of expansion and hence contraction upon cooling from 500°C (932°F) when the glaze has set. They therefore exert a squeeze on the glaze putting it into compression. Later expansion of the body with moisture takes up this compression with little or no crazing of the glaze. Some crazing of functional ware seems inevitable but it need not be excessive or disastrous.

Other clays do not possess this quality but a substitute body can be prepared from ball, china and red clays with some cristobalite to give the necessary compression.

The pleasant salmon pink colour of the maiolica body allows a glaze to be used which is not completely opaque. Not more than 10% of tin oxide, and often as little as 5%, is needed to opacify the glaze sufficiently to give a white. The pinkish body is just visible through this glaze which gives the quality of depth and allows the full suffusion of the glaze to be appreciated. The pictures show a detail from a large dish by Daphne Carnegy, a jug and a lidded ginger jar by Pat Birks and a plaque by Adas Dworski. See also **Colour plates 17, 18, 20, 23, 24, 26, 27** and **72/73** and **Recipe Appendix**.

Before the danger from lead oxide was known, it was used to impart a gentle shine and to enhance the colour. Like tin, the lead gave an elasticity to the glaze which helped glaze fit. Without lead oxide, the brushwork retains a harsh edge which is out of sympathy with traditional maiolica. With leadless glazes therefore it is helpful to prepare pigments as very strongly coloured glazes rather than simply using oxides or stains.

Rob Bibby uses a lead bisilicate recipe at 1100°C (2012°F):

lead bisilicate	65
calcium borate frit	10
china clay	10
flint	5
tin oxide	10
zirconium silicate	4

See **Printing** and **Colour plate 17**.

oxides are used to stain a glaze made white by tin oxide. The traditional method originated by Islamic potters and developed in the Mediterranean countries uses a malm-type clay which is thrown, hand-built and moulded. The ware is

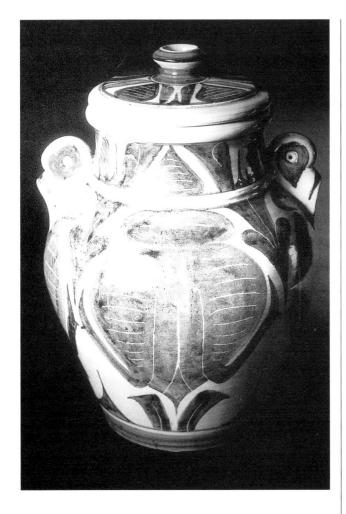

A typical leadless glaze recipe is:

borax frit	60
feldspar	20
china clay	10
tin oxide	10

With any maiolica glaze, the addition of potassium oxide by way of feldspar and boron oxide by way of a frit will help to spread the tin uniformly and produce a smoother white if the granular quality is not required. Small amounts (up to 5%) of zinc oxide and calcium oxide, although not acting as strong fluxes alone at this range, are induced by the main flux to combine with the tin oxide. They help with the opacity and produce a more stable complex silicate, but zinc oxide especially may modify the colours. Zirconium oxide also helps opacity and in small amounts may even help to give a more brilliant shine.

Today many prepared colours are available which were not available to the early maiolica potters. Earlier potters often prepared their own which included a lead antimonate yellow and a manganese purple which were limited in their temperature ranges. Today's prepared colours have a wider range and are often extremely stable, which precludes the softening effect of suffusion.

Majolica

English majolica. A late 19th-century ware with shiny colourful glazes. It was produced as a contrast to the drabber wares of the earlier period. It is not to be confused with tin-glazed maiolica. The majolica body was cane clay which fired to a light straw colour. The ware was richly modelled to provide many highlights which showed the shiny glazes to advantage and with many pockets to collect the glazes.

Malachite

Copper carbonate ore. $CuCO_3.Cu(OH)_2$. A weathered ore of copper which is easily identified by its bright emerald green colour. Small pieces up to half an inch across can often be found on the wash-out tips of old copper, zinc and lead mines. The pieces are easily crushed for use as glaze colourant or brushwork pigment. See **Copper ores.**

Malm

True marl. A clay of fairly recent geological deposition containing a high proportion of calcium compounds. These compounds are calcium sulfate and calcium carbonate, usually referred to as chalk. These could account for as much as 30% of the dry clay. See **Marl**.

Malms usually contain impurities of iron as carbonate, sulfate and sulfide. The iron is bleached by the calcium compounds so that the fired colour is often a yellowish buff. The raw colour can be ochre, brown, green or grey.

Well-weathered malms are plastic and have usually lost the more soluble sulfates. They are used as potting clays for the soft-fired earthenwares like maiolica. The calcium compounds give no fluxing action at the lower temperatures but give valuable anticraze properties. Malms fired over 1100°C (2012°F) deform quickly and melt to a glass by 1250°C (2282°F). See **Calcium oxide**.

The low plasticity malms are used for brickmaking.

Manganese carbonate

$MnCO_3$. The carbonate source of manganese oxides for bodies and glazes. It occurs as the pink-coloured ore rhodochrosite. It decomposes upon heating to form manganese oxide (MnO) and carbon dioxide (CO_2). The manganese oxide immediately takes up free oxygen to become the dioxide (MnO_2). There is some advantage in using manganese carbonate for low-temperature glazes. It is bulkier for its staining power than manganese oxide and therefore gives a more uniform spread of colour if this is required.

Manganese oxide

MnO or MnO_2. A metal oxide used as a colourant for bodies and glazes. It gives blacks, browns and purples. It sometimes occurs in clays but usually it is introduced. Amounts up to 10% give brown slips. More than 15% fluxes stoneware slips sufficiently for them to be called vitrifying slips and slip glazes. Amounts up to 4% are readily dissolved in glazes. More than this is partially precipitated as a crystalline surface. Over 20% gives metallic surfaces. See **Bronze**.

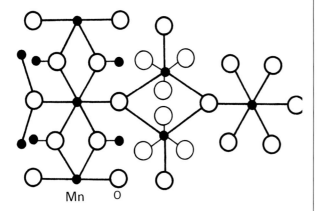

Manganese occurs with iron in many ores and is therefore a common constituent of early slips and glazes, e.g. European slipware and Eastern tenmoku. Manganese oxide is respon-

sible for the fernlike stains in moss agate. A similar effect in pottery is created in slip with tobacco and manganese oxide. See **Mocha ware**.

Manganese oxide occurs in nature as the ore pyrolusite (MnO_2). This is the main source of the metal manganese which is used in the alloy ferromanganese, itself an additive to steel. Other manganese ores are: braunite, hausmannite, manganite, polianite, psilomelane, rhodochrosite, rhodonite, wad. The manganese ores originated in a similar way to iron ores and are often associated with them. The element manganese is a constituent of many igneous rocks. When these weather to clay, some of the manganese oxides are involved in the residual clays while manganese salts are carried away by water. The manganese in solution is precipitated as bog manganese, some of which is integrated with sandstones while some is metamorphosed into concentrated ores. The chief ore deposits are in west Africa, Cuba, Brazil, Russia and India. Manganese is often present in the ores of other metals where it partially replaces iron, aluminium, calcium, barium and magnesium. Manganese oxide is also used in the manufacture of disinfectants, and paint.

Manganese oxide is an interesting oxide in its behaviour. It is introduced into bodies and glazes as the dioxide, a black powder (MnO_2). In this form it is insoluble in water. In a ceramic fusion below 1080°C (1976°F), it is soluble in the alkaline content and as such behaves as an anti-flux or acid with some retarding effect upon the fusion. In this temperature range it gives a dry-looking black colour to bodies (5%–10%) and purplish plum colours to transparent and semi-transparent glazes (up to 4%).

Manganese oxide gives interesting coffee colours with tin oxide. Coarse manganese oxide will give speckled effects in low-temperature glazes but above 1150°C (2102°F) the effect tends to be uniformly dispersed. The following glaze uses iron oxide to give a background beige against which the manganese oxide gives an excellent coffee-coloured speckle at 1040°C (1904°F).

feldspar	10
china clay	5
900°C borax frit	65
tin oxide	10
red iron oxide	5
manganese oxide	5 (unsieved)

A similar colour is obtainable at higher temperatures but the speckle is difficult to maintain. Where the manganese oxide is dissolving too much it can be put unsieved into an engobe which is brushed onto the body. The speckle will burn through the glaze.

Manganese dioxide (MnO_2) starts to decompose as early as 600°C (1112°F). This decomposition increases in rapidity up to 1080°C (1976°F) at which temperature the oxide is completely the monoxide (MnO). In slow firings below 1080°C the manganese oxides in ceramic fusions will be MnO_2, MnO and also the transitional Mn_2O_3 which is

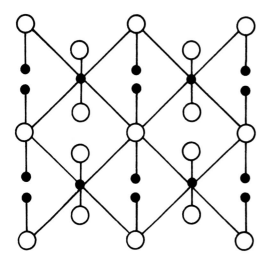

known to give good purple colours when dissolved in alkaline glazes. In fast firings the decomposition happens suddenly near to 1080°C. The change is inevitable and requires no effort at reduction on the potter's part. The two drawings show the dioxide and monoxide structures. The monoxide is a green colour but this colour is never seen because immediately it is formed it is involved in fusion with silica. Like other monoxides, it is an active flux. The manganese dioxide's ceramic role is changed from that of an anti-flux to one of a flux by raising the temperature above 1080°C (1976°F). In combination with silica the monoxide gives violet colours. Amethyst is silica stained with manganese monoxide. When aluminium oxide is also present

the colour tends towards a brown. The brown is a bluish or purplish brown and pleasantly different from the brown obtained with iron oxide. Glazes high in alkali and low in aluminium oxide can be given a beautiful violet colour by 1% to 3% of manganese oxide. The colour can be intensified by a very small amount of cobalt oxide (less than 0·5%).

Manganese oxide was an important colourant in the Rockingham brown wares. With iron oxide in a transparent lead glaze it gives deep rich browns which have some crystalline striations and a reddish colour when seen in sunlight. The following recipe is for a Rockingham-type glaze which has all the qualities of the best Rockingham on buff and red clays at 1120°C (2048°F):

feldspar	28
china clay	14
flint	4
lead bisilicate	40
whiting	4
red iron oxide	3
manganese oxide	7

The liberation of oxygen at 1080°C (1976°F) can cause trouble in glazes which are matured at this temperature. It will be noticed that the examples given avoid this temperature. The use of slips presents even more of a problem because the oxygen must travel the whole thickness of the glaze to escape. If one is firing to 1100°C (2012°F) with a glaze covering a slip containing manganese oxide, one can expect oxygen bubbles in the glaze over the slip and they might spoil the glaze surface also. To avoid this one must fire lower than 1080°C (1976°F), or approximately 1110°C or 1120°C (2030°F or 2048°F) with slow maturing at the end, or use a different colouring in the slip. With the first alternative, the colour will never achieve the rich blacks possible with the higher temperature but some soft purplish greys are obtainable.

It is impractical to start with the monoxide instead of the dioxide. Although stable enough to exist at room temperature, the monoxide will take up oxygen from the air in the early stages of warming up for the firing.

Alone, manganese monoxide is refractory but it melts easily with body interaction above 1150°C (2102°F). Manganese oxide painted onto the body and fired unglazed produces its own glossy surface. A thick layer of manganese oxide produces a fused black matt surface with very thick parts showing a coppery bronze colour which can be polished like a lustre. Therefore for firings above 1150°C (2102°F) one can use manganese oxide as part of a slip or glaze up to 100%. The photographs show a bowl by Peter Wills (page 227) and a detail of a bowl by Lucie Rie (above). The detail shows how manganese oxide produces a thick lustrous metallic surface. In other words, whatever the amount it can produce satisfactory results. It can, of course, produce over-fluxed results that run down the pot. Slips containing over 15% manganese oxide are often fused like glazes and can be used as once-fired slip glazes. See **Bronze, Colour plates 29** and **38** and **Recipe Appendix.**

Manganese monoxide is unaffected by reduction and does not assist iron and copper to give good colours in reduction. It is better to keep it for oxidized wares and it is at its best in slips and glazes for 1200°C (2192°F) and above. Here it does for oxidized glazes what iron oxide does for reduced and neutralized glazes: it gives pleasing and sometimes surprising results in most circumstances. Like iron oxide, it dissolves in stoneware glazes and more is able to dissolve when hot than cold. Therefore the difference is precipitated as crystals on the surface of the glaze during cooling. The amount which completely dissolves in stoneware glazes approximates 4%. The following recipe for 1200°C (2192°F) gives a good crystalline precipitation from the further 2% with the iron oxide:

mixed feldspar	46
china clay	14
flint	14
whiting	16
red iron oxide	4
manganese oxide	6

The crystalline striations, as mentioned in this example and in the Rockingham-type glaze, vary in crystal size according to glaze composition, rate of cooling and amount of oxide. The usual is a distinct grouping of crystals in the line of gravity. There also occurs a smoky lustrous surface of crystals when the amount precipitated is very small and the glaze is of the fully-matured transparent type. A speckled metallic surface like a fine oil spot sometimes occurs. All these effects are available at all temperatures.

Manganite
MnO(OH). A manganese ore and one of the sources of manganese oxide.

Manx stone
Another name for **Cornish stone**.

Marble
CaCO₃. A metamorphosed limestone of fine texture. It is extremely hard but its dust could be used in glazes as a source of calcium oxide. See **Limestone**.

Marbled ware
A marble is a variegated stain. It is achieved by partially blending two differently coloured clays.

The clays must be tempered with openers to make their shrinkages alike during drying and firing. They are blended by kneading or cutting and joining. The blend is usually thrown and later turned to take off the blurred surface and reveal the pattern in clean contrast.

The illustrations show a marbled stoneware vase by Delan Cookson and an agate porcelain dish by Linda Caswell.

Marcasite

White iron pyrites. Iron sulfide. FeS_2. An iron ore which is similar to iron pyrites but light in colour. It sometimes occurs in marls. It can be crushed after controlled 'weathering', when it has partially 'oxidized' to iron sulfate ($FeSO_4.7H_2O$). Its sulfur content still presents a hazard to its use as a colourant because the sulfur is slow to burn away during firing but some soft yellow colours can be produced in solution with lead glazes.

Marl

Specifically a natural clay containing iron oxide and a high proportion of calcium compounds. Marls are used as potting clays for low-fired earthenware and as brick clays. The high proportion of calcium compounds, often called chalk, make marls friable when dry. Other friable clays have come to be called marls although they contain no chalk, e.g. the Old Red Sandstone marls. Following this practice some plastic red clays, although containing no chalk and not being friable, were also called marls, e.g. Etruria Marl in Stoke-on-Trent, England. The term marl is therefore a general one for iron-stained earthenware clays. To specify the original true marls the old name of malm is used.

Ignoring the Old Red Sandstone marls and the marls associated with Carboniferous strata like the Etruria marls, one can consider the true marls as a group of clays having similar properties. They were deposited during different geological periods and under different circumstances over about 150 million years but they all contain soluble salts and are associated with calcium compounds. The marls used by British potters include the Keuper and Tea marls of the Triassic Period; the Oxford and Kimmeridge clays of the Jurassic System; and the Gault and Weald clays of the Cretaceous System.

The iron content is partially bleached by the calcium oxide and often remains so during firing. Marls therefore fire to attractive ochres, buffs and pinks which are suitable backgrounds for tin glazes. The marls were used by the delftware potters.

Marls are used on a large scale for making general building bricks. They are not suitable for making engineering bricks because they vitrify too quickly resulting in too many wasters. For the same reason they cannot be used for stoneware. Instead they are used for earthenware where the high calcium oxide content is an advantage.

For use as potting clays, the marls are weathered and changed from the short crumbly state to a practical plastic state. This weathering can be accentuated by thorough blunging and the removal of the water which contains the soluble salts. Even so, some of the calcareous compounds remain. Calcium carbonate will not be washed away and some marls contain as much as 30% calcium carbonate. This and other impurities act as fluxes above 1100°C (2012°F) which is why marls cannot be used as bodies at these temperatures: they quickly vitrify and deform. At temperatures around 1050°C (1922°F) the calcium oxide is only partially involved in the fusion and gives to the body a high rate of contraction upon cooling. See ***Calcium oxide***. This is not the same as a high shrinkage rate during firing. The high contraction rate puts a compression on the glaze and therefore gives some insurance against crazing. See ***Glaze fit***.

Martin brothers

The four Martin brothers—Wallace, Walter, Edwin and Charles—were pioneers of the artist-potter movement in Britain. From 1873 to 1912 they produced salt-glazed stoneware in London and Southall, making full use of applied decoration and colouring oxides in combination with mottled glazes. Their production included architectural plaques, decorative vases and grotesque animals and birds. Their work is referred to as Martinique ware.

Matting agents

Materials which are added to glazes to give a matt surface. Of the simple oxides, the acidic ones are the easiest to control but they do raise the maturing range of the glaze. The alkaline oxides which are capable of creating matt effects have the opposite effect if present in too small an amount. To overcome these difficulties combinations are created and commercially marketed. Examples of the three types are given. Details will be found indexed under the oxide concerned. See also ***Crystalline glazes***.

The acidic oxides which give matt results are:

titanium oxide, up to 25%
rutile, up to 25% gives buff colour
tin oxide, 15% to 25% (oxidation)

Also included here because of their anti-flux properties:

aluminium oxide, 15% to 25%
red iron oxide, 8% to 25% gives dark brown (oxidation)

It is difficult to give precise amounts for alkaline oxides. The type and composition of the glaze is an important factor. The best amount can be established by a line blend by arranging the test amounts between 10% and 45%. The alkaline oxides which encourage matt crystallization are:

magnesium oxide introduced by magnesium carbonate, talc or dolomite
calcium oxide introduced by whiting
zinc oxide
barium oxide introduced by barium carbonate
manganese monoxide introduced by the dioxide
strontium oxide introduced by strontium carbonate

Combined agents are made from the following recipes:

1. china clay   50
    zinc oxide   50

The mixture is calcined between 600°C and 800°C (1112°F and 1472°F) and reground. The powder is added to glazes in amounts up to 30%.

2. titanium oxide   30
    tin oxide   30
    zinc oxide   30
    whiting   10

The minerals are mixed together and added to the glazes in amounts between 10% and 25%.

3. titanium oxide   40–30
    zinc oxide   30–40
    whiting   30

The minerals are mixed together and added to glazes in amounts up to 30%.

Maturing

Developing and improving. Clays are said to mature if they are stored in wet plastic condition. See *Ageing*. Glaze slops are usually allowed to stand for 24 hours after preparation. This is maturing. It encourages a full wetting of the materials. It is similar to the maturation of clays and, of course, often involves some clay.

Molten glazes are said to mature in the final stages of firing. This is usually considered as a length of time at one temperature. In contrast is the maturation of the body which takes place over a time and temperature range called the maturing range. See also *Glaze: chemistry* and *Grain size.*

Maturing range

The part of a firing, usually considered as between two temperatures, where the body reaches its correct strength and compactness through vitrification. Below this range the body is underfired, being too weak and porous. Above this range the body is overfired and is likely to be so dense and glassy that it is brittle when cool. Most overfired bodies also deform during firing by blistering and collapsing. This is the beginning of the eventual complete breakdown which results in a molten state.

The maturing range is different for every clay. Some red clays, which are rich in fluxes, mature in the range 950°C to 1050°C (1742°F to 1922°F). Some ball clays mature in the region of 1150°C to 1200°C (2102°F to 2192°F). It will be noticed that the range is not always the same length. Some fireclays have a very long maturing range from 1200°C to 1400°C (2192°F to 2552°F) while some special bodies may, by virtue of the active fluxes present, be matured in a range which allows no room for error from 1090°C to 1100°C (1994°F to 2012°F).

Medium

Liquid used to assist the application of colours to pottery. The medium has no part in the fired formula but burns out in the firing. Some media are: water, water with a gum such as arabic or tragacanth, wax emulsion, linseed oil, turpentine, stand oil, rape oil, aniseed oil.

Medium glaze

An intermediate glaze. One which matures in the region 1050°C to 1200°C (1922°F to 2192°F). See *Intermediate glaze*.

Meldon stone

Another name for *Cornish stone*.

Mellor

John W (1869–1938). The British ceramicist noted for his study of the behaviour of ceramic minerals during fusion. He successfully completed and co-ordinated much of the work started by earlier continental ceramicists, some of which concerned the solubility of lead oxide in glazes and the production of lead-free glazes. See *Low sol*.

Melting point

The temperature which divides the solid state from the liquid state of a material. A crystalline compound has a definite melting point which is also the solidifying point. A glaze, on the other hand, has a melting point at the upper end of a melting range. It is not the same as its solidifying point which is at the lower end of the melting range. See also *Glaze: chemistry* and *Grain size*.

Melting occurs when the molecule-to-molecule bonds,

which are responsible for maintaining a solid state, are broken in response to the vibratory pressure of heat. The heat energy is used by the material to break the bonds. See *Heat*.

In a crystalline solid (mineral, oxide etc) there are many identical bonds regularly distributed. These bonds respond to heat in the same way and therefore break within a few degrees of each other around the quoted melting point.

A glaze is an amorphous solid which is composed of many different minerals and oxides linked together by many and varied bonds. These bonds are broken at different temperatures and therefore there cannot be a single melting point. As the bonds are broken the viscosity of the glaze progressively decreases so that the glaze becomes first pliable and then a stiff liquid. When the point is reached at which the bonds between different minerals and oxides have all been broken, the glaze can be said to have melted. It will have reached a liquid state and be capable of flowing.

The melting points of potters' minerals are included in *Table 30*.

Mensuration formulae

Area of rectangle	= base × height
Area of triangle	= ½ (base × perpendicular height)
Area of circle	= πr^2
Circumference of circle	= $2\pi r$
Volume of cylinder	= $\pi r^2 \times$ perpendicular height
Surface of cylinder	= $2\pi r \times$ (height + radius)

$$\pi = \frac{22}{7} = 3 \cdot 14159 \text{ approx.}$$

Mesh

A fabric of interwoven threads producing theoretically square holes between them. Meshes were originally identified by the number of threads per linear inch. Thus a 50's mesh had 50 threads and 50 holes per linear inch. The threads and apertures being approximately equal, the hole was therefore 1/100 inch wide. The method was approximately true for mesh sizes numbered from 8's to 350's. These sizes are called lawns or sieves.

Coarser meshes are riddles which are described by the length of the hole which is assumed to be square. In riddles the wire threads are not the same as the width of the holes but are usually standard throughout a series of riddles. See *Riddle*.

The apertures are now standardized internationally in micrometre measurements. Although some mesh numbers differ from country to country the original meaning is still approximately true. In continental Europe the mesh number approximates holes per centimetre. See *Table 42*.

Meta

A term used in chemical nomenclature to indicate a sense of change. It is often used for a half-way sub-division in an equation and is also used to indicate simply 'with'. For example, metaboric acid is half-way between boric acid and boron oxide.

Metakaolin

The theoretical crystal which exists after firing clay. See *Ceramic change* and *Firing*.

$$\underset{\text{kaolinite (clay)}}{Al_2O_3.2SiO_2.2H_2O} \xrightarrow{600°C} \underset{\text{metakaolin (pot)}}{Al_2O_3.2SiO_2} + \underset{\text{water vapour}}{2H_2O\uparrow}$$

Metallic salts

Crystalline compounds of colouring metals which can be volatilized to transfer colouring to ceramic surfaces as lustres and flashing.

The adjective 'metallic' is used to avoid confusion with salt glazing and with the salts in clays which give scumming.

Typical metallic salts used are sulfates and chlorides of copper, silver, tin, cobalt, manganese, nickel and iron. They are soluble in water and most are poisonous. All should be handled with care. The gases liberated are also poisonous.

The metallic salts are often added to the sawdust which is close to the ceramic pieces in smoking and sawdust firing/carbonization treatments. Alternatively, the metallic salts are dissolved in water and painted or sprayed on the ceramic surface prior to smoke firing. A third method uses little open bowls of metallic salts which are placed close to ceramics in the kiln either in saggars, shielded or on an open shelf to give flash or scorch patches across the ceramic pieces.

A flame kiln will exit the harmful gases and smoke up the flue. When an electric kiln is used, positive ventilation of the site must be provided and alternate firings should be oxidized to restore the protective oxide coating on the elements.

Metal release

The release of poisonous metals from fired glazes during contact with acids. If these metals are not completely involved in the ceramic fusion the surplus metal remains soluble. It can be dissolved by food acids such as vinegar or fruit juice which may be ingested. The metals in question are derived from:

compounds of lead
antimony oxide
arsenic oxide
barium carbonate
beryllium oxide
cadmium and selenium compounds
copper oxide and carbonate
chromium oxide
potassium dichromate
zinc oxide

These substances are particularly likely to remain soluble in low-fired or underfired ware. Also, additions of them to a recipe can disturb an otherwise stable glaze. If painted onto the surface of a raw glaze, or as enamels, the potential release of lead is increased. Prepared stains have a lesser effect on metal release than do oxides. Copper oxide is the most dangerous in this respect.

Food acids which leach out soluble metals are: citric acid in fruit juice, especially lemon juice; malic acid in apple juice and cider; succinic acid in coffee and whisky; acetic acid in vinegar. Alkaline foods such as beans and some green vegetables might also be capable of attack.

Fired glazes are laboratory tested for solubility and must be under the minimum statutory level. In Britain levels are given for lead and cadmium on different shapes.

British Standard 6748 Part 1

Flatware	Lead = 20 ppm (parts per million)
	Cadmium = 2 ppm
Hollow-ware	Lead = 7 ppm
	Cadmium = 0·7 ppm

Storage vessels or any hollow-ware over 1100 millilitres capacity

Lead = 2 ppm
Cadmium = 0·2 ppm

The test involves exposure to 4% acetic acid at room temperature for 24 hours.

British Standard 6748 Part 2

| Cooking ware | Lead = 7 ppm |
| | Cadmium = 0·7 ppm |

The test involves boiling acetic acid in the vessel for two hours followed by a cooling period of 22 hours.

Similar or more stringent limits apply in other countries and some include arsenic, antimony and zinc in the regulations. See also ***Lead poisoning*** and ***Low sol***.

In the USA there is also a restriction on barium release from glaze which must be below 70 ppm.

Mica

A group name for a series of alumino-silicates related to clay, montmorillonite and feldspar, and existing as impurities in them. Mica is present in acidic and intermediate rocks, and is one of the products of their decomposition along with clay, feldspar and quartz. The commonest forms are muscovite and biotite.

Micas have a structure similar to montmorillonites with a gibbsite layer sandwiched between two silica layers. The layers are held together by potassium, calcium and magnesium cations which present a stronger bond than the sodium cations of the montmorillonites. The result is that water cannot enter micas nor do they swell in water. They do not exhibit plasticity but they do not hinder it in clay. They can be cleaved into fine sheets and broken down into very fine particles. The crystals are hexagonal and vary in size from 0·05 micrometres to a couple of feet across! These large crystals are called books, from which thin sheets are split.

When micas are present in clays they do not readily separate from the kaolinite particles by simple sedimentation because their particles are of similar size and density. However, being non-plastic they respond differently to the presence of electrolytes and then settle more quickly than the kaolinite. Fortunately, the presence of some mica is advantageous in providing the slow vitrification of clay. See also ***Illites***. They also provide an excellent filler which is resistant to thermal shock. For this reason, micaceous sands are preferable to quartz sands as openers for ovenware clays.

Muscovite is potassium mica and is given the formula $K_2O.3Al_2O_3.6SiO_2.2H_2O$. When potassium oxide appears in the ultimate analysis of a clay it is likely to be present mostly as muscovite although an accompanying rational analysis might attribute it theoretically to feldspar. See ***Analysis***.

The water content of muscovite and all micas is present as hydroxyl groups within the gibbsite layer. It is driven off slowly from 250°C to 1100°C (482°F to 2012°F). This decomposition period overlaps the slow melting period which starts at 750°C (1382°F). Being a complex structure, muscovite is slow to melt and is responsible for the extended vitrification of many white ball clays and natural stoneware clays.

Biotite contains iron and magnesium. It is very variable in composition and dark in colour. The black specks in granite are biotite and it is also responsible for the pink colour in feldspars and some of the colour in clays.

Microcline

Potassium feldspar. $K_2O.Al_2O_3.6SiO_2$. A feldspar which is chemically identical with orthoclase but has a different crystal structure. It occurs in granites and other acidic igneous rocks and is normally classed as orthoclase feldspar by the potter. See ***Feldspar: types of***.

Mill

General term for grinding and mixing machines, e.g. pug mill, ball mill, grinding mill. On its own it usually means a grinding mill or pan. Like the word kiln, the original word was miln but it has lost the 'n' in most dialects and is now spelt mill.

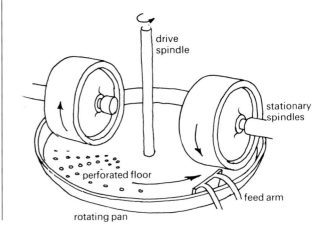

Mineral

A natural material which has a definable chemical formula in whole numbers and a definable molecular structure which gives it a distinct crystal formation. In its strictest sense a substance must be won from the earth by mining or quarrying to be a mineral and must be inorganic, although coal, oil and gas are exceptions.

In its wider sense in pottery, a mineral can also be prepared so that prepared oxides etc are accepted as minerals. The term has sometimes been extended to include raw materials like clay and cornish stone which are of variable composition and therefore cannot be given chemical formulae in whole numbers and do not form single crystal structures. It is better to refer to these variables as materials and reserve the term mineral for substances of predictable chemical composition.

Minerals are identified by general appearance, feel and colour; specific gravity; hardness; fracture and cleavage; and colour streak.

Mirror black

A Chinese glaze, which in Chinese is called black bronze, of the Kangxi period (1662–1722). The colour is from iron and manganese oxides. The surface has a slight grain and is not an absolutely shiny mirror.

Mocha ware

A 19th-century English ware with dark tree-like motifs as decoration often on a pale blue ground. The ware is white earthenware, thrown and turned. The decoration is in coloured slips under a transparent glaze. The motif is produced by mixing manganese oxide powder with tobacco juice. This stain is applied to the edge of the wet, freshly dipped or banded slip. The juice breaks a way through the slip in ever-dividing channels which are quickly filled and thus stained by the manganese oxide. The effect is similar to moss agate which is manganese oxide staining of cryptocrystalline quartz.

Modifiers

Modifying oxides. A general name describing all oxides other than the glass-forming oxides. In creating glazes, one considers that one starts with the all important glass-forming oxide silica. The silica is made to fuse at a convenient temperature by the use of alkaline fluxing oxides. The melt is stabilized by the use of amphoteric oxides and stained by colouring oxides. All these oxides, which are additional to the silica, are modifiers. However, the term is used more specifically when it refers to oxides which are used to alter (modify) an existing standard glaze or colour. One then refers to the glaze and the modifiers and considers the new glaze to be the modified glaze. The term modified oxide arises in referring to a colouring oxide which has been altered in its colouring power by being mixed with, and in some cases fritted with, other oxides.

Mohammedan blue

Cobalt oxide modified by arsenic oxide gives a bright blue. The name was given to cobalt ores with arsenic impurity which were imported into China in the Yuan dynasty. The usual impurity is manganese which subdues the blue. This colour is known as Chinese native blue.

Mohs

Friedrich. The German mineralogist who originated the Scale of Hardness in the early 19th century.

Mohs' Scale of Hardness

A list of ten minerals arranged in order of their hardness and given numbers from 1 (soft) to 10 (hard). The minerals were chosen for their fairly universal availability and consistent structure and hence hardness. Some have a slight difference in hardness between an edge and a face of a crystal but for general field testing this can be ignored. It should be noted that the scale is not one of equal progression but only a convenient sequence.

1	Talc
2	Gypsum (rock salt)
(2·5	Finger nail)
3	Calcite
4	Fluorspar (fluorite)
5	Apatite
(5·5	Window glass and penknife blade)
6	Orthoclase feldspar
(6·5	Metal file)
7	Quartz
8	Topaz
9	Corundum (aluminium oxide)
10	Diamond

The scale is used to provide information about the hardness of substances. For example, dolomite is given the number H3·5 to H4. In fieldwork identification of a mineral or other material, the factors involved are: native colour, general appearance and feel; the colour of its streak when it is scratched across unglazed porcelain; its relative density; its fracture or cleavage; and its hardness. For example, the dogtooth spar of calcite is often mistaken for quartz. The crystals of these two minerals look similar but can be quickly differentiated by their hardness. Quartz (H7) will scratch window glass (H5·5). A penknife cannot cut into the quartz crystal. But the calcite crystal (H3) is much softer and can be scratched quite easily with a penknife (H5·5).

In Mohs' Scale the standard rule is that a mineral of one number is capable of scratching minerals of any lower number but not *vice versa*.

Molecular weight

The total of the atomic weights of all the atoms which make up a molecule. See *Calculations: molecular weight* and *Table 30*.

Molecule

The smallest part of a chemical compound that can exist independently while retaining all the properties of the compound in bulk form. In potting terms, a molecule cannot be seen. What is visible is a grain composed of thousands of molecules. The molecule is used as a theoretical unit in a discussion of ceramic fusions and in calculations of the unity formulae.

Molecular formulae are descriptions of molecules using chemical symbols to indicate the elements present and their relative proportions. In the descriptions of oxides and other compounds in this book, a formula for one molecule is included with the synonyms in the first line. For an explanation of these see *Formula: chemical*.

Molecular compounds are chemical compounds formed from two or more complete molecules, e.g. lead bisilicate.

Molochite

Chamotte. Grog. $Al_2O_3.2SiO_2$. The trade name for calcined china clay produced by ECC International. It is used as a refractory white grog in bodies. In glazes it introduces aluminium oxide without the shrinkage problems of raw china clay. Molochite is calcined at 1500°C (2732°F) and is composed of mullite and amorphous silica glass with no crystalline silica. It therefore has a low and uniform thermal expansion and is an excellent way of introducing mullite into ovenware to increase the resistance to thermal shock. It is low in iron and titanium. See also *Chamotte* and *Grog*.

Molybdenum oxide

Molybdic oxide. MoO_3. A refractory colouring oxide used in the preparation of yellow stains. It acts as a stabilizer in glazes. It is soluble and poisonous. See *Poison*. Molybdenum silicide ($MoSi_2$) is a refractory electrical conductor used in some kiln elements.

Mono

A term used in chemical nomenclature to indicate a combination with one atom or one molecule. For example, lead monoxide (PbO) has one atom of oxygen and lead monosilicate ($PbO.SiO_2$) has one molecule of silica.

Monoxide

In the monoxide molecule there is one (mono) atom of oxygen but there may be one or two atoms of the other element. For example, zinc monoxide has one oxygen atom and one zinc atom in each molecule and the chemical formula is written ZnO; whereas sodium monoxide has two sodium atoms to each oxygen atom and the formula is written Na_2O. See also *Oxide*.

Montmorillonites

A group of silicates produced by the decomposition of igneous rocks. Their particles are extremely small flat hexagonal crystals and hence exhibit plasticity.

They are related to kaolinite and are often referred to as clays. The most important, from the potter's point of view, are bentonite and talc. Both exhibit the property of lubrication which arises from the flat particles. See *Bentonite*.

Mudstones

As the name suggests, these are stones made from mud. It is a name given to rocks which formed from deposits of mud and dust. Another term often used to describe them is argillaceous which implies the presence of some clay. However, mudstones do not necessarily reconstitute into clays, although Keuper marl is an example of one that does. The presence of some directional cleavage, as in shales, is an indication of clay content. Crushed mudstones can be used in glazes. See also *Albany slip*.

Muffle

A thin-walled box to protect ware from direct contact with flames. It is like a saggar but is permanently part of the kiln structure. It is made from a refractory, such as fireclay, sillimanite or silicon carbide, and is as thin as possible to allow the heat from the flames outside to reach the ware inside. There is no direct heat transference from flame to ware, instead all the heating of the ware is by radiation and conduction.

A muffle lasts longer than a saggar because it is handled less. However it is only suitable for small kilns and is only necessary when direct flame contact is undesirable. Such conditions arise with some delicate colourings, onglaze enamels and some lustres. These colours are sometimes called muffle colours. Today's clean fuels—gas and electricity—have rendered a muffle kiln unnecessary. However, electric kilns are sometimes referred to as electric muffles.

A term semi-muffle is sometimes used for up-draught kilns which have a high bag wall.

Mug

A drinking vessel for informal occasions. The examples are by Buddy Bird, Micki Schloessingk, two by Will Levi Marshall, Frank Hamer, David Frith, Cathi Jefferson and John Pollex.

Mullite

$3Al_2O_3.2SiO_2$. An important alumino-silicate which is created within pottery bodies during firing. Mullite crystals are long needles which interlace to produce a strong body. It is named after natural occurrence on the island of Mull.

Mullite is a product of vitrification. As the fluxed molten silica attacks the metakaolin crystal (originally the clay crystal), it removes silica into the melt. The remaining structure readjusts itself into an alumino-silicate of relatively higher aluminium oxide content, and one which does not yet melt. There are a few intermediate stages, but, from 1000°C (1832°F) upwards, mullite is an end product of kaolinite crystal decomposition. The first stage is the ceramic change:

$$Al_2O_3.2SiO_2.2H_2O \xrightarrow{600°C} Al_2O_3.2SiO_2 + 2H_2O\uparrow$$

$$\text{kaolinite (clay)} \qquad \text{metakaolin} \quad \text{water vapour}$$
$$\text{(pot)}$$

Further stages to mullite are:

$$Al_2O_3.2SiO_2 \longrightarrow Al_2O_3.1\tfrac{1}{2}SiO_2 + \tfrac{1}{2}SiO_2 \longrightarrow$$
$$Al_2O_3.SiO_2 + SiO_2 \longrightarrow Al_2O_3.\tfrac{2}{3}SiO_2 + 1\tfrac{1}{3}SiO_2$$

Fractions are used to give a better comparison with kaolinite. The last formula is, of course, mullite ($3Al_2O_3.2SiO_2$).

This rearrangement of lattice can take place within a body as it vitrifies. The resulting mullite crystals are even capable of growing outwards from their origin within the metakaolin crystal which is decomposing, thereby lacing together different particles and creating a structure of their own. Mullite crystals are long, square-sectioned needles which stiffen the vitrified mass and give strength to the final product. This is the valuable strength of stoneware and porcelain which is lacking in earthenware because found in short crystals or nuclei involved in the silica chains. These chains are stiffened by its presence. See **Aluminium oxide in glazes**. During cooling, these nuclei are starting points for the growth of crystals in crystalline glazes, especially glazes high in aluminium oxide like dolomite matts.

Muscovite
See **Mica**.

Mycenaean
The late Helladic civilization of the Greek mainland (1600BC to 1100BC). It was late Bronze Age in development. Mycenaean pottery was strongly influenced by late Minoan wares; in fact, it is likely that many of the potters came from Crete.

The wares were wheel-thrown, had a light-coloured ground and were painted with vitrifying slips. The slips were made from finely levigated red clay with additions of flux.

The best wares were probably the products of a division of labour between thrower and painter. The forms show a maturing style with increasing emphasis upon precision and use of tools. The painting of flowers and sea creatures has affinity with contemporary mural painting and at first continues the natural freshness of the best Minoan pieces. Later, there was a loss of identity with the source of inspiration and a stylized angularity appears in the drawing of figures and animals. The loss of natural freshness is partially balanced by an attractive humour in the figure-painting.

Both forms and painting become angular in the late period and develop naturally into the geometric style of the following Iron Age period.

insufficient metakaolin crystals are involved in the melt. The lesser strength of earthenware is maintained by the glass weld created at the point of contact between the metakaolin crystals etc. Mullite can form as low as 1000°C (1832°F) but its presence cannot be ensured without a firing above 1150°C (2102°F). It grows more readily in oxidation than in reduction. Mullite can be introduced into bodies in the form of Molochite.

In glazes, the mullite is unable to grow as long needles because of the agitated state of the whole melt. Its place is

N

Natch
See *Joggle*.

Natrium potassa
Kalium soda. Sodium potassium oxide. NaKO. See *Kalium soda*.

Natron
The natural form of hydrated sodium carbonate (washing soda) found as efflorescence around soda lakes. Varies from pure $Na_2CO_3.10H_2O$ to $Na_2CO_3.NaHCO_3.2$ to $9H_2O$.

Neolithic pottery
The earliest known pottery. It was made during the Neolithic Period or New Stone Age. At this time the previously wandering hunters became the settled agriculturalists and stock breeders. This is the age of polished stone implements. In this settled existence pottery provided suitable cooking and storage vessels. It also provided the opportunity for decorative expression and therefore made comparatively speedy development. Within 500 years of the introduction of pottery-making, highly decorative vessels of expressive form were being produced and were an important means of artistic expression.

Clay was first used as a modelling material pre-dating pottery by a few thousand years. Various dates have been given for the first pottery including a Japanese find dated as 9000BC, but the generally accepted date is 7000BC for pottery made in Anatolia (Turkey). From here, pottery-making is said to have spread throughout the world reaching the Far East about 5000BC and western Europe about 3000BC.

Nepheline
$K_2O.3Na_2O.4Al_2O_3.9SiO_2$. A feldspathoid mineral variable in colour from white to dark greenish brown. It melts in the range 1100°C to 1200°C (2012°F to 2192°F). Nepheline syenite is a transparent and colourless variety occurring in plutonic igneous rocks. It is given the formula $K_2O.3Na_2O.4Al_2O_3.8SiO_2$ and is a useful substitute for the normal feldspars in bodies and glazes because of its lower melting point. It is an excellent material for the introduction of sodium oxide.

Neriage
A Japanese name for a process which creates repeat patterns of contrasting colours in a clay slab. The colours are streaked together in a roll or slab from which small identical pieces are cut and used to reform a patterned slab. This is then free-formed or used in or over a mould. The photograph shows a detail of a bowl by Dorothy Feibleman.

Network structure
Network. The three-dimensional placing of fixed points on which atoms or molecules of a solid are positioned. If the network is regular as a repeating pattern it is called a lattice and results in a crystalline structure. If the network is not regular it is called a random network and in such cases the substance will be amorphous.

The diagrams show a lattice and a random network. They are calcium oxide (CaO) and an imaginary glaze, respectively. Other examples are given under *Lattice structure, Random structure*, and some of the described minerals.

It is not essential for the potter to study atomic structures

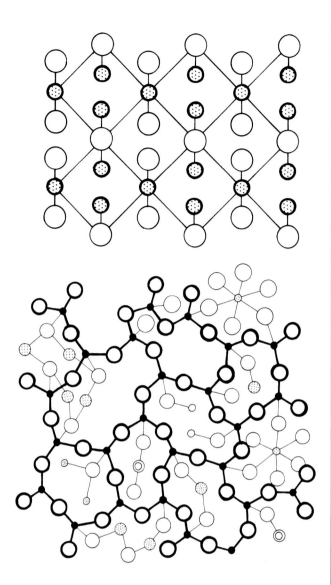

glazes packed with 20%–50% barium carbonate and 10% zinc oxide develop attractive pinks, blues and greens with 1%–3% nickel oxide. The colour varies according to the body, temperature and the amount of barium carbonate. See **Recipe Appendix.**

Nickel oxide is always affected in its colour response by the major flux of the glaze. Of course, all colouring oxides are affected in this way but nickel oxide shows some surprising results. These occur because the major flux causes the nickel atoms to attach themselves to the oxygen atoms in specific uniform ways. Glazes with a mix of fluxes produce dull grey-greens from the nickel atom but glazes formulated around a preponderance of a single flux like potassium, sodium, barium or lithium oxides can produce more striking individual colours.

Nickel is a metal that occurs as ores in association with arsenic and sulfur. The main ores are nicolite (NiAs) and nickel glance (NiAsS) but all ores have iron, copper and cobalt as impurities. Canada is the major source. Nickel is used in alloys, notably stainless steel and nickel silver, and with chromium for resistance wire for kiln and other heating elements. The oxide is extracted from the ore by roasting.

There are three available forms of nickel oxide: the black and green nickel oxide (NiO) and the black nickel oxide (Ni_2O_3). Nickel oxide (NiO), sometimes called nickel monoxide, is the form which enters a ceramic fusion and this is the usual form which is marketed for potters. It is perfectly stable at room temperatures. It is available in a greenish grey form and a black form which are almost identical, being 99% nickel oxide. The trace oxides making up the other 1% influence the colour of the nickel in powder form but do not make any difference to the use of the nickel oxide as a glaze colourant. The oxide becomes unstable at temperatures above 1200°C (2192°F) and, although dissolved in the hot glaze, amounts over 1% tend to separate out of the melt causing a scum on shiny glazes during the cooling.

Nickel oxide is a strong colourant. The limit is about 3% in a glaze. The best colours are obtained with faint tinting using 1% or less in crystalline glazes. Nickel oxide is useful as a strong colourant to obtain black in conjunction with other colouring oxides as in the following colourant recipe:

nickel oxide	2
red iron oxide	5
cobalt oxide	5
manganese oxide	2
chromium oxide	1
	15 parts to every 100 parts of transparent glaze

and bonding. This is the work of the mineralogist who uses the information to identify specimens by their physical characters, and also of the chemist who tries to understand the combinations of atoms. It does, however, provide an allied interest for potters and explains why glazes mature when crystalline solids melt, why kaolinite particles are flat and result in plasticity and differential shrinkages of clay, and why some substances are physically harder than others.

Nickel oxide

NiO or NiO_2 or Ni_2O_3 or Ni_3O_4. A general name for compounds of nickel and oxygen which are used as colouring for glazes. Under most conditions the colour is not exciting, being greenish and brownish greys, although it is a useful modifier for the brighter colours like cobalt and copper oxides. It also produces pleasant greens and greys in combination with chromium oxide. See **Colours**. However, Emmanuel Cooper has shown that oxidized stoneware

Noggin

A very small drinking mug holding only a quarter of a pint (140 ml). Nog is a strong beer.

O

Ochre

Gall clay. An iron oxide ore and a ferruginous clay. The iron oxide ores are hydrated and semi-hydrated forms of iron oxide from $2Fe_2O_3.3H_2O$ to Fe_2O_3. They are crumbly earth ores. See **Limonite** and **Haematite**. When the term ochre is used for a clay it is reserved for fine clays with a very high iron oxide content and especially when these clays are used as a colouring. Ochre wash refers to its use as a slip brushed onto tiles, pots etc, often as only a thin basting from which the iron oxide burns decoratively into the clay or outwards into the glaze. Ochres are also used as colourings for slips, bodies and glazes. If no other colour is mentioned, such as red ochre or brown ochre, the word alone or the words raw ochre imply a yellow colour.

Ochres are the colour of iron oxide in different forms and all stabilize themselves as red iron oxide in an oxidized firing. Thus the term burnt ochre refers to the colour of red iron oxide—that is, terracotta colour.

The different forms of iron oxide found as ochres are red iron oxide giving the bright red colour, a mixture of red iron oxide and black iron oxide giving browns and sometimes grey-browns, and red iron oxide in a bleached state and combined with water giving yellow. The red ochre is almost unchanged by firing. The deep brown and grey-brown ochres have some of the iron oxide in a reduced state. Oxygen has been taken away, possibly by organic action (bacteria and plant). On exposure to air such ochres begin to change to brown. The firing completes this process of reoxidation. Yellow ochre contains iron oxide, the colour of which is distorted to yellow by calcium oxide. When fired, the calcium oxide dissociates itself from the iron oxide to flux any free silica in the ochre itself or in body or glaze. The water evaporates. Thus the iron oxide changes to its red colour, or brown colour when suspended in glass. To keep the yellow colour of the ochre in a glaze, the free silica must be occupied with other fluxes. This is possible in a lime matt glaze where there is more than sufficient calcium oxide present. In reduction firings the iron oxide is reduced to black iron oxide producing olive greens in glazes. See **Iron ores** and **Iron oxide**.

Oilspot

A decorative feature on stoneware glazes exhibiting lustrous spots of excess iron oxide breaking through a black surface. The spots may be brown, black, or, rarely, silvery blue and vary in size from a pin-prick to 5 mm. The oilspot glaze is closely related to those called 'partridge feather' and 'hare's fur'.

The glaze has a high iron oxide and/or mafic content which is late to fuse and erupts into a dark glassy and viscous matrix. The red iron oxide is introduced in a form which has large particles associated with other impurities, as from an estuarine mud. Above $1220°C$ ($2228°F$) this iron oxide decomposes and with the mafic mineral moves to the glaze surface assisted by the oxygen and sulfur released by the decomposition. It does not disappear into the already iron-saturated surrounding glaze but crystallizes on the surface where it forms a thin spreading spot of lustrous crystals which are self-reduced. An oxidized firing is necessary.

It follows that a logical way to achieve an oilspot effect is to use a slip of an Albany or estuarine mud type, which is rich in mafic minerals, under a viscous feldspathic glaze. See also **Iron oxide in glazes**.

The oilspot decoration originated in Henan in northern China on tenmoku wares of the Song dynasty. Many of these wares were copying southern Chinese wares from Fujian such as the famous Jian bowls. However the oilspot never occurred in the southern tenmokus. Our appreciation of oilspot and of all tenmokus derives from the Japanese admiration of them in connection with the tea ceremony.

Oligoclase

One of the plagioclase feldspars. It is mostly sodium feldspar but contains up to 25% lime feldspar.

Once-fired

A description which is given to ware which is finished by a single firing as opposed to the use of two firings (biscuit and glaze).

Historically most pottery was once-fired, notably early unglazed pots, terra sigillata and lead-glazed earthenwares. The tradition continues with salt glaze and earthenware slipware. The advantages of once-firing are the saving in time and fuel, and the simplicity in the method of working which encourages a directness and spontaneity. The disadvantages are the disastrous effects of a single shattered piece on a kiln full of glazed ware, the difficulty of successfully burning out carbon and sulfur from a body which is covered by a glaze, and the difficulties of timing the making and glazing of the ware. See also **Through firing**.

Glazes for once-firing can be applied to the bone-dry ware or to the leatherhard ware. The latter usually contain a large amount of clay and are called slip-glazes.

Any glaze can be applied to raw ware. Exceptions to the method of once-firing lie with the body and the compatibility of body and glaze. Some clays cannot withstand the shock of being dipped in glaze at the bone-dry stage and crack because the wetted parts expand while other parts do not. Others blister as water soaks into the clay and air is expelled. The blisters often occur where slip has been applied or the clay has been previously wetted. Spraying glaze can overcome this problem because a minimum of water touches the clay and this dries rapidly.

Earthenwares which use high-clay slip-glazes, and stonewares which use ash and slip glazes, can be once-fired. Sanitary fireclay ware achieves unity of body and glaze by a number of thin layers of slip, engobe and glaze which again can be once-fired. Pots designed for dipping in slip are characterized by sturdy shapes, rims, handles and feet which withstand handling and wetting when raw, and by glazes which put a smoothness and shine on the body without attempting to mask it completely.

Adjustments to body and glaze may be necessary in order to get a good fit before firing. Glazes for dry ware should be low in clay content (less than 20%) whereas glazes for leatherhard ware need at least 50% clay. Good fit before firing does not guarantee good fit after firing.

Twice-firing was introduced when potters wanted a white covering over an ochre body for painting with colours. It began in Mesopotamia in the 8th or 9th century when potters tried to imitate the much admired Tang Dynasty pots from China. To achieve a whiteness comparable to the Chinese body they covered their darker body with a glaze opacified with tin oxide. The necessarily thick layer applied to raw ware was prone to crawling and they devised the twice-firing to overcome this. The practice continued with Persian and Spanish lustres, Italian maiolica, French Faience and Delftware. It continued in the mid-18th century with the increase of industrial methods. Biscuited ware was safer in less skilled hands and it allowed more delicate decoration. See ***Raw: raw glazing***.

Onglaze

O/G. Onglaze colour. Overglaze colour. Onglaze enamel. O/E. Ceramic colours applied on top of the fired glaze surface and given an extra firing. The firing is at a lower temperature than the glaze firing in order that the glaze is undisturbed while the onglaze colour fuses itself onto the original glaze surface. The temperature involved depends upon the hardness of the original glaze and is about 300°C (540°F) lower. Temperatures from 600°C to 1000°C (1112°F to 1832°F) have been used. The usual temperature for commercial colours is around 750°C (1382°F). A special muffle kiln called the decorating kiln or enamel kiln is generally used.

The term onglaze colours is somewhat misleading because they are really soft-firing glazes, both opaque and transparent, which have been powerfully stained. The main fluxes are the oxides of sodium, potassium, boron and lead. The colours are obtained by the same chemical combinations as other ceramic colours. For example, blues are still obtained from combinations with cobalt or vanadium oxides. But because lower temperatures are involved, a wider range of colours is possible. Some colour combinations which involve elements and compounds that volatilize at higher temperatures are stable at onglaze temperatures.

Onglaze colours are low-fired in an oxidized atmosphere and are fused onto a glaze surface rather than into a glaze. Most are opaque, detectably raised from the glaze surface, and have a smooth but not deep or glassy shine. In these respects they resemble oil or emulsion paints more than any other ceramic colourings. See also ***Inglaze***.

The oxides from which various colours are derived are listed under ***Oxide***. See also ***Colours*** and ***Stains***.

The colours are prepared by fritting and grinding. The colour is thus ready to melt and, because it is finely ground, it melts quickly and smoothly.

Onglaze colours are applied to the previously fired glaze by brush, spray gun, dusting onto a groundlay medium, and by litho and engraved transfer. Oils and varnishes are usually used as carrying media but water can be used.

The disadvantages of onglaze colours are the extra firing required (which must be in a clean gas atmosphere or, preferably, a ventilated muffle kiln); the toxic nature of some of the colours; and the poor resistance to abrasion and chemical attack which is provided by such a low-firing glaze. See ***Poison***.

It is not usual for individual potters to make their own onglaze colours. For one reason they are usually fritted and for another they are usually very finely ground. Both these points are necessary if a particular colour is required which is little affected by its surroundings and fuses quickly and smoothly in the firing. However there is no reason why a potter cannot use self-prepared soft glazes as enamels. Any convenient temperature can be used. A slightly extended firing will be necessary to fuse a coarser and unfritted colour, and many of the colours which must be specially prepared will be impossible to obtain. Care should be taken with regard to the possible toxic nature of these low-fired glazes.

Russell Coates compounds his own onglaze pigments which he uses in Japanese Kutani manner as on the large porcelain platter shown here.

Oolite

Oolitic limestone. $CaCO_3$. A limestone which is composed of spherical particles. The coarse-grained oolite is called pisolite. See **Limestone**.

Opacifiers

Minerals which are included in glaze recipes for their property of opacification. Opacity is the result of light interference inside and at the surface of a glaze. This can occur in three ways: when light strikes opaque matter suspended in the glaze; when light is deflected by crystal facets; and when it is deflected by matter of less than wavelength size.

The popular opacifier is one which does not readily dissolve in the molten glaze but remains as isolated oxide particles which are suspended in and thus cloud an otherwise transparent glaze. Tin oxide is the most dependable additive for a white opacification of this type. Others are the oxides of antimony, cerium and zirconium. The minerals mentioned are separately indexed for details of their use.

Crystalline opacity occurs when crystals form within and at the surface of a glaze during cooling. Crystal growth is encouraged by the inclusion of titanium oxide and/or zirconium oxide. Also excess of the oxides of aluminium, calcium, magnesium, barium and zinc is precipitated upon cooling and forms compound crystals. These oxides can also be responsible for interesting surface qualities. See **Crystalline glazes**.

Aluminium and zirconium oxides have a stiffening effect upon the fluidity of a molten glaze. This stiffness tends to trap minute bubbles which, if small, give a milky quality. If the bubbles are extremely fine so that they cannot be seen individually, even with a magnifying glass, the opacity is called colloidal. Some substances behave in a similar way to these colloidal bubbles. They subdivide and disperse through a molten glaze, but never fully melt. They are not necessarily opaque but interfere with the light waves because of their small size. The elements carbon, phosphorus, sulfur and fluorine can give colloidal opacity. Arsenic oxide and zirconium oxide are also colloidal opacifiers. See **Colloid: glaze**.

Open setting

Packing ware in a kiln without a muffle or saggars. The flames pass between and over the ware so that open setting must be carried out to accord with the chosen flame pattern.

Opener

Any material added to a clay to give it a character and quality. The first requirement of an opener is that it should assist the drying. The opener, by becoming a proportion of the body, cuts down the proportion of clay content to be dried. Porous openers provide ducts for the passage of the moisture drying out and thus the mass dries more uniformly. The opener therefore assists the uniform drying of ware, cuts down shrinkage and helps to prevent warpage. Secondly an opener gives a working character to a body. Some clays are so smooth that without an opener they are difficult to handle on a wheel or by hand-building methods. An opener gives the necessary 'bite'. A third quality from an opener is the balance it gives to the fired quality of the clay. For example, the addition of a refractory grog to a body enables it to withstand a slightly higher temperature.

Openers are divided into ceramic and organic. Ceramic openers become part of the body during firing. They may still show as colour and texture and may play an important part in making the body withstand thermal shock in ovenware and raku. Ceramic openers are grog, pitchers, fireclay and sand. Organic openers give texture and working quality to the body but burn away during firing leaving a series of holes. This can be decorative and also useful in cooking ware. Organic openers are sawdust, husks, chopped straw etc, cow and sheep dung. Shredded paper is added to give strength to raw clay for sculpture. See **Paper clay**.

Orange peel

Pigskin. The texture of the surface of a glaze where there are many small craters resembling pin-pricks. In tenmokus the craters are the remains of bubbles occurring during fusion. Because the glaze is stiff it does not flow together at the surface after a bubble has burst. Pigskin is usually used to describe tenmokus that have a widely spaced pin-holing. Orange peel is used to describe the texture of the surface of salt or soda glaze where the extremely viscous glaze, forming with the clay body, has been unable to form smoothly over irregularities caused by quartz or aluminium oxide particles and pores. See **Tiger skin**.

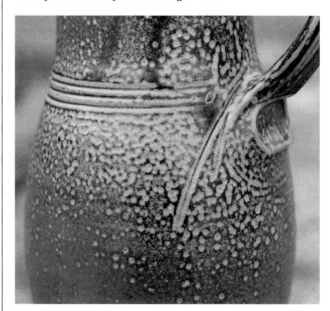

Organic matter

Describes living (and once living) matter. Organic chemistry is that which concerns carbon compounds. Carbon readily oxidizes (burns) to become a gas. Carbon compounds decompose in the kiln during firing and many paint colours and dyes are therefore useless as ceramic colours. But such colourings are very useful as stains for identifying raw materials, slips and glazes before they are fired. Organic matter such as wood and bone contains more than carbon, hydrogen and oxygen. Elements such as potassium, calcium and phosphorus are present so that organic matter, after burning, can be used in pottery as vegetable ashes in glazes and bone ashes in clays.

Ortho

A term used in chemical nomenclature to indicate the straight, correct, equal or normal balance of atoms or molecules within a crystal structure. Examples of its use are orthoclase feldspar, lead orthosilicate, sodium orthoborate. Some explanations of nomenclature are given under *Borate*.

Orthoclase

Potassium feldspar. Pink feldspar. $K_2O. Al_2O_3. 6SiO_2$. The commonest of the twelve types of feldspar. It is used as a flux in bodies and as a major constituent in glazes. It melts at approximately 1200°C (2192°F).

Orthoclase originates in molten magmas and separates upon cooling, occasionally creating masses of practically pure orthoclase which include large crystals. The photograph shows particularly well-formed crystals a couple of inches long. Often the crystals are smaller and integrated with other feldspars and silicates as in granite.

The molecular structure of orthoclase is based upon the oxygen tetrahedra which gives a hexagonal chain. One in four tetrahedra has an aluminium atom at its centre. The other three have silicon atoms. One chain directly fits upon another to form a honeycomb of boxes. The boxes form sites for potassium atoms in eight-fold co-ordination with the surrounding oxygen atoms which have unsatisfied valencies due to the lower valency of aluminium compared with silicon.

Orthoclase is a natural frit containing glass-former, flux and amphoteric stabilizer (silica, potassium oxide and aluminium oxide). It is not soluble and therefore is an important constituent for introducing potassium oxide into glazes and bodies without recourse to fritting. Alone, orthoclase begins to sinter around 1000°C (1832°F) and starts to melt at about 1150°C (2102°F). By 1200°C (2192°F) it has produced a very stiff glass which is rendered opaque by millions of tiny bubbles. See photograph. The high aluminium oxide content precludes the creation of a glass which will flow below 1350°C (2462°F). Thus orthoclase is a mineral which can be introduced into bodies in amounts up to 25% and will provide progressive densification over a wide temperature range. In glazes it is often the major constituent. Because of its stiff nature, extra silica is usually required and additional flux of a different composition. However, its stiff character during fusion is invaluable. See *Aluminium oxide* and *Feldspar*.

Orthoclase, or indeed any feldspar, is so dependable as a glaze mineral that one can start with it as the basis for a glaze recipe. Orthoclase can be progressively fluxed with either a frit for low-temperature glazes or whiting and flint for high-temperature ones. See *Feldspathic glaze*. It is usual to include a small amount (5%–10%) of a clay to aid slop suspension.

Orthoclase, albite and cornish stone are often

interchangeable. They are not alike but the particular properties which they possess may not make obvious differences in complex recipes. Colour responses are similar and rarely give startlingly different results. The greatest difference will be found in the rates of expansion and contraction. In this field substitution is useful in the adjustment of glaze fit. See *Glaze fit*. For inclusion in glazes to be fired above 1200°C (2192°F), orthoclase is often preferable because the potassium oxide content is not subject to volatilization as is the sodium oxide content of albite and cornish stone. See also *Albite*.

Orthoclase is the pure mineral. This is only available as hand-picked specimens. The usual mineral available for potters is more correctly called potters' orthoclase or potassium feldspar. This is not pure orthoclase structure but contains some, perhaps 20%, of other feldspars especially albite (sodium feldspar).

Orton

Edward (1863–1932). The American geologist and ceramic engineer who followed up the work which Hermann Seger had started in Germany. This work was the study of heat upon silicates and had resulted in the Seger cone. Edward Orton continued the research and extended the range of cones. By the end of the 19th century Orton cones were in commercial production at the Ceramic Engineering Department of the Ohio University, where Orton was the Director. Edward Orton's interest in education led to his being called the father of ceramic education. See *Cones*.

Outdoor ceramics

Since the earliest times, pots have been used for plant growing and for garden and courtyard embellishment. The earthenware clay pot is still the choice of many growers in spite of the challenge from plastic plant-pots. Similarly, individual ceramic pieces, such as urns, water features, furniture, abstract shapes and figures, meet the competition from mass-produced concrete and stone composition.

Where the criterion is for something original in concept or traditionally restful, individual makers and small-scale potteries can market their creative talents.

When a ceramic sculptor is commissioned to make a large work for a specific site it can be a dramatic focus in its surroundings. A small-scale piece can be designed to reflect or characterize a very personal, private garden.

Except in frost-free climates, or where pots with their plants will be moved into shelter, all outdoor ceramics need to be made and fired to a frostproof state. See ***Frostproof***.

Further considerations for ceramics in public spaces are stability and security against theft. Pieces need to be firmly anchored against wind and knocks from passing children and animals. User-friendly ceramic sculptures, however, are popular. Children are encouraged to dabble in water pools, wetting surfaces to enhance their colours. Gwen Heeney makes extended, brick-carved seats. In ***Colour plate 57*** she is carving a reclining figure seat which is seen in use in ***Colour plate 58***. The black and white photograph on page 244 shows another restful and rest-providing bench. The slabbed pair of stools is by Jim Robison. His 'Winter Figure' echoes the character of its upland setting, the white inclusions reminiscent of quartz veins in a mother rock. The life-size figure is constructed in three sections and mounted on a base slab. A long bar through the base and the lowest section anchors these pieces to the ground. Sometimes concrete is poured in. The second section is bolted inside to the first. This is reached through the open top before the final cap is cemented on. See also ***Colour plates 30*** and ***31***.

The 'Girl with a Dove' and the 'White-faced Geese' on page 245 are by Janet Hamer, the planter is by Karin Hessenberg and the thrown and assembled urn is by Simon Hulbert. See also ***Colour plate 59***.

Oven
Stoke-on-Trent, England, name for a kiln used for unglazed (bisc) firings.

Ovenware
Pottery used for oven cooking, and, in the case of casseroles, ramekins etc, used for serving the food at table. Function is of primary importance. The forms of ovenware must be carefully considered. The body and glaze must be capable of withstanding the thermal shocks and physical knocks involved. Ovenproof does not mean flameproof. Gas rings with direct flames and hotplates on electric cookers are

hotter than oven atmospheres. Ovenware is not intended to withstand the shock of this extreme heat prolonged at one point only.

The forms of ovenware are traditional. They have evolved with cooking methods and are an integral part of the whole subject. It is not by chance that different foods are called dishes and the name casserole means both the pot and the food cooked in it. As a simplification one could say that there are plates and shallow dishes for pies, ramekins, egg-bakers and other individual portion containers and the lidded oven pots and casseroles. Requirements common to all ovenware are stability, robustness, ease of handling and ease of cleaning.

Stability must never be in doubt. One's general unease in the handling of a hot piece of pottery must not be increased by unsteadiness of the pot. Many oven shelves have uneven surfaces but there is no excuse for the potter to increase the cook's anxiety. The broad base, which is stable, presents a problem in making. A broad base warps more easily than a narrow one which has proportionately more pot above it to stabilize it. Adding a thick foot rim would stabilize a broad base but would increase the overall weight of the pot and would increase the risk of cracks from thermal shock.

Domestic ovens have become smaller. Shelf height is now a problem. The use of more selected foods rather than composite stews has led to a requirement for a wide shallow casserole. The globular stewpot or bean pot is less often suitable. The popularity of the shallow casserole has increased this century and it presents a challenge to the ovenware potter. See ***Casserole***.

Hot and full cooking pots take knocks. Ovenware must be robust in form, and the body and glaze physically strong. Robust does not mean clumsy. The traditional west African cooking pot is robust in form yet extremely light in weight. The form is globular which is the strongest form possible. At the same weight of pot, a flat base would be a decided weakness. Uniform thickness helps to give a pot its strength and at the same time decreases overall weight. By avoiding sharp corners one also increases a pot's robustness. The wide, shallow casserole previously discussed is unfortunately a weak form and it is likely to have the further weakness of a sharp angle between base and side.

Ovenware must be handled while hot. Delicate lug handles and small knobs on lids are impractical. Functional design must be exaggerated in ovenware. The use of unglazed portions on stoneware is often an advantage because the gloved hand can more easily grip an unglazed piece. Glazed surfaces seem to become slippery when hot as they do when they are wet.

In every kitchen there are pots that seem to be in constant use. It is a worthwhile exercise to discover why. Analysis of historical pieces is also time well spent. If one approaches the subject enquiringly one can discover why a pot developed in the way it did over a few centuries. The oval cooking dish is a case in point. The oval shape is easier to handle in and out of an oven. If full of liquid it is less likely to spill when moved because the oval cuts across the swell at an angle. The manner in which oval dishes are thrown, cut across the base and compressed produces a break in the lines of stress spiralling the base. The clay, put onto the base to seal the cut, is compressed more than was the original base. This extra compression adds physical strength to the base. An oval dish will therefore last longer than its round counterpart before it finally cracks from the fatigue of thermal shocks. The example shown and the plate illustrated earlier are by Ray Finch.

Body and glaze present further problems. They are described in detail under **Thermal shock, Dunting** and **Shivering**. Thermal shock is the stress created within the pottery body by the sudden temperature changes which are experienced going into and coming out of the hot oven. The temperature difference between two parts of the same pot is responsible, through expansion, for a size difference between these two parts. There is also the phenomenon of different rates of expansion for body and glaze. These differences create stresses which may rupture the pot.

The temperature range which ovenware must span in use reaches 300°C (572°F). This includes the cristobalite dunting point. Cristobalite dunting is therefore an ever-present danger. It is probably impossible to exclude cristobalite completely from the body but every attempt should be made to do so. Some potters fire ovenware very quickly in order to give less time for the free silica to become cristobalite. See **Silica conversion**. One should think twice before refiring ovenware. Clay, slips and glazes, and in fact the whole workshop, should be free from industrial-type materials likely to contain cristobalite, e.g. a white earthenware body. The accidental introduction of even a small proportion of such material into the clay for ovenware can do untold damage because of cristobalite catalyst action upon other free silica.

But, ignoring the separate problem of cristobalite, the potter is faced with conflicting considerations. An open and porous body is physically weak. A partially vitrified body is stronger and there is a point at which a body reaches its maximum strength through vitrification. As a body becomes too glassy and begins to break down it becomes brittle and is less resilient to knocks. For normal tableware a potter would try to achieve the point of maximum strength in his wares. It is also the point of negligible porosity, which is conveniently practical. However, for ovenware one is faced

with the problem of thermal shock. A body's resistance to thermal shock is almost the direct opposite of its physical strength. A body that is dense and physically strong has a low resistance to thermal shock. A weak body needs to be used thickly to be practical. Raku tea bowls are an example of this resistance to thermal shock. The raku body is porous and physically weak, and the pots are made correspondingly thicker.

The graph shows typical curves for porosity, physical strength and resistance to thermal shock. It relates these to a temperature scale which can only be described as from soft fired to hard fired. Actual temperatures will be different for each body. It should be noted that this graph refers to strengths etc of the finished ware. It does not relate to strengths during the firing. The three lines represent three different properties which are measured in different ways. However, by the relationship of each line to the common factor of temperature certain conclusions can be drawn:

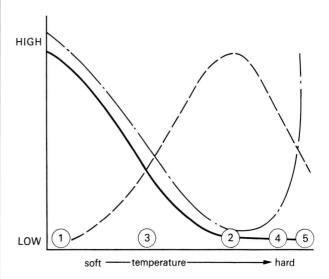

1. Soft-fired ware, although porous and physically weak, has a high resistance to thermal shock. Raku ware is an excellent example of this.

2. A higher temperature of firing produces a denser ware of negligible porosity. Physically the body is at its strongest but the resistance to thermal shock is very low. Providing the resistance was sufficient to withstand boiling water this would be the best condition for tableware.

3. The ideal for ovenware would lie between the extremes of

1 and 2 and would be dictated primarily by the establishment of sufficient resistance to the thermal shock to be experienced, commensurate with reasonable strength.

4. Bodies taken to the vitrification point become glassy and deform. They gain in resistance to thermal shock because most of their crystalline free silica is converted into fused silica. Fused silica expands at a much smaller rate than crystalline silica. However because they are glassy, they become brittle and thus lose their physical strength which was based upon a combination of physical hardness and resilience between the body particles.

5. For completeness, mention must be made of the extreme portion of the graph. Theoretically, the complete vitrification of the body (whereby it becomes a glass) would make the ware more resistant to thermal shock. Glass ovenware makes use of this fact. But pottery in this vitrified state would collapse in the firing. Porcelain comes near to this vitrified state and some, but not all, porcelains are oven-proof. Some potters have perfected this type of ovenware and some have even achieved a porcelain which is also flameproof. Most porcelains, however, are in a similar position to dense stonewares (2) in their relation to thermal shock. They can overcome most tableware shocks, e.g. hot tea in teacups, by being thinly potted.

Overburden

In digging clay or other raw material there is often a layer of soil, decomposed rock or glacial drift on top of the desired material. This has first to be removed before winning can proceed and this non-productive layer is called the overburden.

Overfiring

Firing higher than the required temperature and thus creating defects in the ware. An overfired biscuit has insufficient porosity for glazing. An overfired body warps and bloats. An overfired glaze often blisters by the volatilization of part of its composition. It also reaches a stage where its viscosity is too low to keep it on the pot.

Overfired earthenware glazes lose their character and become glossy and runny. In contrast, overfired stoneware glazes can be attractive. The stoneware body may bloat but in reaching its vitrification point it contributes greatly to the colour and character of the glaze through the body-glaze layer with inspiring results.

Oxford spar

A potassium feldspar mined in the eastern United States.

Oxidation

In pottery this refers to the combination of oxygen with an element or compound. Such an action occurs in the firing at temperatures above red heat and, if required, is achieved by the introduction of excess air to the fire or by allowing pure air to track through the muffle. Small ports set low and high

in electric kilns encourage this movement of air amongst the pots.

The important oxidations are those of carbon and sulfur which occur in bodies. The so-called burning out periods take place between 700°C and 1150°C (1292°F and 2102°F). See **Firing: biscuit**. A kiln atmosphere intended to achieve oxidation is called an oxidizing atmosphere. The opposite is a reducing atmosphere, and one which hovers between the two is referred to as neutral.

Chemists include the removal of hydrogen and the loss of electrons as oxidation. Potters include the decomposition of carbonates, sulfates etc whereby the end product is an oxide which enters a ceramic fusion. For example:

$$CaCO_3 \longrightarrow CO_2\uparrow + CaO$$
$$2CaF_2 + O_2 \longrightarrow 2F_2\uparrow + 2CaO$$
$$2(FeSO_4.7H_2O) \longrightarrow 14H_2O\uparrow + SO_2\uparrow + SO_3\uparrow + Fe_2O_3$$
$$CuCO_3.Cu(OH)_2 \longrightarrow H_2O\uparrow + CO_2\uparrow + 2CuO$$

Some pottery materials require deliberate oxidation to rid them of injurious volatiles like sulfur and fluorine which often occur in muds and feldspathic rocks. Other materials, like tin oxide, are discoloured by lack of oxygen, while others, like lead oxide, are prevented from acting in their ceramic capacity thus causing blistering.

Oxide

A chemical combination of oxygen with another element. To the potter there are two types of oxide, the metal oxide and the non-metal oxide. The metal oxides are numerous and form the fluxes, colourings and opacifiers. The non-metal oxides are few and are the glass-formers and the volatiles. See the individual oxides and **Periodic table**.

In any discussion of ceramic fusions, the majority of compounds are oxides. Very occasionally sulfates, sulfides and single elements are included but mostly all the chemical compounds in bodies and glazes are considered to have decomposed and/or oxidized to become oxides, or a combination of oxides, during a firing. An oxide has physical and chemical properties quite different from its constituent elements.

NAMING OF OXIDES. Oxygen combines with other elements in different numerical combinations. The ones the potter will meet with are: monoxide, where there is only one oxygen atom in the combination but one or two atoms of the other element (RO, R_2O); dioxide, where there are two oxygen atoms (RO_2); trioxide, where there are three oxygen atoms and one or two atoms of the other element (RO_3, R_2O_3); tetraoxide, where there are four oxygen atoms and one or three atoms of the other element (RO_4, R_3O_4); pentaoxide, where there are five oxygen atoms (R_2O_5).

The recommendations on nomenclature by the International Union of Pure and Applied Chemistry allow each of the oxides to be called simply by the element name and the word 'oxide'. Only where it is necessary to make differentiation or be very specific are monoxide, dioxide etc used as with manganese monoxide (MnO) and manganese dioxide (MnO_2) which act differently in a firing. The system becomes cumbersome with the necessary prefixes to the element name as with diiron trioxide (Fe_2O_3) and triiron tetraoxide (Fe_3O_4). Fortunately, potters prefer descriptive names like red iron oxide and magnetic iron oxide. The term sesquioxide for R_2O_3 is still acceptable. In this book the authors have simplified the oxide names and those of other chemical compounds as far as possible.

The stock system, popular in school chemistry and acceptable to the IUPAC, is that of showing the valency of an element by a roman numeral in parentheses after the name. Thus Fe_2O_3 becomes iron (III) oxide while FeO is iron (II) oxide. But Fe_3O_4 becomes iron (II) diiron (III) oxide. Because potters are more concerned with decomposition of compounds than composition the stress on valency seems inappropriate in this book.

Systems no longer acceptable are the use of the Latin and Greek suffixes ~ ous and ~ ic; and the omission of the word 'oxide' with the ~ a ending to the element. This book, however, claims one exception in the continued use of the name silica for silicon oxide.

GEOLOGY. The rocks of the earth's crust are composed mostly of oxides with some carbonates, sulfides etc. The drawing shows proportionately an ultimate analysis of all the rocks. Silica (SiO_2) accounts for almost 60% and aluminium oxide (Al_2O_3) for 15%. All the other oxides and elements account for just over 25%.

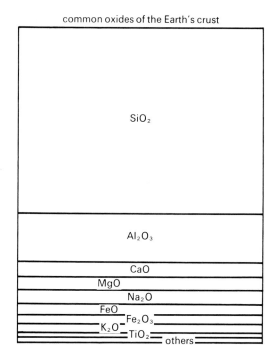

common oxides of the Earth's crust

COLOURING OXIDES. Metal oxides which impart colour to the fired ceramic, e.g. cobalt oxide gives blue. Generally speaking, the colouring power of a single oxide depends upon the amount of vitrification that takes place around it. If it is dissolved in a glaze it will give a stronger colour than in a soft-fired body. To get equal colour strengths at least five times the weight of colouring oxide is required in a body than in a glaze. The following list of colouring oxides gives percentages for colouring a glaze to full strength. The percentage in brackets is the limit that can be put into a glaze and this limit gives metallic, matt and crystalline surfaces, sometimes pleasant. See also the individual oxides and **Colours**.

Antimony oxide	3 (10)	Yellow in soft lead glazes
Cerium oxide	3	Yellow with titanium oxide
Chromium oxide	1 (5)	Grey-green.
		Pink with tin oxide.
		Brown with magnesium oxide.
		Orange and yellow in lead glazes.
		Yellow-green with reduction
Cobalt oxide	1 (10)	Blue.
		Pink with barium oxide.
		Green with rutile
Copper oxide	5 (10)	Green.
		Turquoise in alkaline glazes.
		Pink in magnesium oxide glazes.
		Red and purple in reduction
Iron oxide	12 (25)	Yellow, brown, black.
		Blue-grey and green in reduction
Manganese oxide	20 (100)	Brown.
		Purple in alkaline glazes.
		In reduction pale soft pinks and pale yellow
Nickel oxide	3	Grey-green and brown.
		Blue with zinc oxide.
		Pink with zinc and barium oxides
Praseodymium oxide	5	Yellow-green with zirconium oxide
Uranium oxide	15	Red and orange in lead glazes
Vanadium oxide	5	Yellow with tin oxide and zirconium oxide

A colouring oxide acts as an additional flux or as an anti-flux in a body and glaze. The action can be predicted by the chemical formula. Monoxides like copper and cobalt will be fluxes. Other oxides like cerium and vanadium are anti-fluxes. Details are given under the separate oxides. See also **Periodic table** and **Colour plates**.

The composition of a body or glaze, and the firing conditions, affect the colour achieved with a particular oxide. For example, oxidized copper oxide gives a green that is yellowish apple green in a lead glaze, a brighter bluish green in a borax glaze, and a turquoise blue in high alkaline glaze. Reduced copper oxide gives reds and purples and browns. Most colouring oxides are less bright when used in reduction firings.

Some colours are not very stable, especially when they

depend upon a combination of two oxides. The colouring oxide is therefore combined with others by calcination or fusion, and ground before being added to the glaze. These are known as modified oxides or stains. See **Stains**.

The stoneware dish by Andrew McGarva (right) is painted with iron, cobalt and titanium oxides on a white glaze. The pressed dish is by Bennett Cooper using oxides as underglaze colours.

MODIFIED OXIDE. A metal oxide used for colouring which has been altered in strength or colour by the addition of other oxides. For example a strong blue glaze can result from the addition of merely 0·5% cobalt oxide. In small amounts this is difficult to weigh accurately and not easy to disperse through the glaze without specking. The cobalt oxide is therefore first modified by the addition of feldspar, flint, china clay and possibly aluminium oxide, zinc oxide or barium oxide. This separate recipe batch is fused together and reground. The modified cobalt oxide is not so powerful a stain, is more easily dispersed in the glaze and by control of the additions can be made into different types of blue stain such as mazarine blue and matt blue. See also **Colours**.

P

Paddle and anvil

A method of thinning and compressing the clay wall of a pot by beating it against an anvil with a paddle. The anvil is held inside the pot and the paddle is used on the outside. Alternatively, the paddle is used alternately inside and outside the pot as in the photograph. The paddle is usually a piece of wood but is sometimes a stone slab like a slate. The anvil is dome-shaped and is a pebble, a piece of wood or a piece of fired clay. Different clays require paddles and anvils of different absorbencies.

Paddle and anvil is a useful method to combine with pinching, coiling, slabbing and throwing. Compressing the clay wall strengthens it by reorganizing the alignment of the clay particles. See **Clay: physics**. The clay wall is also thinned so that this is an important forming process. Some potters start from a ball of clay, beat the anvil into it and then, by paddling the clay against the anvil, the whole pot form is produced. As the pot wall is thinned, the clay 'stretches'. To assist the clay to stretch without cracking, the surface is scratched with a comb. This makes the surface larger in area by providing furrows and ridges. The clay can be thinned until this surface is flattened with less risk of cracking than a smooth surface. The paddles and anvils are often pecked, pimpled, scored and ridged to assist this process.

Pan

Grinding pan. Grinding mill. Machine for grinding raw materials. Large mills are used for clay shales and grog. These have two heavy metal wheels up to 8 feet in diameter on a horizontal stationary spindle. The rollers rest on a circular floor which rotates, and materials are directed under the rollers to be crushed. The circular floor is perforated and thus forms a first screening of the crushed material. Although essentially a dry process, some water is often sprinkled into the pan to reduce the amount of blown dust. See **Mill**.

Small pans are used for glaze materials which are ground in water to a slurry. The pan is usually stationary and the wheels go round. Also the pan is not perforated; the same material is ground until sufficiently fine. Sometimes stones, e.g. flint or limestone, are used instead of wheels and these are dragged or pushed around the pan.

Paper clay

A compound of shredded paper pulp and clay. It has surprising green and dry strength and fires like a normal body when the paper has burnt away. Rolled out into very thin sheets it is strong and flexible enough to be used for the printing of etchings, dry points and engravings, surviving the press and peeling away from the plate without tearing. Delicate shapes can be joined dry or wet using a slurry mix to create sculptures. They will have the normal fragility of the fired clay. The paper fibres burn away early in the firing without causing problems in the material but the fumes produced can irritate and firing outdoors is preferable.

Paper is composed mainly of vegetable cellulose fibres produced by plants and trees. The fibres are coated with a thin layer of water-repellent adhesive called lignin which holds them together forming tubes. The mass of flexible tubes evolved to distribute water throughout the plant. This structure is strong and resilient and can expand or contract reversibly with the intake or evaporation of water. This makes the paper pulp an ideal opener in a clay body. The fibrous shreds are tinier than other additions like sawdust, nylon or fibreglass, but large compared with a clay particle. They help to knit the clay together as it dries and interrupt the spread of stress cracks.

The lignin content is non-absorbent so the essential water-absorbing property of the pulp is reduced by a high proportion of lignin. Cotton linter paper contains only 1% so less pulp is needed than when using products from flax (5%) or soft or hardwoods (up to 30%). As a guide, 10% to 30% by volume of squeezed out wet pulp can be added to clay. Non-glossy papers, copy papers and those made from short fibre softwoods which tear easily work well. Ink is not usually a problem but cellophane, waxes, plastics and glues do not dissolve.

Shredded paper is soaked in warm water then blended with thick clay slip. It is important to use slip so that the shreds are fully surrounded by clay particles. The paper clay can then be dewatered and used as normal. Scraps can be reclaimed but wet mixtures do not store well and begin to smell.

The paper shreds give a fine texture to the body but are themselves almost invisible. Paper clay can be used as normal clay but techniques may need to be modified a little. Porcelain paper clay is particularly good for sculptures. In throwing, wet clay rapidly becomes slurry in the fingers. In handbuilding pieces are simply joined with slurry. Wet is added to dry. A strong framework, possibly made from hollow tubes, can be constructed and dried, then fresh wet pieces directly joined on. Joints are reinforced with extra slurry brushed on in different directions. The extra strength and light weight which the fibrous paper gives to green and dry ware is a positive advantage when moving large pieces to the kiln.

The photograph shows a paper porcelain tile by Paul Scott. It was printed in cobalt underglaze from an etched plate and fired to 1200°C (2192°F) with a transparent glaze.

Paper resist

Cut and torn shapes in paper are used to resist a coating of slip, pigment or glaze applied by brush, sponge, spray or dip. Newspaper works well. The resist is removed before firing, thus removing the layer of colour on it. If, by mistake, the paper is not removed before biscuit firing, the coating can often be brushed away with a wire brush. See also *Resist*.

Parian paste

A soft-paste porcelain used for unglazed figures. It is made from china clay 33%, cornish stone 66% and is fired to approximately 1200°C (2192°F).

Paris white

Whiting. Calcium carbonate. $CaCO_3$.

Particle size

Grain size. The term 'particle' is usually reserved for

extremely fine grains in the order of 50 micrometres and less. This size will pass through a 300's mesh and includes those materials which are naturally colloidal, like clay; materials which are ground to a very fine state, like zirconium silicate opacifiers; and divided materials in partial suspension/solution in molten glazes, like the crystal nuclei which give rise to crystalline effects upon cooling.

The term 'grain' is conveniently used for pieces of a size larger than 50 micrometres. Grain sizes are usually measured in mesh numbers. Grains include glaze materials other than colloidal opacifiers and colourants, and all other pottery materials like grogs, sands and body fillers whose grains can be seen with the naked eye or the aid of a magnifying lens.

Particle size has relevance to two main points:

1. In glazes, the particle size is directly related to the time necessary to 'dissolve' the particle in molten glaze. Hence it is also related to whether any of the particle will remain as a crystal nucleus and create opacity and crystallization.

2. In bodies, the particle size of a clay is directly related to the plasticity, strength and shrinkage of the clay. See ***Clay: physics***.

An instance of the importance of particle size follows. A similar consideration of grain size is given under ***Grain size***.

Some pure ball clays compare very closely with china clay when considered in terms of kaolinite content. Chemically these two can be almost alike. Physically, however, they differ in particle size and this means that they will give different results. Ball clay will shrink more than china clay in drying and in firing. In drying, it is the size of the gaps between the particles which is relevant (see ***Clay: physics***); in firing, it is the way in which a clay particle melts. China clay, with its larger particle size (which could be 50,000 times the bulk of a ball clay particle) presents a smaller surface area for its weight. It therefore resists the melting effects of temperature and interaction of fluxes for a longer period. In simple terms, a china clay particle can be 50,000 times the bulk of a ball clay particle, yet it presents a surface area of only 1500 times the size. It will therefore take it 33 times as long to melt. This is comparable to the relative melting times of crushed ice and ice cubes in domestic terms. The actual particle sizes involved are between 20 and 0·5 micrometres for china clay and between 1 and 0·02 micrometres for ball clay.

China clay has the justifiable reputation of being a refractory clay both in bodies and glazes, but ball clay has not. Ball clays often contain impurities which are given the credit for the vitrification which occurs with ball clays, but this is only part of the story.

In glazes, ball clays are often useful because they fuse more readily than china clay. Their larger drying shrinkage is also useful in slip glazes.

The comparison above rests upon the particle sizes of two clays. It should be remembered that the extremely fine particles involved are not always fully dispersed. They tend to form agglomerates of grain size.

Partridge feather

A finer version of the oilspot tenmoku in which a host of fine bright specks of metallic lustre cover a dark brown or black glaze. The effect is associated with iron oxide but can involve other oxides such as manganese and cobalt.

It can be achieved by the use of an under-slip or glaze. This is overloaded with colouring oxide so that it promotes a metallic surface. It melts and bubbles through an already fused and fairly soft upper glaze. This allows the metallic glaze to form spots and circles but keeps them smaller than the oilspot by being more liquid. See ***Iron oxide: in glazes***.

Paste

A prepared 'clay' for a special ware, usually of the porcellaneous type. A paste contains below 40% of clay content, plus fine silica and feldspathic materials.

Clay is a natural raw material possibly refined but without addition. Blends of clays and clays with additions of sand etc are called bodies. A body is therefore a clay or clays prepared for specific use. Bodies which contain very little clay, e.g. porcelain and bone china bodies, are called pastes. Here the clay content is below 40% and the word paste seems a good one. It is descriptive of the texture of the material as one uses it. The words clay, body and paste are used advisedly throughout this book.

Pearl ash

Potash. Potassium carbonate. K_2CO_3. A highly-soluble potassium salt present in wood ash. It is used in glass-making and the preparation of frits. See ***Potassium carbonate***.

Peeling

See ***Shelling***.

Pegmatite

Another name for ***Cornish stone***.

Periodic kiln

An intermittent kiln allowed to cool completely between firings.

Periodic table

A classified arrangement of chemical elements which brings together those elements with similar properties. It was first demonstrated by Dmitri Mendeleev in 1869 and was finalized by Niels Bohr to include all the then known elements in 1930. The table has helped to predict previously unknown elements. Their properties and even their characteristics were known from the table before they were discovered.

Fig. 1. The first 20 elements of the Periodic table

						hydrogen 1	helium 2
lithium 3	beryllium 4	boron 5	carbon 6	nitrogen 7	oxygen 8	fluorine 9	neon 10
sodium 11	magnesium 12	aluminium 13	silicon 14	phosphorus 15	sulfur 16	chlorine 17	argon 18
potassium 19	calcium 20						

The Periodic table and the potter's periodic table, which is an adaptation of the original, help potters to understand and in some cases predict the part a mineral will play in their ceramics. Once the chemical constituents of the mineral have been ascertained they can be identified on the table and their likely actions considered. The significance of the Periodic table to chemistry is explained first. This lays the foundation for the principles involved. In part 2 the significance to ceramics is explained.

PART 1.
To make the table, the elements are placed in the ascending order of their atomic numbers. An element's atomic number is the number of its electrons. This puts the elements in an order which is the order of their atomic weights. There are a few exceptions but they do not concern the potter. Fig. 1 shows the first 20 elements numbered according to their atomic numbers and placed on a framework of eight columns which are progressively filled from the top downwards.

Each of these first 20 elements has at least one property in common with another element which has an atomic number eight higher or lower. For example, helium, element number 2, is an inert gas not naturally forming compounds with other elements. This property reappears with number 10 neon, and again with number 18 argon.

The layout of the table in fig. 1 brings together those three gases in the right-hand column while maintaining the sequence of ascending order of atomic numbers. Each of the other seven columns contains elements with properties in common. Significant for the potter are the two columns at the left-hand side. The far-left column contains lithium, sodium and potassium. All three form oxides which are

dependable strong fluxes in all glazes. The elements in this column are known collectively as the Alkali metals. The second column contains beryllium, magnesium and calcium whose oxides are strong fluxes only at higher temperatures. The elements of this second column are known collectively as the Alkaline earth metals. The other columns do not show common properties which have high significance in ceramics.

The vertical columns of a Periodic table are called Groups. The horizontal rows are called Periods.

In attempting to construct the table beyond element number 20 it is found that the next ten elements from 21 to 30 present new properties which do not fit into the existing Groups or vertical columns. The new properties arise from the increasing number of electrons and the more complex configurations within the atom's structure. See **Atom**. The compact table shown in fig. 1 is therefore separated into two parts in fig. 2, with two columns to the left-hand side and six columns to the right-hand side. Ten extra columns now fit in between. This new block of ten columns is important because it contains the elements which give ceramic colours. The elements of the first nine of these ten columns are referred to as Transition elements.

The inclusion of an extra block in the table to accommodate new properties becomes necessary again between elements 57 and 72. A full table of the existing, identified and projected 118 elements would therefore look like fig. 2. Only the atomic numbers are given here to show how the sequence is maintained.

For completeness, this table includes the division into blocks identified by the letters s, p, d and f. The letter refers to the theoretical shell of the atom which is progressively filled with electrons, element by element, along a horizontal row

Fig. 2. Layout of the full Periodic table

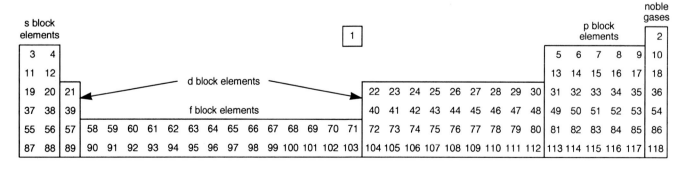

of the table. The noble gases form a separate block because all have completed shells. Hydrogen, atomic number 1, has now been isolated because of its fundamental construction of one proton and one electron.

Fig. 3 (overleaf) is the layout of the Periodic table which is most commonly used by chemists. It gives the atomic numbers and symbols for the elements together with the names of all elements usually associated with ceramics and involved in the descriptions in this book. The f block elements are positioned below the table and named as a series after 57 lanthanum and 89 actinium. The block contains 58 cerium, 59 praseodymium and 92 uranium which find use in ceramic colours. The d block elements, which were separated into two parts in fig. 2, are now together as one block. Period 7 is completed as a full row using the systematic symbols based on the atomic numbers.

The layout in fig. 3 satisfies most people's classification of the properties of elements. However, there are at least four ways of numbering the Groups and Periods which are in general use. The method used here is the one which is recommended by the International Union of Pure and Applied Chemistry in the UK and the American Chemical Society in the USA.

The Groups are numbered 1 to 18 from left to right. The Periods are numbered 1 to 7 from the top downwards. Hydrogen although in Period 1 is not in a specific Group. Its properties are such that it could be placed in more than one Group and therefore it is usually separated from them all.

PERIODIC TABLE (general chemistry principles). From the table some general properties of the elements can be predicted. An understanding of these properties is useful in a general way and helps in understanding the more specific properties of the oxides in the potter's periodic table.

1. *Noble gases.* Vertical Group 18 contains the gases helium, neon, argon, krypton, xenon and radon. They are practically inert because these elements have very limited combining capacity. They do not appear naturally in compounds, never form oxides and so are not used by the potter.

2. *Valency.* All elements except the noble gases of Group 18 have the capacity to combine with other elements and thus produce compounds such as carbon dioxide, iron oxide and calcium chloride. This capacity to combine is controlled by the electrons of the atom and is called the atom's valency. It is the number of these same electrons that dictates where an element should be placed in the table. There is therefore a correlation between which Group an element is in and the way in which it combines.

This correlation is shown by the way in which valency increases across the table. Group 1 has elements that are monovalent. In Group 2 they are divalent. Moving across to Groups 13 and 14 the valencies are three and four. The Transition elements have a range of valencies discussed later.

Oxygen has a valency of two. Calcium is in Group 2 and has a valency of two. Calcium and oxygen therefore combine on equal terms to produce calcium oxide (CaO). Potassium in Group 1 has a valency of one and therefore two potassium atoms are required to combine with one oxygen atom. The result is potassium oxide (K_2O). In contrast, silicon in Group 14 has a valency of four. One silicon atom requires two oxygen atoms, each with a valency of two, to balance it. The result is silicon dioxide or silica (SiO_2). See also **Valency**.

3. *Atom weights.* From top to bottom down any Group or column there is an increase in atomic weight. It is natural therefore that we should find the heavy elements like lead and gold low down on the table and the light elements like hydrogen, lithium and aluminium at or near the top. There is also an increase in atomic weight along any horizontal Period.

4. *Atom sizes.* In general, the atom sizes decrease from left to right along a Period although the weights increase. However, atom sizes increase from top to bottom in each column. Sizes (atomic radii), along with valencies, determine bonding possibilities. See **Valency**.

5. *Alkalis and Acids.* An element has potential to form compounds with other elements. Its valency and atom size determine what compounds are possible. Elements which actively seek to form compounds tend to appear towards the extreme left and right of the Periodic table. This statement ignores the special family of inactive noble gases of Group 18.

Elements at the left-hand side form alkaline compounds. Elements towards the right-hand side form acidic compounds. For example, sodium at the extreme left is involved in caustic soda (NaOH) while chlorine at the extreme right is involved in hydrochloric acid (HCl in H_2O). Sodium is in Group 1 which is a family group of metals known as the Alkali metals. Chlorine is in Group 17 which is a family group of elements known as the Halogens.

Between these two extremes of left and right the elements are progressively less active. Group 2 elements form a family known as the Alkaline earth metals. These form compounds which are alkaline. Elements in Groups 3 to 11 are known collectively as the Transition elements. They are relatively inactive. For example, none of these elements reacts with cold water which is in marked contrast to the alkali metals. They are also between the extremes in valency and many have more than one valency. Iron, for example, can exist as the pure metal and in three stages of oxidation: FeO, Fe_2O_3, Fe_3O_4.

The Transition elements often resemble each other. They have similar properties along a single Period as well as down a single Group. This is convenient for the potter because the Period 4 Transition elements, which include all the common colouring elements, can be considered as one family.

From Group 13 acidity becomes more dominant. Witness

Fig. 3. Periodic table of elements

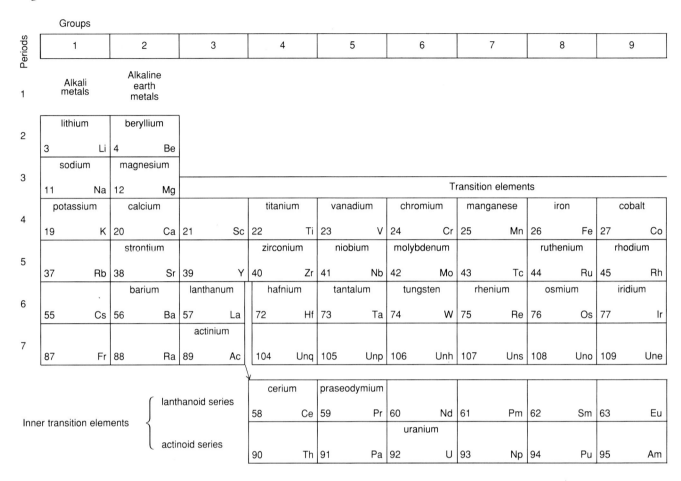

Groups								
1	2	3	4	5	6	7	8	9

Periods

1   Alkali metals | Alkaline earth metals

2   lithium
3   Li | beryllium
4   Be

3   sodium
11   Na | magnesium
12   Mg | | | Transition elements | | | | |

4   potassium
19   K | calcium
20   Ca | 21   Sc | titanium
22   Ti | vanadium
23   V | chromium
24   Cr | manganese
25   Mn | iron
26   Fe | cobalt
27   Co

5   37   Rb | strontium
38   Sr | 39   Y | zirconium
40   Zr | niobium
41   Nb | molybdenum
42   Mo | 43   Tc | ruthenium
44   Ru | rhodium
45   Rh

6   55   Cs | barium
56   Ba | lanthanum
57   La | hafnium
72   Hf | tantalum
73   Ta | tungsten
74   W | rhenium
75   Re | osmium
76   Os | iridium
77   Ir

7   87   Fr | 88   Ra | actinium
89   Ac | 104   Unq | 105   Unp | 106   Unh | 107   Uns | 108   Uno | 109   Une

Inner transition elements { lanthanoid series

cerium
58   Ce | praseodymium
59   Pr | 60   Nd | 61   Pm | 62   Sm | 63   Eu

actinoid series

90   Th | 91   Pa | uranium
92   U | 93   Np | 94   Pu | 95   Am

the progressive acidity from weak to strong of boric acid, carbonic acid, nitric acid, sulfuric acid and hydrochloric acid.

From top to bottom of the Periodic table there is a tendency for compounds to increase in alkalinity. Thus compounds formed around the elements of the top right-hand corner tend to be acids. The alkalis are compounds formed around the elements on the left and in the lower part of the table. See *Acid* and *Alkali*.

6. *Metals and non-metals.* The elements can be simply divided into metals and non-metals. All the noble gases of Group 18 are obviously non-metals. The gases hydrogen, nitrogen, oxygen, fluorine and chlorine are also non-metals. In fig. 4 hydrogen has been moved in with the other gases for convenience. The solids which adjoin this area of gases in the right-hand top corner of the table are also non-metals. It will be noticed that this area includes the elements responsible for the acids. In fig. 4 this area is separated from the other elements by a solid stepped line. All the other elements are metals.

This division is suitable for potters but scientists prefer to have a third division for those elements which show

properties of both metals and non-metals. Seven non-metal elements are semiconductors of electricity. For example, silicon has use in transistors and computer chips. These elements are called semi-metals and are separated from the true non-metals in fig. 4 by a dotted stepped line.

PART 2. POTTER'S PERIODIC TABLE.
Fig. 5 (overleaf). This table shows both oxides and elements because it is oxides which are combined in the fusion of a body or glaze. Only those involved in ceramics are included in this table. Oxides and elements which behave similarly, because they have properties in common, come together in families in vertical Groups, horizontal Periods and areas. About 23 oxides are in common use by potters. About another 14 oxides and 12 elements are in specialized use or exist as important impurities.

The general principles of the table are analysed first. Then the different properties of the oxides and important elements in each area are discussed in turn.

POTTER'S PERIODIC TABLE (general principles). The general chemistry principles of the Periodic table of elements engender parallel principles in the potter's periodic table.

10	11	12	13	14	15	16	17	18	
								Noble gases	
hydrogen 1 H							Halogens	helium 2 He	1
			boron 5 B	carbon 6 C	nitrogen 7 N	oxygen 8 O	fluorine 9 F	neon 10 Ne	2
			aluminium 13 Al	silicon 14 Si	phosphorus 15 P	sulfur 16 S	chlorine 17 Cl	argon 18 Ar	3
nickel 28 Ni	copper 29 Cu	zinc 30 Zn	31 Ga	germanium 32 Ge	arsenic 33 As	selenium 34 Se	bromine 35 Br	krypton 36 Kr	4
palladium 46 Pd	silver 47 Ag	cadmium 48 Cd	49 In	tin 50 Sn	antimony 51 Sb	tellurium 52 Te	iodine 53 I	xenon 54 Xe	5
platinum 78 Pt	gold 79 Au	80 Hg	81 Tl	lead 82 Pb	bismuth 83 Bi	84 Po	85 At	radon 86 Rn	6
110 Uun	111 Uuu	112 Uub	113 Uut	114 Uuq	115 UUp	116 Uuh	117 Uus	118 Uuo	7

64 Gd	65 Tb	66 Dy	67 Ho	68 Er	69 Tm	70 Yb	71 Lu	6
96 Cm	97 Bk	98 Cf	99 Es	100 Fm	101 Md	102 No	103 Lr	7

Fig. 4. Metals and non-metals

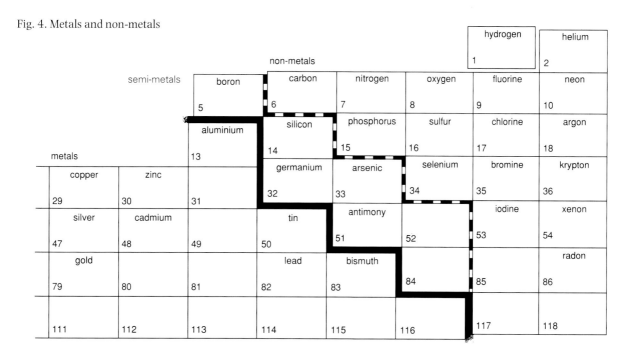

Fig. 5. Potter's periodic table

	1	2	3	4	5	6	7	8	9	10	11	12	13	14	15	16	17	18	
2	Li_2O	BeO											B_2O_3	C	N	O	F		1
3	Na_2O	MgO											Al_2O_3	SiO_2	P_2O_5	S	Cl		2
4	K_2O	CaO		TiO_2	V_2O_3 V_2O_5	Cr_2O_3	MnO MnO_2	FeO Fe_2O_3	CoO	NiO	Cu Cu_2O CuO	ZnO		GeO_2	As_2O_3	Se SeO_2			3
5		SrO		ZrO_2	Nb	Mo		Ru	Rh	Pd	Ag	Cd CdO		SnO_2	Sb_2O_3	Te			4
6		BaO	CeO_2 PrO_2	Hf	Ta	W_3O_8 WO_3	Re	Os	Ir	Pt	Au			PbO	Bi Bi_2O_3				5
7			U_3O_8																6/7

Fig. 6. Valency of Period 3

Na_2O	MgO	Al_2O_3	SiO_2	P_2O_5	SO_3	Condensed Period 3

Valency (1–6)

Fig. 9. Acidic areas

	14	15	16	17	
	C	N	O	F	2
	SiO_2	P_2O_5	S	Cl	3

Fig. 7. Valency of Period 4

1	2	3	4	5	6	7	8	9	10	11	12	13	14	15	16
K_2O	CaO		TiO_2	V_2O_3 V_2O_5	Cr_2O_3	MnO MnO_2	FeO Fe_2O_3	CoO	NiO	Cu_2O CuO	ZnO		GeO_2	As_2O_3	SeO_2

Valency (1–5)

Fig. 8. Alkaline and acidic oxides

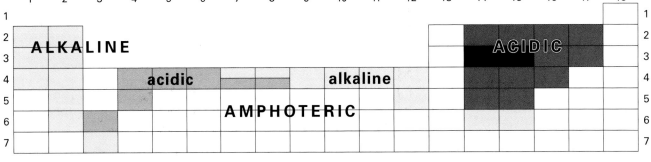

ALKALINE   **ACIDIC**
acidic   alkaline
AMPHOTERIC

Fig. 11. Alkaline area

	1	2
2	Li_2O	BeO
3	Na_2O	MgO
4	K_2O	CaO
5		SrO
6		BaO

Fig. 10. Glass-forming oxides

	13	14	15	16	
	B_2O_3				2
		SiO_2	**P_2O_5**		3
		GeO_2	As_2O_3	SeO_2	4
			Sb_2O_3		5

1. *Valency.* Figs 6 and 7. A general principle is that valency increases from left to right across a Period. This principle is illustrated perfectly by the condensed Period 3 where the oxides contain proportionately more and more oxygen (fig. 6 shows this diagrammatically). Along this Period the valency displayed by each oxide logically corresponds to its position, thus Na_2O shows the monovalency of Group 1 elements, MgO shows the divalency of Group 2 elements and so on.

Along the long Period 4 the general principle is displayed twice which necessitates the inclusion of the opposite to the principle with a decrease in valency to accommodate the two increases (see fig. 7). This diagram also shows that Transition elements have more than one valency and four display this with their oxides used in ceramics.

2. *Alkalis and acids.* Fig. 8. The concept of an alkali/acid reaction is fundamental to all glaze and dense pottery making. Alkalis and acids form opposing clusters on the potter's table. There are alkaline oxides in Groups 1 and 2 at the extreme left-hand side and a pair of acidic oxides in Groups 14 and 15 towards the top of the right-hand side. In between is a large area of amphoteric oxides which play important roles as supplementary fluxes, as colours and opacifiers and as stabilizing links between the alkalis and acids of ceramic fusion. Although theoretically neutral the amphoteric oxides display tendencies towards alkalinity or acidity.

POTTER'S PERIODIC TABLE (analysis of areas). Consideration of the table, area by area, brings out the similarities of the oxides and elements within each area. By reference to the table one can predict the behaviour of an individual from the general character of its family. Of course, no two oxides with different names are exactly alike because no two differently named elements are alike. If they were alike they would be the same element. But families with similar properties do exist and these properties can be defined. Separate articles give full details of individual oxides. See individual names.

1. *Acidic area.* Fig. 9. This contains four non-metal elements which are gases, two non-metal solid elements and two oxides. See also fig. 4.

The gases are:
    N nitrogen
    O oxygen
    F fluorine
    Cl chlorine

The non-metal solids are:
    C carbon
    S sulfur

These six are found in the compounds of many ceramic raw materials but, with the exception of oxygen, they are rarely found in the final ceramic product. With the action of heat, the gases dissociate from their compounds. Carbon and sulfur combine with oxygen to form gases which again dissociate from the original compounds. In the majority of ceramic fusions these elements are unwanted so this decomposition of the material and expulsion of the gases is encouraged, e.g. by oxidation of a biscuit firing in the 700°C to 900°C range (1292°F to 1652°F). These elements often reform as new volatile compounds especially upon meeting the atmosphere outside the kiln. They form acids which corrode kiln structures, etch windows etc. The six elements form a block of non-metal volatiles on the periodic table.

Into this block fit the only two oxides which are truly acidic. All the other oxides which are considered acidic are weakly so and only considered as acidic because of their reaction to circumstances. The two acidic oxides are:

    SiO_2 silica
    P_2O_5 phosphorus oxide

They are both glass-forming oxides and, of the two, silica is by far the more important. Thus silica is sometimes loosely referred to as the glass-former or the acidic oxide.

2. *Glass-forming oxides.* Fig. 10. This area includes, in bold type, the acidic oxides from fig. 9 plus those amphoteric oxides from close-by which have acidic tendencies. The heavy outline on fig. 10 surrounds the semi-metal oxides which are part of this area. Reference fig. 4.

The glass-forming oxides are:

    B_2O_3 boron oxide
    SiO_2 silica
    P_2O_5 phosphorus oxide
    GeO_2 germanium oxide
    As_2O_3 arsenic oxide
    SeO_2 selenium oxide
    Sb_2O_3 antimony oxide

When involved in forming glasses, the elements display non-metallic properties but, with the exception of phosphorus, selenium and oxygen, they can also display metallic properties. Therefore these elements are given the in-between name of semi-metals. See fig. 4.

Germanium oxide and arsenic oxide are rarely isolated but are often present in glazes as trace substances. Antimony oxide dissolves in lead glazes but otherwise remains isolated and produces opacity. Selenium oxide is unstable and rarely used.

3. *Alkaline area.* Fig. 11. The alkaline oxides are the main fluxes. They are sometimes simply called the alkalis. They cause silica, which is the acid, to melt in bodies and glazes. This alkali/acid reaction is fundamental to all glaze and dense pottery making.

The alkaline oxides are also known as the metal oxides although some of the elements concerned are not familiar to us as metals in everyday life. The alkaline oxides are

Repeat of Fig. 5. Potter's periodic table

Repeat of Fig. 8. Alkaline and acidic oxides

Fig. 12. Amphoteric area with some general indications of properties

Fig. 13. Dependable colouring oxides of the transition series

alkaline

6	7	8	9	10	11
Cr$_2$O$_3$	MnO / MnO$_2$	FeO / Fe$_2$O$_3$	CoO	NiO	Cu$_2$O / CuO

acidic

Fig. 14. Lustres

	8	9	10	11	12	13	14	15
4				**Cu**				
5	Ru	Rh	Pd	**Ag**			Sn	
6	Os	Ir	**Pt**	**Au**			Pb	**Bi**

contained in the vertical Groups 1 and 2 at the extreme left-hand side of the table. The oxides of Group 1 are known as the alkali metal oxides. Those of Group 2 are known as the alkaline earth metal oxides.

The alkaline oxides are:

Li_2O	lithium oxide
Na_2O	sodium oxide
K_2O	potassium oxide
BeO	beryllium oxide
MgO	magnesium oxide
CaO	calcium oxide
SrO	strontium oxide
BaO	barium oxide

Each oxide is individually described under its name in this book.

4. *Amphoteric area.* Fig. 12. The oxides of this area are between the alkaline and the acidic in their action and are found in the area between these two extremes on the Periodic table. See fig. 8. The amphoteric oxides are theoretically capable of acting as either alkalis or acids according to the environment in which they are placed, that is, in relation to the dominant properties of contiguous oxides. Fortunately, in ceramic fusions, the environments vary little and so the actions of these oxides are reasonably predictable. Two oxides of Group 13, however, behave more truly amphoteric and this gives rise to important contributions in ceramic fusions.

Boron oxide (B_2O_3) displays both alkaline and acidic properties at the same time by acting as both glaze flux and glass-former. Aluminium oxide (Al_2O_3) also displays both properties and in so doing provides a most important stabilizing link between the alkalis and the acids in the random network of a glaze structure. See ***Aluminium oxide***.

Three rare elements appear below these two oxides in Group 13. Being rare, their compounds are not in common use. One can only speculate on how marvellous it would be if their oxides were readily available.

Aluminium oxide (Al_2O_3) is always cited as the archetypical example of an amphoteric oxide. Aluminium has a valency of three. Alkaline oxides display valencies of one or two. Acidic oxides display valencies of four and five. Aluminium oxide is therefore exactly halfway between these two extremes. These valencies were previously noted in

Fig. 15. RO formulae and the position of the archetypal amphoteric oxide

alkaline		*amphoteric*	*acidic*	
Na_2O	MgO	Al_2O_3	SiO_2	P_2O_5
R_2O	**RO**	**R_2O_3**	**RO_2**	**R_2O_5**
fluxes		links	glass-formers and anti-fluxes	

fig. 6. The ceramic oxides are repeated here in fig. 15 with the addition of RO formulae. The RO formula of an oxide is the first pointer towards its action in ceramics. See ***RO formula***. Unfortunately, exceptions do occur and will be seen in the following lists.

Amphoteric oxides tending to be alkaline in ceramic action, and therefore fluxes, are:

Bi_2O_3	bismuth oxide
CdO	cadmium oxide
CoO	cobalt oxide
CuO and Cu_2O	copper oxide
FeO	black iron oxide
MnO	manganese oxide
NiO	nickel oxide
PbO	lead oxide
U_3O_8	uranium oxide
ZnO	zinc oxide

Amphoteric oxides tending to be acidic in ceramic action, and therefore anti-fluxes, are:

As_2O_3	arsenic oxide
CeO_2	cerium oxide
Cr_2O_3	chromium oxide
Fe_2O_3	red iron oxide
GeO_2	germanium oxide
MnO_2	manganese oxide
PrO_2	praseodymium oxide
Sb_2O_3	antimony oxide
SeO_2	selenium oxide
SnO_2	tin oxide
TiO_2	titanium oxide
V_2O_3 and V_2O_5	vanadium oxide
W_3O_8	tungsten oxide
ZrO_2	zirconium oxide

The amphoteric area includes the transition elements. See figs. 3 and 7. Transition elements have more than one valency. Some demonstrate this in ceramics by having more than one stable oxide form. For example, iron displays valencies of two and three in FeO and Fe_2O_3 both of which are stable at room temperature. However, the Fe_2O_3 stability begins to break down at 1220°C (2228°F) as valency changes slowly to two. See ***Iron oxide in glazes: oxidation***. Another element which changes its valency according to temperature is manganese. Manganese oxide is purchased as MnO_2. Above 1080°C (1976°F) the valency of the manganese changes from four to two. Oxygen is released and the oxide becomes MnO. In this case the change is rapid and complete so that the property of the oxide turns from mildly acidic to strongly fluxing. See ***Manganese oxide***.

In fig. 8 the amphoteric area includes a cluster of acidic oxides on the left, another cluster attached to the strongly acidic area at the right and an alkaline area in between. Note that the acidic and alkaline areas of the transitional series are interlinked because of multiple valencies.

The amphoteric oxides with alkaline tendencies have similar strong fluxing properties to those of the Group 2 oxides like magnesium oxide and calcium oxide (MgO and CaO). However, by contrast, the amphoteric oxides with acidic tendencies must be viewed as different from the archetypical acidic oxide, silica. They are not glass-formers so their action must be seen simply as the opposite of fluxing. They inhibit fusion and so these oxides are referred to as anti-fluxes.

5. *Area of colouring oxides.* Fig. 13. See also fig. 12. All ceramic colours are associated with the amphoteric area. The colouring oxides can be divided into three types: those which always give colour and act as alkaline fluxes; those which always give colour and act as acidic anti-fluxes; and those which only give colour in a particular environment of other oxides. Of course, all colours vary according to which other oxides are present in the ceramic oxide network. See **Colours**. The fluxes give transparent colours. The anti-fluxes give opaque colours, except in small amounts when solubility is possible. See **Oxide: colouring oxides** and the individual oxides.

The alkaline colouring oxides are:

CoO	cobalt oxide
CuO and Cu_2O	copper oxide
FeO	iron oxide
MnO	manganese oxide
NiO	nickel oxide

The acidic colouring oxides are:

Cr_2O_3	chromium oxide
Fe_2O_3	iron oxide
MnO_2	manganese oxide

The colouring oxides requiring a particular environment are:

Sb_2O_3	antimony oxide with lead oxide
CeO_2	cerium oxide with titanium oxide
PrO_2	praseodymium oxide with zirconium oxide
U_3O_8	uranium oxide with lead oxide
V_2O_3 and V_2O_5	vanadium oxide with tin and zirconium oxides

Some colours are developed in the particular environments prior to inclusion in a glaze or body. See **Stains**.

Fig. 12 includes some rare elements in the amphoteric area. These have been used experimentally by ceramic chemists to produce colouring compounds. They are included for completeness and are:

Nb	niobium
Mo	molybdenum
Te	tellurium
Hf	hafnium
Ta	tantalum
Re	rhenium

Tungsten (W) is less rare and has some occasional use. Cadmium (Cd) and selenium (Se) are used to produce yellow, orange and red.

6. *Lustres.* Fig. 14. Ten metals have been used for lustres. Nine of these are together in an area in the middle of the Periodic table. The tenth metal is bismuth at the bottom of Group 15.

The non-tarnishing metals, which are precious metals, come together as a horizontal quartet in the middle of Period 6. They are osmium (Os), iridium (Ir), platinum (Pt) and gold (Au). They are non-tarnishing because they do not readily oxidize.

In vertical Group 11, above gold, are silver (Ag) and copper (Cu). Silver and copper tarnish by combining with oxygen in the air but like all this family of metals they are easy to reduce to pure metal state.

Platinum, gold and silver are used for precious metal lustres on pottery. Copper is also used for lustres. They can all be dissolved in acids and applied to pottery in liquid form. The acid is burnt away during the firing and the gases assist in keeping the metal reduced. See also **Lustres**. Experimentally the other metals close to silver in horizontal Period 5 have also been used to produce lustres on ceramic surfaces. These metals are ruthenium (Ru), rhodium (Rh) and palladium (Pd). From Period 6, osmium (Os) and iridium (Ir) have also been used.

Bismuth (Bi) is a heavy metal in Period 6 close to lead (Pb) and tin (Sn). All three are slow to tarnish. Bismuth creates a mother-of-pearl effect. Tin can be made to produce a lustre by the heavy reduction of raku but in other firings it tends to partially re-oxidize. Lead is too dull as a metal to provide interesting lustre. See **Lustres** and **Iridescence**.

Perlite
Pearlite. An expanded form of perlite rock used in horticulture. It has above 70% silica content and is a useful addition for raku bodies.

Perthite
Mineral name for the combination feldspars sodium orthoclase and sodium microcline. See **Feldspar**.

Petalite
Lithium feldspar. $Li_2O . Al_2O_3 . 8SiO_2$. A feldspathoid used in glazes to introduce lithium oxide, aluminium oxide and silica. Ground petalite inevitably includes some sodium and potassium oxides. It interacts readily with other feldspars and alkaline oxides producing fluid melts. Its range of maturity as a secondary stoneware flux is in the region 1200°C to 1350°C (2192°F to 2462°F).

Pure petalite, like spodumene, has a low expansion rate and is used in flameproof bodies.

Petuntse
See *Baidunze*.

Phase equilibrium diagram
A visual representation of information about the liquid, solid and mixed phases of mineral mixtures at different temperatures. Phase diagrams are based upon the information about the melting points of different mixtures which pinpoint the position of eutectics. See *Eutectic mixture*.

The value of phase diagrams to the potter is that they explain which minerals can be expected to interact, what proportions most easily melt, what temperature range other mixtures require for full maturation and which mineral can be expected to remain non-involved and in what amount. The diagrams are purely theoretical. They assume that no matter how long a temperature is held no further change will take place. The phases are at equilibrium. This is not a state normally encountered during firings which are either rising or falling in temperature. Nevertheless the information on behaviour of one mineral towards another is useful in predicting which area of experiment will be most useful or why particular effects have occurred.

The binary diagram as illustrated here shows composition against temperature and is the one most commonly used by potters, but there are ternary, quaternary and multicomponent systems in use by ceramic engineers.

For example, suppose equal weights of oxides RO and SiO_2 create a eutectic mixture melting at 1200°C (2192°F) and that RO melts alone at 2000°C (3632°F) and SiO_2 at 1710°C (3110°F). The full information would be shown on an equilibrium diagram with four phases. Below 1200°C all possible mixtures will be unmelted so they present a solid phase. Above the V-shaped line from 2000°C on the left down to 1200°C in the middle and up to 1710°C on the right all possible mixtures have melted so this area is labelled as liquid phase. The remaining two areas are mixtures of

liquid and solid. In one case the solid is RO and in the other it is SiO_2.

The information from this diagram can be read as follows: only mixture E (50% + 50%) melts suddenly passing from solid to liquid phase at the eutectic temperature of 1200°C. All other possible mixtures melt over a range of temperature starting at 1200°C. For example, mixture S (80% RO + 20% SiO_2) starts to melt at 1200°C at point T but does not become fully molten until 1800°C (3272°F) at point V. At point T the 20% SiO_2 forms a eutectic mixture with an equal amount of RO and this part of the mixture melts. However, the remaining 60% is solid RO. Between points T and V progressively more and more of the solid RO is incorporated in the liquid melt. To discover exactly how much is still solid at point U, temperature 1460°C (2660°F), a horizontal line is drawn across to the boundary with the liquid phase at W. Point W is directly over mixture X which explains that a mixture of 60% RO + 40% SiO_2 is molten at this temperature. Since mixture S contains only 20% SiO_2 this amount can only involve 30% RO in liquid melt. This is the proportion 40% SiO_2 to 60% RO of mixture X. Therefore at point U there is a liquid composed of 20% SiO_2 and 30% RO with 50% solid RO.

Phosphorite
$Ca_3(PO_4)_2$. A fossil deposit which is a source of phosphorus oxide and calcium oxide for glazes. It contains some fluorine but the amount is variable and is not includable as a definite chemical composition.

Phosphorus oxide
P_2O_5. A glass-forming oxide which is present in many glazes as a trace constituent though it is not often deliberately introduced. In small amounts it gives colloidal opacity as in the Chinese jun glazes. See *Jun*. Large amounts give opacity, a dull surface and blistering. In bodies it gives vitrification without softening and is so used to give translucency to bone china.

Phosphorus oxide is often introduced into glazes via vegetable ashes and bone ash. The phosphorus, with the calcium, is an essential element in plant and animal growth. The amount of phosphorus involved in vegetable ashes may be small but sufficient to give a jun effect. With bone ash the amount of phosphorus can be calculated. See *Bone ash*.

Phosphorus also occurs combined with calcium in the rocks phosphorite $(Ca_3(PO_4)_2)$ and apatite $(3Ca_3(PO_4)_2.Ca(Cl,F)_2)$. These rocks are the origin of superphosphate fertilizers. Phosphorus oxide can be introduced into frits and glazes by the rocks and fertilizers. The lithium ore amblygonite has also been used to introduce phosphorus oxide. The rocks are not so useful as the vegetable and bone ashes because they contain unwanted trace elements like fluorine.

Phosphorus oxide shows as a bluish flush in glazes. The particles of phosphoric glass are separate from the silicic glass though suspended in it. They are of colloidal size and therefore disperse the light. See *Colloid: glaze*.

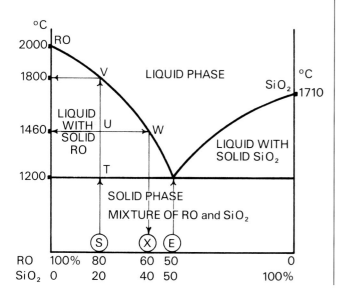

In bodies, the phosphorus oxide produces a very stiff liquid which helps vitrification without allowing a fluid state. The calcium oxide content of bone ash is checked from becoming an active flux by its involvement with the phosphorus oxide.

Isolated phosphorus oxide is a glass which is soluble in water. Like boron oxide it is also deliquescent and is therefore used as a desiccant. Phosphorus oxide cannot be considered in any way as a substitute for silica and does not enter the silica chain. If it were isolated it would vaporize at 300°C (572°F). In compounds it provides a viscous link in the structure at temperatures above 580°C (1076°F).

Phototrophy

Phototropy. The phenomenon of colour change caused by light. Normally glazes are physically unchanged by light although obviously their colourings are dependent upon the light which falls upon them. Glazes which contain rutile or titanium dioxide with a small amount of rutile, totalling 15%, however, darken in colour upon exposure to light. The dark colour fades again with the absence of light and the process can be repeated *ad infinitum*.

The amount of colour change is not noticeable except where a part of the glaze has been covered. For example a saucer will show a lighter circle where the cup has been placed. The image disappears in approximately a minute.

Pigskin

Orange peel. The texture of a glaze surface where it resembles pigskin or orange peel because it is covered with many small craters. Pigskin is usually used to describe tenmokus and glazes with widely-spaced pin-pricks. Orange peel is used to describe irregular glaze surfaces especially salt glaze and heavily-pitted glazes.

Pilgrim flask

Pilgrim bottle. A bottle with thong-loop handles by which it can be carried. Pilgrim flasks exist in all shapes and sizes. Some are flat-sided whilst others are like a barrel on its side. They were made throughout Europe and Asia, and are associated with pilgrimages, sanctuaries and places of holy

significance. They were used by the pilgrims as a means of carrying drinking water for the journey and also for bringing home holy water from a sanctuary. Small bottles with scenes depicting a saint or a religious emblem were often sold at shrines and contained the holy water of the shrine. See also *Costrel*.

Pinching

Forming a pot by the compressing action of fingers and thumb. The pot grows from a ball of plastic clay by pushing a hole in it and progressively thinning the walls. The pot is slowly rotated in one hand as it is pinched with the other.

A soft plastic clay is required. Coarse clays can be used because there is no friction between clay and hands that would tear the hands. If coarse clays cannot be persuaded into pots, their workability for pinching can be improved by a generous addition of bentonite.

Beating compresses the clay and brings moisture to the surface. This strengthens the pot wall and returns the outer layer of clay to a more plastic state when it has started to dry. Some clays become very dry and require to be worked wet. With water, the pinching action becomes a stroking action and it is probable that throwing developed from this technique.

Large pinched pots are enlarged by further beating with a paddle and anvil. Two pots can be joined rim to rim to form a larger pot.

The idea is simple, and pinching is often used as an introduction to pottery-making. The product is the direct

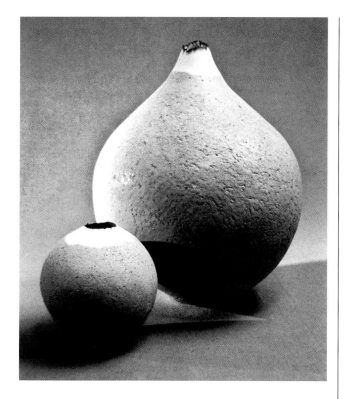

result of the concentration and action of the maker. No tools intervene. Mastery of the technique promotes close observation of the clay's properties and the effects of the hands' actions. With development of skill one can make pots of great sensitivity. Betty Blandino uses a pinched-coil technique in which each coil addition is pinched and thinned in the shaping.

Pin-hole

A small smooth-edged hole in a glaze surface like a pin-prick and a similar mark occurring as a defect on slip-cast ware. See *Casting slip: adjustment*.

The pin-hole in the glaze surface as illustrated here is the result of a burst bubble which has left a crater. The crater has started to heal over but because of insufficient time has been unable to do more than round the edges of the crater. Horizontal surfaces are more prone to pin-holing than vertical ones because they lack the general glaze movement

under gravity. Glazes intended for horizontal surfaces only, like tiles and plates, can afford to be more fluid than other glazes in order to overcome pin-holing.

Pin-holing sometimes occurs in re-fired glazes especially if the refiring is at a lower temperature than the original glaze temperature, e.g. on enamelled ware. This is caused by moisture in the ware which blisters the glaze as it escapes.

Pink

Pink in ceramics is usually achieved by the chrome-tin combination. Some pinkish lilac colours also occur with cobalt oxide and manganese oxide in high alkaline glazes. See *Chromium oxide: chrome-tin pink*. Pink lustre results from a very thin layer of gold lustre on a transparent glaze covering a white body or slip.

Pint weight

Slop weight. Ounces per pint. The weight of one pint of a clay or glaze suspension in water. It is a description of density and is expressed in ounces and is written as a number with 'oz pt'.

Care should be taken to ascertain whether the pint is Imperial measure or US measure.

> 1 US pint = 0·83 Imperial pint
> 1 Imperial pint = 1·205 US pints

Thus a slip of 29 oz pt imperial is of the same density as one rated 24·07 in the USA. See also *Formula: density*.

Pint weights of slips and glazes are noted in order to reproduce the same density in successive batches. However, note that the fluidity of the suspension can be altered by the phenomena of flocculation and deflocculation while the density remains the same. Calculations involving the amounts of dry material and water in suspensions are made with Brongniart's formula. See *Formula: Brongniart's.*

For most slips and leadless glazes the average relative density of the materials is taken as 2·5. This means that for imperial pints the pint weight will lie between 20 oz pt (the weight of one pint of water) and 50 oz pt (the weight of one pint of solid dry clay). Equal bulks of water and clay give a pint weight of 35 oz pt. Equal weights of water and clay give a pint weight of 28·54 oz pt (143 g/100 ml). See also *Slop weight*.

Pipe clay

A white clay found in small pockets often associated with fireclay. It is white, capable of being refined, and vitrifiable at around 1000°C (1832°F). It was used for making clay tobacco-pipes.

Fireclays for making sewer pipes are also referred to as pipe clays.

Pipkin

A late medieval cooking pot, usually glazed inside only and with three legs on which it could stand securely in hot ashes. The straight tapering handle allowed the pipkin to be lifted in and out of the hot ashes by slotting over it a long stick or metal rod with a tubular end.

Pitcher
A large jug often with a relatively small top. It is intended for carrying and storing liquid rather than pouring and serving.

The examples are made by Janice Tchalenko and Michael Casson.

Pitchers
Grog made from the same clay as that to which it is to be added. The word is rarely used in the singular. Pitchers are usually finely ground and are blended with the body to reduce shrinkage and increase workability rather than to give texture.

They are made from ground broken biscuit (soft pitchers) or bisc (hard pitchers). Occasionally glazed wasters are ground into pitchers but the glaze particles can cause unpredictable results. Because pitchers are of the same body as the ware, they do not alter the ultimate composition but are effective in the control of drying and firing shrinkages.

Hard pitchers are used in fine white earthenware. Soft pitchers are used in porcelain where they mature with the body.

Place
To pack ware into saggars. Earthenware and bone china for high-temperature bisc firings are placed in saggars surrounded by sand. The placing of plates in this way is known as nesting. The sand holds the ware in place during firing and thus restrains any tendency to warp.

Bone china is placed in aluminium oxide 'sand' because silica sand would be fused by the ware. White earthenware would be stained by aluminium oxide and is placed in a pure silica sand. The silica sand is smooth-grained but is coarser than the aluminium oxide used. If the sand is too fine it tends to fuse to a solid mass whereas a relatively coarse sand does not. Most individual potters, however, would call the industrial placing sand fine and many use it as an opener in stoneware bodies.

Plagioclase feldspar
Any one of the group of feldspars which has albite at one end and anorthite at the other. The group contains six feldspars which show progression from the sodium to the calcium feldspar.

Albite	$Na_2O.Al_2O_3.6SiO_2$
Oligoclase	
Andesine	
Labradorite	
Bytownite	
Anorthite	$CaO.Al_2O_3.2SiO_2$

Plaster of Paris (historical)
Plaster was known to the Greeks and Romans and it is possible that its absorbent properties were used in bats for stiffening clay and in sprig moulds, but no evidence is available. The first references to the use of plaster by potters is in France of the early 18th century. Between 1745 and 1750 different potters, notably Ralph Daniel and Ralph Littler, both makers of salt-glazed figures, brought the method of making plaster moulds from Paris to improve

their own productions in Staffordshire, England.

The name plaster of Paris remained, although plaster was soon produced not far away from Stoke-on-Trent at Burton-on-Trent. Potters had previously carved gypsum, the raw material for plaster, to make moulds for sprigs. They had also used alabaster, biscuit, copper, brass and wood. Plaster quickly replaced these because of the ease with which the impression could be taken from the original model.

The porosity of plaster enabled larger plates and pots to be press-moulded successfully and was the basis of the development of slip-casting. It is interesting to note that, at the time of its introduction, the potters heralded plaster as a boon to the production of their salt-glazed whiteware. The salt-glazed ware had reached perfection in the struggle to outclass oriental and continental porcelain. Modelled decoration was crisp and pots were thin as a result of great pressure from metal moulds. Plaster was seen as a means of quicker and easier production. But plaster moulds wear quickly and there was soon a loss in crispness of detail and a resulting clumsiness in thickness of ware. The plaster moulds helped the rival creamware industry more because of its simpler approach with use of soft glazes and colour. Creamware overtook salt glaze in popularity and plaster of Paris can be seen to be a major contributing factor.

Plaster of Paris (technical)

Semi-hydrated calcium sulfate. Calcined hydrated calcium sulfate. $2CaSO_4.H_2O$. Plaster of Paris is a white powder prepared from gypsum by driving off part of the water of crystallization.

$$2(CaSO_4.2H_2O) \longrightarrow 2CaSO_4.H_2O + 3H_2O\uparrow$$
$$\text{gypsum} \qquad\qquad \text{plaster} \quad\ \text{water}$$

To manufacture plaster of Paris the powdered gypsum is heated in steel pans. As the water escapes, the powder looks as if it is boiling. Plaster of Paris is sometimes called boiled plaster or boiled gypsum. If the gypsum is overheated it is called overburnt and is difficult to recrystallize. If it is completely calcined it is called dead plaster. Underburnt plaster quickly recrystallizes and so does plaster which has been able to absorb atmospheric moisture. By so doing it has begun to form the crystals which make it set.

To make plaster of Paris into a hard substance one adds the powder to water. After thorough mixing the plaster takes up sufficient water to form its crystals. That is, it takes back the water that was driven off in its manufacture and could be said to return to its gypsum state. Excess water, and there is always some, is removed from the set plaster by drying in a warm draught (25°C or 77°F).

The ratio of water to plaster affects the setting time, the final strength and the absorbency of the set plaster after it has dried. See chart. The weakest practical mixture is 100 parts of water to 110 parts of plaster by weight. The result is a light plaster with about 50% absorbency but it is not physically strong. The strongest mixture is 100 parts water

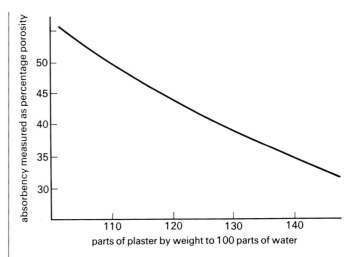

to 140 parts plaster. This gives strong heavy plaster with about 35% absorbency. These mixtures are called 110's mix and 140's mix. With the 110's mix there is about 7 minutes available between mixing and commencement of setting. With the 140's mix the time is about 4 minutes. The 140's mix is used for cases and any originals which need to remain intact during the parting process. A 130's mix is used for pressing moulds, casting moulds and jolley moulds where these moulds form the outside of the articles. A 120's mix is a general mix for hump moulds and absorbent bats where absorbency with reasonable strength is required.

Some potters find difficulty in mixing plaster but no difficulty should be experienced if a careful routine is followed. First, the measured amount of powdered plaster should be sifted through a 20's mesh and then sprinkled into the measured amount of water. The sprinkling is intended to give a thorough wetting to each particle. This is further ensured by allowing the mix to remain unstirred for one minute. Patience at this point is rewarded because a thorough wetting prevents the formation of lumps. This is also the reason for the sifting. When a stirring begins it must be thorough and continuous but frothing or entrapping of bubbles should be avoided.

From the commencement of stirring to the time setting begins, is the pouring time, and this varies with the mixture ratio. A fresh plaster in good condition should give 3 to 6 minutes of pouring time. An old plaster which has had time to absorb moisture from the air may give only 1 minute. This time is further altered by retarders and accelerators. Some retarders are borax, gelatine, alum and sulfuric acid in the water, and lukewarm water (20°C–30°C) instead of cold. Accelerators are crystalline salts, e.g. potassium sulfate, chloride and nitrate, also hot water (above 40°C) and already-set plaster. The presence of only 1% of set plaster will cut down a pouring time of 5 minutes to 30 seconds. Cleanliness of mixing utensils is obviously essential or one may find one's hand set in the plaster as soon as stirring begins. Also it is necessary to store the plaster of Paris powder in a dry place, otherwise it becomes pre-set.

As the crystals form and interlock in the setting plaster an overall expansion takes place. This continues through the first 24 hours. It is only 0·4% but it is a useful aid to the parting of two blocks of plaster, such as a case and a mould. Heat is generated by the crystallization and reaches a maximum of 35°C (95°F) from water at room temperature. To reach maximum temperature during crystallization takes up to 30 minutes from mixing. The times on the chart are given as minutes after pouring. The point of maximum temperature can be taken as the point at which the plaster is strong enough to be moved. It is sufficiently accurate to judge this temperature by touch. The heat is also a useful aid to parting because it causes the set plaster to sweat. This softens a water-bound parting agent like soft soap thus enabling the parts to be more easily separated.

To calculate the amounts of water and plaster of Paris powder required, the following system can be adopted. The volume of the space to be filled is estimated or calculated by measurements. This volume multiplied by 5 and divided by 7 is the volume of water that will be required. The volume of water is taken as the unit from which the weight of plaster is calculated for 120's, 130's or 140's mix. A few examples are given:

	120's mix	130's mix	140's mix
per 100 ml	120 g	130 g	140 g
per ½ imp pt	12 oz	13 oz	14 oz
per imp pt	24 oz	26 oz	28 oz
per ½ US pt	10 oz	11 oz	11½ oz
per US pint	20oz	21½ oz	23 oz

In calculating the volume to be filled, the following formulae will be found useful:

To change cc to imp fl oz multiply by 0·035
To change imp fl oz to imp pints divide by 20
To change cc to US fl oz multiply by 0·034
To change US fl oz to US pints divide by 16
To change cubic inches to imp fl oz multiply by 0·58
To change cubic inches to US fl oz multiply by 0·55
Further capacity equivalents are given in **Table 18**.

Chart of plaster mixes

Parts by weight Water Plaster	Minutes pouring time	Further minutes setting	% absorbency	Use
100 110 } 91 100 }	6	13	50	patching moulds
100 120 } 83 100 }	5½	18	45	absorbent bats; hump moulds
100 130 } 77 100 }	5	20	40	casting moulds; jolley moulds; blocks
100 140 } 71 100 }	3	18	35	cases

Plastic clay

Clay in plastic state, that is, in a state in which it can be formed easily by moderate pressure and yet retain the new form without collapse. However, contrary to what the novice may wish, no clay is ready for use. All clays require some preparation by wedging and/or kneading immediately prior to use.

The term plastic clay is also used to imply a clay with high plasticity. The term long clay and fat clay are also used. The opposite is a short or lean clay.

Plasticity

The unique property held by clays which combines the strength of a solid with the fluidity of a liquid. Plasticity allows the solid to be reformed without rupturing and allows the new form achieved to remain without any attempt to return to the original form. That is, there is no elasticity involved.

The measurement or assessment of plasticity is subjective and is judged for the purpose and by the potter using it. The properties of a clay become evident to the potter using it as a 'plastic' clay or as a 'short' clay. Plasticity can be defined in terms of slide, moisture retention and strength. Slide or 'shear' is the initial response to pressure; a plastic clay gives easily, a short clay resists or is bouncy because there is too much friction. A clay which can hold a high proportion of water without becoming too weak has a long working range. Strength, or the ability to hold its shape when formed and reformed is given by a balance of particle size using some larger grains, and thixotropy which holds fine particles in a strong network.

If one has a clay that lacks plasticity, one can add this property by adding a clay of high plasticity. The resulting blend will be proportionate. Even 10% of a highly-plastic ball clay will make a noticeable difference in the workability. It is sufficient to knead the two clays together in a plastic state. It may also be necessary to add a little extra water.

Ten per cent of a light-coloured ball clay will have little effect upon the colour of a clay. It will, however, affect the general drying contraction and firing shrinkage. Plastic clays tend to have high wet-to-dry contraction and dry-to-fired shrinkage rates.

Another plastic material is bentonite. Though strictly not a clay, it is so called. A clay which is very low in plasticity can be made workable by 5% or 6% of bentonite. A usual amount added to many clays is 1% or 2%. This is a dry-weight measure of bentonite to the dry weight of the clay. However, bentonite cannot be added as a powder to plastic clay. It must first be mixed with about twice its own weight of water. It then swells to a slippery mass rather like a greasy soap. This is added to the clay by slicing the clay with a wire, poking holes in the slices and sandwiching the bentonite before re-kneading. The bentonite provides so much 'slide' that the process is not an easy one.

Of course, the ideal way is to start the improvement of plasticity at an earlier stage of preparation. To do this one needs to understand the major factors that contribute to plasticity. See also ***Preparation of clay***.

The photographs (page 269) show Julia Land making use of plasticity, and one of her finished teapots.

PHYSICS OF PLASTICITY. Plasticity depends upon:

1. clay particle size
2. true clay content
3. moisture content
4. particle uniformity
5. plasticizers
6. strength of particle bond

These factors are now discussed in relation to the preparation of clay by the wet process, that is, rendering the clay to a slurry which is refined and dewatered to plastic state.

1. *Clay particle size.* The size of the clay particles has a direct bearing on plasticity. The smallest particle sizes give the most plasticity. Even non-plastic materials like quartz and zircon exhibit plastic tendencies by mutual particle attraction if their particles are small enough. However their plasticity is nothing compared to that of clay.

The fineness of particle which gives plasticity is not a question of a mesh size. The clay particles are infinitely smaller than could be separated by sieving. The particles involved are of colloidal size and individually invisible to the naked eye. The largest size involved is in the region of 3 micrometres in diameter. A micrometre is one ten-thousandth of a centimetre. To give a comparison: the holes in a 100's mesh are each 150 micrometres across.

The 3-micrometre clay particle is that of a coarse clay. Such a clay is not very plastic, e.g. china clay.

In comparison, a ball clay has particles averaging 0·25 micrometres and bentonite 0·05 micrometres. Particles of this size are often packed together as large grains. To break down these grains into particles and thus achieve full plasticity it is necessary to soak the clay in water and age it or use a blunger, preferably of the high-speed type. The more water that is available at any stage of clay preparation, the more plastic the final clay is likely to be because the water penetrates between and divides the particles giving more particles of smaller size. See ***Ageing, Weathering*** and ***Preparation of clay***.

2. *True clay content.* Whilst it is impossible to use a mesh to separate the different sizes of clay particles, it is perfectly possible to separate a lot of the non-clay particles from the clay particles by its use. Non-clay particles detract from plasticity since they exhibit very little or no plasticity themselves.

Pieces of shale and sands are the commonest non-plastic constituents of clays. These can be removed by a suitably-sized mesh. A test amount of very thin slip should be run through a series of sieves until the most efficient one is found. See ***Preparation of clay*** and ***Analysis: mechanical***.

If the sand is too fine and sieving is impractical, the process of levigation can be used. This provides a very fine clay in the region of 90% true clay content. It involves a very watery suspension and a lot of settling. See ***Levigation***.

The ball-clay miners used to assess the purity and hence plasticity of their clay by the bite test. If a small piece of clay is put between the teeth, the grittiness or smoothness of it can be assessed. With a little practice one can almost tell the grain size and amount of the non-plastic material. This does not truly test plasticity because a non-plastic clay like china clay is smooth, but it tests a clay's possibilities. It is a suitable test in ball clay pits where particle sizes are of a similar range and plastic potential depends upon the amount of impurities of quartz, mica and feldspar. Here one is trying to arrive at a rational analysis which states the proportions of true clay and non-clay content.

If a clay is purchased from a bulk supplier it may be possible to obtain a rational analysis and a mechanical analysis which will help to assess the clay's potential. See ***Analysis***.

3. *Moisture content.* A plastic clay is one which can hold a high proportion of water before becoming too weak to retain a shape. This is important to the potter when hand forming or joining shapes. It gives a longer working period. The quantity of water which is contained depends largely on the proportion of fine particles which can support more water content than coarse ones. To extend this ability fine ball clay or bentonite can be added. The question of plasticity in casting slips is also related to moisture content. See ***Preparation of clay: control of moisture content***, and ***Water of plasticity***.

4. *Particle uniformity.* Consideration was given earlier to the mechanical analysis of clay, mainly with regard to removing unwanted non-clay material. Size uniformity of the clay content itself must also help to get closer packing of particles which will give extra strength. However it is worth mentioning that a clay can be so highly plastic that it lacks workability. Such a clay is sticky and very soft. It deforms easily with little initial resistance and lacks sufficient strength to support its own weight.

The optimum correction for this state can only be decided upon after consideration of a few trials each involving additions of different materials. China clay, a sharp sand and a sharp fine grog can be tried. All these provide friction between the particles, thereby adding bite. See ***Preparation of clay: control of grain size***.

5. *Plasticizers.* Plasticizers encourage the slipperiness of existing clay particles or introduce highly-plastic particles to act as a lubricant for the clay and other materials.

The addition of bentonite has been described in the introduction to plasticity. It increases plasticity by introducing minute particles and an extra proportion of water. It is probably the most popular and the most effective plasticizer for clays. It is not a chemical but a variable mineral of the montmorillonite group. This group is closely related to the kaolinite group and therefore bentonite is often called a clay. Bentonite can be safely added to clays up to 2% of the total weight of the clay. About 6% is the limit. See **Bentonite**.

Other plasticizers which provide lubricating qualities are polymerized carbohydrate pastes, bacterial colloidal gels, and synthetic inorganic colloids. These give a clay a plastic, slippery feel because the lubrication lessens the friction. This is useful in some forming processes such as jigger and jolley where a mould supports the clay. In fact, a weaker clay is less likely to tear because it deforms readily.

However, it is not acceptable to have a plastic but weak clay for throwing and handbuilding. To be strong enough for these purposes it must have a high proportion of fine particles. The addition of a plasticizer assists the thixotropy, the strength of bond between particles, but this effect does not necessarily penetrate to the finest mesh of the structure.

Laponite, Macaloid and Additive A are trade names for synthetic colloids used as plasticizing gels. As additions to porcelain bodies they have the advantage over bentonite of being pure and colourless. They are also said to improve the strength of green ware.

The plasticity of clay can be encouraged to improve in storage by the addition of some weak acid and/or a bacterial agent such as Jeyes fluid. This promotes the thixotropic attraction which develops between fine particles when given sufficient time.

The thixotropic attraction which holds clay particles together is affected by the acidity or alkalinity of the soluble environment. As the clay is aged or stored the remnants of organic plant material are broken down by bacteria which multiply and produce amino acids. A weak acid or neutral water allows attraction between relatively larger particles. An increasingly acid environment shifts the attraction to one between the increasingly minute particles, below one micrometre or colloidal. That is, a colloidal gel is formed. Instead of the larger particles being flocculated and attracted, it is now the finer particles; and these form a fine strong mesh which supports the large particles and also can quickly reform after disruption.

When weathering is simulated by blunging this creates smaller particles which are capable of high plasticity. But the violent action destroys the attraction between them. This must subsequently be restored by storing and souring. This is a similar circumstance to when a viscous slip becomes fluid when stirred and needs time to regain its thixotropy. In natural weathering the break-up of particles is slower and thixotropic strength is built up at the same time.

The strength achieved in this way is important to a potter making fine and demanding shapes, especially with soft clay on the wheel. The kind of clay which is needed is one which has little initial resistance—it gives easily in the fingers because there is little attraction between the larger particles, but it can be repeatedly reformed because there is very strong attraction between the smallest particles. It has long lasting strength. A fuller explanation of this phenomenon is given in the book *Clays* by Frank and Janet Hamer.

6. *Strength of particle bond.* The strength of a clay is vital. There is obviously some strength from friction between clay and non-clay particles as described in 4, but there is also a strength derived from the structure created by the clay particles in plastic state.

Clay particles are flat hexagons. They are lubricated with water and are able to slide past one another with ease. The flat faces of two adjacent particles provide an excellent suction area when lubricated with water and this gives clay adhesive qualities and much of its strength (fig. 1).

It is difficult to form a break at right angles to the particles, because of the brick-like structure which they form (fig. 2). Pulling the clay particles closer together by de-airing adds to the strength. See ***De-airing***.

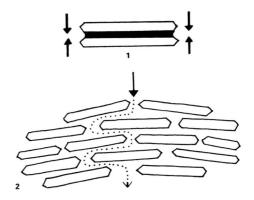

The plasticity of a clay lies with its capacity to allow its particles to slide past one another. There is a point at which the resistance of the clay is overcome by pressure. This is called the yield point. The strength is a combination of physical abrasion and mutual attraction bonds between the particles. Once the initial resistance is overcome, the plastic clay should deform with slight pressure. There may be a certain bite from the friction of a sand or grog but the shearing of bonds continues as a sequence of bond break-and-remake. On release of the pressure the bonds establish themselves strongly to hold the new form. This is the property of thixotropy. See ***Workability***.

Thin flat particles present a large surface area for very small weight. They therefore respond to the mutual forces of attraction which, at the exceedingly small size of ball clay and bentonite particles, become increasingly larger forces proportionately. See ***Forces of attraction***.

Clays with a correct balance of plasticity and strength will withstand the pull occasioned by their own weight in

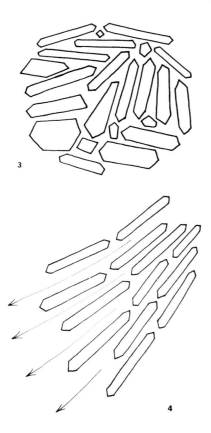

wide or tall free-standing clay structures (fig. 3). A clay with too much plasticity and insufficient strength collapses. It deforms by its own weight and uses its plasticity to enable it to do so (fig. 4). A clay with too little plasticity and too much strength also collapses. But it does so by tearing between the particles. Here the so-called strength was all in initial resistance to movement. Such clays feel dead to knead and often have a stodgy or bouncy feel to them. Their strength resists shear by compression or sideways displacement but cannot resist a tension tear. They cannot withstand that most crucial potter's test: the pulling of a handle (fig. 5).

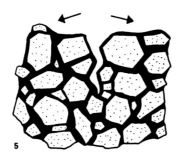

The general strength of a clay is improved by bringing the particles closer together. The bonds and suction are increased even though the ability to slide, the true plasticity, is not increased. Ageing, wedging, pugging, especially de-aired pugging, help in this way to improve overall workability and hence apparent plasticity.

Plucking
The spoiling of a foot rim or lid by chips from the edges caused by the rim sticking to the kiln shelf. This occurs especially in salt glaze and vitrified clays.

Plumbic
Of lead or with lead from the latin plumbum, e.g. plumbic glaze contains lead. For information on lead glazes etc, see ***Lead oxide***.

Pneumoconiosis
See ***Silicosis***.

Poison
A substance that injures the living organism when absorbed. The potter handles many potential poisons. Some are directly harmful if introduced into the lungs and digestive system. Some substances are harmless until altered by heat when they liberate poisonous gases or decompose into poisonous substances. Most of the poisons are rendered sufficiently insoluble by complete involvement in ceramic fusions but low-fired ware and underfired ware are always suspect. See ***Lead poisoning, Metal release*** and ***Health hazard***.

Substances which should be handled with respect and should be fired correctly are: antimony oxide, arsenic oxide, barium compounds, beryllium oxide, unfritted borax, cadmium and selenium compounds and colours, cobalt compounds, colemanite, copper compounds, chromium compounds, raw lead compounds, lead silicates, lustre preparations, manganese compounds, nickel compounds, potassium dichromate, vanadium compounds, zinc compounds. The list covers many materials and is a salutory reminder to act respectfully. See ***Safety***. Potential poisons must be stored away from accidental misuse.

The previous list contains substances which can become poisonous by mishandling in the firing but there are substances that liberate poisonous gases during correct firing. These are the sulfides, chlorides, fluorides and, to a lesser extent, carbonates. For example, cornish stone, crude feldspars and low-grade fireclays, fluorspar, gypsum, lepidolite, cryolite.

Some substances volatilize when overfired and produce poisonous fumes. They are the antimony, boron, cadmium, lead, selenium and zinc compounds and the precious metals. Many of the substances used in ceramic printing, especially photographic processes, are hazardous.

Lastly, remember that many household cleaners, detergents, bleach, glues, solvents, thinners, pigment mediums, wax fumes, propane and methane gases are harmful. Also many plastic products give off toxic fumes if heated.

Porcelain
A vitrified, white and translucent ware. A few wares fit this description. The one usually implied is that fired at 1300°C (2372°F) plus. In this, the body and the glaze mature together to create a very thick body-glaze layer which gives

the whole piece an important strength. This ware is sometimes called hard-paste porcelain or *grand-feu*. There is also the soft-paste or *petit-feu* porcelain. Here the body and glaze mature together but at a lower temperature. To achieve translucency, the body contains a high proportion of glassy frit which requires very accurate firing. Wasters are consequently frequent.

China, both bone china and non-bone china, overcomes some of the difficulties of both hard- and soft-paste porcelains. The body of a china is fired to a translucent state as an unglazed bisc. It is prevented from warping by being embedded in ground aluminium oxide. See **Place**. The ware is given a soft-firing glaze.

A few pieces of the 18th-century white salt-glazed ware are also translucent and could be considered porcelain.

The name porcelain is said to have been coined by Marco Polo in the 13th century from *porcelino*. This was the name of the translucent cowrie shell which looked like a little pig or porcelino. He likened Chinese porcelain to this translucent white shell. The Chinese have always defined porcelain as a development of fine stoneware, valuing resonance as important as translucence. This takes into consideration a good body-glaze layer and a well-fitting, non-crazed glaze. Porcelains were being developed in the 10th century when the emperor Hou Zhou Shi Zong pronounced that Chai ware should be 'as blue-green as the sky, as clear as a mirror, as thin as paper, and as resonant as a musical stone of jade'. In Jingdezhen today (the centre of Chinese porcelain production), a modern version of these lines, adapted to describe eggshell white ware is quoted:

> As white as jade,
> As thin as paper,
> As bright as a mirror,
> As sound as a bell.

An essential ingredient for the body of these high-fired porcelains was a plastic white-burning clay. The Chinese name was *kao ling* which survived in the English kaolin and china clay. The discovery of suitable clays in Europe in the 18th century enabled Western potters to emulate the Chinese success but European clays are not so plastic as the Chinese ones. This has meant that pressing and slip-casting have been more frequently employed.

Potters have tried various body recipes to achieve a throwable porcelain body. But the addition of even a small amount of ball clay tends to darken the body. Some whiteness can be retrieved by hard reduction but this tends to encourage premature collapse. David Leach has successfully overcome the problem of plasticity by the use of bentonite.

His body recipe is:

china clay	55
potassium feldspar	25
quartz	15
white bentonite	5

His glaze recipe is:

feldspar	25
china clay	25
flint	25
whiting	25

A number of potters' suppliers now offer plastic porcelain bodies which have some translucency fired at approximately 1280°C (2336°F). Some are whiter than others but there is a tendency to sacrifice whiteness for workability or *vice versa*. When scraps of porcelain body are reconstituted there is sometimes a problem of bloating at a previously satisfactory temperature. This body must then be processed in a de-airing pug mill. The use of these bodies for hand-thrown or modelled, small, delicate and colourful pieces also takes advantage of small and fast-fire kilns, and new stable body stains. The porcelain pieces illustrated are a blue and white Qing Dynasty bowl, a landscape bowl by Maggie Andrews, a painted bowl by Derek Clarkson, an agateware bowl by Linda Caswell and a teapot by Jakes Michal. See also *Colour plates 80/81*.

Porosity

The ability of a fired body to absorb water by capillary action. In a plastic clay the interstitial spaces between the clay and other mineral particles are filled with water (fig. 1). After the ceramic change at 600°C (1112°F) these spaces are empty. Clay fired at or just above 600°C becomes an extremely porous body (fig. 2). As the temperature increases above 600°C the feldspathoids and free silica are fluxed by the alkalis which are present. The resulting molten silicates begin to fill the spaces and the whole mass shrinks as a result. Thus there is less space left and the body is less porous (fig. 3). The fluxing action continues until all the spaces are filled and the porosity is nil. This is complete vitrification. Beyond this point the body deforms and eventually melts.

If one is using the normal soft biscuit, the biscuit firing should be chosen to give the optimum strength, with maximum porosity. In practice this means between 900°C and 1000°C (1652°F and 1832°F). Above this it is difficult to get the glaze to adhere in a uniform layer. Below this the biscuit ware is so soft that it is easily damaged and large pieces cannot always survive the shock of dunting when cooling.

The porosity in earthenware is overcome by the use of the impervious glaze covering which of course should not be crazed. In stoneware the glaze is theoretically unnecessary and is for decorative and hygienic reasons. Crazing can be decorative in stoneware without trouble from porosity.

Although potters theoretically seek to get a porosity which is nil in their stoneware bodies, for practicality a very slight porosity is preferable. A porosity of 1% or 2% gives a much stronger body than one with no porosity at all. This is because the glassy nature of the latter is brittle and allows no chance of movement between the particles except by fracture. The graph shows typical porosity and strength curves for a stoneware clay when fired to different temperatures. By relating these two one can appreciate the relationship between porosity and ovenware. Ovenware based upon normal clays is usually porous between 5% and 10% in stonewares.

The normal test for porosity is to take a sample piece of fired body and whilst warm from the kiln to weigh it accurately. It is necessary to use a balance capable of weighing to within a hundredth of a gram. The test piece is put in boiling water for five minutes and left in the water as this is allowed to cool. When cold the test piece is taken out and dried, preferably with a damp sponge. This is better than a cloth which can leave fibres behind on the test piece. The test is then weighed again and the increase in weight is calculated as a percentage of the original dry weight.

$$\frac{\text{Wt after soaking minus wt dry}}{\text{weight dry}} \times \frac{100}{1} = \frac{\text{percentage}}{\text{porosity}}$$

Posset cup

A 16th- to 18th-century large cup sometimes lidded. There is often a long spout or tube coming from the bottom and attached firmly to the inside or outside appearing near the rim as a spout from which the posset was sucked. Posset is hot milk curdled with wine or ale.

The photograph shows a late 17th-century slipware example made in Staffordshire, England. The spout is visible on the right and one of the two handles on the left.

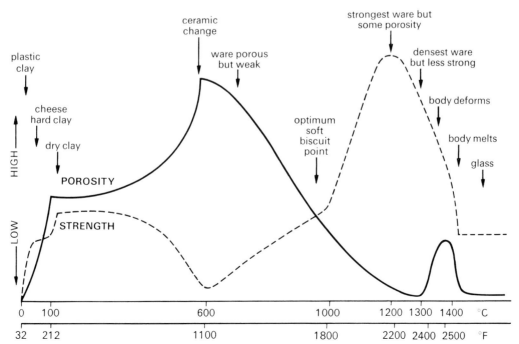

Potash
Potassium carbonate. K_2CO_3.

Potassium carbonate
Pearl ash. Potash. K_2CO_3. A highly-soluble salt used in the preparation of frits and glass. During firing, decomposition takes place to give the flux potassium oxide and carbon dioxide:

$$K_2CO_3 \xrightarrow{900°C} K_2O + CO_2\uparrow$$

Potassium carbonate is the true potash. It is so called because a solution of water and carbonate (lye) was evaporated in iron 'pots'. The carbonate was derived from the ashes of burnt vegetable matter. Wood ash when used for glazes will be found to contain soluble potassium carbonate. At least half of the potassium carbonate content of wood ash is soluble and if not washed from the wood ash before use in the glaze slop it will be found to dissolve in the glaze tub. If these glazes are stirred by hand one can feel the alkalinity of the water. In extreme cases the amount is sufficient to have a caustic effect and irritate sensitive skins and remove nail varnish.

This caustic action of wood ash solutions was used historically as a cleaning solution (lye) for textiles and is the origin of soft soaps.

Alone, the pure white crystals of potassium carbonate are deliquescent. They pick up water from the atmosphere and dissolve in it to become a solution.

Potassium dichromate
(Bichromate). $K_2Cr_2O_7$. A soluble crystalline material with a bright red-orange colour. It is used to introduce chromium oxide into low- temperature glazes. Because the chromium oxide is combined with the potassium oxide, it is more effectively dispersed in the glaze. It is possible to obtain a bright red colour with potassium dichromate in lead frit. See *Chromium oxide: chrome red*.

Care should be taken with potassium dichromate because it is soluble and poisonous. See *Poison*.

Potassium feldspar
See *Orthoclase*.

Potassium minerals
The potter's main source of potassium oxide is orthoclase feldspar. Some other igneous minerals also contain potassium oxide, e.g. cornish stone and nepheline syenite. The decomposition of these rocks gives the soil in which plants grow and potassium has become essential to plant life. Therefore, vegetable ashes contain potassium and are a source of potassium oxide for glazes. Feldspar is 10% to 15% potassium oxide. Wood ash is up to 15% potassium oxide but at least half of this is very soluble. Potassium carbonate is 68% potassium oxide which is all soluble and therefore potassium carbonate is used in making frits.

There is slightly more potassium than sodium in the earth's crust. This potassium is mostly in insoluble compounds like igneous rocks whereas the sodium is mostly in soluble salt deposits. A few soluble potassium salt deposits exist. They give:

sylvine	(KCl)
carnallite	$(KCl.MgCl_2.6H_2O)$
kainite	$(KCl.MgSO_4.3H_2O)$
potassium nitrate	(KNO_3)

Potassium oxide
Kalium oxide. K_2O. One of the three strong alkaline fluxes for ceramic fusions. The others are lithium and sodium oxides. Potassium oxide is soluble in water but exists in feldspars in relatively insoluble form. Feldspars are used in glaze-making and most clays contain some potash in feldspathic combinations. Potash is introduced into frits by feldspar and potassium carbonate.

Potassium is a similar metal to sodium but it is not quite so chemically active. See *Sodium minerals*. The compounds of potassium are therefore not quite so soluble as those of sodium. The potassium feldspar (orthoclase, $K_2O.Al_2O_3.6SiO_2$) is relatively insoluble. In geological time the potassium oxide content can be dissolved and it, with other feldspars, is the source of china clay and indeed all clays. Feldspar is therefore a constituent of all clays with the exception of pure kaolinite.

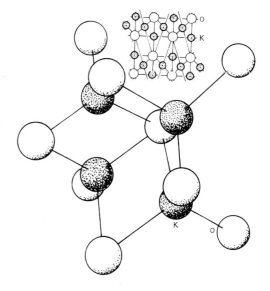

Potassium oxide feldspar can therefore be introduced into clays and bodies. It provides a non-plastic shortening and a fusible content which gives hardness to the finished product. The potassium oxide is the flux which instigates the interactions which give the denser ware.

One cannot help comparing potassium oxide with sodium oxide, the slightly cheaper but slightly more active glaze flux. As if to compensate, potassium oxide begins its action a little earlier than does sodium oxide, at 750°C (1382°F). Its action is uniform throughout all glaze ranges and it does not suffer from soda's defect of high-temperature volatility. See **Sodium oxide in glazes**. The resulting melt of a potassium oxide glass is not quite so fluid, but when set, it is more resistant to abrasion and to solubility attack than is sodium oxide glass.

However, potassium oxide cannot be used alone as a flux. Potassium oxide glass is brittle and as a glaze would be unstable and certainly crazed. Potassium oxide, like sodium oxide, is a valuable constituent in the manufacture of frits and glazes, including lead-free glazes, and in the making of hard glass. It encourages alkaline colour responses which again are similar to but not identical to those of sodium oxide. Because it is soluble, it is introduced into glazes by frits or as a second flux by way of feldspar. This use as a second flux cannot be overstressed. It brings to glazes an excellent, wide-ranging and predictable fluxing activity; it provides stability, adds brilliance and provides opportunity for balance of contraction rate. See **Glaze fit**.

Powder blue

Soufflé blue. Blue produced by cobalt oxide dusted on to or blown on to body or glaze. The action isolates the blue as specks on a white ground which gives a luminosity to the colour.

Praseodymium oxide

PrO_2. One of the lanthanide oxides in the amphoteric area of the periodic table. It is used in the production of yellow stains in combination with zirconium silicate. Such stains are not powerful but have wide temperature and glaze ranges.

Preheating

Process of warming-up prior to the firing of clay. What is apparently perfectly dry clay still contains water in the pores between the clay particles. This water turns to steam and escapes at temperatures over its boiling point, 100°C (212°F). Once this water is removed, a firing can proceed fairly rapidly but if this water has not been removed there is a grave risk of exploding the clay with a build-up of steam pressure. When pots are being fired in the sudden fierce heat of brushwood and grass bonfires this preheating is most important and is done by holding the pots over a small fire until hot. With pots set in a kiln the preheating is done by starting the firing very slowly. This period up to 120°C (248°F) is called the water-smoking period of kiln-firing.

Preparation of clay

Pockets of clay of perfect consistency and ideal composition for a particular product can be found. This proves that the preparation of clay for working is a natural process of events. All that the potter does is to simulate nature's ideas, accelerate them and emphasize one or another to produce the clay required. It is important to appreciate this and to try to work with nature rather than against it.

In a similar way one should consider working with clay so that one need not lift and move it more than necessary.

An economical time-and-motion sequence for preparation and storage is important to release the potter for making pots. To this end, many potters buy prepared clays but they will also find that a knowledge of their purchases will help them to use their clays effectively.

A few clays are suitable for potting as dug from the ground. Some are potentially good clays but require preparation. It is all too easy to assume that the earliest potters used their clay 'as dug'. The exceedingly coarse nature of some of the bodies of Bronze Age pottery might lead one to think that no selection or preparation was carried out. However, a closer study of primitive pottery proves this to be wrong. The pottery made now by people whose civilization is classified as Stone Age shows a remarkable understanding of the practical necessity of clay preparation, even if the technology is not understood.

Anthropologists have been amazed to see a potter take the trouble to remove sand from a clay only to replace it with sand from another locality. Either the explanation of the avoidance of dunting was misunderstood or the reasons for this time-honoured practice had been forgotten.

Clay preparation aims to produce a homogeneous material with sufficient workability for the job in hand. It is therefore necessary first to understand what demands will be made of the clay in one's chosen way of working. See **Workability**. Having assessed the requirements, one can consider the preparation in four steps: the control of plasticity; the control of grain size; the control of moisture content; and preparation prior to forming. The first two may be taken in either order.

A typical preparation sequence to produce a throwing clay from a raw clay would be:

1. weathering ⎫
2. blunging ⎭ plasticity
3. screening—grain size
4. settling
5. dewatering ⎫
6. wedging ⎬ moisture content
7. storage ⎭
8. preparation for the wheel

CONTROL OF PLASTICITY. One usually wishes to increase the plasticity of a clay. To this end one adds ball clay to one's own clay, or adds a plasticizer like bentonite. Ten to twenty per cent of ball clay will improve an otherwise dead clay. It will also lengthen the workability range. Two to four per cent of bentonite will give a similar feeling of plasticity but it will not have the same effect upon the workability range. See **Ball clay, Bentonite** and **Plasticity: physics (plasticizers)**.

These are additions to an existing clay but it is possible that more consideration of the earlier preparation could have rendered this doctoring unnecessary.

Plasticity can be related directly to particle size. The most plastic clays have the finest particles. See **Plasticity**. Some clays have naturally large particles. The particles themselves

Description of clay processing from raw materials

are large, orderly crystals. These clays are usually chemically pure kaolin and they are not very plastic, e.g. china clay and some fireclays. Other clays have fine particles which are compacted to form larger particles often called grains. These clays also are not very plastic, e.g. some fireclays and ground shales. However these clays have a high plastic potential if the particles forming the grains can be separated. Some clays have fine particles which are already separated. These clays are highly plastic, e.g. ball clays.

A clay particle is composed of thousands of clay molecules. These molecules link together to form strong sheets. The sheets are held together by comparatively weak links called hydroxyl bonds. A few hundred sheets form a tiny crystal. The tiny crystals are similarly held together to form the larger particles and so on. At the size easily visible to the naked eye these particles are often called grains.

In ordered kaolinite, the tiny clay crystals are so neatly packed together that they form what is virtually one large crystal. However, in disordered kaolinite the tiny crystals are slightly distorted. They cannot fit together neatly and so their particles are formed of a more random packing of crystals. The bonds between these crystals, and hence between particle and particle, are weaker than in the ordered kaolinite. These hydroxyl bonds (O-H-O) are the first cousins of water (H_2O). Water is able to infiltrate the bonds in the disordered particle by becoming part of them until the bond is only loosely held across a chain of water. At this point physical force can shear the sides apart. The physical force is available in nature as rain or impact during transportation. This process, which breaks up the grains into smaller particles, is called weathering.

A clay in its first stages of disintegration may take a hundred or a thousand years to become weathered. Ordered kaolinite, requiring the first stage to disordered kaolinite before the weathering can have effect, will be millions of years before it becomes a fully plastic clay.

At the other end of the scale are clays that once were fully plastic but by pressure and drying have now become compacted again and consist of large grains. These grains are vulnerable to weathering so that a clay of this sort will show surprising disintegration after one year's weathering. These clays are rock-like fire-clays, marl shales etc. After millions of years in the earth as rocks they weather to plastic clays in a few years, the hardest taking perhaps twenty.

An important agent in disintegration is the frost. Water alone will slowly penetrate the clay grain that has plastic potential but frost greatly accelerates the process. Water expands as it freezes. Thereby the gap between the particles is widened and floods with water upon thawing. Once water has entered one end of a potential gap it drives a wedge inwards by the alternate actions of freezing and thawing. Following the frost, the particles are only loosely held by water bonds. Now the physical action of rain beating upon the clay is sufficient to move the particles apart.

Secondary clays that have been transported by water, ground and tossed about in rivers, and finally allowed to rest below a lake, tend to be plastic. However, if these clays have also dried out, been compressed or otherwise dehydrated, they will tend to have lost their plasticity. The particles will be packed tightly together to form large grains. From this one learns that, even on the smaller scale of the workshop, it is a retrograde step to allow intended plastic clay to dry out at any stage. For a clay to realize its full plastic potential, it requires water between the particles. Clays which are weathering should therefore be kept wet also if this is possible.

The foregoing has been described in detail to emphasize that an accurate assessment must be made of a clay's potential. Not all clays will improve by weathering: only those which have plastic potential. A study of the geological origin of the clay will help to identify the clay type. See also ***Weathering***.

Weathering can be simulated by blunging. A whole winter's weathering can be achieved in ten minutes of high-speed blunging. See ***Blunge***. This literally forces the particles to collide with shattering impact. At this shock instant the water seepage is rapid. See drawing. The standard slow-speed blunger or the hand blunger is best used as a follow-up to part the particles already loosened by open-air weathering.

Weathering also allows soluble salts to be washed away. It is true that blunging will also achieve this. However, there is the point that during weathering an amount of chemical decomposition takes place. For most clays this decomposition and solution is desirable. The most common product is calcium sulfate which, if not washed away, causes scumming. See ***Scum***. Chemical correctives can be added at the blunging stage to complete decomposition and precipitate the salts as harmless compounds. The abrasive action of blunging disturbs the thixotropic strength of a potentially plastic clay. This strength is restored by keeping the clay wrapped in storage for as long a time as possible. See ***Ageing*** and ***Sour***.

After all this treatment, some clays may be found to be too plastic and sticky. These clays are difficult to handle but improve in workability by the addition of some non-plastic material. As a general rule, the fine non-plastics decrease the plasticity more than the coarse ones. It is sufficient to add grogs and sands at the kneading or pugging stage, but powders must be added at the blunging stage. See also ***Filler***.

Powders, even wet powders, do not seem to mix thoroughly. They create agglomerate grains of their own if added to the clay at its plastic stage. Such powders are china clay and quartz flour. It may seem a nuisance to add these to the suspension, only to screen them and dewater them, but they do not seem to mix otherwise. It is of course pointless to add material of a size that will later be held back by a screen.

A further point on plasticity is mentioned later under storage. The physics of plasticity are dealt with under ***Plasticity***.

CONTROL OF GRAIN SIZE. The foregoing weathering and blunging has been concerned with the improvement of plasticity. Blunging is also a preparatory step to the control of grain size which, in itself, has some effect on overall plasticity. A sandy clay is less plastic than the same clay with the sand removed. It may not be more workable but it will be more plastic. This presents a difficult problem which arises from the potter's use of the word plastic. He uses it to embrace the idea of workability. A clay which behaves itself well under all the conditions to which it is subjected is often called 'highly plastic' when it would be better to call it 'highly workable'.

A plastic clay, at its full potential, is a collection of plate-like particles. These particles are lubricated with water and electrostatic repulsion. Such a clay is too slippery for use and requires tempering with a non-plastic or low-plasticity material. A fine grog or a sand will theoretically position itself between the particles causing a friction where none existed before. This will stiffen the clay and give it a strength in its plastic state. The word 'theorctically' is used here because, in fact, the clay particles are much smaller than the sand.

Throwing clays often require some grog for this purpose. It ensures that as more water enters the clay, the clay particles do not slide too quickly past each other. The end result is that about 10% of fine grog (60's to dust) often improves the 'throwability' of a clay.

Large size grogs, however, present a different picture. They introduce large objects into the clay around which the clay particles must fasten in layers in an attempt to keep the mass plastic. If the grog is too large, and the size is relative to the clay particles, the clay takes on an awkwardness in its workability. It appears stiff and yet is soft. In throwing it feels stiff but softens suddenly. It lacks the in-between size of grain that would enable large objects and fine clay to flow as a whole. The addition of a medium/fine sand or grog can improve the workability of such a clay. This is a point to remember when introducing grogs for textural effect.

It is difficult to assess what needs to be added to a clay or taken from it except by trial and error. However, one can obtain some idea of what a clay contains by a simple experiment. One requires a glass bottle that will hold about half a litre. This is half-filled with water and about half a teaspoonful of the clay is added. It can be added in any convenient state, but the idea is to get it into suspension by vigorously shaking the bottle. When the clay is in suspension, the bottle can be almost filled with water and shaken again to mix the suspension. The bottle is then put at a slight angle. See drawing.

As the water comes to a standstill, the heavy material immediately settles and progressive sedimentation of different grain sizes follows. If there is sufficient plastic clay present to make a suitable potting clay, the mixture should remain completely cloudy for at least two hours. In fact it will take at least a day to completely settle.

The slight tilt on the bottle emphasizes the sediments into identifiable layers against one side of the glass. If the test is carried out on a window sill the light shining through the bottle helps one to identify the particles. A magnifying glass can be used through the side of the bottle.

Bentonite can be added to a clay which has insufficient of the ultra-fine particles. This would be a clay that settled completely in four or five hours. Two per cent of bentonite is usually sufficient.

With a locally dug clay it is often necessary to take out unwanted material. This material may be large like twigs, roots, leaves and stones,or it may be small like sand or shale.

Large objects can be sorted by hand: a process used by primitive potters and one which does not take as long as one might think. If the clay is in plastic state, small pellets are broken off and squashed between finger and thumb. Large unwanted pieces are felt and removed. Some carbonaceous matter present as hair roots is often advantageous to plasticity. It will certainly help in the souring.

A larger problem is unwanted sand and shale. Weathered shales are often difficult in this respect, containing a lot of flat slatey pieces that do not reconstitute as clay.

The only way to get rid of this unwanted material is by turning the clay into a very thin slurry with water. In this state pieces of wood and carbonaceous matter often float and can be skimmed off. Very large and heavy material sinks and can be left behind in the container. Finer sand and shale is removed by screening.

An appropriate mesh size is chosen for the required final clay. A 60's mesh gives a good general potting clay. Some potters prefer finer clays and use an 80's or a 100's mesh, but take the suspension through a 20's or 40's mesh first. Too much coarse material might otherwise accumulate and tear the finer mesh. A brush should be used sparingly. There is no point in forcing material through the mesh because this is unlikely to be clay material. A brush can be used to keep the mesh clear. A vibrating screen is the best method. The use of a very thin or watery suspension helps to break the clay content into its finest particles. Overnight soaking before screening will help to reach plasticity potential and will help the suspension to flow through the mesh without clogging.

Some clays will not settle after this process. The addition

of some acid to the water will increase the settling rate but fine clays, and these are the plastic clays, will always settle slowly. This is a good sign. Two or four days is not too long to wait for a good clay. The use of a test, as previously described, will give some indication of the mesh size to select and the time required for decanting the suspension from the first heavy sediment.

Clays, which contain unwanted material which is as fine as the wanted clay, can be refined by levigation. The process involves the use of the different densities of the clay and the unwanted material. The heavier material of higher density sinks in water quicker than the lighter material. See **Levigation**. On a large scale, timed settling and elutriation are also used. The process is sometimes necessary to remove sand specking from light-coloured clays. Porcelain bodies are sometimes refined in this way to get the maximum plasticity and purity.

CONTROL OF MOISTURE CONTENT. The correct moisture content for a plastic clay is a matter of personal choice. However, one could say that each clay has a moisture content amount at which its full plastic potential is realized.

The plasticity of a clay and the fluidity of a slip are dependent upon the moisture content in relation to the behaviour of the clay particles and other material. A clay's behaviour depends upon its particle size and its electrostatic charges.

For slip-casting the electrostatic charges are emphasized in one direction in order that the particles can slide past one another. Also in large-scale preparation of plastic clay, the electrostatic charges are rebalanced. For small-scale preparation of clays it is sufficient if the potter realizes that slight alkalinity or acidicy in the water of the clay can affect its plastic behaviour. For example, in the blending of two plastic clays from different sources, one is likely to find that one clay affects the other. The usual effect is that the slightly more acidic one opens up the other and creates spaces for more water. Two quite soft clays will then give a stiff blend which requires extra water to bring it to workable consistency. The phenomenon is dealt with under **Flocculation** and **Deflocculation**.

One should also be aware of the effects of the acidic and alkaline waters in the clay and as used for throwing. Alkaline clays soften quickly. Alkaline water feels slippery but softens clay quickly. Acidic clays are often 'thirsty' to throw with. The effect of acidity on strength is dealt with under **Plasticity** and **Sour**.

Suspensions of clay etc and water, which are required to be constituted as plastic clays, are dewatered by settling and siphoning. They have been mixed with as much extra water as is convenient because this ensures a full wetting of the clay, eases screening and washes away solubles. After siphoning, the resulting thick slip is poured into drying troughs (see **Dewatering**), onto absorbent boards, onto a heated floor or just left in the open air to dry. Frequent attention is required to forestall any tendency to dry out too much at the edges.

On a large scale, which is anything requiring more than 50 kg of plastic clay daily, a filter press is used. This is used instead of the settling process. A deflocculant gives extra fluidity for screening and the clay is returned to its stiffer and more permeable state by a flocculant. This thick slip is pumped under pressure or suction into a series of demountable boxes whose sides are made of a permeable, fine, strong cloth. The water passes through the cloths and the clay is held back to produce a 'cake'. See **Filter pressing**.

Most plastic clays are stored in a slightly over-wet condition. This assists ageing. Therefore plastic clay often requires a slight dewatering before use. It is achieved by wedging and kneading on a slightly absorbent bench. If the clay is too soft, it may be necessary to use a very absorbent plaster block or porous board to achieve correct moisture content. Alternatively, arches of clay, left on a board outside in a breeze, quickly stiffen and can be wedged and kneaded. Clay which has required much in the way of this late dewatering does not reach its maximum plasticity without a further rest in storage.

Clay that is too stiff can be remixed with water in a pug mill, a reconstitutor popularly called a dough mixer, or by hand. It is a laborious process by hand but can be done by cutting the clay into slabs, poking holes in the slabs and adding water or slurry before sandwiching. The lump is kneaded a little, wedged and kneaded again. Again, this clay will benefit from storage.

Clay which has dried out completely, as scrapped pots or the edges of clay which is dewatering, should be resoaked if possible. This is the only way to achieve full plastic potential.

PREPARATION PRIOR TO FORMING. The usual preparation is wedging followed by kneading. Wedging compresses and mixes the clay. Kneading prepares the specific amount required and makes it homogenous. **Wedging** and **Kneading** are separately indexed.

Prepared

When used to describe clay this means that more than one clay or mineral has been blended together. The word 'body' is usually used rather than the term 'prepared clay'.

A prepared mineral or prepared oxide is one that has been chemically produced in contrast to one that is a selected and ground raw material. For example, red iron oxide can be crushed haematite or a prepared oxide precipitated from a ferriferous solution.

A prepared colour is one that has been manufactured from a number of ingredients, e.g. colouring oxides, alumino-silicates and fluxes. The ingredients are calcined or fritted and reground as a homogeneous powder ready for use.

Press-moulding

Forming pots by pressing plastic clay slabs onto and into absorbent plaster moulds. The clay slab is coaxed into place against the mould by the hands, sponges, leathers and rubber kidneys. As the clay stiffens, it retains the form of the mould and can be removed for fettling.

Hollow forms are sometimes made in piece moulds which are put together with a slab of clay in each piece. The slabs are joined together to form the pot before the mould is dismantled.

Large plates are often press-moulded because it is easier to make them in this way than to throw them. Non-circular plates and bowls must be moulded in some way. Also the method is useful for pre-forming pieces from which larger pieces are to be constructed.

The pictures show a pressed serving dish by Andrew McGarva and a vessel pressed into a plaster mould by Carol Peevor. The making sequence (right) shows the processes employed by Bennett Cooper. See also **Colour plate 68**.

PRESS-MOULDING CLAY. Clays for press-moulding need not be highly plastic. In fact, clays of low plasticity (short clays) often press well and have the merit of freeing themselves from the mould fairly quickly. Being relatively coarser than highly plastic clays, they are more open and the water can be drawn from the clay more quickly. There is also less water to be drawn from the clay before it stiffens and therefore there is less shrinkage. See **Water: of plasticity** and **Drying.** The low shrinkage is important where contact with the mould could involve tightening onto a deep mould.

Primary clay

Residual clay. A clay found in its place of origin. The only common examples are china clay and bentonite. See **Clay: origin**. Clays which have been removed from their place of origin and deposited elsewhere are called secondary or sedimentary clays.

Printing

This term can be used for any method of transferring pigment to a ceramic surface to create decoration. It often implies a repeated shape which creates a pattern or a repeatable image used in mass production. The techniques of printing multiple images on paper via engraved or etched metal plates were well established before the ceramics industry took up the idea. A system for printing on ceramics, using paper transfers, was eventually developed towards the end of the 18th century, taking over almost completely from hand painting. See **Liverpool**. Modern ceramicists are now exploiting sophisticated, commercial printing techniques, adapting them to create images on ceramics.

The simplest, direct ways of printing colour onto a ceramic piece, use fingers, cut sponge or rubber stamps dipped in ceramic pigment and pressed onto the surface at any stage prior to final firing. The process (overleaf) shows Rob Bibby applying stains using cut sponges and a finished bowl. See also **Colour plate 17**. Carved plaster, biscuit stamps or found objects can be used to imprint into the clay creating a surface into which coloured slip can be inlaid. Early studio potters, reacting against all industrial methods which distanced the maker from the initial creative

idea, preferred to use these ways of decorating, along with uncomplicated brushwork. In recent times, the pendulum has swung back to recognizing the body of knowledge which resides within the industrial tradition. Students in colleges have access to workshops teaching various craft skills and industrial technology. They have inter-married techniques, adapting them on their own terms, either for small-scale repetition, or to enliven design for industry, or the creation of novel personal styles. Ways of printing images have been culled from the fine art printmaker, and more noticeably, from the photographer. These processes, going through many stages, can be intriguing but laborious and are usually only attempted on a flat surface and often produce only one item. Flat tiles or slabs of clay or porcelain are sometimes subsequently folded and assembled to produce three-dimensional sculptures.

Most of the processes involve transferring the chosen image in the form of ceramic colour to a pottery tissue paper, or decal, which can be pressed onto the clay thus transferring the image to that surface. Silk screen printing is a popular way of manipulating shapes, either directly onto the ceramic, or via a decal. A stencil design may be created on the screen as in the textile printing industry. The screen is coated with a photosensitive emulsion. Any opaque object placed on the screen will protect some areas from the UV light to which it is then exposed. The screen will then carry the image in the form of open or blocked areas of mesh. This can then be used to screen-print ceramic pigment either on to a decal, or directly onto the ceramic surface.

Illustrated are three printed porcelain works by Paul Scott. The vase shape uses underglaze pigment printed from screen-printed decals fired onto a previously fired glaze. The second illustration shows an etching printed onto paper porcelain in cobalt oxide and glazed with a transparent glaze. The image size is 9 cm by 7 cm. The third is a detail of an etching printed onto paper porcelain and fired without glaze to 1200°C (2192°F). The image is 20 cm by 6 cm. See also **Paper clay** and **Colour plate 61**.

A photograph can be used as a stencil if put through a photocopier to create a black and white image. The white is made transparent using an oil. A half-tone photographic image can be reproduced by having a half-tone film positive made by a commercial print workshop. A film positive is a photograph printed on a transparent sheet instead of paper. Alternatively a photosensitive gummy emulsion may be painted directly onto the ceramic. A film positive is interposed and exposed to light. The areas protected from the light remain sticky while other parts are hardened. Pigment is then dusted onto the sticky areas. A variation of this technique is to mix the pigment with the emulsion and to subsequently wash away the un-exposed areas.

Many of the materials used in these processes, and the photographic chemicals, e.g. ammonium dichromate and acetic acid, are irritant, corrosive and flammable. Ultra-violet light is carcinogenic. Some pigments and resin lustres present hazards. Great care and good ventilation are essential. See **Health hazard, Safety** and **Colour plates 60** and **61**.

Proto-porcelain

Stoneware which was the forerunner of Chinese porcelain. The body was grey, the glaze was feldspathic and the ware must have been fired at least to 1200°C (2192°F). It developed contemporaneously with the lead glazes of the Han dynasty and probably superseded lead-glazed wares for general use during the Tang dynasty, when it emerges as white stoneware or porcelain.

Pug mill

A machine for mixing and compressing a plastic clay. It mechanizes the handwork of wedging and kneading. Knives rotate on a central shaft and force the clay through a tapering barrel and out through a compressing nozzle. Illustrated are a de-airing horizontal pug mill and a vertical model, both manufactured by Ratcliffe.

Pugging achieves some mixing of clay consistency but is more important for its effect upon compression. Compression improves the strength and thus workability of a clay. See also **Ageing, De-airing** and **Wedging**.

Pull

Draught. The energy exerted by the chimney on the kiln gases.

Puzzle jug

A popular tavern joke jug of the 17th to 19th centuries in Europe. The handle was hollow and the ale was drunk by sucking it up through one of the spouts. To make the suction work, all the other holes, both obvious and secret, had to be covered. The example is a 19th century Sunderland version.

Pygmy cups

Small ritual vessels, only 6 cm to 8 cm in diameter, of the Middle and Late Bronze Age. They are found in round cairn burials of 1600BC to 1400BC especially in western Britain.

They are called pygmy because they are small. They were usually used along with the large overhanging rim urns and held a few small bones or accessory treasures, pendants, amulets etc. Being able to perform their accessory function easily they were not subject to the normal functional design found in the larger pieces. This allowed their makers the opportunity for experiment. No two are alike. There are globular ones, straight-sided ones, conical ones and open bowls. Decoration is impressed, incised and punctured. Their precise significance in the burial is still unknown.

Pyrite

Iron pyrites. Iron sulfide. Fool's gold. FeS_2. An iron ore occurring in crystals which have a light yellow metallic shine. It occurs as impurity specking in fireclays, and because it weathers very slowly and is harder than the clay it is impossible to grind it into a uniform colouring. The ore is too hard to grind for use as a pottery colourant.

The word pyrite comes from the Greek word for flame because it is possible to burn pyrite like coal. The particles in clay burn away part of their sulfur before 600°C (1112°F) but the remainder (FeS) forms compact particles which are difficult to oxidize. Above 1200°C (2192°F) these particles melt, causing unpleasant blemishes on unglazed ware and sometimes erupting through a glaze in an unsightly way. It is possible with very small particles to achieve solution in the glaze as a decorative speckle.

Pyrite is also used as a general term for the other iron sulfide ores and for the copper and iron ore called copper pyrites.

Pyrolusite

MnO_2. The chief manganese ore and source of manganese oxide.

Pyrometry

The measurement of temperature and heat-work.

Temperature is measured by pyrometers using a thermocouple or pyrocouple and a potentiometer. The thermocouple is two dissimilar metal wires joined at one end and introduced into the kiln. The heat generates a small current which is measured at the other ends of the wires and related to temperature. Pyrometers measure the temperature inside the kiln and can be linked to the kiln control to switch off, soak or control temperature rise and fall. See **Instrumentation**.

Heat-work is measured by pyroscopes. These are expendable objects made from carefully proportioned ceramic minerals. They are similar in composition to glazes and thus sinter, fuse and melt at predicted points as a result of temperature and the time subjected to the temperature. The temperature/time factor is called heat-work and is referred to as a temperature with the understood significance of a particular rise in temperature expressed in degrees per hour. Pyroscopes may be used as the visible check of heat-work during a firing and the kiln fired by means of these. Also they may be strategically placed for recovery after firing. The popular pyroscopes are cones, bars and rings.

Q

Quartz

Silica. SiO_2. The popular name for the mineral rocks specifically called milky quartz and crystal quartz. They are used as sources of silica for glazes and bodies and are introduced as a powder or as quartz sand. Quartz as the specific term for the primary phase of silica is separately described.

QUARTZ MINERAL. Milky quartz, sometimes called quartz rock, is an opaque white, greasy-looking and sharply angular rock. It occurs as veins through other rocks and, being hard, survives as white pebbles which are often included in conglomerate rocks. Crystal quartz has larger crystals which can be seen with the naked eye and while from a distance the quartz looks white, upon closer inspection the individual crystals are often perfectly clear and colourless. Large crystals over 50 cm in length are not unknown and those of 3 cm or so are quite common.

Both rock and crystal quartz are hard and are used as a measurement of hardness as number 7 on Mohs' scale. Quartz will therefore scratch window glass.

Disintegrated rocks have provided white sands, some of which are agglomerated as gritstone while others remain as beds of soft sand. The sand is quarried and marketed as quartz sand or silica sand. Some is ground to provide powdered quartz.

Quartz sand added to a clay or body acts as a grog. As a non-plastic material it opens a body and decreases the plasticity and shrinkage in the raw state. It gives visual texture and bite for workability especially for throwing. During firing it makes a body more refractory and during cooling increases a body's thermal contraction. Sand does not fuse but retains most of its crystalline structure in bodies thereby adding its high contraction rate to that of the body. See **Grain size** and **Glaze fit.**

Quartz sand is also used as a placing sand and as a source of silica in glass-making and frit manufacture.

Powdered quartz is used in glaze recipes. It is 100% silica (SiO_2) and therefore its addition to most recipes raises the glaze's melting point, increases the resistance to abrasion of the final glaze and improves its glassiness. See **Glass-former**.

Powdered quartz is occasionally added to stoneware and porcelain bodies to assist vitrification.

QUARTZ PHASE. Quartz is one of the four conformations, called phases, which silica can take. The four are quartz, cristobalite, tridymite and silica glass. They are alike

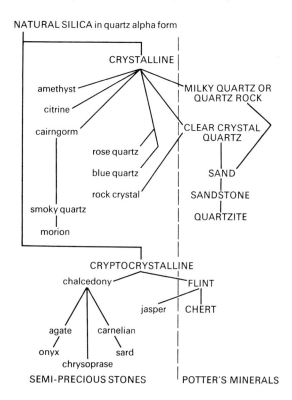

chemically but differ physically in their molecular structures.

Silica found as rock or sand is almost invariably of quartz phase. The other phases are extremely rare in nature and when required in ceramics are created by conversion from quartz phase.

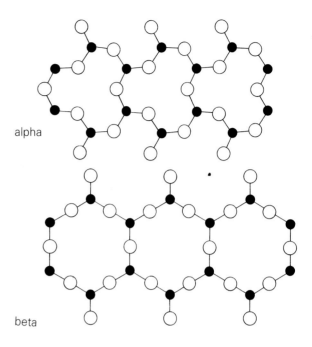

The quartz phase of silica occurs in crystalline form as quartz rock or milky quartz, quartz crystals or crystal quartz, quartzite, sand and sandstone. It also occurs as the semi-precious stones rose quartz, blue quartz, citrine, amethyst, cairngorm and rock crystal. There exists also a cryptocrystalline form of quartz in which the crystals are too small to be discernible under the normal optical microscope. Natural forms of cryptocrystalline quartz are flint, chert and the semi-precious stones jasper and chalcedony. The colours of the semi-precious stones are due to impurities such as iron, manganese, nickel and rutile.

The quartz phase of silica is subdivided into two forms known as alpha quartz and beta quartz. Alpha quartz exists only at temperatures below 573°C (1063°F) and beta quartz only above this temperature. The difference is in the angle of the silica-oxygen-silica bond which changes at 573°C.

This change occurs every time crystalline quartz passes this temperature in either direction. It is called a reversible change or silica inversion. There is a decrease in size from beta to alpha and this may cause cracks called dunts in pottery bodies. See **Silica** and **Dunting**.

Quartz which has become part of a molten glass or glaze is no longer crystalline and does not become crystalline on cooling. This fused quartz is not subject to inversion and would, strictly speaking, no longer be the phase called quartz but would be called by the overall name of silica or the specific name silica glass.

Quartzite

Pure silica rock used as a refractory in some salt-glaze kilns. The rock is composed of a quartz sand naturally cemented by silica. A sandstone which has undergone metamorphism is also called a quartzite but is not necessarily a refractory.

R

R

Chemical symbol, which is not used for any of the elements and therefore can be used to denote an unknown element in a chemical formula. For example, R_2O_3 where R could be Fe or Al.

It is usual for potters to use R but also available and sometimes used are D, G, M and X.

Raddle

Reddle. Ruddle. Haematite. A red ochre with a high iron oxide content. Fe_2O_3.

This ochre is associated with iron ores and iron stones which produce reddish powders when disintegrated and crushed. It was considered the blood of the mother earth by primitive peoples and used by them to decorate pottery and themselves.

Radiation

Transference of heat through space by energy waves from the heat source outwards in all unhindered directions. The heat is absorbed when the waves meet cooler obstacles. In the kiln, radiation takes place from all hot objects—kiln wall, pots, electric elements, muffle, saggar. It takes place in still air and evens out the heat distribution differences. In moving air, convection replaces radiation. The wavelengths involved in radiation are between a tenth and a thousandth of a centimetre.

Radical

A group of atoms which preserves its identity although it passes from one compound to another. For example, when the carbonate identity (CO_3) moves from barium carbonate ($BaCO_3$) to calcium carbonate ($CaCO_3$).

$$CaCl_2 + BaCO_3 \longrightarrow BaCl_2 + CaCO_3$$

Barium carbonate is added to clays at slip stage when such clays show unsightly finger marks on the fired, unglazed ware. The finger marks are caused by the crystallization of soluble salts on the surface, being broken by handling.

Rainbow effect

Extremely thin layers of the metals silver, bismuth, copper and tin on the surface of glazes may produce lustres with mother-of-pearl colouring. Some light usually passes through such a layer so that one sees the colour of the glaze and body beneath as well as the lustre. Light is reflected from both the top surface and the under surface of this metallic layer. Thus light reflected from the under surface travels a longer distance before reaching the eye. If this distance corresponds to a half wavelength of a particular colour the two sets of waves, one from the top and the other from the under surface, are travelling in opposition and cancel one another out so that the particular colour is not seen. The other colours of the spectrum are seen instead of white light. This phenomenon is called interference. Thus the slight variations of thickness of the thin metallic layer and the angle at which it is viewed present partial spectral effects. The metallic layer itself does not need to be coloured. The effect is like that of oil on water which is an extremely thin transparent film. See *Iridescence*.

Raku

Japanese word freely interpreted as 'enjoyment'. It was an ideograph engraved on a gold seal and given by the ruler Hideyoshi to Chojiro in 1598. Raku thereby became his family title. Chojiro is credited with being the first to produce, in 1580, a low-fired glazed pottery by a direct process which involved putting the pots into and taking them out of the red-hot kiln. See *Colour plates 70/71*.

The raku process gives the potter control of colourful expression when subjecting pots to oxidations and reductions during their cooling. The openness of the body and the soft nature of the glaze enable subtle variations of colour to be achieved. Originally only oxidation was used following neutral firings. Reduction was introduced in the mid-20th century by Paul Soldner in the USA. The use of the term raku is sometimes widened to include low temperature treatments involving reduction and smoke. See *Fuming*, *Smoking*, *Carbonization* and *Metallic salts*.

Popular modern raku is often recognized by a velvety black body contrasted with black-stained crackle of white, yellow, blue and turquoise glazes some with lustrous glints of reduced copper red. Glazes are often poured so that they overlap and integrate but leave areas of unglazed black body as important shapes in the composition.

The fact that the work is fragile is accepted as a small price to pay for the quality achieved. Also some of the effects of lustre created by an extremely thin layer of metal at the surface are only temporary. Bright lustres, especially copper, might last only months before tarnishing by oxidation. Polishing will temporarily restore the shine by rubbing away the surface layer but since the metallic layer is only 100 or so atoms thick the whole layer will eventually be removed. Some protection can be given to a lustre by a clear lacquer.

RAKU BODY. Almost every clay can be made to work as a raku body. Most will require the addition of approximately 40% of an opening material.

Red clay gives soft pink blushes through semi-transparent white glazes. Additions of china clay or ball clay to red clay can improve the quality of the pink. White clay, often a prepared body, is used to give brighter colours to underglaze and coloured glazes. A porcelain body which is intended for much higher temperatures remains highly porous at raku temperatures. It therefore absorbs carbon readily in post-firing reduction and smoking, turning from white to a dense smooth black on the unglazed parts. It can be used in a pure form or with additions of calcined china clay.

Coarse stoneware clays give visual and tactile texture. 'T' Material is popular because of its whiteness, working strength and fired strength. Crank bodies, white, buff and brown give colour and texture. They are invigorating to use and easy to fire. The opportunity should not be missed to experiment with local clays. This gives fuller involvement and individuality which are part of the raku ethic.

A simple light-coloured body might contain:

ball clay	67 (plastic state)
fireclay grog	33 (dry wt. 40's to 100's)

This is a basic recipe from which many more can be developed by subdividing and substituting within the clay and non-clay amounts.

A more complicated brown body might be:

plastic red earthenware clay	17
stoneware clay	13
fireclay	33
talc	3
sand	34

Additions which are made to raku bodies in order to improve the resistance to thermal shock do so in four ways:

1. Course materials open the body. (Fireclay, grog, sand, vermiculite, perlite.) See ***Opener*** and ***Thermal shock***.
2. Materials which burn out also open the body. (Sawdust, shredded nylon fibres, chopped straw.)
3. Materials of low thermal contraction decrease the overall contraction of the body proportionate to their inclusion. (Sillimanite, spodumene, petalite, talc.)

4. Materials of slow vitrification improve the sintering of the clay particles during the biscuit firing and thus improve the body's strength. (Feldspar, petalite, spodumene, wollastonite.) See ***Sinter***.

Fireclay and non-clay additions provide between 20% and 40% of the body. From its beginning with small teabowls, raku now includes very large sculptural works of at least 1 metre high, making these relatively inert bodies essential.

RAKU BISCUIT FIRING. A biscuit firing is necessary to enable the ware to be handled and to prepare it for the thermal shocks of the glaze firing. A popular temperature is 900°C (1652°F) but it depends upon the body, its refractoriness and the amount and type of volatiles which it contains. If the same body is tried as both a very soft and a hard biscuit it will be seen that the more delightful soft colourings occur on the softer ware. Porous bodies are susceptible to oxidation, reduction and smoking, and thus provide the opportunity to produce the most exciting colours. One must accept that porous bodies are easily broken. The biscuit firing cleans the body. See ***Firing: biscuit firing (burning out)***. From 700°C (1292°F) the unwanted elements carbon, sulfur and fluorine are liberated from a clay in gases. If these were liberated during a glaze firing they would discolour and bubble the glaze which is melting over the same temperature range.

RAKU COLOURINGS AND GLAZES. First, there is the colour of the body. Second, there are slip coatings. A white or light-coloured body gives brighter colours to the glaze. A dark-coloured body gives interesting variations with reduction. Both can be given washes of coloured slips which, because of the coarseness and softness of the body, appear to have a translucent quality. Slips are more effective when brushed on rather than dipped. They also adhere better when brushed because of the coarseness of the body. Third, there are pigments which are painted on the body before glazing or over the glaze before firing. They are metal oxides, carbonates etc, and are sometimes mixed with some glaze to encourage integration.

Fourth, there are the glazes themselves. The range of raku glazes is 750°C to 1000°C (1382°F to 1832°F). Raku glazes contain a larger proportion of flux than glazes for higher temperatures and therefore the effect upon the colour to be obtained from the popular oxides is more marked. The fluxes—lead oxide, boron oxide and sodium oxide—are the bases of the three main types of raku glaze: lead, leadless and alkaline, and give plenty of scope for exploiting the colour possibilities. Suggested starting points might be:

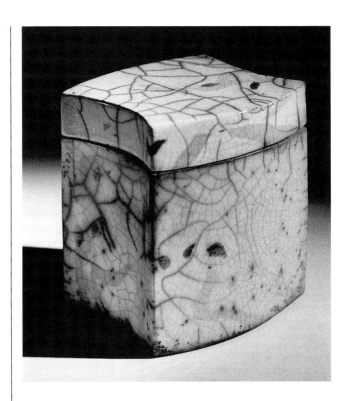

Oxide or other compound	Low sol [lead oxide]	Leadless [boron oxide]	Alkaline [sodium oxide]
Iron 2%–15%	yellow to brown to dark red	browns and greens	blues and blacks
Cobalt up to 1%	blue	blue	purple
Copper 0·5%–7%	green	green (reds and lustres in reduction)	turquoise
Manganese 5%–15%	purply brown	purply brown	mauve
Tin 5%–15%	——— milkiness to white opacity ——— (some lustre in reduction)		
Titanium 5%–15%	——— bluey milkiness to creams ———		
Other stains	——— all colours possible ———		

The traditional glaze given by Bernard Leach used 66% white lead. Lead glazes are attractive because of their soft yet brilliant shine and their deep generous-looking colours. They were popular because during the firing they melt and smooth out easily so that it is not difficult to see when the glaze has fused. This assumes a clean oxidized firing. Lead glazes cannot be successfully reduced during the firing although they give excellent post-firing reduction results.

To avoid the danger of using raw lead, glazes using low solubility lead frits have been developed. See **Lead frit**.

lead bisilicate	90·5
quartz	4
china clay	5·5

This glaze is almost a eutectic mixture and will melt before 700°C (1292°F). It can thus be used in a kiln which reaches only the dull red heat of 750°C (1382°F).

The low clay content of this glaze makes it very friable on the ware so that parts of the glaze are easily knocked off when a piece is being placed in the kiln. It is therefore necessary to add some binder to the glaze such as gum arabic or cellulose paste.

The concern over handling potential poison and producing toxic fumes during the firing has been responsible for the use of leadless glazes. From the raku point of view there are two types: borax frits and alkaline frits.

A borax frit can usually be substituted, weight for weight, for a lead frit in a glaze recipe. The leadless frit should be a soft one melting alone at around 850°C (1562°F). A typical recipe therefore is:

frit	94
china clay	5
bentonite	1

Alkaline glazes are leadless glazes which rely upon oxides of sodium, potassium and lithium as the main fluxes. These oxides brighten the colours, notably giving a turquoise with copper oxide. See **Alkaline glazes**.

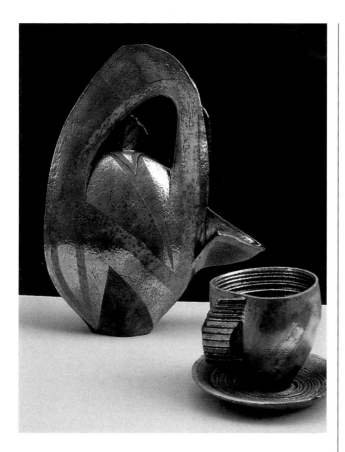

Alkaline raku glazes are essentially frit with suspender:

high-alkaline frit	96
bentonite	4

All low-clay raku glazes settle quickly in the glaze tub and require a liberal addition of calcium chloride. Alkaline frits settle and set hard without adequate suspension.

Alkaline glazes do not bite into the body to form a body-glaze layer and are therefore susceptible to flaking, crazing and chipping.

The photographs show a toucan by Jennie Hale, a box by Joan Doherty, David Jones removing a pot from a top-hat kiln operated by fork-lift, and a teaset by David Jones. See *Colour plates 33, 34* and *35* and *Recipe Appendix*.

RAKU GLAZE FIRING. The raku kiln is often seen as a symbol of experimental involvement with heat and ceramics. Raku has been described as a state of mind rather than a technique. The Zen philosophy of self discovery through contemplation, of allowing accidents to happen, is respected. But Western potters tend to throw much creative energy into designing and building new kilns and burners, mixing glazes and conferring about post-firing reduction materials. Spontaneity flourishes during the intense and heated period of withdrawing hot pots and reducing and cooling them. A philosophic attitude may be developed when assessing the results! The firing is planned for the glaze result and not for the body.

The kiln is often a temporary affair built out-of-doors and fired by charcoal, coke, coal, wood, oil or gas, although small electric kilns can be used. Long flame wood, oil or gas can be used in kilns with through flames reaching the wares. Oil and propane are popular because they are more easily portable to temporary sites. Solid fuels like charcoal and coke which use direct contact for heat transference are used around a muffle which contains the ware. The excellent insulation properties of fibre, preferably the noncarcinogenic or 'body-soluble' type make possible custom-built kilns to suit the fuel supply and situation. These are easily portable to raku event sites. Fibre is used to line a supporting casing which may be a wire mesh frame, shaped like a large 'tea cosy' to be lifted over the pots, or shaped to form a cylindrical top-loader. Alternatively, a metal dustbin or a large oil drum can be lined. The firing is so fast that it is often feasible to fire single pots consecutively. As kilns get lighter, so the ceramic work gets bigger. A 'top hat' fibre kiln or lined oil drum type may be lifted free of the work, or dismantled, in order to move a large piece to a pit for reduction.

The ware is either previously biscuited or biscuited in the raku firing during its warming-up period. In the latter case the pieces are taken out hot by means of long tongs. When cool they are glazed, decorated, dried thoroughly and replaced in the red-hot kiln with the long tongs.

There is usually some heat loss at this point and the kiln is further baited to raise the temperature. The range used is between 750°C and 1000°C (1382°F and 1832°F). In a short time the glazes have melted and the red-hot pots, now shining with melted glaze, are withdrawn with the long tongs. During the next few minutes as each piece of work cools it can be subjected to oxidation, to varying degrees and types of reduction and to differing rates of cooling, all of which bring their own particular effects to the various parts of the piece.

RAKU POST FIRING. Making raku is one of the few areas where the cooling cycle is manipulated to create effects as an essential part of the total firing process. The techniques involve controlled, probably quick, cooling, and reduction of body and glaze before the glaze has fully set.

In the original Japanese method, the pot was withdrawn and held in the air to allow the glaze to smooth out. In the making of the higher-fired black-glazed 'Kuro' ware, the pot was dunked in water to achieve the black colour from the iron oxide which in a slower cooling would have produced a reddish brown. Quenching in water to produce large crackle, or sprinkling with water to make partially crackled areas, is now used by many makers.

The other ways of creating reduction effects have become very popular. As soon as the glaze has smoothed and begun to dim, the pot is immersed in combustible material such as sawdust, chippings, wet straw, grass and leaves, finally being dunked in water to seal the effect. There is a degree of unpredictability in the colouring effects which is a large part of the fascination. Very large pieces can be smoke reduced in the kiln, or transferred for reduction to a pit, dug in the ground and lined with corrugated cardboard.

Metallic lustre effects have become one of the most characteristic features of raku. This can be encouraged firstly by using an alkaline type glaze and secondly by using very heavy reduction. In addition to this, metal salts can be added to the base glaze. These salts are soluble in the glaze slop and so tend to migrate to the surface, leaving a film of metal to be reduced. Some reduction during the firing will help to promote the formation of this film. Silver nitrate is used for yellow/gold effects, and bismuth subnitrate for mother of pearl. Lustre colours are obtained from potassium bichromate (green), copper sulfate or copper chloride (turquoise), tin chloride (attenuator), gold chloride (pink), and iron chloride (ochre). These chemicals are poisonous and must be treated with great care. They also release toxic fumes in the firing which must be ventilated effectively. See **Poison** and **Health hazard**.

Lead glazes can be used but any reduction in the up-firing may lead to a dull bloom and muddying of the lustre.

If the ware is left to cool sufficiently in the reduction material, the smoking deposits carbon in the body giving a velvety black which contrasts well with the colours and lustres.

Ramekin

Ramequin. An 18th-century French cheesecake. Also the small mould in which it was baked. Hence in modern potter's usage, a ramekin is any small deep bowl, often with a single side-handle, and often with a lid, used for both baking and serving individual portions. The one illustrated is from the Leach pottery.

Random structure

Random network. The three-dimensional placing of fixed points on which atoms or molecules are positioned in relation to one another. The random network does not follow a regular pattern but it must keep within a number of possibilities. Amorphous solids, and this includes glazes, are random structures. Glaze structures are usually imagined to be in chains, some of whose links are joined to other chains. The diagram shows this chain idea related to a structure.

Regular structures, which are also called lattices, give crystals. The difference between the random and the regular structures explains why a glaze and other amorphous substances have melting ranges whereas crystalline substances have melting points. The random chain breaks down slowly because some links are weaker than others. In the crystal the links (bonds) are equally strong throughout the substance, or more usually, there are a number of types of bond spread regularly throughout the substance. Each type has its own detachment temperature which results in a sudden collapse of the substance when one type of structure gives way throughout the substance. See also **Network structure.**

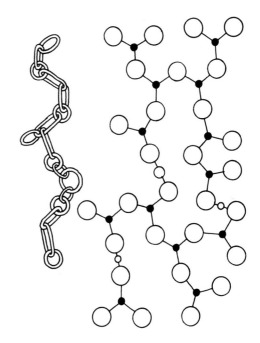

Range

The variation of temperature/time that a clay or glaze can withstand without being over or underfired.

Rankine

°R. Degrees Rankine are Fahrenheit measurements of temperature starting at 'absolute zero'. Therefore 0°R equals –460°F and the freezing and boiling points of water are 492°R and 672°R, respectively. See also **Kelvin**.

Rare earths

Rare earth elements called lanthanoids. A group of fifteen rare metallic elements with properties resembling aluminium. So far only cerium and praseodymium have been used by individual potters although about six have commerical pottery value.

Ratio

The relationship between quantities expressed in the same form of measurement. For example, 6 grams and 2 grams are in the ratio of 6:2 or 3:1. Glaze ratio is a phrase used to describe the proportional amounts in the glaze of the alkaline, amphoteric and acidic compounds expressed in relative numbers of molecules. Glaze ratio has a direct relationship to melting temperature. See **Formula: unity (in use)**.

Raw

Uncooked, unfired, in original state. The term is loosely used to describe materials and processes, and can lead to confusion, especially with glazes and glaze materials. A number of definitions follow.

RAW CLAY. Clay as dug before it is processed by crushing or removal of stones. The phrase has been used by some potters to mean clay which has not been fired but the word clay alone implies this since when fired it is no longer clay.

RAW GLAZE (*Noun*). A glaze compounded of materials that have not been previously fritted. The exception is wood ash which if considered strictly would be called a frit but which is always considered a raw material. The opposite of a raw glaze is a fritted glaze or one containing frits.

Raw glazes for stoneware are not difficult to compound because whiting, dolomite and wood ashes provide cheap fluxes. Below 1100°C (2012°F) the only cheap fluxes available are lead, sodium and boron compounds. Lead has the disadvantage of being poisonous. Sodium and boron compounds need to be fritted because they are soluble in water. Raw glazes receive attention by potters because of three factors:

1. They use more readily available materials which require little preparation.
2. They are cheaper than glazes for which prepared frits are purchased.
3. In pioneering pottery away from commerical supplies of

frits, the preparation of one's own frits in sufficient quantity can be very irksome. The pioneering spirit remains with many potters even within reach of a supply of frits so that there is some pride in scorning the prepared frit and using raw materials which potters feel are nearer to a native or indigenous way of working.

RAW GLAZING. RAW GLAZE. (*Verb*). In contrast to the above, this is the action of glazing raw—that is, on raw ware. This may be with a raw glaze but it could equally be done with a fritted glaze. The reasons which lead a potter to use a raw glaze, namely directness of approach and cheapness, also often lead to glazing wares at raw stage, thus cutting out the extra firing to biscuit. The glaze and clay mature together, and since they start together, full integration of clay, slips and glazes for decorative effects is possible.

Raw glazing can be done on the dry ware, in which case the glaze is often one containing frits, other non-clay minerals and less than 10% clay. Bentonite often replaces clay in those glazes. It overcomes the friable and flaky natures of fritted glazes low in clay, sticks the glaze to the ware yet allows rapid drying. It presents fewer side effects than the use of glues. See **Bentonite**. The glazing techniques are very similar to those used with biscuit. One advantage is that dry clay ware has a less variable porosity than biscuit ware from an uneven kiln and thus glaze thickness can be more accurately controlled.

Raw glazing can also be done at all other stages from soft through cheesehard to black-hard. Each has its own advantages in directness of approach or control of thickness. Glazes for these stages usually contain a high proportion of clay, 30% to 100%, and are thus vitrified or melted slips. They are often called slip glazes or, in the cases where a fusible clay is used alone, clay glazes. They are applied to the pots as are slips by pouring, dipping and brushing and can thus be directly integrated with other slips and the body clay. Sgraffito through the slip glaze into the body is possible with very rich results as in the 11th- to 13th-century northern Chinese wares.

In the first photograph the potter is raw glazing a sprig decorated jar at the Red Star Factory, Yixing, China. She walks backwards round the pot as she directs the glaze onto the upper edge and runs a finger on the rim to prevent the glaze from running inside.

In the second photograph, Peter Wills is brushing glaze onto a dry bowl. The bowl is inverted on a plastic container centred on the wheel and is held steady by a finger on a plastic bottle cap on the foot.

Besides the approach to working, the high proportion of clay in these glazes gives a characteristic matt surface not easily obtained by other means, but slip glazes must be applied at exactly the right stage. This can be a disadvantage. A batch of pots must be brought to this stage together for economical glazing as a group. If they are glazed when too wet or too dry, the glaze may be too thin, too thick, may not adhere and thus crawl in firing, or even flake off before firing. Or the pot itself may crack. Glazes for dry ware give one a longer time in which the pots can be waiting but if the glazing is done too soon and the pots are not absolutely dry the glaze may well flake away.

General disadvantages of raw glazing are that for ware fired below 1100°C (2012°F) the glaze may melt so soon as to seal off the escape of gases from the clay. This would result in bubbled glazes and with clays nearing vitrification, bloating can also occur. The bubbling of glaze can often be overcome by slower firings and slight glaze modification. Quick firings in the early stages can also result in pieces exploding with steam build-up. Such explosions tend to send fragments into far too many pots where they stick because the ware is glazed. Explosions rarely happen to the work of the experienced potter but are frequent enough with students' work to make raw glazing hazardous in schools and colleges.

There has been some misunderstanding of the advantages and disadvantages of raw glazing. It should be remembered that in Europe a biscuit or bisc stage has been used for less than 300 years and is still not used by every potter. If one considers the reasons for introducing biscuiting, raw glazing is seen in more correct perspective.

RAW LEAD. Lead compounds—galena, litharge, white lead and red lead. See **Lead oxide**.

RAW MATERIALS. Any materials which the potter uses. The name implies that they have not yet been processed. Although, strictly speaking, raw materials should only include clay minerals such as flint and feldspar the term may be extended to cover wood ashes and grogs. The latter two have already been subjected to heat. The potter may even include lead silicates or other frits etc. The fact that feldspar, cornish stone and quartz were formed by heat is always ignored since they are won as raw minerals.

RAW WARE. Pottery etc before it is fired.

Reaction

The effect two or more substances have on one another producing a change in the substances. For example, the combination of wood ash and clay to produce a glass at high temperatures. See also **Interaction**.

Reactive slip

A fusible slip, often containing rutile, which creates a mottled effect as it erupts through a covering glaze. The slip's fusion range is different from the glaze's. The effect varies according to thickness and the temperatures of fusion, and the result is sometimes large in texture like a **Lizard skin** glaze.

Readsorption

The intake of water from the air by the empty pores of dry clay.

Clay pores are filled with water when clay is in plastic state. Most of these pores drain during drying but the smallest pores retain their water by capillary tension. The size of pore which is able to retain its water is determined by the humidity of the air and the atmospheric pressure. The amount of water in air-dried clay therefore varies from day to day.

Not only do the pores dry out to this determined point but also those pores which were empty fill up to this point by taking water from the air. This is readsorption.

Clays can withstand these daily adjustments of water content without ill effect. However, if clay is dried thoroughly and then allowed to readsorb moisture a slight expansion takes place which causes cracks with some clays in certain sections.

The clays most prone to readsorption cracking are prepared bodies which contain a large proportion of non-clay material. These have insufficient strength at this stage to withstand the tension exerted by the expansion.

The pot section which is vulnerable to readsorption cracking is the slowly tapered rim. The greatest expansion takes place where readsorption from both sides can meet. This is around the rim and thus the clay next to it in the pot is pulled into tension. If the clay is weak it may crack but the crack will be unseen until after the firing. In fact such a crack is difficult to see in biscuit but shows as a fine line of thicker glaze immediately after dipping. It usually opens more during the glaze firing to reveal a crack about 1 cm in length at right angles to the rim.

Therefore if pots are dried on a kiln top they should be fired while they are still warm rather than after allowing them to cool completely, especially if conditions are humid.

The readsorption of moisture is in two stages. The first moisture to be readsorbed is attracted electrically to the clay particles. There is always a layer of water around each clay particle but its thickness varies from one to four molecules according to prevalent humidity. This variation accounts for the slight expansion on readsorption. The layer is known as the bound layer and is not completely removed by drying but is removed at red heat when the clay becomes pot. See *Ceramic change*.

In itself this layer accounts for the smaller part of the readsorbed moisture but it encourages the second stage of readsorption, which is the filling of the pores between the particles. Here pore water reforms by a process called capillary condensation. The surface tension of the water within such a small space is able to condense the water from the vapour in the air, not chemically as in the case of the water around the clay particles, but physically by tension.

The word should not be confused with reabsorption which is the capillary action of dry clay taking up liquid water as opposed to water vapour. Reabsorption is called soaking by potters but there is no simple potter's word for readsorption.

Recent

Geologically, the last period extending to the present day. It is part of the Quarternary or Pleistocene period which is the last million years, and recent deposits are unsatisfactorily defined as those containing remains of flora and fauna still existing in the locality. To the potter, recent deposits are those he can see still being built. River and sea sands and the clays and muds of river and estuary are recent as opposed to deposits like the clay beds of glacial origin.

Reclamation

Reclaiming clay from turnings, broken unfired pots etc is easily done with most clays by softening the dry clay in water and drying out the resulting slops on plaster or absorbent boards, with the possible aid of powdered clay or grog. This latter process is called dewatering.

Some very plastic clays are so fine that without an opener they resist the softening action of water by forming a waterproof skin. This happens especially with leatherhard clay. In such cases it is necessary to thoroughly dry the clay first. After this it can be more easily slaked. If the clay is exceedingly fine and of the highly plastic type, such as pure ball clay, it will be necessary either to dry it and repowder it before wetting or else bring it to a slip by blunging.

Some clays, if reclaimed immediately after throwing, appear to have become tired and less plastic. A resting period of a few days puts this right. Casting slips which have been allowed to dry should not be reclaimed because of the deflocculant balance.

Porcelain bodies, and some fine stoneware bodies, because of the regular size of their particles, need the pressure of de-airing to restore them. Without this air pockets accumulate and cause a premature bloating effect in the firing.

Red

Red and orange are colours of wide interpretation in pottery. The rust reds and orange colours are called red in reference to clays. See *Red clay*. The colouring is from red iron oxide which is the only practical deep stain for bodies.

For glazes there is a wider choice of red and orange stains. Iron oxide gives orange and reds at low temperatures in lead glazes. A bright colour requires complete oxidation. Accidental reduction, however slight, dulls the hue. Iron oxide also gives good rust colours at stoneware temperatures. See *Rust, Iron oxide* and *Colour plate 67*.

Chromium oxide gives reds in lead silicates and the combination is useful for producing pools of red glass on ceramic tiles. See *Chromium oxide: chrome red, and orange*. There is also the crimson pink colour which results from the chromium oxide-tin oxide combination. See *Chromium oxide: chrome-tin pink*.

Bright red (*sang-de-boeuf*) glazes are obtained at temperatures above 1100°C (2012°F) by staining with copper oxide. The copper oxide is reduced during the firing to the colloidal copper state. See *Copper oxide: in reduction* and *Colour plates 1, 2, 3, 4, 15* and *82*.

The brightest reds and oranges are dependent upon special conditions. The use of prepared stains helps to stabilize fugitive colours. Uranium oxide and lead silicate combinations have now been replaced by cadmium selenide stains. These require precise use to achieve brilliant colours and are mostly used in prepared onglaze colours although stained glazes are also available. See **Cadmium** and **Selenium**.

Red clay
Red earthenware clay. The potter's name for brown clay. When fired to about 1000°C (1832°F) these clays burn to a deep orange colour, sometimes called flowerpot red. The red colour is due to 5% to 8% of red iron oxide (Fe_2O_3) which is often heightened in its brightness as a red by the natural presence of some titanium oxide (TiO_2). The titanium oxide may only be a trace amount below 1% but it has an effect upon the iron oxide during firing. Red clays vitrify below 1200°C (2192°F).

Some of these clays are quite a bright orange when dug, some are a deep rich brown, while others are a dull brown. The blackish clays which also burn to a similar red, are more often called grey clays and terracotta clays. The yellow clays which burn to red are referred to as ochres. Some red clays, and notably the English Staffordshire red clay from around Stoke-on-Trent, are sometimes erroneously called marls. A true marl is a pink-burning clay in which calcium oxide has a bleaching effect upon the iron content.

Red clays are usually highly plastic clays. They have been finely ground and sorted into pockets of extremely fine clays by being deposited, removed and redeposited over the last few million years. The youngest deposits of less than a million years of age are probably redeposits of previous deposits dating back 500 million years or more. The same process that ground the clays to fine state was often responsible for the addition of impurities of which the important ones are iron oxide and free silica. The free silica is sometimes in the form of quartz sand of large enough grain to be seen with the naked eye. This provides an excellent 'bite' to the clay for use on the potter's wheel.

The qualities of high plasticity, rich colour and workability endear this clay to potters today as they have to potters in the past. It is an ideal clay for fast throwing of plant pots; for providing the body for slip decorated ware, for modelling figures of the larger type like portrait busts and for making teapots. It is usually biscuit fired at around 950°C (1742°F) and glaze fired at around 1080°C (1976°F).

Red clays are ideal for blending with other clays. They possess sufficient character in colour and plasticity to assist poorer clays to become blends with excellent workability.

Red copper oxide
Copper monoxide. Cu_2O. See **Reduction**.

Red-figure ware
The peak of Classical Greek pottery; it was decorated with red-brown figures on a black background. The red colour was a fine slip on the red body over which were painted the black background and the details on the figures. See **Attic pottery**.

Red heat
The temperature at which the pots in a kiln are seen to be glowing red hot. 700°C to 750°C (1292°F to 1382°F). See also **Incandescence**.

This phrase is usually used when the kiln is cooling. When the temperature of the pottery has dropped to red heat it is a sign that the crucial temperature of dunting is approaching and holes which would allow draughts into the kiln are sealed. It is also the temperature at which lead glazes begin to set. Above this temperature it was the practice amongst many slipware potters to allow clean air to enter the kiln through the raked-out firebox to brighten the shine of the glaze. Most stoneware potters clam up the kiln earlier than this in the 1000°C to 900°C (1832°F to 1652°F) range—clear red heat.

Red lead
Red lead oxide. Minium. Triplumbic tetraoxide. Pb_3O_4. See **Lead oxide**.

Red ochre
Raddle. Reddle. Fe_2O_3. The soft earthy variety of iron ore. It often contains some clay substance. See **Haematite**. Calcined yellow ochre is also sold as red ochre.

Redox
Portmanteau word for reduction and oxidation. It is used as an adjective to describe situations which involve reduction and oxidation or to describe compounds which act as agents in these situations.

Reduction
The action of taking oxygen away from metal oxides. The potter uses reduction to coax different effects from the same metal oxide in the clay or glaze, e.g. black pots from a red clay, or a metallic lustre from a white tin glaze. This is achieved by controlling the atmosphere surrounding the pots during the firing and/or cooling. Altering the atmosphere alters the metal oxide used for the colouring. Reduction is used during porcelain firing to assist the integration of body and glaze, and to counteract any tendency towards a cream colour in body or glaze caused by iron oxide.

Reduction of stoneware firings affects the iron oxide in the body making this an effective flux. Thus, integration of body and glaze involves colour also, so that colour from the body burns into and smooths the glaze in a decorative unifying way. A small amount of reduced iron oxide in a glaze gives the colouring called celadon. See **Iron oxide: in glazes** and **Celadon**.

Copper oxide gives a startling colour change when reduced. The oxidized copper oxide gives a green colour and the reduced copper oxide gives a red colour in glazes. See **Copper oxide: in reduction** and **Colour plates 1 to 4, 69** and **82**. It is also possible to completely deprive the copper of its oxygen to create a layer of metal on the glaze surface. Tin, silver, platinum, gold and bismuth are other practical metals for lustres. See **Lustres**.

Raku colourings often involve reduction. Here the reducing atmosphere is localized by the proximity of sawdust etc but the phenomenon is scientifically the same as when a kiln full of ceramic birds is reduced.

REDUCING ATMOSPHERE. The atmosphere inside a kiln either contains oxygen which, it can give to the metal oxides, or else is lacking in oxygen and takes some from the metal oxides. These are called, respectively, oxidizing and reducing atmospheres. A kiln atmosphere often fluctuates between oxidizing and reducing, and is called neutral. Sealed muffles and saggars tend to have neutral atmospheres. To achieve reduction, carbon is introduced into the kiln atmosphere. This carbon, if hot enough, will combine with the oxygen in the atmosphere to form carbon dioxide. When nearly all the oxygen is used up, carbon monoxide is formed and to reform carbon dioxide this takes oxygen from the metal oxides.

Electric and gas muffles are reduced by the introduction of gas, wood or other burnables at the correct time and temperature. See also **Silicon carbide**. Open set kilns are reduced by restricting the flow of secondary air into the combustion chamber. Solid fuels, fuel-oil and gas are thus only partially converted to carbon dioxide.

Smoke appears when there is incomplete combustion due to insufficient oxygen, but merely producing smoke does not guarantee reduction. To effect a change within the clay and the glaze the carbon must be in a finely divided form and hot enough to form a gas with the oxygen. It is necessary to form carbon monoxide gas which is hungry for oxygen. A reducing kiln may be producing only a wisp of smoke at the chimney. The necessary reducing atmosphere is maintained inside the chamber by control of the pressure by the damper, by 'spoiling' the draw of the chimney, or by limiting the intake of secondary air.

A heavily reducing atmosphere will cause the temperature in the chamber to drop since less energy is being produced by the inefficient burning. To achieve a temperature rise with sufficient reduction is a fine balance

and may require the use of a digital pyrometer. A faster temperature rise needs more fuel with an adjustment of more air, making reduction firing more expensive than oxidized firing. During the actual firing the degree of reduction is judged by a slower rate of temperature climb, flame colour from the chimney and spyholes, and pressure in the chamber. Black smoke pouring from chimney and from cracks in the structure indicates early restriction of oxygen. Leaking carbon monoxide gas is highly poisonous and must be avoided. See **Carbon monoxide**.

THE ORDER OF REDUCTION. Some oxides are held together by weaker bonds than others. There is an approximate order in which the metal oxides are willing to part with their oxygen atoms when subjected to reduction.

A slight reduction affects antimony oxide but it does not improve its colour. Antimony oxide is kept for oxidized glazes. Slight reduction next affects tin oxide. If the glaze has not melted the eventual glaze will be reduced to grey. If the glaze has already melted, only the surface is affected giving an iridescence on a white glaze. Thus tin oxide is suitable for reduction effects produced during cooling as with raku.

As reduction becomes heavier it affects the oxides of lead, bismuth, copper, zinc, nickel, cobalt, iron and manganese, and lead silicate in that order.

Where lead oxide is required as a flux, it appears that bismuth and copper oxides cannot be reduced without affecting the lead oxide detrimentally. Fortunately lead oxide quickly reoxidizes and once involved in a silicate its position in the above list is at the end. Thus bismuth and copper oxides can be reduced in a lead glaze. Like tin oxide they can be reduced below 700°C (1292°F) a phenomenon made use of in raku.

Zinc, nickel, cobalt and manganese oxides are difficult to maintain in reduced state. Zinc oxide is lost by volatilization if it is reduced. See **Zinc oxide: flux**. Iron oxide has a stable state as reduced iron oxide (FeO) and can be reduced above 700°C (1292°F). See **Iron oxide: black**.

To reduce the oxides of aluminium, vanadium, titanium, cerium, barium, magnesium, chromium, calcium, sodium, potassium and silicon requires a very strong reduction beyond the capacity of pottery kilns. Their use in pottery is in fully oxidized state whether this is from a reduced or an oxidized firing.

Refine

Usually refers to the processing of clays whereby unrequired materials, called impurities, are removed. Methods include dry and wet sieving, elutriation, levigation, settling and the use of magnets.

Refractive index

The number which indicates the ratio of the velocities of light outside and inside a material. As light enters a glaze its speed is reduced. The light rays therefore bend (are refracted) at the point of entry. The refractive indices of silicates used as frits and glazes lie between 1·4 and 1·8. Opacifiers have indices between 2·0 and 2·4. As light meets an opacifier it is therefore bent further or reflected from the surface. Both effects scatter the light. Opacifiers are not part of the general silicate structure but are isolated nuclei and particles which affect the light separately. See also ***Colloid: glaze***.

Refractory

Resistant to high temperatures. The potter uses refractory materials for building a kiln. The materials therefore have to withstand not only high temperatures but constantly changing temperatures, uneven temperatures in close proximity and various gases. Industrially, refractory may mean temperatures of $1700°C$ ($3092°F$) but the individual potter would count clays and other materials as refractory if they withstood $1300°C$ ($2372°F$) without deformation.

Fireclay is used for blending with clay to make the mixture coarser, or to withstand higher temperature or thermal shock. It was the potter's original refractory and is still very useful for making special expendable pieces of kiln furniture and for kiln patching and stopping. China clay is also a useful refractory for patching etc. Manufactured kiln shelves and furniture are made from sillimanite, aluminium oxide, zirconium silicate and silicon carbide. Each has its own advantages dependent upon the order of preference one puts on their properties, e.g. initial cost, strength, weight, purity when considering staining of ware, reaction to kiln gases such as reduction atmosphere or salt vapour.

Refractory cement, which with suitable aggregates makes refractory concrete, provides an easy way of casting awkwardly shaped kiln arches, flues etc, which cannot be made from standard bricks. Refractory cement is built around aluminium oxide and silica, whereas the usual cement is a combination of calcium oxide and silica. Aluminium oxide and silica have melting points above $1700°C$ ($3092°F$) and do not overflux one another or easily break down upon attack.

New materials developed for use in spacecraft and jet engines include ceramic fibre which is used for kiln insulation. It extends the range of insulation materials in the high temperature category and has the advantage of being lightweight. See ***Insulation***.

Refractory is also used as a comparative adjective for clays and glaze materials.

REFRACTORY COATING. A layer of refractory material used to insulate or to isolate a kiln wall from the effects of gases, or kiln shelving from the fluxing of bodies and glazes. It is usually administered as a thin slurry painted on the surface and called flint wash, zircon wash, aluminium oxide wash, bat wash etc. The choice of refractory depends upon the type of protection required.

Relative atomic mass

r.a.m. See ***Atomic weight***.

Relative density

r.d. (previously called specific gravity). Relative density is expressed as a number for each material. For example, the r.d. of china clay is 2·5. Specifically, this represents the weight of a chosen volume of the material at $20°C$ divided by the weight of the same volume of water at $4°C$. Since 1 ml (cc) of water weighs 1 gram the r.d. is the same as the weight in grams of 1 cc of the material. See also ***Formula: density***.

For potters, r.d. represents how much heavier a material is than water. China clay, r.d. 2·5, is two-and-a-half times as heavy as water. It therefore sinks in water. Black cobalt oxide, r.d. 6, sinks rapidly.

A dry slip, engobe or glaze can be given a relative density calculated from the r.d. of the individual recipe materials proportioned as the recipe. For general purposes these average as r.d. 2·5 for slips and leadless glazes, r.d. 3 for low sol glazes, and r.d. 4 for glazes containing 80% of lead bisilicate. See also ***Calculations: percentage to batch recipe*** and ***Slop weight***.

Relative formula

Another name for Unity formula.

Relative molecular mass

See ***Molecular weight***.

Relief decoration

A relief is achieved by modelling the surface of the clay, by adding pieces of clay (sprigging), by pushing the clay out from the other side (repoussé), and by using relief moulds. One photograph is of part of an 18th-century mould for a dish in which the decoration shows as raised lines between which areas of slip were painted. See also **Applied decoration** and **Sprigging**. The other photograph is of an 18th-century Chinese wall panel in coloured glazed earthenware. See also **Resist**.

Repetition throwing

The act of throwing repeat items on the potter's wheel. It is essentially a production method but has excellent value for all students. While much depends upon the judgement of the eye for the silhouette and size of the rim, a great deal of judgement remains with the feel of the pot in the hands. This skill requires much practice with concentration upon what effect each pressure and movement is achieving. A good thrower realizes the necessity for each movement made and naturally comes to an economical use of energy. This, rather than hurried movements, gives speed. The thrower uses lumps of prepared clay of the same weight to assist accuracy. This and the rhythmic use of economical movements gives repeat items. As a further check a thrower often has a pointer, which is a stick with or without a rubber flexible tip or feather end, to define where the rim should come. There may also be other simple measuring sticks handy.

When the judgements by hand movements and sight are keen, then use can be made of repetition throwing on a stem, also called off the hump. For this, a large piece of clay is put on the wheel and centred by patting into a cone. Then, by judgement, sufficient clay is centred at the top of the cone of clay and is thrown in the normal way. A necessity is the positive compressing of the base of the pot in a combined centring and opening process. Without this compression the clay in the base of the pot does not match the clay in the rest of the pot and subsequently cracks. See **Crack: H**.

A measuring stick or callipers may be used as a check on size, but movements and the eye are usually sufficient. Trimming by rib or other tool includes making a notch at the point where the pot is to be cut off. The cutting-off wire is placed or allowed to run in this notch for cutting off. The use of a twisted wire helps the two parts, pot and clay lump, to separate more easily and so does a peeling action when lifting the pot. It is difficult to cut a very thin base and most potters use some later turning. The clay lump is rarely used to the last bit but until its size is no longer convenient.

Repetition throwers were paid by the number of pots thrown. In some of the traditional rural potteries, especially those making plant pots, interesting methods of making calculations have been used. Payment was by the weight of clay thrown calculated as so many casts, cakes, lumps, slugs or pieces. These were the particular size of clay convenient for handling in the store and from the pug and varied from 20 lbs to 50 lbs. Other payment was by the board, which was the plank upon which the pots were arranged in definite numbers according to size. Plant pots were often known by numbers such as 12s, 48s, 60s, which referred to the number of pots coming from one lump or cast of clay. It is interesting to note that the small plant pots were sold by the 'yard' when stacked together in the store shed.

The use of an assistant, called a passer, greatly speeds up the output. The passer prepares and weighs the clay and lifts the pots from the wheel. The disadvantage in using a passer is that speed becomes more important than pot. Passing for oneself enables a continuous critical appraisal of each pot to be made as it is lifted from the wheel.

For anyone learning to throw, whether intending to do repetition work or not, the skill of the repetition thrower is worth consideration and can be analysed under three points.

1. Use of thoroughly prepared clay weighed out to exactly the same weight. This means that mistakes on one piece can be corrected on the next and achievements are more easily consolidated.

2. Consideration of every movement the hands are making. Think of what they are achieving in terms of moving the clay. Repeat successful movements until they can be strung together in a rhythm.

3. Thinking positively towards creating a good pot with as little as possible thinking in terms of rescuing a bad pot. Getting rid of a bad pot and starting another good pot is quicker in the long run for both satisfactory production and learning.

Residual clay

Primary clay. Clay which is found in its place of origin. China clay, bentonite and a few fireclays can be called residual clays. All other clays have been removed and deposited elsewhere and are called secondary or sedimentary clays. See **Clay: origin**.

Resist

The action whereby area decoration as pigment, slip, glaze or carbon is prevented from colouring selected parts of the ceramic piece.

The simplest resist is newspaper cut or torn to shape and attached to the pot at leatherhard or earlier stage by slip or wetting with a sponge. Subsequent dips or brushings of coloured slips therefore cannot adhere to the part protected by the paper. As the slip begins to dry the newspaper comes loose and can be peeled away. A variation is to treat the resist as a stencil using only part of it to protect earlier decoration from sponging, spraying or the addition of very soft clay applied with the fingers.

The first four photographs are of paper resist: a stoneware plate by Janet Hamer using cut paper shapes to resist sponged slips under the glaze; a slipware dish by Josie Walter showing torn paper resist; a 'wave and gargoyle' by Annie

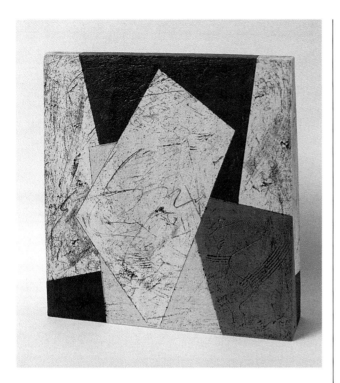

Horner where torn strong paper (wallpaper) was temporarily attached to the biscuited piece with latex glue, coloured glaze was sprayed onto the bowl and the resist and latex removed before the final glaze was sprayed overall; and a slabbed form by Bernard Irwin which involves the use of layers of resist decoration with sgraffito.

Wax is used to resist a glaze, e.g. on a foot rim, or to resist a second dip of glaze or a colouring brushed onto an unfired glaze surface. The area to be reserved is dipped in wax or has wax brushed on to it. The colour or glaze, being mixed with water, cannot adhere to the wax.

Hot wax is made from approximately equal parts of paraffin wax (candle wax) and paraffin oil (kerosene), sometimes with thin machine oil. The wax and oil are melted together in a tin over a low gas flame or electric ring remembering that it is an inflammable mixture. If it catches fire, smother the flame with a fireproof board and turn off the heat.

Cold wax emulsions are marketed by potters' merchants. These are like the wax/water emulsions used in canvas waterproofing for tents. The water dries out leaving the wax as a resist or water repellent. There is no need to remove the hot or cold waxes since they burn out completely in the firing. The photograph is of a planter by Frank Hamer using brushed hot wax resisting a dipped glaze to contrast toasted unglazed body with white glaze.

Liquid rubber or latex resist works well on unfired glaze, resisting a covering colour or glaze. Its additional advantage is that it can be peeled away before firing allowing further decoration in the resisted shape. The press-moulded stoneware dish by Archie McCall uses brushed-on latex to resist a black glaze over white glaze, with oxides and gold lustre used in the resisted areas.

Where colours are being applied over an already fired glaze a water-soluble resist is used. This can be gum, dextrin or a water paint. The surface must be cleaned of grease by wiping over with whiting. The resist is applied and dried before the oil-based pigments are applied by groundlay, spraygun or brush. Colour which remains over the resist and the water-soluble resist are washed away but the oil colour remains intact.

Paper, wax, latex and soluble resists most naturally give hard-edge definition to the colour contrast. This hard-edge style can be exploited and enhanced by the use of angular or pointed shapes. If a softening of the edge is required this can be done by coarse brushing of the colour in a 'dry brush' technique which allows some background to show through the brushed colour, or by the use of colours which bleed in the glaze. A very delicate soft edge can be achieved if newspaper is torn rather than cut, and the slip it is resisting is used thinly. With wax resists, if the wax can be used thinly or the glaze can be thick, it is possible to get specks of the resisted pigment or glaze adhering over the wax. These specks eventually fuse onto the underneath surface especially with glazes and give a delightful speckled effect which successfully breaks the otherwise harsh contrast. See **Paper resist** and **Wax resist**.

The pedestal jug by Sasha Wardell shows a resist effect on

slip-cast bone china. The jug was partly painted with acrylic medium on the dry clay. The non-water-soluble medium resisted the erosion of stroking with a damp sponge giving high points to the relief decoration. Shellac knotting, nail varnish and other quick-drying but non-water-soluble

paints will work with this technique. The paint burns away in the biscuit firing.

In smoking and raku, a popular development with many variations uses clay and glaze as resists sometimes involving paper and wax also. Ashraf Hanna puts slip onto biscuit and scratches through this layer to expose the body. The dried work is smoke fired. The slip sticks to the biscuit piece sufficiently to form a good resist but is removable because only very lightly fired and not fused on. The photograph shows a piece being washed clean after smoking. The dried work has its decoration enhanced by beeswax. See also **Smoking**.

The lidded jar is by Tim Andrews and shows the remarkable control of shapes combined with the relaxed style of carbonization. This piece was given a high bisc firing prior to slip coating and glazing. Parts of the covering were scratched away and the piece was raku fired and smoked. The slip coat sticks to the biscuited piece well enough to withstand the fire but can be removed after smoking. The glaze seals the resist shapes more effectively than slip alone thus giving large crackle patterns. However, it is removable because it adheres to the slip coat and not the pot. The jar was finished with beeswax to improve the tonal contrast and give a tactile satisfaction. See also **Raku**.

Rhodochrosite

Manganese ore. Manganese carbonate. $MnCO_3$. A transparent, lustrous, pink ore sometimes polished as a gemstone. It decomposes on heating to MnO and CO_2 and takes up oxygen to become manganese dioxide, MnO_2.

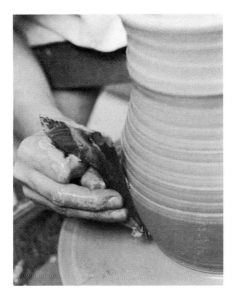

Rib

Any object or tool, such as a piece of slate, metal or wood, used in throwing pots on the wheel (see photograph above). Originally animals' ribs were used.

Rich clay

Very plastic clay. Fat clay. Long clay. Sticky clay.

Riddle

Coarse mesh used for separating dry materials into two sizes of particles: those that will pass through the riddle and those that will not. Its use is in sorting crushed dry clays, shales and soft rocks. A riddle is named by the size of its holes which are theoretically squares produced by interwoven wire warp and weft. Thus a 5 cm riddle has holes 5 cm × 5 cm. It should be noted that shales and some grogs have particles which are flat and long and these could pass through a hole diagonally and lengthwise. Thus the material which passes a 5 cm riddle can have pieces 7 cm at least amongst it. See *Mesh*.

Riffles

Barriers set across channels down which a slurry is run to catch the heavier particles and thus separate, by weight if not by size, the sand etc from the clay. With clay processing one usually considers the sediment as impurity and this is thrown away, but in ore washings such as gold the sediment is what one is collecting and the impurities are washed away. See *Levigation*.

Rings

See *Bullers rings*.

RO formula

The unitary system invented by Prof Hermann Seger (1839–94) to assist in the analysis of the properties of different bodies and glazes. The system involves the grouping of ceramic oxides as RO, R_2O_3 and RO_2. For any one body or glaze the total number of molecules of one group is brought to one and the other two groups are then expressed in proportion. For bodies the R_2O_3 group is brought to unity and for glazes the RO group. See *Formula: unity*.

Following the use of unity formulae, RO, R_2O_3 and RO_2 have become accepted shorthand expressions for monoxide, sesquioxide and dioxide in ceramic writings.

Rockingham

A pottery factory at Swinton near Rotherham, Yorkshire. From 1826 to 1842 a porcelain was made in an extremely lavish Rococo style.

Roll

A pronounced thickening of glaze used as a decorative feature, especially on bowls. Glazes for this treatment must be stiff and of the aluminium oxide type. Use is made of surface tension to collect the glaze at the lowest point of the glazed area. These glazes are applied thickly.

Rolled inlay

Method of rolling pieces of coloured clay into the surface of a pot or clay slab from which a pot is to be made. This produces a strong colour contrast similar to sprigging but without the relief surface which a sprig makes. See also *Encaustic*.

Two photographs show how Sabina Teuteberg composes thin cut-out shapes and rolls these into the main slab which is then jiggered as a plate. The third photograph shows a curled form made from an inlaid slab by Cathy Beetham.

Romano-British pottery

Civilian pottery produced under Roman occupation, probably under Roman direction and mostly for the military and Roman civilian use. The indigenous British wares in the form of burial urns continued through the occupation and after, with little obvious influence from the occupation, but the domestic ware is more difficult to trace as a continuous line.

Romano-British pottery owes something to the precision of Graeco-Roman tradition and often shows an almost mathematical consideration of form. It was obviously influenced by the Samian ware which was imported from Gaul, but it never copied the fully-oxidized red colour.

Instead, the Romano-British ware always shows signs of reduction, sometimes of extreme reduction, and varies from pale greys and slate blue-greys to lustrous blacks.

Most of the ware is plain and wheel-thrown and very rarely is it glazed. The forms vary greatly, some being exceedingly free. Small feet are a typical feature on bottles, beakers and jars. The bottles swell to a fully round form before closing to the neck sometimes with rich throwing rings showing. The rims and handles are generous and show a feeling for plastic clay. Jars vary from very small to very large. The widest part is usually above half-way giving a high shoulder and top-heavy appearance over the small base. The rims are flared.

Other wares from Eastern England are decorated with relief lines and dots in both the body clay and in a white clay apparently trailed onto the pots as a thick slip. These are called the Upchurch and Castor wares and are associated with the later Roman period after AD200 when difficulties in trade with Gaul resulted in a dearth of Samian ware.

ROMANO-BRITISH KILN. The kiln used in Britain during and after the Roman occupation was a development of the simple trench fire. It was less sophisticated than one might expect of the Romans, yet it involved many features including those for slow water-smoking and reduction.

The kiln was a low beehive structure sunk into the ground with a dome which was remade over the closely packed pots for each firing. There was no chimney, only an exit hole in the dome, and the firemouth was a pit leading to a circular area with a central clay column supporting the chamber floor. By digging the kiln out of the clayey ground the kiln became a fired pot unit but was probably considered fairly expendable since more than one is usually found at one site. They also face different ways, perhaps to make use of different winds.

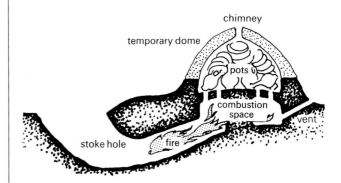

Recent experiments using kilns copied from the Roman ones, and with actual Roman kilns, have shown that the Romano-British kiln was capable of producing oxidized red ware as well as the common black and grey wares. Yet few reddish pieces have been found and this may be due to the potter's realization of the additional strength of the denser reduced body.

Roping

A slip-casting fault which is like a series of strings on the slip side of the cast. In vitreous and dense bodies the marks sometimes show on the outside (mould side) of the cast after firing. See ***Casting slip: adjustment***.

A similar effect also occurs with glazes that are over-flocculated. This shows after firing as uneven ripples and looks similar to the 'stringing' effect of highly-fluxed ash glazes. See ***Ashes***.

Roulette wheel

A small wheel, notched or carved on the rim and held by its spindle or a handle. It is run across the surface of a pot thus giving a line of relief pattern. The example is a Jane Hamlyn jug.

Rubbing stone

Rubbing stick. Originally a piece of fine-grained gritstone from the English Pennines used for the removal of blemishes by hand where the normal grinding wheel cannot reach. Now all sizes of sticks, discs, rectangular blocks and mouse-shaped stones are used. These are manufactured from silicon carbide, corundum and diamond-impregnated resin.

Ruby lustre

A copper lustre which is half-way between a complete metal and the red copper glaze. Its colour is a deep red tending to purple with lustrous shine. It has always been a popular colouring, being even richer in colour than the deepest gold lustres since it has the backing of the red glaze. It is effective as an all-over lustre on modelled surfaces and as brushwork.

There are three ways of producing a ruby lustre: one uses a copper compound in the glaze; another uses a copper compound painted onto the glaze; and a third transfers the copper from a removable coating.

In the first method, 2% to 8% of copper oxide or carbonate is mixed with the glaze. The amount is dependent upon the composition of the glaze. Adjustment of the amount is made upon the principle that too much copper compound produces a poor-quality red while insufficient gives a poor lustre. A good-quality red with some iridescence is called a rouge flambé. A full lustre with little or no red

background is a copper lustre. The glaze must be soft, mature below 1000°C (1832°F) and contain some lead. It is fired oxidized to maturity and upon cooling is reduced either intermittently down to dull red heat, or more intensely in the 750°C to 600°C (1382°F to 1112°F) range or even given an extra reduction firing in this range. See ***Copper lustre***.

The second method uses similar reduction techniques below 1000°C (1832°F) but the glaze can be harder, even fired as high as 1200°C (2192°F). The colouring is only at the surface and is therefore more easily reduced although the glaze is harder. Decoration is painted onto the unfired glaze with a pigment composed of glaze, copper compound and a very small proportion of iron oxide which reinforces the reduction. Varying amounts of reduction give variety of lustre from red to metallic.

In the third method a paste composed of clay and copper compound is painted onto the surface of the already-fired glaze. The glaze can be transparent over a white body or of the tin-opacified type. A low-temperature reduction firing in the region of 700°C (1292°F) transfers the colloidal copper into the glaze surface. See ***Transmutation lustre***.

Ruckling

Another name for the glaze defect called crawling.

Run (1)

Glaze run. The amount by which a glaze moves under gravity during its fluid state in the firing.

The distance a glaze will move is dependent upon its thickness as well as its fluidity or viscosity. A thick glaze having more bulk and proportionately less friction on the body will move further than the same glaze applied thinly. The distance moved can often be seen where an iron fleck is dragged or other colouring streaks exist. Movement up to 5 mm does little harm. The extra amount of glaze at the foot will usually be held there by its surface tension as a thickening or roll. More than 5 mm of movement is unusual except for some of the very streaky art glazes. These glazes, popular in the 1920s and 1930s, always required the pots to be supported on high stilts. The pots had to be severely ground at the base to restore a foot rim.

A shiny glaze needs to have been through a state in

the firing during which it was very fluid. This allows the surface to smooth out completely after the disruptions of fusion.

Many other glazes have a very fluid state which causes excess run, sometimes called skating, and yet these glazes may be crystalline glazes or near-crystalline glazes. For example, stoneware wood ash and feldspar glazes, earthenware titanium matt glazes. In such cases it is an unnecessary risk to allow the glaze to run too much. The crystallization obliterates the colouring effects or the possible high shine which the long run could give. On the other hand a glaze which is so viscous that it cannot move at all tends to have an uninteresting surface which looks unmoved and dead.

The melting of the glaze and the speed with which it will melt over a given range is dependent upon the flux:silica ratio. The higher the temperature and/or the longer the time taken, the greater the proportion of silica which can be melted, varying from 1:2 to 1:7. But the run is governed by viscosity and this is dependent upon the aluminium oxide:silica ratio. The greater the proportion of aluminium oxide, the stiffer the molten glaze will be. Thus a glaze with no aluminium oxide at all will run very quickly once it has melted. It will also craze badly.

Since unity is always kept for the aluminium oxide when considering the aluminium oxide:silica ratio, the appearance is that the silica amounts are being varied. In practice, however, it is the aluminium oxide amounts in the recipe that are being varied. For example, a very runny glaze might have a ratio of 1:20 but a very viscous glaze would have a ratio more like 1:6. This latter is the ratio of potassium feldspar which does not succeed in becoming a runny glass at 1300°C (2372°F) although it begins to melt at 1160°C (2120°F).

To effect a change in the glaze recipe which is too runny the simplest way is to introduce aluminium oxide by way of china clay. China clay has an aluminium oxide:silica ratio of 1:2 so that it introduces a high proportion of aluminium oxide for its introduction of silica. Empirically it can be substituted in the glaze recipe for some of the flint or quartz content which is pure silica. If the glaze is too viscous, the reverse is true. Substitute flint for some of the china or ball clay. Some stoneware glazes can withstand as much as 30% of china clay in the recipe. However, in any glaze to go on biscuit, an amount of any raw clay over 10% might result in shrinkage cracks during drying and a viscous glaze which crawls away from the cracks in the firing.

Run (2)

Bleed. Blur. Describes the action of certain colours which when used as underglaze or similar decoration are partly dissolved by the glaze giving a diffused edge. Copper oxide, cobalt oxide and manganese oxide are typical examples.

The effect is partly due to the action of the glaze flux and partly to the fluxing action of the colourant. Lead oxide in a glaze is very active. Lead glazes move considerably during fusion and absorb silicates and colouring from the adjacent body. This accounts for the blurred edges under lead glazes especially those compounded with raw lead. However it does not account for the blurred edges under stiff glazes like feldspathic stoneware. Here the run is local to the colour. Copper oxide, cobalt oxide and manganese oxide are strong fluxes, which, even though combined with aluminium oxide, silica, etc as underglaze or other colourant, will actively attack the adjacent glaze and diffuse into it. High alkaline fluxes and frits, and also boron oxide encourage the running of colouring oxides.

Rust

Hydrated iron oxide. $2Fe_2O_3.3H_2O$. The surface coating which forms on iron when exposed to moisture and air. Rust sometimes refers to similar coatings on other metals, though tarnish is a more usual name. Iron rust and rusty pieces of flaking iron are used by potters to produce iron speckling in bodies and glazes. See ***Iron oxide***.

The rust colour in glazes is produced by red iron oxide at the surface. In stoneware, this effect is called kaki by the Japanese. See also ***Tessha*** and ***Tenmoku***. It can be achieved in three ways:

1. By overloading the glaze with iron oxide so that there is more than can be dissolved in the eventual solid glass. The extra iron oxide is precipitated during cooling and forms a coating at the surface. This method requires distinct oxidation in the firing and cooling. The results are not a bright rust colour but can be improved by including up to 0·5% nickel oxide.

2. By hard firing with suitable clays which form a deep body-glaze layer resulting in a crystal formation through the glaze to the surface. The red colour of red iron oxide (Fe_2O_3) is due to its crystal structure. A thin glaze layer helps the crystals to reach the surface. This is first evident on rims of pots where rust patches break through a black glaze. See ***Tessha***. Oxidation is essential. The use of clays with a high iron content increases the strength of colour and helps to form the crystal layer. The use of white clay or white slip as a buffer layer between the body and glaze helps to create a brighter colour. In methods 1 and 2 the presence of boron oxide assists the formation of a brighter colour. The two methods are often combined.

3. During the firing of glazes, which contain less than a saturation of iron oxide, the iron oxide in solution is not uniformly distributed. It tends to gravitate away from the glaze surface and towards the body, collecting in a concentrated layer. This leaves a comparatively clear layer of glaze above it. Some of the iron oxide can be persuaded to collect at the surface of the glaze by the use of a reduction atmosphere over the period when the glaze melts. This oxide is not red iron oxide (Fe_2O_3) but black iron oxide (FeO) and is said to come to the surface to gain oxygen to revert to the more stable form of Fe_2O_3.

At the molten stage, the iron oxide is in solution. It should be noted that there is not an excess amount when compared with the glaze as a whole. It is not the same as method 1. The iron oxide however is precipitated out of solution as separate crystals upon cooling because it has concentrated at the surface where it has produced a layer of glaze which is saturated. If this black iron oxide is further oxidized at this precipitation stage it becomes red iron oxide, producing a bright rust crystal. Quick cooling keeps the crystals small and avoids a matt surface. This method forms the brightest rust colour because the crystals cover a volume of colourless glaze through which the light can reflect. See ***Iron oxide: in glazes***.

The photograph shows a close-up of the concentration of iron oxide crystals at the surface known as segregation.

Rutile

TiO_2. Natural titanium oxide with up to 15% iron oxide. When rutile is used in glazes, creams, yellows and oranges can be produced in association with tin oxide and red iron oxide, and yellow-greens with cobalt oxide and copper oxide.

Rutile is one of the three oxide ores of titanium. It is found associated with sandstones in Australasia. The other oxide ores are brookite and anatase. The three are chemically alike but identified by their different crystal structures. Rutile always contains impurities, mostly iron, and such is the colour-heightening power of titanium oxide that only a trace is sufficient to give a yellow colour in glazes. Rutile containing much impurity is a dark brown, almost black. But the purest rutile is grey in colour because of its crystal structure and, because it is slow to dissolve in a glaze, it always darkens glazes more than does titanium oxide.

Amounts of rutile, up to 10% in a glaze, give a broken colouring effect due to crystallization. In association with tin oxide a whole variety of streaked and mottled effects are obtained. These effects in lead and low sol glazes, fired at approximately 1050°C (1922°F), were popular under the name of art glazes up to 1960, and are being explored again.

Rutile readily produces a crystal structure in a glass on cooling and therefore opacity and a matt surface due to crystals can be produced by introducing up to 25% rutile in a glaze. See also ***Crystalline glazes***.

Glazes containing 15% or more of rutile or rutile and titanium oxide are subject to phototrophy after firing. Phototrophy is the ability to change colour by the absorption of light. Such glazes darken with the light and grow pale with the lack of it. This process is reversible and continuous *ad infinitum*.

Rutile containing over 25% of iron, calculated as FeO, contains sufficient iron titanate ($FeTiO_3$) to be called by the ore name of ilmenite.

Rutile is a good electrical insulator and is used with very small amounts of plastic clay in the making of electrical condensers. See also ***Titanium oxide***.

PLATE 67 COLOURS FROM IRON OXIDE

Mike Bailey

Emmanuel Cooper

Janet Hamer

John Jelfs

John Jelfs

Jill Dick
Photo: Tessa Bunney

Christine McCole
Photo: Roger Brann

Detail, Ray Finch
Photo: Janet Hamer

Other photos by the makers

Clive Bowen
Photo: Janet Hamer

PLATE 68 OXIDATION FIRING

Betty Blandino
Photo: G O Jones

Clock, Anita Peach
Photo: J Hamer

Dish, Molly Curley
Photo: Martin Avery

Will Levi Marshall
Photo: W L Marshall

Jude Jelfs
Photo: Jude Jelfs

Bennett Cooper
Photo: Stephen Brayne

PLATE 69 # REDUCTION FIRING

Michael Casson
Photo: Petra Reynolds

Denise Wren

Bernard Leach

Pauline Paterson

Oldrich Asenbryl

David Leach

Frank Hamer
Photo: Frank Hamer

Other photos by Janet Hamer

PLATE 70 # RAKU

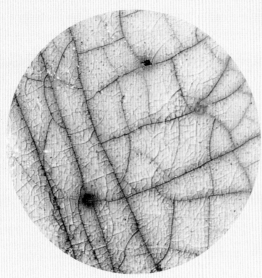

Dramatic crackle patterns result from rapid cooling. The stress of thermal shock produces cracks in the glaze which are then stained by carbon. Glazes containing copper oxide become red and metallic when they lose their oxygen to carbon-burning materials.

FIRING INSIDE THE KILN

At around 1000°C (1832°F) the body is unaltered but the glaze is fused. The glaze creeps into the body interstices giving anchorage.

Glaze pinhole

Fast climb to temperature

Section showing the wide range of particle size in the biscuited body. Grog, silica and feldspathic materials compose up to 50% of the body.

grog

clay

clay

flint, quartz or sand

clay

feldspar

clay

Unglazed surface which eventually gets blackened

1000°C

900°C

800°C

700°C

600°C

500°C

Approximate firing hours   1   2

PLATE 71

RAKU DISH
by Frank Hamer.
(photo: Frank Hamer)

COOLING OUTSIDE THE KILN

The fused glaze shines and bubbles disappear. The pot is lifted from the kiln and cooled rapidly to around 750°C (1382°F). The glaze surface stiffens which protects it from physical damage.

1000°C

The still-hot pot is smothered in combustible materials which begin to burn. Smoke (carbon molecules) is drawn into the still-pliable glaze in search of oxygen and is sucked into the porous body.

750°C

Combustibles: sawdust, grass, leaves etc ignited by touching hot glaze.

Slower cooling in combustibles

Parts of glaze still oxidized and coloured green by copper oxide (CuO).

When cool, the pot is cleaned. Most of the copper oxide is reduced to its red state (Cu_2O). A very thin film of pure copper metal has been drawn to the surface leaving a lustrous sheen.

Carbon-blackened body

4   5

PLATE 72 # MAIOLICA

The traditionally used marl clay is calcareous with a high coefficient of expansion and contraction. Upon cooling, this puts the glaze under compression and helps to avoid crazing. A body may be made up from ball clay, china clay and red clay with some cristobalite. The fired body remains porous and the glaze is fused on but with little body-glaze layer.

1100°C

1000°C

Tin oxide is the traditional white opacifier in the glaze but zirconium silicate can be used. Typically, the glaze has a granular surface texture sometimes erupting as tiny smoothed white glaze bubbles which show through painted colours.

900°C

800°C

The body is biscuited to around 1000°C (1832°F) and coated with the tin glaze. Colours are then brushed onto the unfired glaze which has a friable and porous surface. In the firing some pigments sink partly into the glaze while fusible oxides such as cobalt bleed and present blurred edges.

700°C

600°C

500°C

Approximate firing hours   4   5   6

PLATE 73

Where the body fires to a light red it is detectable through a semi-opaque white glaze. The hand painting of bright colours allows personalized imagery, heraldry and commemorative lettering.

1100°C

Skilled brushwork is the hallmark of maiolica.

ALBARELLO from Deruta and, on left, a detail of a TILE SHOWING A HARE from Seville.
(photos: Janet Hamer)
TILED PANEL (above) and JUG by Pat Birks.
(photos: Miles Cort)

8   9   10   11

PLATE 74 CRYSTALLINE GLAZES

FIRING

1280°C

1200°C

1100°C

1000°C

900°C

800°C

700°C

600°C

500°C

The steep rise to top temperature fuses the glaze but avoids unwanted contamination by aluminium oxide and silica from the body.

900°C

BOTTLES on left by Avril Farley.
(photos: Martin Avery)
BOTTLE on right by Derek Clarkson.
(photo: David Seed)

Crystals and crystal-free matrix take up colour
with distinct priorities dictated by the colourant's
crystal-field energy strength.

Approximate firing hours

2   3   4   5   6   7   8

PLATE 75

COOLING

1280°C

Double 'axe-head' shape.

The glaze is of low viscosity. An initial rapid cooling controls its flow and prevents the formation of microcrystals in the matrix.

Molecules reform in fluid glaze making new compounds. Cooling is arrested to give more time in the optimum crystal-growing temperature ranges. Unfused seeds of titanium oxide provide nuclei from which crystals expand radially.

1090°C

Crystal growing from nucleus.

1020°C

Crystals expanding in a repeated step to form halos.

Cobalt takes precedence to stain zinc silicate crystals but copper and nickel are also taken up. Manganese and copper have more affinity with the matrix but will stain crystals in the absence of cobalt.

10   11   12   13   14   15   16   17

PLATE 76

SALT & SODA FIRING

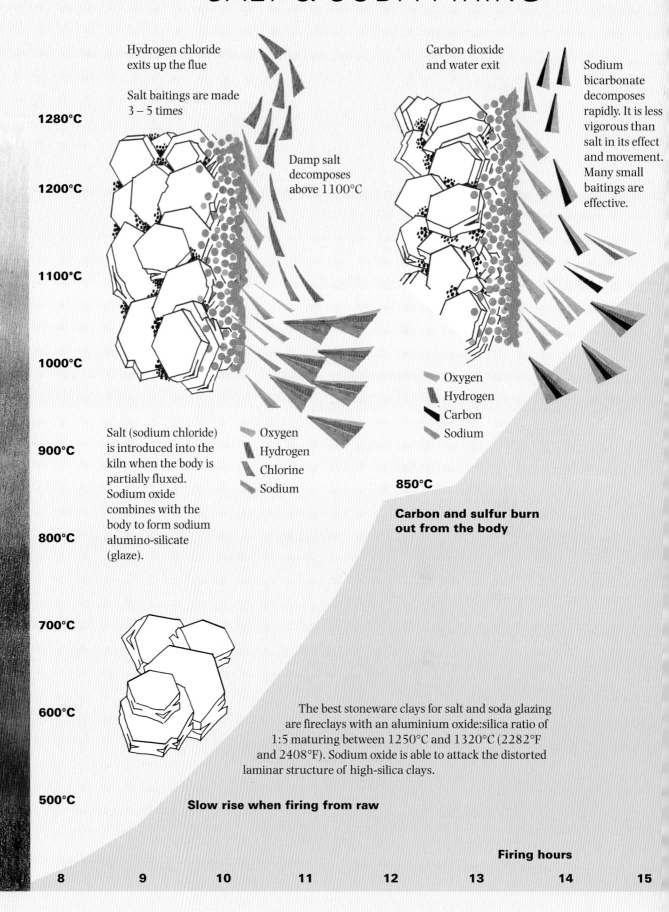

Hydrogen chloride
exits up the flue

Salt baitings are made
3 – 5 times

Carbon dioxide
and water exit

Sodium
bicarbonate
decomposes
rapidly. It is less
vigorous than
salt in its effect
and movement.
Many small
baitings are
effective.

1280°C

1200°C

Damp salt
decomposes
above 1100°C

1100°C

1000°C

Oxygen
Hydrogen
Carbon
Sodium

Salt (sodium chloride)
is introduced into the
kiln when the body is
partially fluxed.
Sodium oxide
combines with the
body to form sodium
alumino-silicate
(glaze).

Oxygen
Hydrogen
Chlorine
Sodium

900°C

850°C

800°C

**Carbon and sulfur burn
out from the body**

700°C

600°C

The best stoneware clays for salt and soda glazing
are fireclays with an aluminium oxide:silica ratio of
1:5 maturing between 1250°C and 1320°C (2282°F
and 2408°F). Sodium oxide is able to attack the distorted
laminar structure of high-silica clays.

500°C

Slow rise when firing from raw

Firing hours

| 8 | 9 | 10 | 11 | 12 | 13 | 14 | 15 |

PLATE 77

Salt and soda-glazed ware is very strong, hard and acid-proof.

Oxidizing soak for 1 hour

1280°C

Baitings

Fast cool to avoid formation of cristobalite

Heavy salting can produce a pronounced texture. Raised beads of glaze, often coloured, crawl away from colourless dimples and craters. This characteristic effect is popularly called Tiger skin.

The surface is often pitted like orange peel. The very viscous molten glaze did not smooth over a pin-holed texture.

SODA-GLAZED BOTTLE by Trevor Chaplin.
SALT-GLAZED FLAGON by Sheila Casson.
SODA-GLAZED BOTTLES by Ruthanne Tudball.
(photos: The potters)

PLATE 78

STONEWARE

1280°C

1200°C

1100°C

A transparent glaze will gain some colour from iron oxide in the body and wood ashes. Phosphorus from the wood ash may give a crystalline opacity. Iron oxide may speckle the glaze.

The body has variously-sized particles of fireclay, ball clay, grog, sand and bentonite with traces of iron oxide. It matures slowly above 1200°C (2192°F) to produce a strong vitrified material with 1% to 2% porosity.

Fluxes in the body and glaze fuse the silicates as the glaze flows into pores in the body. Long needles of mullite knit the whole together making a strong body-glaze layer which eases stress between body and glaze.

1000°C

900°C

Glaze mix with wood ash often used in stone ware glazes

800°C

Washing wood ash

700°C

Wood ash from a bonfire

600°C

500°C

1   2   3   4   5   6   7   8

PLATE 79

Some larger particles of iron oxide may resist fusion and remain as spots of colour in the glaze or break the surface. Reduction will smooth these out by changing the trioxide to the more fusible monoxide.

Oxidizing slow soak to 1280°C

Rapid cool to 1000°C with damper out

Reduction

JAR on left by Phil Rogers.
SQUARED BOTTLE by Janet Leach.
FISH PLATE by Frank Hamer.
BRENT GOOSE by Janet Hamer.
(photos: J & F Hamer)

Firing hours

| 9 | 10 | 11 | 12 | 13 | 14 | 15 | 16 | 17 |

PLATE 80

PORCELAIN

1300°C
1280°C

1200°C

1100°C

1000°C

900°C

800°C

700°C

600°C

500°C

Around 1300°C (2372°F) the mullite crystals form a new strong network which bonds together the reformed kaolinite resulting, when cool, in the strongest ceramic body.

Mullite needles, body and glaze interact and fuse to create a very thick body-glaze layer.

Mullite forms in the glaze but long needles are precluded by movement in the melt.

Decomposition of kaolinite crystals above 1150°C (2102°F) produces mullite crystals which grow into long needles.

Firing hours

1   2   3   4   5   6   7   8

PLATE 81

The translucent quality of the pure, white body gives glazes extra brilliance.

Oxidizing soak up to 1300°C

Reduction assists the body-glaze layer

The strength of porcelain body allows thin-walled translucent forms to survive.

Brightly-coloured enamels are fired onto the previously fired high-temperature glaze in a further firing at a lower temperature.

THREE BOTTLES by Peter Wills.
(photo: Peter Wills)
TEAPOT by Michael Casson.
(photo: Petra Reynolds)
BOWL by Linda Caswell.
(photo: Linda Caswell)
SMALL TRAY, Chinese Qing dynasty, c.1800.
(photo: Janet Hamer)

10   11   12   13   14   15

PLATE 82

COLOURS FROM COPPER OXIDE

Peter Wills
Photo: Peter Wills

Kevin de Choisy

Mike Bailey
Photos: Mike Bailey

Janet Hamer

Detail:
Derek Dixon

Frank
Hamer

Mike Bailey
Photo: Mike Bailey

Ned Heywood

Triana Lustre

Michael Eden

Other photos by the authors

S

Safety

Working conditions which are intelligently and efficiently organized. Pottery making uses many complex processes involving storage and movement of raw materials, a lot of carrying and handling, use of machinery, heat treatment, water, electricity and gas. Potential hazards to safety abound but thoughtful planning, layout and working habits can and must overcome all of them. Potters should keep a visible first-aid box and know how to use it.

Recent safety legislation does not exempt the self-employed, nor indeed the part-time student. It does recognize however, the problems which the individual faces when required to comply with industrial standards. The potter is legally responsible for him/herself, employees, whether full-time or casual, and for visitors. The studio or workshop must be a place safe from accidents and health risks even when the potter is absent. The **Bibliography** contains a list of notifications on health and safety.

Notices to oneself and others are worthwhile. They are obligatory for certain situations like those involving unguarded machinery and for materials which are hazardous. Some international symbols exist and are being introduced by EEC Regulations. Official Regulations are often difficult to understand but Codes of Practice are couched in everyday language. The obligatory precautions and recommendations might seem excessive to the individual potter who has to interpret them for personal use but they do show the seriousness of the risks described.

Some obligatory precautions are given below, followed by examples of hazards which are difficult to define officially but, nonetheless, present a danger to the potter.

Early planning of the pottery workshop should keep water, electricity and gas as separate supplies. The main water stop-cock, main electricity switch and primary gas stop-tap should be easily accessible but separate from the hub of workshop activity where accidents are most likely to occur. Keep water supply at least arm's length from electricity plugs and switches. Ceiling pull switches are safer than wall switches but an earth-trip switch on the supply at the meter gives the safest installation. Individual trip switches plugged into socket outlets are an alternative.

Plan the workspace with an awareness of accidents and emergency evacuation. Consider what to do in an emergency, especially where there are a number of people involved. Have an agreed procedure. If working alone the procedure still needs to be decided upon and remembered. Take advice from the local fire prevention officer. Potteries have been known to catch fire!

When kiln building or doing other construction work, wear industrial boots or shoes with steel toecaps. A firebrick weighs 4 kg. When lifting sacks of clay and other heavy weights let the legs do the lifting by bending at the knees and keeping the back straight. Keep the arms close to the body. Plan storage with consideration of the lifting and turning involved.

Store wax and inflammable liquids like paraffin, white spirit and lustre thinning medium in a closed cool place.

It is injurious to the eyes to stare into the brightness of kilns at red to white hot temperature. The light contains energy of a wide spectrum including ultra-violet and infra-red. The ultra-violet energy (UV) causes temporary blindness commonly known as snow-blindness which eventually cures itself. The infra-red energy (IR) causes permanent damage. Sunglasses and ski goggles give protection against UV but very little against IR. Although almost all glass, including normal spectacles, gives a little protection against IR, the only true protection is by the green glass which contains iron. Welders goggles are ideal. Recent research has produced a pale green glass which is effective for kiln work and is not so difficult to see through as the very dark green glass necessary for arc welding. Thus, looking into kilns to see cones or glaze fusion can be done safely and easily. With practice, the adjustment of a gas flame can be done accurately and it is even possible to stoke a wood fire when wearing goggles.

Wear protective clothing. Wear eye protection when doing any work involving sharp ceramic or metal particles as when grinding and drilling, or when using reactive chemicals like strong acids and alkalis. Don't wear swinging jewellery. Fasten back loose hair.

Strict regulations cover the use of abrasive wheels. Protective eye goggles and sometimes gloves should be worn when grinding pot bases or when sharpening tools.

Toxic materials must be clearly labelled and should be kept in a cupboard where they are less likely to be accidentally used or spilt. Whether the cupboard is locked or not depends upon who else, like a child or visitor, might investigate the workshop. See also **Health hazard** and **Poison**.

If in doubt at all about legislation or hazards, seek advice from ROSPA or the Health and Safety Executive. Both organizations are represented in all regions of the UK. See ***Appendix*** on page 424.

The wearing of protective clothing does not lessen the need for care. Some hazards in the workshop are obvious. Protruding brackets, levers and handles are evident obstacles, as are steps, boxes, or spilt slurry on the floor. They are less visible when one is concentrating on carrying a board of pots. Uneven floors are not obvious but can cause a fall. For these and many other hazards there is no legislation so the potter must seek to develop a safe working practice by being aware that hazards exist.

All sharp tools should be stored safely. A wall rack or row of hooks is popular and effective.

Insulating gloves, which are essential for handling tongs, tea-cosy kilns and pots for raku, are a hazard if they become wet. The heat is then transmitted through the gloves almost instantaneously.

Thick gloves will protect the hands from warm and rough kiln bricks and shelves. Splintered glass where glaze has stuck to a shelf is often an unseen hazard when unpacking a kiln. Such a shelf must be chiselled clean as the next operation. Pots with glazes that are shelling off should be consigned to the rubbish bin straight away. Beware of fine splinters of glass which easily lodge themselves into wooden table tops.

Heat is an essential component of pottery making but remember that when unpacking a kiln of warm pots the assistants also need gloves. With gas kilns under reduction, flames often leak around doors and bungs and are invisible in sunshine as are the flames at short chimney vents. Very hot currents of air are also emitted from electric kilns at ventilation holes and spyholes. Hot wax for resist is very hot.

Lifting heavy weights has already been mentioned. Legal limits are based upon 25 kg for men and 15 kg for women. But throwing on the wheel also puts a strain on the back and here the method and amount of throwing are factors which cannot be tailored legally to the individual. Cold and damp conditions make matters worse. Keep warm and analyse the throwing method. Potter's back is an all too common complaint.

Saggar

A refractory box to protect ware from direct contact by flames and gases or sudden changes in temperature. Pots are packed in saggars which are then piled in bungs inside the kiln. See ***Bung*** and ***Wad***.

Salt glaze

A glaze derived from salt, usually common salt, which is introduced into the kiln fire. The salt decomposes and volatilizes, the most important product being sodium oxide which combines with aluminium oxide and silica from the hot pottery body to produce sodium alumino-silicate, i.e. glaze. The glaze varies from a light glossing of the surface to

two millimetres in thickness depending upon the number of baitings, position in the kiln, and the amount of body which the volatile sodium oxide is able to flux. The volatile sodium oxide enters the pores at the surface of the body when the aluminium oxide and silica are hot enough for immediate combination. Salt-glazed pots are recognized first as light grey, buff, or brown stoneware, glazed in a range of similar colours and with a characteristic orange-peel, mottled or pin-holed surface. See ***Tiger skin***.

HISTORY. Salt glazing probably originated in the Rhineland. Here stoneware was developed during the 12th to 14th centuries and salt glazing appears to have been a part of this development. The Rhenish stoneware consisted largely of wine bottles, beer mugs and storage jars. This type of ware was made in Britain from the 17th century, notably by John Dwight at Fulham and later, more imaginatively, by the Martin brothers at the end of the 19th century.

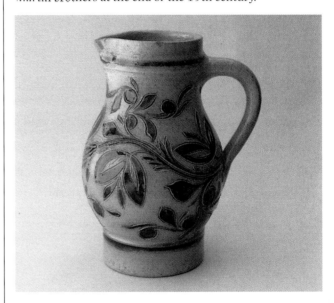

Salt-glazed ware is still sometimes referred to as German salt glaze if it is brown and Dutch salt glaze if it is grey. The brown colour which is often a rich reddish-brown, is due to iron oxide in the clay and sulfur in the fuel. The grey colour is given by a small quantity of reduced iron oxide. The Dutch salt-glazed ware was often painted with cobalt oxide. This painting followed lines scratched in the soft clay and gave it the name of 'scratch-blue ware'. Cobalt oxide blue is almost the only colour seen on historical pieces as it was the only oxide which successfully integrated with the salt glaze when used in direct painting. Iron oxide and other refractory colours tend to inhibit the formation of a good glaze.

Individual potters use salt glaze today but its industrial use for chemical containers and sewer pipes had ceased in Britain by the mid 1970s. Because salt glazing relies upon vapour to create the glaze on the pot, the insides of all but the shallowest bowls remain unglazed. Insides of pots may be glazed with slip-glazes prior to firing where the traditional once-firing process is being practised.

KILN. The salt vapour also attacks all surfaces within the kiln and deposits glaze where it can combine with an alumino-silicate material. The kiln lining and shelves need to be of resistant composition. Good quality high aluminium oxide or high silica firebricks are to be preferred. Fibre is not suitable and HTI bricks need a zirconium silicate coating. Shelves should contain a high percentage of aluminium oxide in order that they do not become glazed.

The kiln used must be efficiently ventilated by using flues. Both up- and down-draught kilns can be used. For sewer pipes, a down-draught kiln was used and the pipes were stacked over some of the exit flues in the floor. The insides of the pipes were thus glazed along with the outsides.

PROCESS. To produce an effective salt glaze the salt must be quickly decomposed to create volatile sodium oxide. Salt is sodium chloride. To achieve decomposition water is added to the salt to produce sodium oxide and hydrogen chloride as gases.

$$2NaCl + H_2O \longrightarrow Na_2O\uparrow + 2HCl\uparrow$$

salt   water   sodium oxide   hydrogen chloride

A temperature of 1100°C (2012°F) is needed for this decomposition and for the sodium oxide to combine with the body. Dry salt thrown earlier into the kiln would melt at 800°C (1472°F) and be lost as it combined with the clinker or the base of the kiln. For this reason wet salt is introduced at temperatures above 1100°C (2012°F). In traditional salt glaze therefore, three to six saltings are used between 1180°C and 1250°C (2156°F and 2282°F). Individual potters may continue with more saltings as far as 1300°C (2372°F).

The salt must be damp but not too wet as excessive steam would cause explosions in the kiln. The firemen used to shovel the damp salt into the fireboxes of the kilns. With smaller kilns, potters make small paper bag parcels to throw in. The use of vaporized oil for kiln firing presented a problem to salt glazers. There was no open fire onto which the damp salt could be thrown. An answer to the problem was found in the use of salt and borax. This combination, already known to give more fluid and smoother glazes, can be handled as a dry granular material. As such it can be introduced into the combustion chamber by blown secondary air. Borax is a combination of sodium and boron oxides with water. The water assists the decomposition of the borax and also the salt. Up to 10% borax is used in the mixture. The equation is:

$$Na_2B_4O_7.10H_2O + 20NaCl \rightarrow 11Na_2O\uparrow + 2B_2O_3\uparrow + 20HCl\uparrow$$

borax   salt   sodium   boron   hydrogen
       oxide   oxide   chloride

Propane gas provides water vapour allowing the use of dry salt blown in. Another way of introducing salt is as a saturated brine solution of water and salt. This is organized as a supply entering the oil pipe to the burner. The two, oil and brine, do not mix and can be seen as separate quantifiable amounts on their way to the burner. The advantages of this system are the efficient use of salt as it gives good coverage for a less amount and therefore decreases air pollution. A disadvantage is that deposited salt clogs the burner end and must be cleaned off. See diagram.

CLAY. Not all clays are fluxed by the sodium oxide because many contain insufficient free silica, e.g. china clays, ball clays and stoneware clays with aluminium oxide:silica molecular ratios approximating 1:2, 1:3 and 1:4. The best clays for salt glazing are fireclays which are high in silica. These have aluminium oxide:silica ratios of 1:5 and higher. The distorted structure of disordered kaolinite is fluxed more easily than ordered kaolinite. See **Colour plates 76/77**. Extra silica is sometimes added to clays as quartz sand but silica in isolation does not take a glaze. Some aluminium oxide is necessary.

A good salt glaze is very hard and chemical-resistant, hence its former use for sewer pipes and acid containers. Alkalis from the body join the sodium oxide in the formation of the glaze. Small amounts of calcium oxide and magnesium oxide help to stabilize the glass. But aluminium oxide plays a more important part and is necessary if a glaze is to be formed at all. The simplest salt glaze is sodium alumino-silicate with a unity formula of:

$$Na_2O \ . \ 0.5 \text{ to } 1.0Al_2O_3 \ . \ 2.8 \text{ to } 5.5SiO_2$$

The aluminium oxide content is always high which accounts for the stiff nature of the glaze and its stability.

INDIVIDUAL POTTERS. As industrial salt glazing was phased out, the unique quality of the ware, and its rarity, have made it more highly valued. Individual potters have experimented with smaller kilns and studied more precise firing tactics. Most noticeably they have extended the range of colours and glaze effects using patterns of slips, stains, additional applied glazes, especially silica-rich grass or bracken ash glazes, and higher temperatures.

The photographs (overleaf) illustrate a large bowl by Michael Casson; a teapot and a bowl with looped handles by Walter Keeler; a vase with paper resist decoration of swimmers by Michael Casson; a slabbed planter with impressed and applied decoration and another with oxide sophisticated pieces find that using a biscuit firing is more convenient than the traditional once-firing. The extra firing cost is balanced by less risk of damage in packing the glaze kiln and a quicker salt firing.

To obtain brighter colours fine white stoneware body is used, and frequently, porcelain. Whereas in earlier wares cobalt was the only colour which successfully integrated with the body, now rich reds, orange, cream and green appear. These are achieved by mixing colouring stains and oxides with other glazes to fuse them since otherwise they do not take salt glaze well. These colours are poured, trailed, brushed and used with paper and wax resist in decorative patterns. A bright orange colour is also achieved by minimizing the amount of glaze which is deposited in certain areas to give flashing which ranges from a dry surface to a light glossing. This can be used to give fairly random effects from salt fumes which flow unevenly through the kiln by keeping the damper open with an oxidized temperature rise and a not too generous supply of

decoration both by Paul Stubbs; and a large jug by Michael Casson.

The new breed of potters closely control the kiln packing and firing schedule to achieve optimum effect of glaze and colour. Kilns are idiosyncratic in their firings and so there are no absolute rules. Many potters making more salt. It can also be achieved in more controlled shapes by applying areas of high aluminium oxide slip which will take a less thick glaze than other parts. All this gives further richness so that the final effect is a bouquet of colourful chemistry. The way in which salt glaze emphasizes textures on a pot surface, darkening grooves with thicker glaze and burning light on high-lights, is exploited by generous, sometimes excessive, use of ribbing, incising, impressing and neo-baroque handles.

Variations on salt mixtures are also tested. A 50/50 mixture of rock salt and sawdust is used to encourage an orange-peel texture, or 10% borax to give a smoother glaze. The sawdust and 5% sugar or baking flour are also added to hold a reduction atmosphere. Amounts of salt and number of saltings vary.

Many potters use periods of reduction during the temperature rise from approximately 1000°C to 1200°C (1832°F to 2192°F) to develop the applied glazes. These are followed by oxidation to clear the atmosphere before salting. This may be necessary to clear sulfur, from the burning of oil fuel, which could be sealed on the surface by the salt and result in a dull grey bloom. Temperatures up to 1300°C (2372°F) may be used. A quick cooling down to 1080°C (1976°F) is popular to avoid the formation of cristobalite. Cristobalite in a stoneware body makes it prone to dunting. See ***Dunting: cooling dunts***.

Temperature readings in a salt kiln can only be measured against previous readings from the same kiln. The reduction atmosphere and salt fumes affect pyrometer probes and cones so that they cannot perform as promised by manufacturers. Bars and rings which can be withdrawn and inspected for progress of glaze build-up give the best indication. Safety respirators and goggles must be worn during these operations for protection against corrosive gases and heat glare. See ***Health hazard*** and ***Safety***.

The question of air pollution by fumes from salt firing is of concern to potters. The products of the dis-association of sodium chloride which reach the chimney vent are toxic. Hydrogen chloride gas (HCl) in association with water vapour forms corrosive hydrochloric acid vapour. Surplus sodium oxide may also escape as sodium vapour, especially on a hot dry day and when the kiln is reducing. In contact with water vapour this will form caustic soda (NaOH). These fumes can be diverted via a washing tower, called a scrubber, where a swirl jet of water washes out much of the acid and chlorine. The run-off water can be neutralized by running over limestone chips but this still leaves the problem of the disposal of carbon dioxide (CO_2). Serious industrial pollution has been progressively restricted by legislation since 1876 in the UK. Subsequent Acts tightened the regulations and, in the 1950s and 1960s, Clean Air Acts effectively brought industrial salt glazing to an end. The UK Environment Protection Act of 1990 instituted a system of licensing but small craft potteries can apply for exemption. However, recent controlled studies of emissions from salt and soda kilns conducted by concerned potters and chemists have shown that pollutants from the salt or soda are an insignificant part of the total emissions from fuel combustion.

See also ***Soda firing*** and ***Colour plates 6, 7, 22, 41, 52, 53, 54*** and ***76/77***.

Sand

Natural ground quartz. Sands vary in composition from pure silica to a mixture of silica, calcium compounds (shells), clay and soluble salts. There are often colouring impurities of iron and manganese, and traces of other minerals like titanium oxide and zirconium silicate.

Pure silica sand is a source of silica for frits, glazes and glass. It is used as a filler in both earthenware and stoneware. In earthenware, fine sand which will convert into cristobalite is often used. In stoneware either a very fine sand which fuses or a quartz sand which remains as quartz phase is used. See *Grain size*.

The less-pure sands are useful additions to clay often providing interesting speckle.

Sang-de-boeuf

See *Copper oxide: in reduction*.

Sassoline

Sassolite. Italian mineral containing boric acid. See *Borax*.

Satin matt

Vellum matt. A low-temperature matt glaze on which the matt surface is caused by extremely fine crystals of zinc silicate, zinc titanate and possibly, lead titanate. Satin matts are produced by adding up to 18% of zinc oxide and 4% of titanium oxide to soft runny glazes. Tin oxide and zirconium silicate are often added for extra opacity.

Satin matts rely upon the zinc oxide to remain isolated in the molten glaze but sufficiently loosened in molecular bonding to remake permanent bonds with titanium oxide and silica. The effect is lost if the zinc oxide acts as a flux and becomes involved in the melt. Satin matts are therefore restricted to temperatures below 1085°C (1985°F). They are usually fired below 1050°C (1922°F) with lead and boric oxides as the main fluxes. See also *Crystalline glazes* and *Zinc oxide*.

The molten glaze must be very fluid for the orientation of the zinc oxide and titanium oxide to take place. Satin matts are therefore runny glazes, often low in aluminium oxide content, and are restricted in practical use to horizontally fired surfaces like tiles and decorative plates. Their fine crystals provide a very smooth surface which does not mark and stain as do other crystalline glazes. The zinc and lead in crystalline compounds, however, make satin matts impractical for tableware on toxicity grounds.

The following is a recipe for a white satin matt used by Harry Fraser. It is fired at 1050°C (1922°F):

lead bisilicate	50
borax frit	20
zirconium silicate	12
titanium oxide	3
tin oxide	3
zinc oxide	6
china clay	6

Saturation

The point at which the limit has been reached for dissolving one substance in another. A solution is a combination of a solvent and a solute. The solvent is usually liquid and keeps its identity as a liquid. The solute is often a solid which loses its identity as such. If more solute is present than is required for a fully-saturated solution, the excess remains undissolved.

In pottery, the term saturation usually refers to colouring oxides which are dissolved in glazes. The dissolved amounts give clean colours but the excess tends to give scummy or metallic colours. The saturation is different with each colourant and with each glaze but some typical amounts are:

iron oxide	8%
cobalt oxide	1%
nickel oxide	3%
copper oxide	3%
manganese oxide	5%

The concentration of the solution is dependent upon temperature. In glazes it is possible to dissolve more colourant when hot than cold. The difference between these two could be as much as a quarter of the colourant. This difference is precipitated out of solution as the glaze cools and is responsible for some interesting crystalline effects with iron and manganese oxides. See *Rust* and *Kaki*.

Sawdust firing

A simple system of firing in which pots are set in sawdust within a brick or metal box with lid. The sawdust burns slowly achieving sufficient heat to turn the clay into pot. Pockets of oxidation and reduction are caused which produce interesting decoration especially on burnished red clays. See also *Jutland ware* and *Burnishing*. Many potters now use this process to produce integrating colouration and also some reduction to lustre of copper and silver salts on previously biscuited pieces. See *Smoking*.

The photograph shows the special care taken by Duncan Ayscough in setting his bottles into coarse sawdust. He uses large metal containers densely packed for a slow burn taking two or three days. This lengthy process helps to evolve the intensities and depths of the surfaces. See also *Terra sigillata.*

Pat Clark's 'Chimney pot' shows the variation of black carbon deposit on a white body.

SCMC
Sodium Carboxymethylcellulose. A glaze binder which is added to friable glazes that contain little clay content. Up to 3% may be used. SCMC also has deflocculatory power which is useful in low-clay glazes to keep them in suspension. Beware of over-thinning. It cannot be used in conjunction with calcium chloride in glazes of high clay content. SCMC is used in engobes and slurries for clay stage joining where it provides useful fluidity without too much water content.

Scratch-blue
A method of decorating in which a deeply-scored line in soft clay is painted with cobalt oxide. It was first used on salt-glazed ware in the 17th century and later copied on creamware. See photograph. See *Salt glaze* and *Creamware*.

Screen
A framework across which is fastened an interwoven mesh or possibly a grid created by holes in a flat sheet of metal. A screen is used to separate materials by size; particles that will go through the holes and those that will not. Screening can be done wet or dry. A screen used for materials in suspension in water is also called a sieve. A coarse screen which is made from interwoven wire and is used for dry material only is also called a riddle. The terms screen and screening imply a continuous process and are therefore more common in industry than in the individual potter's workshop. However the term screening is sometimes used by the individual potter to mean the use of a middle-sized mesh between the fine sieve and the coarse riddle. This would be between 40's and 10's mesh for wet or dry work but might include coarser meshes in wet work. See *Mesh*.

Scum
The light-coloured marks which appear along edges and as finger prints on unglazed ware and biscuit. They are caused by the soluble salts in the clay which crystallize at the surface as the water evaporates. The salts may have entered the clay from the water supply. The crystals are broken in handling and leave remarkably clear finger prints which show only after firing.

Extra moisture is drawn to edges which catch the movement of air during drying. These edges therefore get an extra amount of the salt crystallization. During firing the salts become oxides and in a very soft biscuit are on the surface as a dust but with a harder biscuit or an unglazed stoneware they flux the body from the surface and cannot be removed. If the ware is to be glazed many glazes will absorb the excess oxide which is mostly calcium oxide. However, thin layers of glaze on a fine body may not take properly on the rims and edges of handles. This is especially so on a medium to hard biscuit which is over-fluxed at these places. The salts are of sodium, potassium, calcium, magnesium and iron. Some have entered the clay by its association with salt water or by the weathering of sulfides in proximity. The commonest mineral is calcium sulfate.

Some of the salts in the clay can be rendered harmless by

the addition of 1% to 2% of barium carbonate. The barium carbonate is only slightly soluble and must be mixed thoroughly with the clay at a slurry stage. Blunging is preferable. Merely mixing with the clay is insufficient. The barium carbonate becomes 'soluble' in contact with the soluble salts with which it exchanges radicals. The new carbonate is precipitated as an insoluble powder or is a less soluble compound which cannot be carried to the surface of the clay by the water. The barium salt does not cause scum. The equations are:

$$MgSO_4 + BaCO_3 \longrightarrow BaSO_4 + MgCO_3\downarrow$$
magnesium   barium   barium   magnesium
sulfate   carbonate   sulfate   carbonate

$$CaSO_4 + BaCO_3 \longrightarrow BaSO_4 + CaCO_3\downarrow$$
calcium   barium   barium   calcium
sulfate   carbonate   sulfate   carbonate

The soluble barium chloride can also be used.

$$CaSO_4 + BaCl_2 \longrightarrow BaSO_4 + CaCl_2$$
calcium   barium   barium   calcium
sulfate   carbonate   sulfate   chloride

Sodium oxide and potassium oxide are also involved. They do not cause white scum but do cause over-fluxing. They cannot be precipitated because all their compounds are soluble. If the clay is worth the effort it can be 'washed' in plenty of water, settled and the excess water siphoned off.

Secondary clay

Sedimentary clay. A clay which has been removed from its place of origin by natural forces and deposited elsewhere. A primary clay is one that is still in its place of origin. China clay is the obvious example of a primary clay, but most clays have been washed away by rain, carried in rivers and settled in lakes or the sea to form beds of plastic clay. Sometimes the clay beds have been subjected to pressure and heat to become mudstones, shales and even slates. During transportation, the clays are ground to fine particles, pick up the impurities including colour and are often sorted by levigation into fine and coarse clays. Secondary clays are therefore of many types: ball clay, red clay, stoneware clay, shales, marls, fireclays. See also ***Clay: types*** and ***Disordered kaolinite***.

Sedimentation

Settling. The sinking of particles in a suspension. For example, the potter uses sedimentation to consolidate a slurry for reclamation as clay. The required clay settles and the water can be siphoned off the top.

The term is also used to describe the method of separating coarse, unwanted particles like sand from the finer, wanted particles of clay. The mixture is blunged—that is, thoroughly mixed with an excess of water. There must be

an excess of water in order to make the slurry very fluid (thin). The slurry is allowed to stand still so that the heavier particles are no longer able to keep in suspension and settle out. After the desired effect of separation is achieved (it is usually documented as a time), the required slurry is run off through a sieve and allowed to settle fully over a number of days before the water is siphoned or run off.

Sedimentation is a convenient method of washing and separating wood ash. It is also used commercially for special clays, in which case large tanks are used and a deflocculant is first added to increase the suspension life of the clay and make the slurry more fluid for the passage of the unwanted sediment. When the wanted suspension has been run into a second tank, a flocculant is added to hasten the sedimentation of the clay.

Sedimentation uses the same physical idea as levigation to separate particles without screening, but levigation uses a constant motion past riffles.

Seger

Hermann A. (1839–94). The German ceramicist who worked in other industries as a chemist before concentrating upon clay and heat treatment. He is known for his fundamental rules for overcoming crazing which followed his study of expansion rates and glaze fit; for his system of analysis, now called rational analysis, which describes clays in terms of pure kaolinite, feldspar and quartz; for his method of describing a glaze by the proportions of the constituent molecules, now called the unity formula method; and for his development of a method of gauging heat-work by pyrometric cones. All these systems originally carried his name (Seger rules, Seger analysis, Seger formula and Seger cones) but, with mid-20th century perfection of them, his name has been dropped from use, with the exception of the official Seger cone. See ***Cones***.

Selenium

Se. A non-metal which under special conditions gives red colours. It is volatile and can only be used under controlled conditions at low temperatures. It is used to produce red glass but in pottery its greatest use is in onglaze colours.

The red colour develops when selenium is combined with cadmium to give cadmium selenide (CdSe). This is a dark maroon red which with cadmium sulfide becomes a bright red and orange. The colour must be fired quickly because it is volatile.

Selenium dioxide is a glass-former but it has no place in glazes. See ***Poison***.

Sepiolite

Hydrated magnesium silicate. $3MgO.4SiO_2.5H_2O$. A natural soapstone similar to talc and used as a body flux in some medium temperature porcelains up to $1300°C$ ($2372°F$). It affects some colours unpleasantly—notably reduced iron and cobalt.

Sesquioxide

An oxide in which the combination of atoms which form the oxide molecule are in the ratio of two of the element to three of oxygen. For example, aluminium oxide is aluminium sesquioxide, there being two aluminium atoms to every three oxygen atoms in the aluminium oxide molecule. The chemical formula is written Al_2O_3. See also ***Oxide***.

Sesquisilicate

A combination of a stated compound and silica which involves three molecules of silica to every two molecules of the other compound. The definition (and the molecular formula) is sometimes expressed as one-and-a-half times the other compound which is literally correct since 'sesqui' means 'and one-half added'.

The usual use of sesquisilicate is to describe the lead frit, lead sesquisilicate, which is given the molecular formula of either $PbO.1·5SiO_2$ or $2PbO.3SiO_2$. See also ***Silicate***.

Setters

Special refractories shaped to hold pots in the kiln. These may be for biscuit or glaze firing. Some pots require to be held firmly to prevent warpage. This is especially true in high-temperature bisc firings where setters are used in combination with sand or aluminium oxide. In some porcelain glaze firings setting rings are used to keep cup rims round, the rims being unglazed. The cups are fired upside down.

Setting

Kiln packing especially of repetition pieces and bricks.

Sgraffito

Sgraffiato. Scratched decoration especially when the scratched line or area reveals a different colour. The word comes from the Italian '*graffiare*' to scratch and the adjective '*graffiato*' is sometimes used in English for textured areas. Sgraffito refers to decoration which is in scratched lines and sgraffiato to decoration using areas which have been scratched. By general use however sgraffito embraces all types of scratched decoration including textured areas.

Sgraffito is such an obvious and direct method of patterning a surface that its qualities are often overlooked. There is a natural desire to mark a clean surface and the obvious way is to attack it and scratch it. This is seen in many primitive pots where the simple action of scratching has given a very successful decorative quality. The best examples of sgraffito make full use of the textured area in relation to the whole pot. The normal considerations of distribution and balance in area and line must be realized.

The technique is easier to acquire than using a brush, especially for those who normally write and draw with an inflexible tip. The feeling of sgraffito should be freedom and movement. Impressed and applied decoration, in contrast, are static.

Sgraffito can be of various types. The simplest is a scratching of the surface of the clay at leatherhard or whitehard stage. This reveals a different texture of clay. The scratched lines and areas will probably show as a coarser texture even if the surface is glazed. Such scratches can be emphasized by rubbing with metal oxides. Or the lines may show through a semi-opaque glaze because the glaze is thicker on the lines. This effect can be made more marked by the use of a vitrifying slip. The first photograph shows vitrified slip sgraffito in a porcelain bowl by Sheila Casson. The slip may or may not be coloured differently from the body but it should contain sufficient soft flux to make the slip coating more dense than the body after biscuit firing. Thus the exposed body will be more porous and take to itself a thicker layer of glaze during glaze dipping.

With coloured slips the contrast becomes more marked and the removal of the slip at all stages from freshly dipped to bone-dry gives distinctive effects. The second photograph shows a honey jar by Graham Adamson.

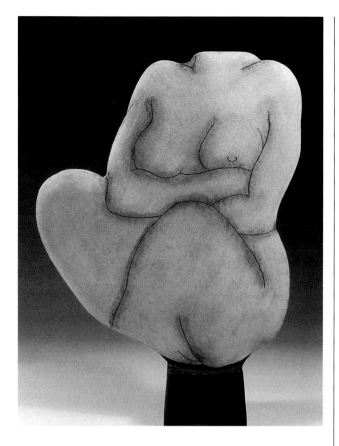

The use of a slip-glaze with stoneware opens up great possibilities because the contrast in colour and texture can be very effective. Because the body is incised the effect is very rich. Sgraffito is one of the best reasons for wanting a slip-glaze. Glazes on biscuit can also be sgraffitoed but the effect is not so rich. One can, however, gain a certain vitrification and colouring on the scratched surface by leaving a dusting of glaze there. Alternatively, another glaze over the top, possibly with further scratching, can give an infinite variety of decorative effects. The coffee pot by Michael Cardew shows the deep incision possible through a slip-glaze.

Shale

Flue. A clay in the form of small compressed flakes. The disc-like clay particles have orientated themselves at right angles to pressure producing a cleavage. In this arrangement they can be packed more tightly and form hard, flat flakes up to an inch across.

Pressure put onto plastic and cheese-hard clay is resisted by a partial reshuffle of particles across the line of pressure. This occurs in clay kneading, centring on a wheel, throwing, and burnishing after turning. In clay deposits the pressure may be great and continuous over millions of years, resulting in all the clay particles being lined up in the same direction. This produces shales. If heat is also present, the clay is partially 'fired' and the result is slate which exhibits cleavage along the lines of least resistance between the particles.

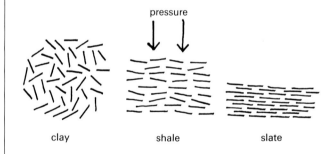

Terms such as wet sgraffito, cheese-hard sgraffito and dry sgraffito have been used to define such methods. Finger-combing is an example of the directness of fresh slip sgraffito. At a leatherhard stage the slip can be attacked with many tools from single cutters such as pieces of wood and metal to multiple texturizers, such as hacksaw blades.

The photograph of 'Sitting Pretty' by Jude Jelfs illustrates the individual way sgraffito can be used. Black slip has been painted on the leatherhard piece, burnished, then covered with an orange-coloured slip. Sgraffito lines were drawn through the top slip to reveal the black slip. After biscuit firing more black slip was rubbed into the lines and smudged to give the effect of a charcoal drawing. The final firing was to 1095°C (2003°F) and the piece was given a beeswax polish while still warm.

Shales—that is, clay shales—occur in all ages of rocks. The oldest ones are the Silurian shales of 420 million years ago. The Carboniferous System also has shales. Both the culm measures and the productive coal measures contain shales, some of which are fireclays. These are over 280 million years old. The Tea marls of the Triassic Period of the New Red Sandstone System are also often shaly. These are about 200 million years old.

All these shales will weather to clays. The process can be accelerated by crushing and blunging. Many shales can be converted into excellent potting clays by the addition of bentonite. Weathered shales are sometimes referred to as hungry clays.

Shape

The two-dimensional qualities of a pot or ceramic. These can be analysed as silhouette, outline, contrast of colour and tone, proportions and angles. Shape is often used as a synonym for form but correctly shape should be used in the consideration of a pot's silhouette, its comparative dimensions or proportions and its decoration. The confusion has arisen because of consideration of pots at a drawing board stage.

Shelling

Flaking. Peeling. A glaze, or glaze and slip, defect in which the glaze falls from the body in flakes. It often occurs where there is a slip on the body and mostly on low-fired ware or on porous bodies. It is caused by insufficient bond between glaze and body. This bond is lost when stress is placed on the article by handling or by normal expansions of the body and glaze.

The poor bond is the result of underfiring the glaze which melts itself but produces no body-glaze layer. Or, in the case of wares with slip covering, if the slip is put on the ware when the ware is too dry, or possibly greasy, it never properly adheres. After the glaze firing, the glaze is pulling at the slip, which parts its bond on the body. Shelling is usually in evidence on rims when the wares are taken from the kiln or in the period soon after. Complete shelling may take place in extreme cases.

Where there is sufficient bond between body and glaze, but flakes of glaze leave the ware, this action is called shivering and is described elsewhere. Shivering is characterized by the way the sliver of glaze shears off the pot, tearing part of the body with it.

Sherd

Shard. A piece of broken pottery. The term is often used archaeologically with the collective noun shraft.

Shigaraki

A pottery-making valley in rural Japan. The distinctive wares made for over seven centuries have gained an esteemed place in the aesthetic of Japanese woodfired stoneware. The storage jars and tea-ceremony wares were made in the low-iron clay and fired in anagama kilns. This produced attractive, light iron colours enlivened by small white dots of partly melted feldspar granules and natural ash runs.

Shino

A popular high-temperature transparent glaze from Japan.

nepheline syenite	75
ball clay	25

Usually used over a dark body and white slip. The nepheline syenite produces a deep orange colour from iron in the body. See ***Colour plate 43***.

Shivering

A glaze defect in which slivers of glaze shear away from the pot. It occurs especially on sharp outside edges, e.g. rims, the edges of handles, relief decoration and throwing marks. The flake of glaze has a very sharp edge and takes with it some of the body to which it was attached. It is known as a glaze defect although the fault often lies with the body. It is a result of poor glaze fit and is the opposite of crazing. It occurs more on stoneware than earthenware. In stoneware the body and glaze mature together and become integrated. If the glaze does not fit it takes with it part of the body. In earthenware and immature stonewares, the lack of this integrated body-glaze layer means that the glaze can leave the pot without tearing the body. This phenomenon is called shelling.

When a pot cools after firing, the glaze sets at approximately 500°C (932°F). From this temperature down to room temperature the body and the glaze lie side by side as two solids which should be bonded to each other. The body and the glaze each contract at a different rate. This puts the glaze on the finished pot either under tension or under compression by the body. Some compression is desirable as an insurance against crazing but too much compression results in shivering. It is impossible to know how much is too much until shivering occurs. Since the correct balance is a fine one and shivering when it occurs is dangerous with tableware and ovenware, some potters prefer not to have their glazes under compression at all. To be sure that there is no compression, they welcome a very slight crazing. According to the type of ware being made, one must steer a course between the two extremes of shivering and crazing. The problem is discussed under ***Thermal shock***.

To overcome shivering, the glaze, or the body, or both must be altered in composition. The glaze must be made to contract more on cooling. This can be done by substituting other oxides of greater contraction rate for some of the fluxing oxides. The problem is discussed under ***Glaze fit***. Shivering is typical of glazes of high clay content which are high in aluminium oxide, and also of aluminium oxide and magnesium oxide matts. It will be seen from the table of expansion rates that these oxides are at the low expansion end of the scale.

Conversely, the body may be made to contract less on cooling. The method is the opposite to that used for the glaze. However, most bodies do not contain fluxing oxides in the way that glazes do. The fluxes are part of raw materials and they cannot be isolated. One must therefore turn one's attention to the free silica in the body. Free silica exists in the body as crystalline quartz before firing. During firing, some of the crystalline quartz becomes involved in vitrification and becomes fused silica. As fused silica, it has a lower expansion rate than crystalline. A prolonged or higher firing will therefore result in more of the free silica becoming fused and the result will be that the eventual body will contract less on cooling than it did before.

However, one must not jump too quickly at this means of correcting shivering. Shivering usually occurs on stoneware where the body and the glaze mature together, and it is on the densest of stonewares, with the most vitrified bodies, that it occurs most. This is contrary to the correction theory just expounded because in practice the extra vitrification makes the body more brittle. It also decreases its physical strength. The stress between body and glaze, though lessened, may still exist and be sufficient to rupture the bond between glaze and body, ripping away the top layer of body embedded in the body-glaze layer. With a prolonged firing there is also the possibility that some of the crystalline quartz which is not fused may be converted into crystalline cristobalite. This would result in even greater body contraction than before. See ***Silica conversion*** and ***Cristobalite***.

At this point one should not confuse the overall shrinkage from raw to fired ware with the contraction which takes place on cooling. The two are entirely separate and independent. A body that shrinks a great deal may still have a contraction rate that is low or high. Shrinkage is an irreversible process dependent upon vitrification. Contraction is the result of temperature fall and is reversible with heat. Correction of body composition must therefore be sought in another way. Aluminous grog has a smaller contraction rate than silica sand, so if grog were used instead of sand the overall contraction would be less. If there is no additional sand in the body which can be replaced by grog it is possible that the addition of some grog may cause less contraction. It is not a certainty because some grogs contract more than some stoneware bodies. An aluminous grog should be tried. Even sillimanite and zirconium silicate have been used in extreme cases but these are expensive and an alteration of glaze is preferable.

If shivering occurs on some pots and not on others, one should note any temperature differences in their firings. One should also consider the forms themselves and the angles on which shivering occurs. Shivering often occurs on pots in which the clay became tired in throwing. Sandy bodies which have been oversponged on the rims, leaving them composed of sand rather than clay, are prone to shivering. A change in throwing habits and the use of a buffer slip may show immediate success but a change in the physical properties of the body and glaze should also take place.

Short clay

Lean clay. Clay which has little plasticity and strength. It is a relative term because clay can only be termed short when it has insufficient workability for the job in hand. A general

standard amongst individual potters is that a clay should be capable of being thrown on a potter's wheel. This requires a high standard of workability. A simple test is the tie-a-knot test described under ***Workability***. The short clay will show signs of tearing, if not complete rupture.

Short clays are often very difficult to knead. They have little capacity to slide; they have also a high resistance to pressure. That is, their yield point is high. They have a stodgy feel that is almost a bounce, like a bread dough. Many have such little strength that they sag under their own weight, especially as they become wet in throwing.

A natural clay which is short can have a plastic clay like ball clay blended with it. Alternatively, a plasticizer can be added or more deliberate preparation may be required. See ***Plasticity*** and ***Preparation of Clay***.

Shrinkage

Decrease in size due to drying and firing. Drying shrinkage is reversible with the return of water, but firing shrinkage is due to chemical and physical changes in the clay and is permanent. See ***Drying*** and ***Firing***. Shrinkage should not be confused with contraction, which is the opposite of expansion and is the result of temperature differences.

The chart compares the shrinkages of two clays and a prepared body. Note how the body which contains 20% non-plastic material has a low shrinkage during drying. This non-plastic material is however a densifying addition which increases the firing shrinkage up to the densification point at 1100°C (2012°F). The photographs show the drying shrinkage of a patch of natural clay and the firing shrinkage of a red clay at the different temperatures of 850°C, 1000°C, 1130°C, 1180°C and 1250°C (or 1562°F, 1832°F, 2066°F, 2156°F and 2282°F).

Siderite

Chalybite. Iron carbonate. $FeCO_3$. A low-yield iron ore formed when iron in solution replaces calcium oxide in a limestone. To differentiate this from the high-yield ores, the siderite is often called an ironstone. Ironstones occur as replacement deposits which do not necessarily follow the strata. There are also partial replacements, referred to as ferruginous limestones, and crystals in shales called clay ironstones. The star shape of the cluster of crystals gives the ore its name, siderite: the stone of the stars. These ironstones can be empirically used as glaze colourants and fluxes. See *Iron oxide*.

Sieve

A frame or rim with a lawn or fine mesh across it used for separating by size the coarse material from fine, or unwanted from wanted etc. It is usual to sieve materials when they are suspended in water. In this form they are easier to handle. Industrially, the word sieve is used in connection with test work, and screen is used in production. The individual potter uses the word screen for coarser meshes and riddle for very coarse. Screening may be done wet or dry but riddling is done with dry materials. See *Mesh*.

The photograph shows an electric vibrating sieve in use.

Silica

Silicon dioxide. SiO_2. The glassy substance which is the most important constituent of pottery glazes and which is an integral part of clay and many potters' minerals. It occurs naturally as quartz rock, flint and sand. It also occurs in combination with other oxides in what are called silicates. An analysis of all the substances in the earth's crust shows that 60% is silica.

Silica is a hard glassy substance which melts at 1710°C (3110°F) to a transparent glass. This temperature is too high for a potter's kiln and so some way of melting silica at a lower temperature is used in order to make a glaze. Fluxes are mixed with the silica. These have the effect of bringing down the melting temperature to within the range of the potter's kiln. The resulting melt is a mixture of silica and other oxides which link together on cooling to form a glass. Silica is the necessary constituent of this glass. There are many fluxes but only one silica. The only substance which gives similar results to silica is boron oxide. This is also a glass-former, but without silica it will not give a satisfactory glaze.

Clay is a combination of silica, aluminium oxide and water. The chemist calls clay hydrated alumino-silicate. The word silicate is a common one and explains that silica is present as an important constituent. Theoretically, pure clay is 47% silica but in practice it contains more silica than this. The extra silica is not integrated in clay particles but is present as sand or as extremely fine silica. This is called free silica and is important because it forms a glassy binding for the clay particles which gives strength to the finished pottery body.

Silica occurs naturally as quartz rock (also called milky quartz), quartzite, ganister, sandstone, sand, flint, chert and a number of semi-precious stones which are listed under *Quartz*. All these occurrences contain some impurities. Sand, sandstone, ganister and quartzite may contain 10% impurities in the form of iron oxide, calcium oxide, feldspathoids and clay. Flint and chert contain up to 5% calcium oxide. Quartz rock is the purest occurrence being 99% silica and only 1% impurity.

In a glaze the silicas from different sources would behave slightly differently because of the impurities. As a general rule, impurities help the silica to melt more easily. Impurities may also give some colouring. Quartz and flint are the popular silicas for glazes and are bought in powder form.

Preparation of one's own silica is a difficult process because it is so physically hard. Quartz is crushed and ground. Flint is calcined and then ground. There is little difference between quartz and flint in a glaze because free silica in a glaze recipe rarely exceeds 20%. Flint should melt more easily than quartz but a mixture of the two will probably be found to melt more easily than either alone because of the phenomenon of interaction.

The addition of silica to a body makes the fired ware harder and more durable. Sand may also give a pleasing texture. Silica also alters the amount by which the body contracts in cooling after firing. The lattice structure of silica is capable of a number of forms and can change from one to another during firing and cooling. These are changes in size, called inversions, and can cause stresses which can result in cracking. See **Silica inversions** and **Dunting**. The amount by which the body contracts is also important for correct glaze fit. Silica is therefore added to a body for a number of reasons which must be balanced against one another. As a general rule, flint is to be preferred for earthenware because it converts to cristobalite more easily than quartz. Quartz or quartz sand are preferable for stoneware because they do not convert so easily to cristobalite.

The addition of silica to a body normally renders the body more refractory, that is, it will withstand a higher temperature because silica itself is refractory. However, there are some natural clays which are not refractory and yet contain a fairly high proportion of silica. This anomaly is explained by the fineness of some or all of the free silica. If the grain size is finer than a 600's mesh then the silica seems capable of fluxing itself.

Silica also occurs naturally in combination with other oxides in silicates such as feldspar, cornish stone, talc and wollastonite. It is also present in vegetation, being responsible for the sharp edges of grasses and the stinging needles on nettles. Vegetable ashes therefore contain silica. Some contain a very high proportion of silica but act as fluxes because of the phenomenon previously explained whereby extremely fine silica crystals or grains can flux themselves.

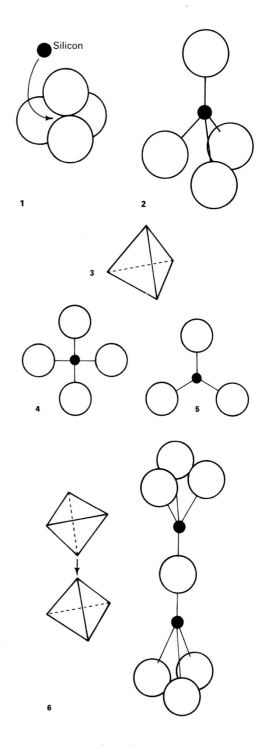

SILICA STRUCTURE. If four oxygen atoms are packed together as in fig. 1, there is a space inside them large enough to accommodate a silicon atom. The four oxygen atoms satisfy the valency and co-ordination requirements of the silicon as in fig. 2.

This triangular pyramid of four oxygen atoms around a silicon atom is the SiO_4 silica molecule and is referred to as the silica tetrahedron. It appears in many structural drawings as a solid tetrahedron, fig. 3, or as a simple square of oxygen atoms, fig. 4, or as a top view ignoring the apex oxygen, fig. 5.

Adjacent silica tetrahedra are joined together by a common oxygen atom as in fig. 6. In this way the valency of this oxygen atom is satisfied. When each oxygen atom is bonded to two silicon atoms and each silicon atom to four oxygen atoms, a series of interlinked chains is formed with twice as many oxygen atoms as silicon atoms. Thus the chemical formula overall is SiO_2.

When two tetrahedra are joined by their common oxygen there are three possible positions for the top triangular 'base' of the upper tetrahedron in relation to the 'base' of the lower one. See fig. 7. The three different crystalline structures (a) quartz, (b) cristobalite and (c) tridymite result if the relationship which characterizes each pair is continued throughout a lattice. See **Crystal**. Inconsistency

7   a   b   c

results in the amorphous phase of silica glass. Slight changes in the angle at the point where the tetrahedra join occur during the silica inversions as described later. Another method of describing the structures is given under ***Cristobalite: physical***.

SILICA PHASES. The main types of silica are quartz, tridymite and cristobalite. The phases of silica are all chemically the same, having the formula SiO_2, but differ in the way in which the atoms are bonded together in the lattice structure. A silica phase is subdivided into silica forms which are given identification by alpha, beta etc. Phases are sometimes called principal forms and are also called silica conversions because they are produced by converting one phase of silica into another. Some phases have no subdivisions and so are themselves called forms which could cause confusion. Fortunately, apart from silica glass, they are phases unknown to the individual potter.

SILICA

phases	forms
QUARTZ	∝ quartz β quartz
TRIDYMITE	∝ tridymite β tridymite
CRISTOBALITE	∝ cristobalite β cristobalite
SILICA GLASS	silica glass

SILICA FORMS. The subdivisions of the main types or phases of silica, e.g. alpha quartz, beta quartz, alpha cristobalite, beta cristobalite. Also types of silica which have no subdivisions are themselves called forms, e.g. silica gel, silica glass, silica W, keatite, compacted vitreous silica, suprapiezo-vitreous silica, coesite and stishovite.

All silica forms are chemically identical, having the formula SiO_2. They are all composed of silica tetrahedra. See photograph, ***Silica structure*** and ***Crystal***. The difference between one form and another is in the way these tetrahedra units are joined together. If they are joined together in a regular pattern a crystalline form results, e.g. alpha quartz. If they are joined in random manner an amorphous form results, e.g. silica glass. If they are joined together in an open network which leaves spaces in

between, the form will be light in weight, e.g. silica W with a relative density of 1·98. If they are joined in a very compact manner the form will be heavy, e.g. stishovite with a relative density of 4·35. Alpha quartz has a relative density of 2·65 and is the commonest form of silica that the potter will meet. Indeed, although there are over twenty forms of silica the potter need be concerned with only five of them. These are alpha quartz, beta quartz, alpha cristobalite, beta cristobalite and silica glass. The differences between alpha and beta quartz and between alpha and beta cristobalite are the angles between the lattice bonds. The alpha form changes to the beta form upon heating. This is a rapid change and is called a silica inversion.

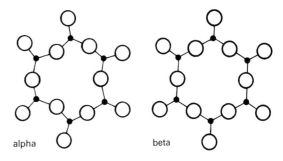

alpha   beta

SILICA CONVERSION. The action by which one type of silica is transformed into another type of silica. The types of silica are correctly called phases. The conversions of free silica of the quartz phase into free silica of the cristobalite phase or into silica glass are the only conversions that really matter to the individual potter.

Potters require cristobalite in their earthenware bodies because of its silica inversion property which acts against the tendency of glazes to craze. Potters therefore attempt to convert the free silica in an earthenware body into cristobalite. They do this using temperature and time in what is commonly called soaking in the presence of other substances which assist. These other substances are called catalysts.

Potters convert the quartz phase of silica, which is crystalline, into the glassy phase, which is non-crystalline, in order to make glazes. Again they use both temperature and time with the assistance of other substances which in this case become intermixed with the new phase.

The commonest phase of silica is called quartz. This is a technical term used to describe silica which has a particular type of crystalline lattice. Quartz occurs naturally in quartz rock, sandstone, sand, flint and chert. If this quartz phase is heated, a change in the lattice structure begins to take place at 870°C (1598°F). This is an exceedingly slow change requiring days to complete and is called a conversion. The new phase is called disordered cristobalite. Further heating above 1470°C (2678°F) results in another slow conversion to the pure cristobalite phase. On cooling the new phases remain. Natural occurrence of cristobalite is extremely rare. This is because it usually cools under pressure within rocks and when under pressure it converts back to quartz which is a more compact or denser phase. Therefore quartz is the phase of silica which a potter is likely to have in clay and glaze minerals.

The difference between one phase and another is the way in which the silica tetrahedra are joined to one another. There are many possibilities. Some produce fairly open networks, some produce very dense networks, some networks are regular and some networks are random. For a conversion to take place, the existing bonds between the silica tetrahedra must be loosened by heat or pressure or a combination of both and sufficient time allowed for the network to be rearranged.

Time is an important factor in all conversions. For example, at 1300°C (2372°F) it takes ten days to convert 100% quartz to 100% cristobalite. The time can be reduced by assisting the conversion with catalysts which do their work without changing their own states. The time would then be measured in hours rather than days. The first conversions to be discovered were dependent only upon temperature and time at atmospheric pressure and the new phases remained on cooling. Hence the term conversion has some hint of a one-way transformation. However, it has since been discovered that a conversion is reversible if the cooling occurs under pressure.

The potter may meet with another phase of silica called tridymite. Tridymite is a complex phase having two major subdivisions and nine minor subdivisions called forms. Quartz converts to tridymite between 870°C and 1470°C (1598°F and 2678°F) if suitable catalysts are present. It cannot exist indefinitely above 1470°C but at this temperature begins to convert into pure cristobalite. On cooling tridymite will remain as tridymite at atmospheric pressure. If under greater pressure, tridymite will convert back into quartz which is a denser phase. For this reason very little tridymite occurs naturally as a mineral. Tridymite has industrial application as silica bricks and in combination with cristobalite in earthenware bodies. The inversion properties of its nine forms combined with the inversions of cristobalite can give control of a tendency to craze, coupled with a higher resistance to thermal shock.

Tridymite and disordered cristobalite can obviously exist side by side at temperatures below 1470°C (2678°F). The same catalysts that assist the conversion of quartz to tridymite also act as catalysts for the conversion of both into disordered cristobalite. Therefore the easiest way is to consider these conversions from quartz into tridymite, disordered cristobalite and pure cristobalite as one and include these phases under the name cristobalite. This simplification is used throughout this book except for the explanation of tridymite inversions under **Silica inversions** and in the article on **Cristobalite**.

The potter is interested in conversions to cristobalite and to glass. In considering conversions a number of factors are involved.

1. Only the free silica of quartz phase which is in crystalline or cryptocrystalline state can be converted into cristobalite. Silica which is of an amorphous phase cannot be converted into cristobalite. This is because from the potter's point of view the silica has reached its ultimate state. The ultimate state is that which it would reach at its melting point of 1710°C (3110°F). When it reaches this state before this temperature by the action of fluxes it has passed the conversion stages. The quick cooling that pottery receives precludes the return to crystalline state possible in nature. Amorphous silica has no crystal structure and is present either as previously fused silica or as silica already involved in a liquid melt. Both quartz and cristobalite can be converted into fused silica—that is, silica glass.

2. Time is necessary for a conversion and therefore a conversion is not inevitable in a firing. This is in contrast to an inversion which is sudden and is unavoidable.

3. For the potter the lowest practical temperature for a quartz to cristobalite conversion is 1100°C (2012°F). At this temperature a long time is required. Three or four hours soaking at 1100°C would only convert a small proportion of the quartz to cristobalite. At higher temperatures proportionately less time is required.

4. The grain size affects the time required. Fine powdered quartz converts quicker than quartz sand at the lower temperatures.

5. The presence of suitable catalysts speeds the process of conversion. Calcium oxide and magnesium oxide are considered catalysts for the conversion of quartz to cristobalite. For conversion to tridymite the list is extended with oxides of potassium, sodium, aluminium and iron and combinations such as feldspar and cornish stone. For conversion to the glass phase the catalysts are called fluxes and the list includes all oxides, especially alkaline oxides.

6. A conversion is a progression. Once the conversion has started, the presence of some cristobalite stimulates the conversion of more quartz into cristobalite and the conversion goes ahead with increasing speed. Cristobalite itself is therefore an important agent or catalyst in the action and some potters add ground cristobalite to bodies to start conversion. The same can be said of conversion to the glass phase. Potters add previously fused silica to glazes and bodies in the form of frits.

Cristobalite is desirable in earthenware bodies as an anti-craze agent. See **Silica inversions** and **Cristobalite**. For this reason flint is added to earthenware bodies. Flint contains about 5% chalk as an impurity. The chalk becomes calcium oxide in the calcination of flint and is an important catalyst in the conversion of the flint, which is the quartz phase of silica, into cristobalite during the firing. Ground rock quartz or sand would not convert so easily. Before the silica conversions were understood potters added talc to earthenware bodies as an anti-craze device. They had discovered this use of talc empirically. Talc is magnesium silicate and would itself convert and assist conversion of free silica to cristobalite during firing. Also magnesium oxide in bodies works against the tendency to expand with moisture as explained under **Silica inversions**.

In stoneware bodies it is not desirable to have much cristobalite, if any. The more brittle nature of stoneware with its thicker glazes renders it more susceptible to cristobalite dunting. Therefore for stoneware bodies clean quartz sand is used in fireclays or ball clays. If red clay is added, the marl types, which are high in calcium oxide, are to be avoided.

It will be seen that conversions are slow changes requiring time. The conversion of quartz to cristobalite is not inevitable. A potter who does not want cristobalite in the body can reduce the amount of quartz converted to cristobalite by reducing the free silica present, by a quicker firing and cooling and by reducing the amounts of the catalysts present. Thus the silica conversions from one phase to another can be avoided or at least controlled. In contrast, the silica inversions from one form to another within a phase cannot be avoided.

SILICA INVERSIONS. Minor changes in the lattice structures of silica. Inversions are responsible for sudden expansions and sudden contractions of pottery bodies which might result in cracks. Such cracks are known as dunts. Inversions can be used to control crazing of glazes especially on earthenware.

The inversion change takes place at an inversion point or temperature. At temperatures above the inversion point the lattice structure is strictly regular but at temperatures below the inversion point the lattice structure is compressed and in parts irregular. This means that at the inversion point a change in size occurs. An increasing temperature past the inversion point results in an increase in size of up to 3% volume. A decreasing temperature past the inversion point results in an equivalent decrease in size. An inversion is therefore a reversible change and will occur every time a silica passes its inversion point.

The two forms of silica, one below and one above the inversion point, are called alpha and beta, respectively. Some phases of silica have more than one inversion point and thus more than two forms. The forms are called alpha, beta one, beta two etc.

Inversions only take place in crystalline silica where there

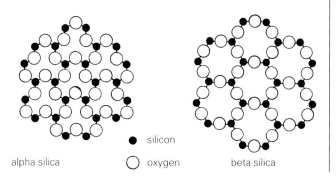

alpha silica   ● silicon   ○ oxygen   beta silica

is a large regular lattice of silicon and oxygen atoms. Once silica is fused in a molten glaze the silica network no longer exists as a large network. It is broken down into smaller units which move freely amongst other small units of other oxides. The different units form random chains or networks of oxides on cooling. The silica units do not have time or opportunity to re-establish contact with one another and so the original state of crystalline silica does not exist in the glaze. A glaze is therefore not subject to silica inversions. However, a body does contain crystalline silica, also called free silica, and this silica will invert and will therefore change its size.

Silica is the name of the chemical compound silicon dioxide. Silica can be subdivided into a number of different phases of which quartz and cristobalite are of concern to the potter. Phases of silica are chemically identical but are physically different and therefore behave differently. The inversion in the quartz phase takes place between 550°C and 575°C (1022°F and 1067°F) but is usually regarded as taking place at 573°C (1063°F). As the temperature rises the lattice straightens itself or regularizes itself as in the earlier diagram. It is always considered a sudden change but it is a change which starts at about 550°C (1022°F) and accelerates rapidly, reaching completion suddenly at 573°C (1063°F). The graph below shows the reversible expansion of quartz when heated. Alpha and beta quartz are therefore subdivisions of the phase quartz. Quartz is a phase of the chemical silica.

The cristobalite inversion takes place between 220°C and 280°C (428°F and 536°F). It is a sudden change, unlike the quartz inversion which is a change with accelerating result from alpha to beta. Also unlike the quartz inversion it does not occur at an exact temperature but can occur at any temperature between 220°C and 280°C (428°F and 536°F). The cristobalite inversion is more important to potters in its cooling from beta to alpha and the temperature at which it changes is dependent upon the length and temperature of the firing from which it is cooling. The comparatively short

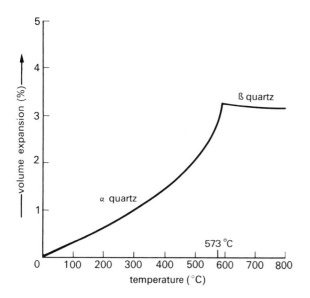

firings used by the individual potter make the cristobalite lag to the lower end of the range of change before inverting so that it is usually below 230°C (446°F). A popular temperature is 226°C (439°F) and it is used throughout this book for simplicity.

The graph below shows the reversible expansion of cristobalite when heated. It will be noted that if cristobalite is in the body then the whole pot will contract suddenly at this temperature during cooling. Ovenware has to withstand sudden cooling from a hot oven at possibly 290°C (554°F). In the making of ovenware the potter tries to exclude cristobalite. The problem is treated more fully under **Thermal shock**.

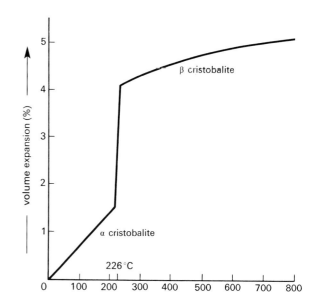

The inversion of tridymite will be mentioned for completeness. Its inversion gives further contrast to the previous two. The tridymite inversion takes place between 75°C and 200°C (167°F and 392°F) in nine stages. To further complicate things, these nine inversions are divided between two main phases of tridymite. Tridymite exists along with disordered cristobalite when quartz is converted with the help of catalysts as explained in **Silica conversion**.

Industrially, the balance of the phases of tridymite and the types of cristobalite existing in disordered cristobalite is controlled to give a series of small inversions rather than one large sudden inversion. The advantage of this is that the necessary overall contraction can be achieved in a smoother action than the sudden large contraction of a cristobalite inversion. The preparation of tridymite is beyond the scope of the individual potter, so for simplicity tridymite and disordered cristobalite are considered as simply cristobalite in this book. It is unlikely that much tridymite will exist in the pot bodies fired by the individual potter because the conversion takes a long time. However, it may be introduced under the name of cristobalite as a purchased powder.

The amount of free silica in different bodies varies between 5% and 50% of the body. During a firing, the

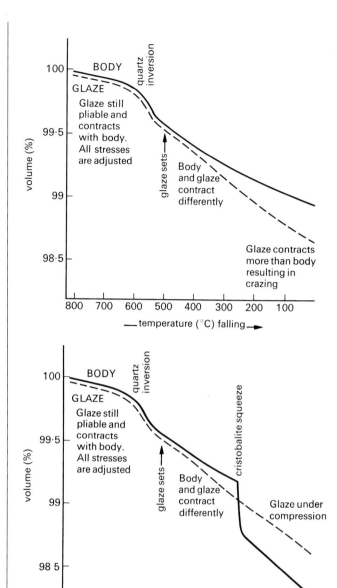

volumetric change in size of this silica, as quartz and disordered cristobalite, will be between 3% and 4·5%. The overall volumetric change in size which it will create in a body cannot exceed 2·25%. Most of this will be part of a gradual expansion and contraction but part will be associated with the silica inversions. Quartz has a volumetric change in size of approximately 1% during inversion and cristobalite a size change of approximately 3%. In practice, this could mean a change in size of a pottery body in the order of 0·5% at the quartz inversion of a body containing 50% free quartz silica, and a size change in the order of 0·45% at the cristobalite inversion of a body containing 15% free cristobalite silica. Both these are extreme cases. Average bodies would give changes of 0·2% and 0·25%, respectively. Even so this amount is sufficient to set up considerable stresses within the body itself and between the body and the glaze.

If the body is not strong enough to contain the stresses which are created within it then it ruptures. This is called dunting. Dunts to the body are usually caused by the quartz inversion at 573°C (1063°F) on cooling from a biscuit firing. If the biscuit is too soft and weak or the cooling too sudden then the body is not strong enough to contain the stress. Dunts may also be caused by the cristobalite inversion at 226°C (439°F) on cooling from a stoneware firing. Unglazed stoneware is sometimes brittle and in such cases may not be strong enough to contain the stress imposed by the cristobalite inversion. The opening of a kiln too soon, causing quick and unequal cooling, will result in dunting of stoneware if there is cristobalite in the body. The problem of cristobalite in stoneware is more fully dealt with under *Silica conversion*.

The cooling quartz inversion at 573°C (1063°F) is not likely to cause stress between body and glaze. At this temperature the glaze is still sufficiently plastic to allow itself to be compressed by the body when the body suddenly contracts. The cooling cristobalite inversion at 226°C (439°F) produces a stress between body and glaze because at this temperature the glaze is solid. The body contracts but the glaze cannot do so. The result is that the body tries to

compress the glaze. If the stress is not too great this state is desirable for earthenware and tableware. It is not desirable for ovenware and is not necessary for true stoneware. This compression of the glaze means that it cannot craze. A glaze crazes when it is too small for the body which it is on. Such a stress between body and glaze is therefore the opposite of the state of glaze compression. Being brittle, the glaze cracks to accommodate the stress and the cracks are called crazes. Obviously a glaze under compression cannot craze.

Earthenware body is porous and although completely sealed by a layer of glaze it can still absorb moisture from the air through the covering glaze by a means as yet unexplained. The absorbed moisture makes the body expand. The glaze does not expand. If the two, body and glaze, were originally lying side by side without stress then the glaze would craze. However if there exists between body and glaze a stress of compression on the glaze, all that can happen when the body expands with moisture is an easing of the stress. If the stress was originally sufficient, crazing will not occur.

If the stress between body and glaze created by a cooling cristobalite inversion is too great the body may crack. Theoretically the glaze would be cracking the body by pulling it apart. As it cracks there is usually some sideways displacement and the glaze cracks also. This is called cristobalite dunting. Alternatively, if the body is strong the glaze may flake off in slivers which are sharp-edged and often take with them part of the body. This occurs mostly on rims, edges of handles and throwing ridges. This is called shivering. A glaze can withstand ten times as much stress in compression before it shivers as it can withstand in tension before it crazes.

Silica gel

A form of amorphous silica. The units of silica gel are the standard silica tetrahedra but they are not joined together in a regular lattice. Instead they attach themselves to one another in a random manner so that no crystal formation exists, therefore it is called amorphous.

Silica glass

Fused silica. Silica which has been melted and cooled again so quickly that the silica tetrahedra have not been able to establish a pattern of structure. The silica is therefore amorphous, that is, non-crystalline. The tetrahedra units

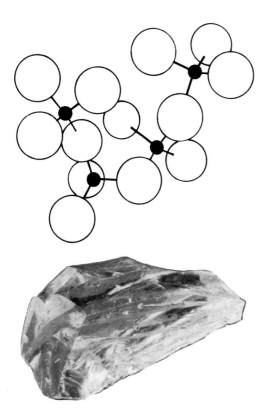

are attached to one another in random manner. If they had been able to attach themselves to one another in a pattern a crystalline structure would have followed and the silica would have become one of the crystalline forms.

Silica glass is sometimes called fused silica, or vitreous silica. Silica which is incorporated in a finished glaze or glass is sometimes referred to as fused silica because it has been unable to re-establish itself as a silica crystal lattice. Silica glass and fused silica are sometimes erroneously called quartz glass and fused quartz. Quartz may have been the original mineral used but since quartz is the technical term for a crystalline phase of silica it cannot be also used for the non-crystalline silica glass.

Silica glass is not subject to inversions as are the crystalline phases. Its thermal expansion is very low compared with quartz and cristobalite. This shows markedly in the graph.

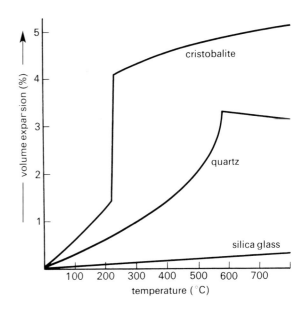

Silicate

A compound involving silica as an important part. Specifically the term implies that the ratio of silica to the other oxides is such that a crystal structure can be established. For example, kaolinite is hydrated alumino-silicate ($Al_2O_3.2SiO_2.2H_2O$) and zircon is zirconium silicate ($ZrO_2.SiO_2$).

In prepared silicates the crystal structure is unlikely to be formed because of the glass-forming properties of silica. Hence lead bisilicate ($PbO.2SiO_2$) is an amorphous solid and not crystalline, although doubtless a crystal could be grown. When crystals have not grown it is impossible to classify it as a balanced compound on its physical appearance and yet many glasses which may not be strictly silicates are described as such. The term 'silicates' is there-fore extended to include all glasses which are founded upon silica as an integral part of the substance. Thus all glazes and frits are occasionally referred to collectively as silicates.

Mineralogically there are many silicates which have

found ceramic use. They include the groups called feldspars, micas, pyroxenes, amphiboles and zeolites.

Siliceous

Refers to minerals, especially clay, which contain a high proportion of free silica.

Silicon carbide

SiC. An artificial compound of silicon and carbon made from baked sand and coke. It is extremely hard, even harder than aluminium oxide and nearly as hard as diamond. It is therefore a useful abrasive both as a powder and as grind-stones, and is sold under many trade names.

Silicon carbide is an electrical semi-conductor and is used to make kiln elements of the bar type. These are often tubular and mounted vertically in the kiln passing through the floor and roof to the terminals. Again different trade names are used. See *Element (2)*.

Silicon carbide is a refractory and can withstand over 2000°C (3632°F). It is therefore used for kiln furniture for high-temperature work up to 1400°C (2552°F), and for reduction firings and salt glazing because it is not affected by these atmospheres. See *Furniture*.

SILICON CARBIDE REDUCTION. Since the 1930s in the USA, silicon carbide has been used as a local reducing agent by adding it to glazes and slips. By its use copper oxide can be induced to give reds and iron oxide can give celadon colourings. The process is called autoreduction and because the effects are achieved in an oxidized firing they are also called local reduction. Only a selected part of the pot, e.g. the glaze, is reduced. Total reduction using a reducing atmosphere affects the whole pot and also the kiln furniture.

If silicon carbide is introduced into a glaze recipe it remains unchanged until about 1000°C (1832°F). Mesh size 200's is used. Above this temperature it is attacked by a molten glaze which causes a breakdown or dissociation of the silicon and carbon. Each then seeks oxygen to become silica and carbon monoxide and dioxide, respectively. The oxygen is taken from the surrounding glaze thereby reducing a part of it. The silica joins the glaze melt. The carbonaceous gases form bubbles in the glaze, rise to the surface, burst and escape.

If copper oxide is present in a glaze it is not difficult to reduce it from CuO to Cu_2O or even to the metal Cu. It readily gives up its oxygen when presented with oxygen-hungry silicon and carbon. An equal weight of silicon carbide to copper oxide will be sufficient—approximately 0·3% of each. Too much copper oxide—over 0·5%—gives a muddy colour. Bubbles sometimes remain in the glaze and also blister the surface. An extended firing will allow these bubbles to escape but also runs the risk of reoxidizing the copper. Extremely fine bubbles in suspension give a pleasing bluish jun effect. See also *Autoreduction*.

The reduction will take place when the glaze melts. From that point to the end of the firing the glaze needs to be sealed and there needs to be present at least one stabilizer if re-

oxidation is not to take place. For copper reds a useful stabilizer is tin oxide. One per cent of tin oxide is sufficient and this amount is practically dissolved by the glaze. Any excess reduced tin gives a pleasant lustrous surface. Theoretically, zinc and iron oxides will also act as stabilizers and the fluxes lead oxide, calcium oxide and sodium oxide will assist in forming and keeping a clear colour. Each situation is different because there are more than the chemical factors of the glaze involved.

To get rid of the bubbles of carbon monoxide and dioxide a prolonged firing may be necessary with a potter's standard glazes. This gives too much opportunity for re-oxidation of the copper. To speed the liberation of the bubbles it may be necessary to alter the glaze recipe by cutting out some of the aluminium oxide. A glaze low in aluminium oxide is very fluid and will therefore liberate its bubbles and seal the surface easily. It may be too runny. Therefore a balance has to be found between the glaze that is too fluid but clears well and the glaze that is too stiff and traps the bubbles.

The effect of large burst bubbles preserved at the glaze surface may be deliberately sought. A mesh size of 50's to 150's is used. See *Crater glazes*.

Silicosis

The sealing of the lung capillaries by lung tissue which surrounds inhaled silica particles. Free silica in the air as fine dust of less than 5 micrometres is able to enter the lungs with the air. Here it remains, is embedded by new lung tissue and causes the lung to choke up. Silicosis is no longer isolated as a separate disease but included officially as pneumoconiosis.

Silicosis is a potter's disease which must be guarded against by avoiding all forms of dust, especially of free silica. Asbestos dust similarly gives rise to asbestosis. See also *Health hazard*.

Sillimanite

Kyanite. Fibrolite. Andalusite. $Al_2O_3.SiO_2$. A hard and refractory mineral occurring in metamorphic rocks. Kyanite, the softest variety, is reconstituted as sillimanite kiln shelves, props etc and used as a low-thermal-expansion grog in raku bodies.

Sink-in decoration

Onglaze decoration which is fluxed into the glaze thus rendering it dishwasher proof. Normal firing of onglaze decoration leaves the enamel attached but very much at the surface. Higher temperatures or prolonged firings which achieve better integration tend to destroy many of the brighter colours. But very fast firing to high temperatures softens the base glaze, allowing the decoration to sink in, and does not fade the colours.

Sinter

To fasten together by mutual adhesion without apparent fusion. The word comes from the German for cinder and this explains its link with a partial action (partly burnt or partly fused) and its use in metallurgy.

All ceramic materials, simple oxides or complex minerals, pass through a stage of sintering before melting. There is no liquid (molten) phase involved and yet the individual particles stick to each other. One could consider it a phenomenon of electrical friction involving some re-arrangement of structure at the surfaces. The result is that materials which start as powders become solid at a temperature which is only half-way to the melting point. See *Tammann temperature*.

It is a difficult phenomenon to assess with the complex minerals of pottery but its action can be seen in clays which melt above 1200°C (2192°F) and yet have cohesion after being fired to only 600°C (1112°F). When the clay has been completely dehydrated at 600°C, the resulting pot would be, theoretically, a pile of dust with no cohesion and yet many historical primitive pots had only this low firing. Also, present-day primitive societies use a low firing to produce cooking pots. There is undoubtedly some incipient fusion of low-melting constituents, like fluxes, but the strength is due to sintering and thereby has an elasticity not associated with glassy vitrification. The elasticity enables these pots to be used for cooking directly on a fire.

It is probably this phenomenon of sintering that enables pots to be piled upon each other in a biscuit firing without crushing the one beneath during the ceramic change.

SI units

Systéme International d'Unités. The units accepted and used internationally especially for scientific measurements.

Slabbing

Forming a ceramic from sheets of clay. The slabs (sheets) are wire cut, beaten out or rolled out. They are then cut and used in soft state or stiffer to construct the projected piece. Joints are usually scored and slurried.

Slabbed objects tend to be more angular and less organic than those formed by pinching, coiling and throwing. They can thus have a very dynamic character. See also *Paper clay*.

Slabs can also be used in a method similar to coiling. The form is beaten and sometimes turned. Beating helps to strengthen the clay sheet which is otherwise less strong than the wall of a thrown or coiled pot. Careful beating of joints should be undertaken with consideration of the clay structure. See *Clay: physics*.

The photographs show a stoneware Canada goose of slab construction by Janet Hamer; Jim Robison rolling a slab, and constructing a form from pre textured slabs; and 'Tripod Vase Form' by Jim Robison using extruded leg supports for the textured slab which has been impressed on the studio wall of concrete blocks. The other photographs are a slabbed form with textures emphasized by slips, oxides and dry glaze by Ian Chapman; lustred slabbed bird by Peteris Martinsons; and John Glick (right) assisting Peteris Martinsons to position Peteris's two slabbed forms.

Slake

To disintegrate in water. Clays are said to slake if from their dry state they can be completely wetted by immersion in water. Such clays crumble as the water surrounds and separates the particles.

Some clays will not slake from the cheese-hard state but need to be thoroughly dried first. Some very fine clays, such as ball clays, will not slake at all but create a waterproof layer on the outside of the lumps with the first water absorbed.

Slaking is the simplest way of rendering raw clay down to a thin slurry for sieving and future preparation. Clays which will not slake must be ground exceedingly finely, e.g. airblown fineness, or else blunged. Some clays even require a very vigorous machine blunging to separate the particles.

Slip

A homogeneous mixture of clay and water.

Slips are used for coating clays to give colour and a

smooth textured surface. See **Slipware**. There is also a process for forming pots from slip. See **Slip casting**.

Although the simple mixture of clay and water is a slip there are often other ingredients. These are added for colouring and to make the slip fit the body during drying, firing and when finished, and to provide the necessary bonding with the body beneath and, if necessary, the glaze above.

The following are colouring oxides for slips with suggested minimum and maximum amounts to give pale and full strength colours. Combinations are possible. See individual oxides.

Chromium oxide	1–5%	grey-green
Cobalt oxide	1–5%	blue
Copper oxide	1–5%	green glazed, buff unglazed
Iron oxide	3–15%	cream to brown and black
Manganese oxide	5–15%	browns
Nickel oxide	2–5%	grey-brown

Other additions to a slip can be feldspars etc for densification and strength; flint for hardness and whiteness; fluxes and frits for vitrification and bonding. A fusible slip containing perhaps 20% flux or 30% frit comes into other categories. See **Slip-glaze, Engobe** and **Buffer layer**. Additions of non-plastic material reduce the stickiness of a slip and decrease the drying shrinkage.

It is usual to have a slip which is finer and richer—that is, more plastic—than the body which it covers. Such a slip fits the body better at raw stage because it has good adhesion (stickiness) and a slightly higher drying shrinkage than the body. This should not be confused with firing shrinkage which is dependent upon vitrification.

Light-coloured slips are often based upon a plastic ball clay and slips prepared from the body clay are passed through a 60's to 100's mesh. This takes out some of the grog and sand making the slip clay richer than the body.

Slip-casting

A pottery-forming process which uses moulds to give the forms and uses liquid clay (slip). The slip is poured into porous moulds which absorb some of the water from the slip. A layer of clay thus builds up against the wall of the mould to give a cast. When the excess slip is poured out, the clay forming the cast is left adhering to the mould. See fig. 1. The cast is stiffened, removed from the mould, dried, fettled and fired in the usual way.

The moulds are usually plaster of Paris with a porosity of approximately 40%. This is achieved by a 130's mix, that is, 130 parts by weight of plaster to 100 parts by weight of water. Moulds are 'one-piece' for simple objects like short cylinders and tapering objects. See fig. 2. The slight contraction of the cast as it dries assists freeing and removal.

However, with increased complexity of form the number of mould pieces increases. Fig. 3 shows two alternatives for a 2-piece mould. Figures and animals may require 20- or 30-piece moulds. There is usually a 'head' or 'spare' (A in fig. 3)

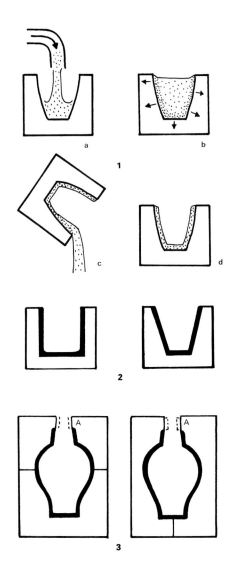

which is cast with the form and is trimmed away. It ensures a sufficient thickness at the required rim by providing a head of slip. This head gives a pressure inside the mould and obviates the necessity for a continual topping-up as the water soaks into the mould.

The moulds are filled with a special deflocculated slip. See **Casting slip**. A mould is filled in one operation and as quickly as possible as it rotates on a whirler. This ensures an equal distribution of slip to all corners of the mould. Sufficient time is then allowed for the required thickness of clay to build up. The slip sinks in the head of the mould as the water is absorbed so that at least one top-up is often necessary. When the build-up is of sufficient thickness the excess slip is poured out.

The mould is left inverted to drain until the cast has dimmed. Different moulds require different treatments but it will be found that most moulds drain better if left at a slight tilt. When the cast has dimmed, the spare is removed. This leaves a firm rim. See A in fig. 3. There is an ion exchange between plaster mould and slip which helps to stiffen the cast.

The cast is removed when the clay is firm enough to stand. It is dried, fettled by scraping the seams, and quickly sponged with a fully wet sponge.

The porcelain box was made by Nigel Wood.

The 'shoal' vase and bowl in bone china are by Sasha Wardell. They are cast using more than one colour of slip by emptying out one colour and refilling with another. At the bone-dry stage, layers are cut away with a scalpel blade to reveal the different colours as decoration. The thinnest sections become very translucent. See **Bone china**.

The 'pour-back' slip can be collected for re-use. It should be resieved through a 40's sieve without brushing. Slip should be stored in tall containers so that only a small surface area meets the air.

Freshly-mixed slip is best. Slip cannot be stored indefinitely but can be kept for about twenty days if the storage tank is non-corrosive and reasonably airtight. Wood or plastic containers are best. During storage a skin forms on the surface of the slip where it meets the air and unwanted foreign matter collects at the bottom. The skin must not be

stirred into the slip because it contains carbon dioxide from the air. This acts as a flocculant which spoils the fluidity of the slip. Some potters put a layer of oil on the top of the slip to prevent this neutralization.

For the same reason, scraps of broken casts, trimmings etc should not be added to the slip. They have become partially flocculated by the air and by the calcium sulfate of the plaster of Paris. Bulk scraps can be reblunged but will require more deflocculant. The amount can only be established by trial. Reclaimed slip never seems to be so good as new slip.

4

Fig. 4 shows a tall storage tank which gives only a small area of slip at the surface. It shows the airtight lid with stopper, return funnel with stopper and return sieve. The tube from the funnel is long so that returned slip does not become mixed with the skin. The run-off tap is above the sediment layer. It is necessary to ease the stopper in the lid when slip is run off.

There are a number of well-known problems in slip-casting. The faults arising from these are dealt with under **Casting slip**. Preparation of the slip is also dealt with there.

Slip-glaze

Vitrifying slip. A glaze that contains over 50% of clay and is applied as a slip to the raw ware. The slip may be a naturally-occurring clay or mud which contains sufficient fluxes to make a glaze when sieved. It will often contain iron and make a tenmoku glaze. Slip-glazes are also made from the body clay or ball clay and fluxed with feldspar, dolomite, wood ash or whiting and coloured with colouring oxides or stains. In character they range from barely fused colours to thick, unctuous and shiny glazes.

Slip-glazes widen the scope for decoration. They can be used with sgraffito or resist, can be once-fired or biscuited and can be further glazed.

Slip stone
A small, slender abrasive stone used for removing blemishes on pots and for sharpening metal tools.

Slipware
Earthenware pottery decorated with coloured slips under a transparent (traditionally lead) glaze. The effect of the mellow shine of a lead glaze coupled with the richness of colour from the slips make slipware a justly popular ware. It developed as a rural or peasant ware in Europe and America reaching its peak in Staffordshire in the late 17th and 18th century. It is therefore often called English or Staffordshire slipware even though it was made in many more places and countries.

Slipware is domestic ware and was largely thrown, but large oven plates were pressed. The body was red or buff and slips were made from this clay with added oxides of iron, copper and manganese. White slips were made from ball and china clays or the small deposits of pipeclays and white fireclays.

The making of slipware demands great skill and is time consuming. It naturally suffered in competition with increasing industrialization and production of simpler more sophisticated wares in the 19th century. Today's potters develop the generous quality of slip decoration in domestic ware and special commemorative pieces. The photographs show Mary Wondrausch slip trailing; one of Mary's commemorative plates; a Punch and Judy plate with Lion and Unicorn supporters; and a trailed and combed platter by Andrew McGarva. See **Recipe Appendix, Feather combing** and **Finger combing**.

Slipware employs the idea of coating a leatherhard clay with what is often a contrasting colour of slip either by dipping or pouring. The slip coating can then be decorated by finger-combing or when dry by sgraffito; or while the first slip is wet, other slips can be added and encouraged to sink into the ground slip in what is called slip trailing as shown in the photograph.

To obtain a good fit it is usual to make a slip from a clay that is more plastic than the body clay. Pure ball clay is often satisfactory but the addition of some frit will improve its fired adhesion to the body and integration with the glaze. A borax frit is an ideal addition because this encourages the bleeding of coloured slips into the glaze as the body-glaze layer is formed. This blurred outline of the slip softens the contrast and enriches the decorative qualities. Some pleasing colours can be obtained by using copper and cobalt oxides with up to 20% borax frit in the slip. Dark slips are usually made from the body clay by the addition of iron and manganese oxides. They should be sieved to take out some of the sand etc thus providing a smoother surface for the glaze.

Traditional slipware employed a raw lead glaze which gave a rich surface shine and partially dissolved the slips beneath, producing a softened effect. A low sol glaze is now essential and while this can give the rich surface shine it does not produce the same integration with the slip. However the use of a borax frit in the slip, as mentioned

earlier, will achieve this softening. A low sol glaze for 1080°C to 1100°C (1976°F to 2012°F) follows:

feldspar	12
china clay	10
flint	8
whiting	5
lead bisilicate	50
borax frit	15

If an amber glaze is required, a red body clay should be used instead of the china clay. It should be noted that although this is a low sol glaze the stability can be upset by heavily stained slips. See *Metal release* and *Low sol*.

Slop

A homogeneous mixture of glaze materials and water. A slop is the most convenient form in which to handle glaze materials. It is applied to the ware by dipping, spraying or brushing. The water soaks into the ware and then dries out. The glaze materials are left in a layer on the surface ready for the firing.

The thickness of the layer, especially from dipping, is dependent upon the porosity of the ware and the density and fluidity of the slop. Densities are measured by weight per volume of slop. See *Formula: density* and *Slop weight*.

The usual method of preparing a slop is to measure the water first into the mixing container and follow this with the weighed amounts of powder. The powders are thus able to soak before being blunged and sieved. A convenient mesh size is 100's to 120's with coarser sizes for ash glazes and finer for uniform colours and slops for spraying.

Some glaze materials require to be ground and these are put into a ball mill or jar mill.

Glaze materials are heavier than water and settle to the bottom of the glaze tub. Slops made from uniform materials, like completely fritted glazes, tend to do this more than those made from a variety of materials and those including clay. See *Suspender*.

Slop weight

Density. Slop weight or density is expressed as a weight for a specified volume. For example, the slop weight of a typical glaze at thick dipping consistency is 150 g per 100 ml. This glaze could be given slop weights of 1·5 g per ml; 1500 g per litre; 30 oz pt imp; and 25 oz pt US. These are different ways of expressing the same slop weight. See also *Table 19*.

Slop weight can only be a guide to consistency for slips and for glazes of high clay content because added acid or alkalis released by wood ash, feldspathoids etc. flocculate or deflocculate the suspension. Fluidity changes but slop weight remains the same. However, the slop weight is necessary in calculating the dry content of a slip or slop by Brongniart's formula.

Slop weight can be used to calculate the relative density of the suspension as a whole. For example, 150 g per 100 ml gives $150 \div 100$ (both are expressed in the same measure of grams) $= 1 \cdot 5$ r.d. Relative density is expressed as one number. Slop weight has two numbers, one for weight and one for volume.

Slug

A length of clay from a pug mill. A slug is a measured length containing a known amount of clay. It can be any convenient size and enough for one pot or more.

Slum

Fireclay containing a large amount of fine coal which makes it necessary to fire the clay very slowly although the coal does help the firing if sufficient oxygen can be introduced.

Slurry

An uneven mixture of clay or glaze and water. If the slurry was more evenly mixed and sieved so that it was in a homogeneous state, it would be called slip or slop.

Smithsonite

Zinc carbonate. $ZnCO_3$. A zinc mineral which is decomposed to zinc oxide and carbon dioxide by heating to 300°C (572°F).

Smoked lustre

A transmutation lustre.

Smoking

The creation of black and tonal shading on pot and modelled surfaces by burning carbonaceous matter around the pieces. Unglazed biscuit pieces are smoked in sawdust or leaves to give partial carbonization. Direct burning contrasts soft-edged blackened shapes with areas which have been protected by unburnt material or the proximity of other pots. The black is carbonization by the infiltration of carbon into the pores of the body. The bowl by Sheila Casson has been smoked in this way. These bowls are set in sawdust, sometimes in saggars, then covered with newspaper which is lit from the top. The burning takes three to five hours and the temperature varies between 200°C and 500°C (392°F and 932°F). The mule in the photograph has been selectively smoked by Susan Halls.

Controlled patterns are effected by using resist slips and glazes. Ashraf Hanna applies a resist slip on the biscuited piece which is scratched through to create striped patterns. See photograph opposite.

Christine Gittins sprinkles salts into the sawdust near to the pot surfaces. These flash the pot with soft colours (see above). Shadow smoking is evident on the globular vase by David Price.

Variations on these techniques are glazes and metallic lustres. See also ***Raku: post firing, Sawdust firing, Fuming, Copper lustre*** and ***Colour plates 32, 36, 37, 49, 50, 55*** and ***56***.

Snake skin
See ***Lizard skin***.

Soak
A term used in kiln firing schedules when the temperature is maintained at the same level for a given period. It is frequently done at the top temperature and implies that time is allowed for glaze and body to mature. Unevenness of temperature within the chamber should be balanced and any remaining glaze bubbles smooth out during this time without the increase of temperature which would over-fire the ware.

Soaking is also done during the cooling cycle to allow the growth of crystals in crystalline glazes.

Clays which contain more than an average amount of carbon and sulfur, such as surface clays and estuarine muds, need a soaking period or slow rise between 700°C (1292°F) and 1150°C (2012°F) to ensure that this material is thoroughly burnt away. This is called 'burning out'. See ***Firing***.

Soda
A general term covering the sodium compounds of:

soda ash (sodium carbonate)	Na_2CO_3
washing soda (sodium carbonate)	$Na_2CO_3.10H_2O$
baking soda (sodium bicarbonate)	$NaHCO_3$
caustic soda (sodium hydroxide)	$NaOH$

The active part in glazing is sodium oxide which is released when the compounds decompose. The word soda is no longer accepted internationally as an abbreviation for sodium oxide.

Soda ash

Sodium carbonate. Na_2CO_3. Originally the ashes of burnt sea plants. See **Barilla** and **Kelp**. Now the terms soda ash and sodium carbonate are used synonymously although soda ash is produced from sodium chloride (NaCl) rock salt by the Solvay process.

Soda firing

A glaze can be formed directly onto the pot surface by introducing sodium compounds into the hot kiln. The sodium compounds decompose enabling sodium oxide to combine with the alumino-silicate, which is the body, to form sodium alumino-silicate, which is a glaze. Sodium carbonate and bicarbonate, known commonly as soda, are the most often used compounds. The unused product of the decomposition is carbon dioxide in a quantity which is a negligible addition to that which is produced by the burning of fuels in any firing.

$$Na_2CO_3 \xrightarrow{\text{above } 860°C} Na_2O \uparrow + CO_2 \uparrow$$
sodium   sodium   carbon
carbonate   oxide   dioxide

$$2NaHCO_3 \xrightarrow{\text{above } 270°C} Na_2O \uparrow + H_2O \uparrow + 2CO_2 \uparrow$$
sodium   sodium   water   carbon
bicarbonate   oxide   (steam) dioxide

The use of sodium carbonate and sodium bicarbonate began as a safer and less polluting alternative to sodium chloride (salt) which was traditionally used in industry and is now used by individual potters when salt glazing. Both soda firing and salt firing produce a glaze which is characterized by orange peel and tiger skin textures, and colourings strongly affected by the corrosive and leaching action of the sodium compounds. The use of sodium chloride has been discontinued on a large scale because the decomposition produced hydrogen chloride gas which has a corrosive effect on kilns, and when emitted into the atmosphere is destructive of the environment and the human breathing system.

The chief difference in the firing process and its effects is that without the forceful pressure of released hydrogen chloride the sodium oxide is not distributed so readily to all the pot surfaces. Hydrogen chloride is a very active gas produced from the disassociation of wet sodium chloride. It carries the sodium oxide efficiently to all the surfaces within the kiln. See **Salt glaze**. However, in experimenting with other ways of dispersing the sodium oxide throughout the kiln chamber, soda-firing potters have developed ingenious techniques and engendered a new aesthetic. The soda is often introduced into the kiln by spraying. A supersaturated solution of sodium bicarbonate may be injected using a garden sprayer approximately every fifteen minutes. A uniform glaze coating is necessary for functional ware but

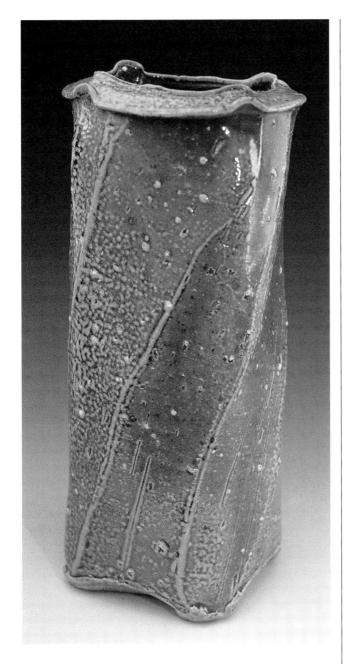

addition to that combined within the clay particle. Larger particles such as quartz sand inhibit the formation of the glaze because the presence of aluminium oxide is also necessary. Sodium oxide performs its function of interacting with the clay body by breaking into the sheets of laminar crystals and disassociating the components.

The glaze which is produced on the surface ranges from a smooth, transparent gloss to an orange peel pitted surface, to heavy texturing called tiger skin or leopard skin. The glaze is formed from a very stiff, aluminous melt. This can only smooth out over a very smooth body and where a relatively thin layer has had a sufficiently long oxidizing soaking to allow it to settle following the disruptive effect of the sodium oxide introductions. More characteristically, there is a build-up of glaze which is affected by underlying irregularities and forms increasingly high beads of stiff glaze which link into a pattern. See **Orange peel** and **Tiger skin**. In cases of higher temperature and heavier introductions of sodium oxide the glaze often seems to have boiled and is too stiff to smooth out. The effect is emphasized by colour which may be finely divided iron oxide from the body, or cobalt oxide and other fluxing colouring oxides from slip coatings. These are leached out by the destructive action of sodium oxide leaving colourless glaze in hollows where the glaze is thin and on rims and edges of sprigging which were attacked on three sides.

Other types of glaze fluxed mainly with sodium oxide have low surface tension and viscosity but in salt and soda firings, without other fluxes to assist fusion, the aluminium oxide content overrides these characteristics. However, the high expansion and contraction rate of sodium oxide often produces crazing. As stoneware, salt- and soda-glazed wares are usually considered hard and strong but they are slightly less strong than stoneware glazed with slip and feldspathic glazes. Excessive attack by sodium oxide into the body and crazed glaze have a partial weakening effect. See **Salt glaze.**

The corrosive attack of sodium oxide into the surface of the pot body has a pronounced effect on colours. The desired colours can be produced by controlling the amount of glaze build-up in a particular area, as well as by applying coloured slips, engobes and glazes. Where a surface has been largely protected from the attack of sodium oxide there is only a slight glazing which can appear as a bright orange flashing. This may be the result of its position in the kiln or may be produced by applying a sodium oxide resistant coating. Potters use dips and brushstrokes of slips containing china clay, titanium oxide and rutile to obstruct the action of the sodium oxide. Rutile exhibits uneven and delayed contractions and a dense, overall coating is best avoided. A coating of iron oxide also inhibits the formation of glaze. The iron oxide must be incorporated in the body or in a slip in a finely divided form to allow the sodium oxide to react with it. The iron oxide is leached out into the glaze. In small amounts this produces cream yellow and tan. Larger amounts produce browns. A body containing calcium oxide encourages yellow. Similarly, other colours can be controlled

varied glaze textures, flashing and soft colours can be exploited in the field of creative ceramic expression.

The photographs show a jug and a bowl by Jack Doherty and a three-footed teapot and a tall squared vase by Ruthanne Tudball. See also **Inlay** and **Colour plates 64 to 66** and **76/77**.

Potters' observations of cause and effect sometimes seem to be contradictory but this is likely to be because the situation is complex and every pot, kiln and firing sequence is at least slightly different. The principles are constant but what creates a particular effect is usually a combination of causes.

The pots may be fired from raw or biscuited. The best clays for soda firing are those with a high proportion of free silica, that is, where there is very finely divided silica in by incorporating colouring oxides in slips which encourage or discourage their entering into the glaze. Thus a slip with more than 50% china clay gives paler colours than one with more than 50% ball clay.

The bright alkaline colours associated with sodium compound fluxes—turquoise blue from copper oxide, mauve from cobalt and manganese oxides, and blue from iron oxide—can be obtained with a lighter glaze deposit but in thicker layers the aluminium oxide dulls these colours. Often potters decorate their pots with engobes and glazes which fuse themselves and produce denser colours. Startling colours and effervescent areas may appear where the sodium oxide interferes with the glaze fluxes to produce a complex chain of fusion. See **Recipe Appendix.**

The rate of cooling can have an effect on colour. Many potters choose to crash cool down to 900°C (1652°F) but traditionally the practice was to cool slowly with oxidation to allow reduced iron to re-oxidize and give brown ware which was thought to be superior. Rapid cooling tends to produce greenish blacks from the black iron oxide. A greyness within the glaze is blamed on carbon trapping. If reduction is unnecessarily heavy, surplus carbon enters the body and can be trapped there when the glaze surface has sealed over. Sometimes crystals form near the surface in an effect similar to an aventurine glaze. Occasionally they are loose on the surface and can be brushed off. This phenomenon is popularly called 'Christmas glitter'. See **Sodium oxide** and **Christmas glitter**.

The same kind of fuel-burning down-draught kiln is used for soda as for salt. The inner structure and furniture must be resistant to sodium oxide attack. Although not so corrosive as the sodium chloride vapours, sodium oxide does damage kiln interiors and leaves a crust which can flake from walls and can block burners. Dense 'alumina' or high silica firebricks are the standard but high temperature insulation bricks and ceramic fibre have both been used. These can be protected by a refractory and sodium oxide resistant coating made from aluminium oxide or zirconium silicate. Purimachos and Furnascote are trade names for such coatings. Shelves and props must also be protected. To assist the circulation of vapour to all parts of the kiln, John Teiser has built a cylindrical kiln with burners directed

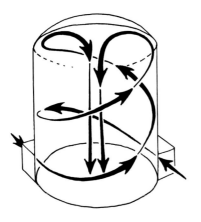

along the walls. The kiln also has multiple ports for sodium compound introduction to achieve optimum distribution.

The firing schedule includes a period of reduction above 900°C (1652°F). This reduces red iron oxide in the body to black iron oxide which begins to flux the body and assist glaze formation. The reduction is followed by a short oxidation to avoid carbon trapping. Then a neutral atmosphere or light reduction is maintained.

The sodium compounds are introduced into the kiln at temperatures from 1260°C to 1300°C (2300°F to 2372°F). Better results are achieved when small amounts are introduced over a longer period, approximately two to three hours, than when using salt. This is also a safer method where water is involved. Water is added to the sodium compounds to assist the decomposition. The steam created also helps the dispersion. Sodium carbonate (soda ash Na_2CO_3) is soluble in water and can be introduced as a drip feed. Hydrated sodium carbonate (washing soda crystals $Na_2CO_3.10H_2O$) can be introduced by throwing in paper bagfuls or pushing a measured amount down a metal angle iron into the fire. Sodium bicarbonate (baking soda, $NaHCO_3$) begins to decompose at temperatures above 270°C (518°F) so that, when it is introduced at a much higher temperature, the action is very rapid causing a more forceful dispersion of the sodium oxide. Amounts used range from 500 g to 5 kg, according to preference and the size of kiln. Additions of about 10% of borax are often included with the sodium compounds. This has a low melting point which helps to initiate glaze fusion and helps to overcome crazing in the final glaze. Additions of oil and sawdust have been tried to help to improve vapour circulation.

The flow of vapours through the kiln can be improved by manipulating the chamber pressure. By closing the damper before introducing the sodium compounds, pressure is built up in the chamber. When released this helps to pull the fumes through. Spraying a boiling saturated solution with a pressurized spray near to the burners avoids the localized expansion of water into steam but is potentially dangerous. Martin Goerg injects the sodium compounds with the fuel, using burners with a special tube inserted for the purpose. Test rings are drawn from the kiln to check the glaze build-up. Most potters fire to cone 10 well down, followed by an oxidized soak, which helps to clear surplus sodium oxide and smooth the glaze surface.

Sodalite
$3(Na_2O.Al_2O_3.2SiO_2).2NaCl$. Sodium alumino-silicate and chloride. A sodium feldspathoid which is one of the mineral constituents of nepheline syenite and other alkaline (basic) igneous rocks.

Sodium bicarbonate
Sodium hydrogen carbonate. $NaHCO_3$. Source of sodium oxide when soda glazing. See **Soda firing**.

Sodium carbonate
Soda ash. Sal soda. Na_2CO_3. The chief source of sodium

oxide for glazes. It is highly soluble and therefore can only be used in frits. It is used in combination with sodium silicate as a deflocculant for casting slips. See ***Defloccuation***.

Until the discovery of the LeBlanc and Solvay processes at the end of the 18th and middle of the 19th century, sodium carbonate for glass-making was produced by burning seaweed and salt-marsh plants. Hence the name soda ash. The processes now employed use rock salt and sea water.

Sodium chloride
Common salt. Rock salt. NaCl. The most abundant natural compound of sodium. It is indirectly the source of most of the sodium oxide used in glazes, the sodium chloride being converted into sodium carbonate for inclusion in frits. Sodium chloride is used with water, or with borax, in salt glazing. See ***Salt glaze***. The fusion of a small pile of salt on a tile was once used as an indication of temperature in the kiln. The melting temperature is 800°C (1472°F).

Sodium feldspar
See ***Albite***.

Sodium minerals
The element sodium is a metal which is very reactive and quickly combines with adjacent elements to form compounds. Sodium is therefore never found as a native ore but occurs in a number of natural materials. Sodium is essential to animal life and to sea-plant life. Sodium compounds occur widely but by far the most common is sodium chloride which occurs in the sea and salt lakes and as rock salt. Household compounds are sodium chloride (NaCl), common salt; hydrated sodium carbonate ($Na_2CO_3.10H_2O$), washing soda; sodium bicarbonate ($NaHCO_3$), baking soda; and borax ($Na_2B_4O_7.10H_2O$).

Sodium oxide for glass- and glaze-making is derived from the following, which are separately indexed:

sodium carbonate	Na_2CO_3 (soda ash)
borax	$Na_2B_4O_7.10H_2O$
albite	$Na_2O.Al_2O_3.6SiO_2$ (sodium feldspar)
nepheline syenite	$K_2O.3Na_2O.4Al_2O_3.8SiO_2$
sodium chloride	NaCl (common salt)
sodium nitrate	$NaNO_3$
sodalite	$3(Na_2O.Al_2O_3.2SiO_2).2NaCl$
ulexite	$NaCaB_5O_9.8H_2O$
cryolite	Na_3AlF_6
barilla and kelp:	ashes from burnt sea plants

There are over twenty sodium compounds which could be used in frit-making, but some are uneconomical. The simpler compounds are processed from rock salt by the Solvay process, the cheapest and most convenient compound being sodium carbonate. Borax, which introduces boron oxide is also popular.

Sodium oxide is the most soluble of all the oxides that the potter uses. Potassium and lithium oxides are close seconds

but occur in non-soluble minerals. The so-called non-soluble sodium minerals are likely to lose some of their sodium oxide into solution. The most convenient minerals are albite and nepheline syenite.

Sodium nitrate
Soda nitre. Chile saltpetre. $NaNO_3$. A highly-soluble sodium salt which is used in fritting for its oxidizing properties. As a source of sodium oxide it is too expensive.

Sodium oxide
Natrium oxide. Na_2O. One of the three strong alkaline oxides providing active fluxes in ceramic fusions. The other two are lithium oxide and potassium oxide. See ***Periodic table***.

Sodium oxide is an active flux from 800°C (1472°F) upwards and creates glazes which give exciting colour responses. The more notable responses are a blue from copper oxide, and purples from cobalt and manganese oxides.

Sodium oxide and most sodium compounds are soluble. Sodium oxide is therefore introduced into glazes in the form of frits, and sodium oxide feldspar. Sodium oxide is rarely used in bodies except where it has been introduced primarily as a deflocculant for casting slips. See ***Defloccuation***.

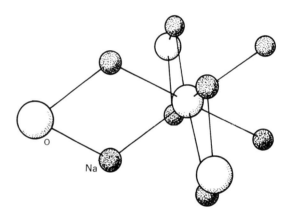

SODIUM OXIDE IN GLAZES. Sodium oxide is important on four counts: colour responses; fluxing action; contraction rate; solubility.

Sodium oxide encourages bright and exciting colour responses from the colouring oxides. For example copper oxide gives turquoise blue, cobalt and manganese oxides give mauve, and iron oxide gives blue. Some of these colours are fickle and their ranges are limited but all are sufficiently exciting to make their pursuit hopeful. See also ***Alkaline glazes***.

To get the colour response, the glaze must be highly alkaline and this usually means high in sodium oxide. Lithium oxide and potassium oxide give similar but not identical results. At least two-thirds of the flux needs to be sodium oxide and this presents its own problems of crazing and solubility. Aluminium oxide must be kept very low, which presents the problem of over fluidity and instability. The only way is to work empirically from an existing colour which can be obtained by the use of the soluble materials, home-made frits or commercial frits. This test will need to be progressively improved to a glaze which is an acceptable compromise between colour and stability.

Sodium oxide is an active flux for all temperatures, its action beginning at approximately 800°C (1472°F). It is at the lower temperatures that sodium oxide is most useful in the making of lead-free glazes, assisted by boron oxide, potassium oxide and lithium oxide. Sodium oxide is combined with boron oxide in the mineral borax and therefore is included in borax frits.

From 1100°C (2012°F) upwards there are other fluxes available which can be used in combination with sodium oxide. Calcium oxide is the most popular but barium oxide is used where a more alkaline flux is required.

Sodium oxide becomes unstable at temperatures above 1200°C (2192°F). Some sodium oxide will volatilize from high sodium oxide glazes at these temperatures, although the glazes may have matured. However, complex glazes with at least equal amounts of three other fluxes suitably engage the sodium oxide. The property of sodium oxide to volatilize is used in the creation of salt glaze. Here wet salt, or salt and borax, is thrown into the firebox where it volatilizes. The resulting glaze deposited on the pots is a sodium alumino-silicate. See **Salt glaze**, **Soda firing** and **Colour plates 76/77**.

Simple combinations of sodium oxide and silica give freely-flowing but brittle glazes. They can be used in hollows on tiles that are fired horizontally. Flint can be fluxed with soda ash or washing soda. The ingredients are dry-ground together and the powder is packed into the hollows. These glazes give exciting colour responses as mentioned above. However, they are very unstable and have insufficient resistance to weathering and abrasion. The sodium oxide remains soluble and will even be attacked by a damp atmosphere. Acids dissolve them. The extreme example of their quality is water-glass. This is a sodium silicate and it is completely soluble in water.

To stabilize these dry-powder glazes it is necessary to add some aluminium oxide by feldspar or china clay, and to increase the number of fluxes. Calcium oxide is successfully used in glass-making. More than minor alterations will dull the colour effect.

It will have been noted that the high alkaline glazes are prone to crazing. Sodium oxide has the highest coefficient of expansion of all the glaze-constituent oxides. Its inclusion in a glaze means that it will bring to the glaze a high rate of expansion proportionate to the amount present. A glaze depending mostly on sodium oxide for fluxing is therefore certain to craze. The high expansion, and hence contraction, rate of the glaze will be greater than the expansion rate of the body. Sodium oxide also creates rather brittle glazes which naturally cannot withstand the tension and therefore rupture. Elasticity is given to glazes by lead oxide and, to a lesser extent, by boron oxide and calcium oxide. Boron oxide and calcium oxide provide excellent counter-action to the crazing caused by sodium oxide. See **Glaze fit**.

The solubility of simple soda-silica glazes has already

been mentioned. Even the sodium oxide contents of the minerals albite and nepheline syenite are partially soluble. Sodium oxide is the most soluble of all the potter's oxides and therefore cannot be used alone in clay bodies and glaze slops. Instead, sodium oxide is first rendered insoluble by a process called fritting. In fritting, the sodium oxide is first melted with aluminium oxide, silica and other fluxes to produce a glass. This glass is ground to a convenient powder. See **Frit**. Cryolite is used mostly in vitreous enamels but albite and nepheline syenite are widely used in bodies and glazes. Albite and nepheline syenite are of igneous origin and can be considered to be natural frits.

Sodium oxide is present in most glazes and contributes its extreme properties of active fluxing and high contraction without which the balancing of satisfactory glazes would be very difficult.

Sodium silicate

Sodium metasilicate. Water-glass. Na_2SiO_3 or $Na_2O.SiO_2$. Sodium oxide and silica combined in approximately equal proportions. It is soluble in water and is used as a clay deflocculant in casting slips. See **Deflocculation**.

Sodium silicate is usually bought as a concentrated solution whose density is expressed in degrees Twaddell (°TW). It is in this form that it is introduced into casting slips. This stiff solution has given it the name of water-glass. The dry form is brittle, glassy and crystalline.

Sodium silicate is prepared from sodium carbonate and quartz. As water-glass, its composition can be varied but that used for deflocculation is usually calculated as the anhydrous formula given above. Water-glass is used as a glue, an egg preservative, a fireproofer and a binder and hardener in concretes and artificial stones.

Water-glasses have melting points between 1000°C and 1100°C (1832°F and 2012°F) and can be used with clay to make paste glazes. The method is not particularly satisfactory and is more expensive than using soda ash or washing soda.

Sodium silicate is difficult to store. It combines with carbon dioxide in the air to give sodium carbonate and silicic acid. Its deflocculating power is then altered.

Soft

Low temperature. In describing glazes the term means 600°C to 1050°C (1112°F to 1922°F). Soft fluxes are those which can be used for these glazes and include oxides of sodium, potassium, lead and boron. Soft glazes are physically soft and are easily scratched.

Soft as a relative term means at a lower temperature not necessarily referring to below 1050°C. See also **Hard (2)**.

Soft soap

Mouldmaker's size. Soft soap, as opposed to hard soap, is used as the parting medium in plaster mould-making. When prepared it is a liquid which can be painted on to the first piece to fill the pores. Excess is wiped away with a damp sponge before the plaster is poured on.

Soft soap is potassium soap; hard soap is sodium soap. Detergents have replaced soft soap for household and most commercial uses but some is still sold for hair conditioning. When purchased it is of the consistency of soft butter and is prepared for the mould-maker's use by dissolving it in an equal amount of warm water. It can then be stored ready for use. It should not be boiled.

A passable substitute is sodium soap which has been dissolved by soaking in warm water. Also some of the liquid detergents are effective parting media.

Solenoid
A powerful electromagnet used to lift and hold open a valve on a kiln gas supply. See *Instrumentation*.

Solid solution
A term used to describe glazes implying that the now solid state is really more than one substance and was achieved by a mixture and/or combination of substances in a liquid state.

Solubility
Measurement of a substance's capacity to go into solution. The word is often used when referring to fired glazes and their capacity to withstand the dissolving action of food acids, drinks etc. See *Lead poisoning* and *Low sol*.

Soluble materials
Most raw materials contain some soluble matter as sodium oxide, potassium oxide, sulfates and phosphates. Small amounts cause no harm but large amounts can be the cause of scumming, non-uniform fluxing and unwanted flashing of glaze onto unglazed surfaces. Soluble materials also cause cementing of glaze slops in the bottom of tubs.

Unwanted solubles can be removed by washing or the addition of chemicals which combine with the solubles to produce insoluble precipitates.

Sour
Age. To improve the plasticity of clay by damp storage. Many clays begin to smell, some in an overpowering way. The introduction of some of this very sour clay into fresh plastic clay will assist the souring of the fresh clay.

If sufficient workshop space is not available for souring of all clay then clay for special purposes, such as handles, is soured. Clay which has been thoroughly wet, as is wheel-trough scrap, is suitable.

There is usually some temporary discolouration of soured clay due to organic breakdown. The clay regains its colour on contact with the air and with firing. The blue colour associated with red and cream plastic clays is an indication that souring is taking place. Clay which is intended to be sour must not be allowed to dry out otherwise its especial property gained over months of souring is lost.

The action is bacteriological. In the breakdown of organic plant material carbon is released and this discolours the clay. Oxygen is used by the bacteria which multiply and produce amino acids. The acid flocculates the finest particles of clay producing a colloidal gel which gives the clay its improved strength.

All clays improve their plasticity with keeping, especially over the first few days after making up from dry. This, however, is not souring but the natural balancing out of the water distribution in the clay. Weathering which uses the action of frost also improves the plastic potential by splitting up particles. Souring develops the clay's strength. See also *Plasticity* and *Ageing*.

Spall
To crack with temperature change. The word is usually reserved for kiln brickwork where it is considered the result of the wide difference in temperature between the hot face and the interior of the brick coupled with silica inversions. The resulting expansion and contraction and the inability to adjust because of the rigidity of brickwork results in cracks both into the depth of the brick and across the brick shearing away flakes.

The term spall is not applied to pottery. Pottery is thinner than brickwork so the temperature differences through a pot are small and any difference in expansion can be absorbed. Pottery cracks are more commonly the result of silica inversions and therefore are called dunts. Indefinable cracks are said to be the result of thermal shock which is an all-embracing term covering both spalling and dunting.

Spar
A miner's term for crystalline rocks which break easily along lines of cleavage. They are rocks containing large crystals which are comparatively soft, like feldspars at hardness H6 and fluorspar at hardness H4.

Specific gravity
Superseded by *Relative density*.

Spinel
A mineral having the composition $RO.R_2O_3$. It is a compound of an alkaline oxide and an amphoteric oxide which is acting as the acid. Natural spinels are magnesium aluminate $(MgO.Al_2O_3)$ and beryllium aluminate $(BeO.Al_2O_3)$ with some replacements by other metals. Many other spinels have been artificially produced and provide stable colourants for bodies and glazes. The following are examples:

$CoO.Al_2O_3$	purple
$CrO.Al_2O_3$	pink
$MnO.Al_2O_3$	pink
$ZnO.Al_2O_3$	green
$CdO.Cr_2O_3$	green
$NiO.Cr_2O_3$	green
$FeO.Cr_2O_3$	brown

There are also combinations called spinel-type combinations which form in glazes, e.g. lead antimonate yellow, chrome-tin pink and calcium borate opacity. See **Colours** and **Stains**.

Spluttering

Sputtering. A glaze defect in which small pieces of glaze fall from the ware during fusion and are found fused to the shelf after the firing. The glaze layer sometimes heals over but sometimes crawls.

Spluttering is caused by a loose glaze layer which fails to adhere during fusion. This can occur with wet ware in a glaze firing and with glazes containing colemanite which releases its water content around 800°C (1472°F). See **Wet ware** and **Colemanite**.

Spodumene

Lithium feldspar or feldspathoid. $Li_2O.Al_2O_3.4SiO_2$. A natural material of the feldspathic type occurring as isolated crystals in granites. Selected specimens can be given the ideal formula above. It is used in bodies and glazes to introduce lithium oxide, aluminium oxide and silica. Ground spodumene inevitably contains some potassium oxide and sodium oxide.

Pure spodumene has a low expansion rate compared with other feldspars and has been used in experimental flameproof stoneware bodies. Lithium oxide has a lower expansion rate than most of the other alkalis and spodumene contains sufficient aluminium oxide to involve free silica in mullitic and other non-dunting fusions.

In glazes, the spodumene introduces an extra alkali with some potassium oxide and sodium oxide. By interaction, small amounts have beneficial effects in lowering the fusion range, increasing gloss and improving stability. However, spodumene alone is high in aluminium oxide (28%) and is therefore comparatively refractory for use as a feldspathic material. Alone it matures very slowly in the 1250°C to 1400°C range (2282°F to 2552°F).

Spoil

Removable bricks at the base of a kiln chimney. In conjunction with the damper, the spoil affects the quality of the chimney's draw. The spoil is used to control chamber pressure, oxidation and reduction. The spoil is also the place where a small fire is made at the beginning of a firing to start the drawing action of the chimney.

Spout

A projection on a pot to assist pouring. Spouts are of two types, the open or jug type and the closed tubular type used on the teapot. These are shown (opposite) in the bowl by Willie Carter, the small teapot by Janet Hamer and the soda glazed teapot by Ruthanne Tudball.

Jug spouts may be pulled or squeezed from the pot body (figs. 1–3) or added as separately-formed pieces (figs. 4–6).

1. Snip spout or lip, knocked or tapped from coarse clay or clay of low plasticity.

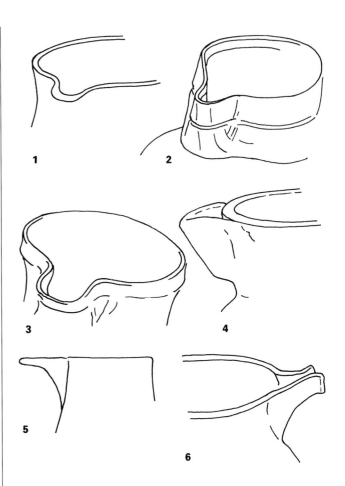

2. Squeezed spout from fine clay of low plasticity.
3. Pulled spout from plastic clay.
4. Parrot beak modelled from coarse clay.
5. Monk's hood, pressed or cast.
6. Thrown and cut spout, luted into position.

The different types have evolved for different thicknesses of liquid to be poured and to suit the pot to be poured from. Some spouts are for generous pouring, others for controlled dropping of small amounts. The clay also influences the type of spout that can be produced.

General principles are that there should be a single flow-line from the belly of the jug out and over the lip. The sides of the spout should throw the liquid into the spout. The lip of the spout should cut the flow effectively and preferably without a drip. A thin section or sharp edge to the tip is the most effective non-drip finish but this is vulnerable in pottery and a compromise has to be made with a thicker section. The effect of the sharper edge can be partially gained by the sudden curl over of the spout end.

The spout is the giving part of the jug. It should look generous, even extrovert; never mean or introvert. Jugs suffer by under-emphasis rather than over-emphasis of their spouts. The photographs overleaf show two different methods of pulling a spout. The usual pulling of a spout using two hands is followed by the thinning of the lip. The thinning and raising of a lip with one hand is followed by a

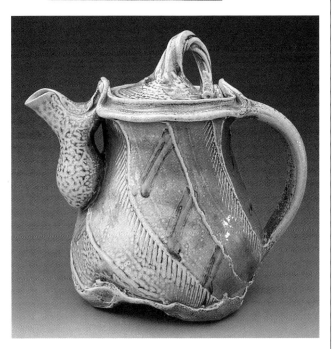

further shaping using two hands. Pictures of whole jugs are given under *Jug*.

The tubular spout is used for teapots and coffee pots. It is made separately by throwing, pressing or casting and is luted into position while still softer than the body of the pot.

For the coffee pot a hole is cut in the pot wall and the spout fitted over it. For the teapot the wall is perforated to become a strainer. The holes should be pierced or drilled at the same angle as the flow of liquid through the spout. The wall thickness may be shaved down to make less resistance in the holes. In this way they are less likely to be blocked by the glaze and later the tea leaves. Some potters cut the holes with a tapering spike which leaves them wider on the outside which again counters blockage. The holes should not be too small. About 5 mm is popular. It is impossible to hold back every tea leaf but the composite action of restricted flow helps to keep the tea leaves in the pot.

The cross-sectional area of all the holes should be larger than the area across the exit of the spout. This gives the pressure within the spout to thrust the tea out over the rim. For this reason teapot and coffee pot spouts should taper noticeably towards the exit. The taper may become less at the end where the spout becomes a directional pipe (fig. 7). A short spout, while providing thrust by taper, gives no direction to the flow (fig. 8). The resulting ideal has concave sides in which the underneath line of the spout joins the body of the pot to form a smooth line of flow (fig. 9). It is important to remember that it is the inside of the spout that should be considered as the taper. The inside of the spout should also be smooth and without throwing ridges which would impede the flow.

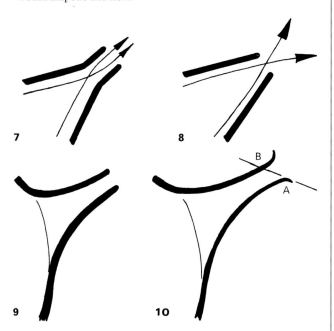

The end of the spout is often cut diagonally (fig. 10). This brings the end nearer to a horizontal so that the lower lip, over which the liquid pours, protrudes further. A smoother flow is thereby achieved because there is no drag on the upper part as the liquid is released. Directional flow is also improved because the slight out-turning of the rim, as shown in the photograph (bottom right, p.347), is used effectively at A, while the part B is cut away. If B were left it would slow down the rate of flow and disperse the liquid multi-directionally. The cutting-off edge can be separately modelled or carved to effect a cleaner non-drip end.

Long spouts if wheel-thrown will twist in firing especially if fired to a vitrified state. Seen from the exit end, a spout will twist in a clockwise direction if it was thrown on a wheel turning anti-clockwise. The amount varies with throwing technique, clay and firing but can be as much as 45°. The cutting of the end of the spout must also be twisted to allow the clockwise rotation of the spout in the firing to bring it to correct alignment. See **Clay: physics of**. The whole spout

will also pull itself across the pot like the hand of a clock. This is only noticeable on long coffee pot spouts and the amount is small.

The angle of attachment for a spout depends upon the body of the pot. The spout should use the body of the pot as its first direction of flow and continue this movement through itself. Approximately 45° is a popular angle and a good general starting point for consideration. The top of the spout should come at least above the upper level of the liquid if not above the level of the rim of the pot.

Sprigging

Adding more clay on to the main pot form. The sprigs may be in the same clay as the body or in clay of a contrasting colour. They may be freely modelled after being applied to the pot or they may be previously pressed in a mould and applied with enough pressure to make them adhere without deforming the detail.

Some means of softening the two surfaces to be joined must be used. With fine clays and preformed sprigs, water is sufficient. With coarser clays, slurry or slip is better and this probably led to the use of coloured slips and differently coloured sprigging clay. The method is very direct and gives scope for both colour contrasts and modelled forms. If different clays are used some adjustment of shrinkage by the addition of a fine ball clay to create more shrinkage, or of fine grog to reduce shrinkage, may be necessary.

The photographs show a Chinese garden seat (where the decoration in light clay has been applied by finger, thumb and a wooden tool) and a Lambeth water filter with sprigs produced from moulds. See also **Lambeth, Dod box, Applied decoration, Relief decoration** and **Elers brothers**.

Springing

The defect of incorrectly joined handles which part from the pot at one end. See **Crack S**.

Stabilizer

A modifying oxide added to a glaze, frit or colour to stabilize the colour or the oxides. For example, in the making of lead frits, small amounts of the oxides of aluminium, titanium and calcium are included and these dramatically reduce the solubility of the lead content. See ***Low sol***. The intermediate or amphoteric oxides are also generally referred to as glaze stabilizers.

Staffordshire cones

The earlier name for Harrison Pyrometric Cones. See ***Cones***.

Stains

Ceramic stains. Prepared stains. Prepared oxides. Modified oxides. Inorganic colouring, usually purchased in powder form, for adding to bodies, slips, glazes and enamels, and for use as underglaze and inglaze decoration. Organic dyes which are used to colour raw materials, slips and glazes and which burn out during firing are sometimes referred to as distinguishing stains.

A stain is included as part of a recipe for a body, slip, glaze or decoration pigment. Alternatively, it is added as an extra to a standard recipe for a colourless body etc. The amount of stain depends upon the intensity of the required colour and the ceramic material it is staining. Full colour is achieved with approximately 5% of stain in transparent glazes, 10% in opaque glazes and 15% in bodies. For uniformity of dispersion without trace of specking it is necessary to mix the stain with hot water and sieve it separately through a 200's mesh before adding to the bulk of the material. The different colours of stain from one manufacturer are approximately equal in staining power.

Ceramic stains are used in preference to colouring oxides where a more stable and predictable colour is required. The difference is explained under ***Colours: oxides and prepared stains.***

Zirconium silicate is the basis of many high-temperature stains. In the late 1940s in the USA, it was discovered that colouring atoms together with sodium atoms could be secured inside the refractory structure of zirconium silicate. This was the start of a new range of clean and stable colours which subsequently has been added to so that a wide range of dependable stains is now available. Most are unaffected by temperatures up to 1300°C (2372°F) and are reasonably resistant to reduction although they are usually manufactured for oxidizing conditions. Heavy reduction and prolonged firings cause breakdown of a stain's structure and result in colour change. Breakdown is influenced by the particular glaze or body composition.

The zirconium-silicate stains are often identified in catalogues by the word zirconium or zircon with the colouring metal. Zinc oxide and tin oxide are also used as stabilizers. These stains (and incidentally almost every stain using copper colouring) are more easily affected by reduction than the zirconium-silicate stains but are perfectly stable in oxidized firings.

Low temperature stains are still used for their special colours and some give attractive variation across brush-strokes as do straight oxides. But the stability of all stains can be linked to their refractoriness. All stains have a temperature limit above which the colour is lost or changed but some are so refractory that studio potters are unlikely to overfire them. The highly refractory stains might adversely influence the vitrification or fusion of a glaze. It is then necessary to rebalance the recipe by decreasing the amount of china clay. Alternatively, the stain may be added with up to an equal weight of soft glaze. The best soft glaze for this purpose can only be found by trial and error. It must be one which counteracts the refractory influence on the body or glaze without dissolving the stain too much and thereby destroying the colour. It should be noted that it is not just a case of increasing the fluxes to balance the addition of a refractory material. It is a fusible glass that is required and this often means a borate glass even though boron oxide fiercely attacks some refractory stains.

In practice very few bodies and glazes by whatever method they are coloured give identical results in oxidation and reduction. Similarly a stain gives slightly different colours in different bodies and glazes.

A single prepared stain is a versatile material. It can be used as a body and slip stain, an underglaze colour, for inglaze painting and as a glaze and enamel stain. See relevant articles.

Stains are finely ground and in powder form should be handled with care since they quickly become air-borne dust. Some contain toxic materials and silica. See ***Health hazard***.

Stannic oxide

SnO_2. See ***Tin oxide***.

Stanniferous painting

Painting on an unfired tin glaze as in maiolica ware. See ***Maiolica***.

Mug by Alan Caiger-Smith.

Steger's bending bar

A method of measuring the stress between body and glaze. A thin bar of clay is biscuited, then glazed on one side only. It is fired with one end fixed and the other end free in space. As the glaze sets in cooling the difference in contraction between body and glaze bends the bar and is measured while bending is in progress. The idea can be used with thin test tiles to discover what sort of stress exists between body and glaze.

Stibium oxide
Sb_2O_3. See *Antimony oxide*.

Stiff glazes
Glazes with little or no run during firing. Some glazes, like pale celadons, are effective only when thickly applied. Such glazes need to be stiffer than average and this is achieved by a high aluminium oxide content. The aluminium oxide:silica ratio is between 1:6 and 1:8. Feldspar and china clay are important ingredients and therefore feldspathic glazes are stiff glazes. See *Feldspathic glaze* and *Aluminium oxide: in glazes*.

Stiff glazes are characterized by a semi-opacity due to suspended fine bubbles and sometimes crystals. They have a high surface tension and are not so shiny as runny glazes. See also Run.

Stokes's law
The law which declares that if particles of a substance are suspended in a liquid the particles will settle in order of their decreasing size. Therefore in a mixture of clay and water the sedimentation of the largest particles takes place first and the finest particles sediment last. The finest particles, if smaller than 10^{-4} cm in diameter, will be of colloidal size and may never settle and these are controlled by a movement called Brownian movement. Stokes's law explains the natural sorting of clay sediments in lakes and is made use of in levigation of clay.

Stone
See *Cornish stone*.

Stoneware
A hard, strong and vitrified ware, usually fired above 1200°C (2192°F), in which the body and glaze mature at the same time and form an integrated body-glaze layer. The quality of the glaze owes much to the establishment of this layer and it is therefore the glaze quality which determines a ware's acceptance as stoneware. This quality shows as an integration of the colours of body and glaze. Stoneware glaze surfaces are scratch resistant.

The photographs are of a large platter by David Frith, a large bowl by Phil Rogers and a large casserole by Pauline Paterson.

Under *Earthenware*, the division between earthenware and stoneware is given as depending upon the porosity of the body. While this criterion is often taken for deciding what is earthenware, it is rarely taken as the criterion for stoneware. There are many porous stonewares with well-integrated body-glaze layers in which much of the quality of the glaze is derived from the body beneath. Their porosity does not invalidate their claim to be stonewares. See *Porosity, Hard* and *Vitrification*.

The following are stonewares:
Stoneware: body and glaze integrated in a firing above 1200°C (2192°F); body of less than 5% porosity.
Ovenware: body and glaze integrated; body up to 10% porosity.
Red stoneware: Non-porous body or less than 2% porosity;

firing temperature between 1100°C and 1250°C (2012°F and 2282°F).

Salt-glazed wares: body and glaze integrated; low porosity; physically hard.

Porcelain is a special type of stoneware which has a white, completely vitrified and often translucent body. See **Porcelain**.

China uses a porcelain body with a soft (earthenware) glaze. See **China**.

STONEWARE CLAY. Clay suitable for making the dense ware called stoneware. It must be plastic with a good workability range. It must have a long vitrification period with an almost dense end-product that is strong but not brittle. It should have an interesting colour, take glazes well and preferably not break down in reduction.

Most stoneware pottery is thrown, for which a high degree of plasticity is required. Good plasticity is often accompanied by a long workability range which allows turning and the adding of handles etc.

In the firing, the clay needs to vitrify slowly so that whatever the product it can mature without distortion. Potters who make stoneware tableware aim to get an end-product which is theoretically vitrified and therefore is non-porous. This takes the body near to its point of deformation. With most clays this vitrification also gives a brittleness or rather a lack of resilience. It is preferable that the body shall have an absorbency of 1% or even 2%. In this state it has resilience and can withstand physical knocks. Below 1% absorbency, most stoneware clays decrease in strength to the point of vitrification where they may be only half as strong as at 1% absorbency.

This connection between strength and absorbency/vitrification cannot be related to porcelain which is quite different. In porcelain the body is homogeneous; it does not contain variously-sized particles of sand, grog etc. The body therefore becomes of equal vitrification and the glaze is of similar composition to the body and integrated with it. The combined body and glaze unit is very strong. In stoneware, while some integration takes place, there is always a stress between body and glaze that must be considered. The ideal stoneware clay is therefore one which can be accurately fired to required porosity.

Many stoneware potters use reduction to gain more integration of body and glaze for reasons of strength and colour response. Good stoneware clays should respond favourably to reduction and give added colour interest. All clays vitrify more quickly under reduction and some may become too brittle to be practical for stoneware.

The base of a pot will always be unglazed in stoneware and the body will show. The siliceous clays often take glazes better than the aluminous ones because they integrate well in the early stages of firing.

Natural stoneware clays exist and have been used for industrial stoneware for 150 years. They are usually a type of ball clay which contains colouring impurities. Normal ball clays can be adapted for stoneware. They are usually too fine and long, and need to be shortened by grog, sand and other clays. Ball clays are also rather insipid in colour.

Heavy clay industrial stoneware uses fireclay. These fireclays are often classified as low grade because they contain many impurities but, if weathered well, they make excellent stoneware clays. If the impurities are potassium oxide and other fluxes with some finely-divided iron oxide, the clay will make a stoneware clay. It may be necessary to blend it with ball clay for plasticity and/or to add some bentonite for plasticity. A very short fireclay may require 5% of bentonite but 2% is more usual.

Strain
The condition of a ceramic body that has been subjected to stress. It can be measured as a linear displacement or a percentage distortion from the ideal.

Stress
The force exerted between two parts of a ceramic body. It can be measured as energy. There is always some stress between body and glaze, and between one part of a pot and another, e.g. foot rim and sides. Stress results in strain which is the effect upon the body and is measured as a distortion.

All pots contain stresses. Sometimes the stresses are such that if a pot is dropped it bounces. In this case the stresses created by the collision are in opposition to, and are counteracted by, the existing stresses. On the other hand a pot is sometimes given a slight knock that results in the shattering of the piece. In this case the existing stresses were finally overloaded. Pots do not always crack where we would expect because we are unaware of the existence of the stresses.

Striking in
Warming in. The process of re-heating potential copper-red glazes to achieve the optimum red colour.

The quality and strength of the visible red colour depend on the size of the copper metal particles produced in the firing of the glaze.

Copper red glazes sometimes come from their top-temperature firing looking patchy, pale or even colourless. The amount of copper metal in the glaze is small. Only 1 in every 800 atoms of glaze material is copper and individually the particles of pure copper are too tiny and too widely spaced to emit sufficiently strong pulses of energy to register in the eye. Re-heating the glaze will activate the copper atoms and soften the glaze enough to allow the copper atoms to agglomerate. They will then form particles or crystals of appropriate size to give a pure red colour. The particles are, in size, equal to only a fraction of the thickness of this paper yet each contains between 0·25 million and 3 million atoms. These collectively can emit a strong signal which the eye will see. See **Colours, Colloid** and **Copper oxides**.

The temperature required for any particular glaze can only be found by experiment. Between 500°C and 1100°C

(932°F and 2012°F) have been used but 700°C (1292°F) seems the most popular. Holding this temperature for up to one hour allows time for the agglomeration to take place. It is usual to strike in using an oxidized firing. It can also be incorporated in the cooling from the normal top temperature by holding the temperature for an hour at 700°C (1292°C). Too long a soak will darken the colour because the particles will become too large.

Possible side effects include: pin-holes if the work has been allowed to meet dampness before striking in; noticeable dulling of the glaze surface by devitrification; cracking of ware if the glaze thickness is not uniform.

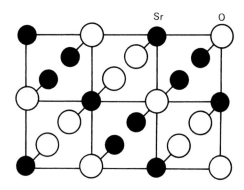

Strontianite

Strontium carbonate. $SrCO_3$. Insoluble strontium mineral associated with lead ores in limestone replacement lodes. It is a source of strontium oxide for frits and glazes. Strontianite is named after the village of Strontian in Scotland, where it was first discovered.

Strontium carbonate

$SrCO_3$. Source of strontium oxide in glazes. The oxide form is soluble in water therefore the carbonate is used in a glaze batch. If the strontium carbonate is prepared from the crushed ore it usually contains some calcium carbonate. Strontium carbonate decomposes by 1075°C (1967°F) to give the oxide:

$$SrCO_3 \xrightarrow{1075°C} SrO + CO_2 \uparrow$$

Strontium oxide

SrO. A useful glaze flux for all temperatures, once it has been incorporated in a frit. If introduced into a glaze batch as strontium carbonate its fluxing action is limited to temperatures above 1090°C (1994°F). It is similar in effect to calcium oxide and zinc oxide.

Strontium occurs in the minerals celestine ($SrSO_4$) and strontianite ($SrCO_3$). The metal strontium can be isolated and melts at 757°C (1395°F) but the oxide is a refractory, melting at 2430°C (4406°F).

The fluxing action of the oxide is effective from around 650°C (1202°F) upwards to any pottery temperature and it is unaffected by reduction. To be effective at the lower temperatures, however, it must be incorporated in a frit. When strontium oxide is introduced into a glaze by means of the insoluble strontium carbonate, its fluxing action is not realized until 1090°C (1994°F). In this way it is similar to calcium oxide.

The action of strontium oxide is often compared with that of calcium oxide. The thermal expansion and the fluxing powers are approximately the same, although the interaction power of strontium oxide is more akin to that of zinc oxide. Like both calcium oxide and zinc oxide, it requires interaction to be effective as a flux, and also like them an excess precipitates a crystalline matt surface.

For the individual potter who uses raw glazes, strontium oxide, via the carbonate, is a useful additional flux to give interaction in the middle temperature range, 1100°C to 1200°C (2012°F to 2192°F). Although little used, strontium oxide is not a new flux. It has been used since the late 19th century when it was tried as a substitute for lead oxide. The glaze experiments were successful and lead-free and zinc-free non-poisonous glazes were produced. Strontium compounds are not poisonous. The price of strontium minerals precluded their use and strontium carbonate is still about three times the cost of whiting, so there is no point in such a substitution. However, as a replacement for lead oxide on a molecular basis it will be found to be of approximately the same price and here strontium oxide is worth consideration for glaze recipes calling for small amounts of lead oxide.

Super-cooled liquid

Undercooled liquid. A technical term meaning that a liquid has been cooled below its freezing point without crystallization.

A glaze is a super-cooled liquid because it cools so quickly that there is usually no time for crystals to grow. If a glaze were cooled very slowly, various crystals would grow and separate themselves from the liquid, e.g. calcium silicate, orthoclase, quartz. After such a slow cooling the glaze would be a complete mass of crystals, as is granite, and would not be a glass. Because a glaze cools quickly it sets without this opportunity and is therefore scientifically regarded as a liquid although it has set to a solid state.

The terms solid solution and amorphous solid are also used to describe a glaze. Both are linked with the conception of a glaze as a liquid which is so viscous as to present the appearance of a solid. Therefore a glaze which is reheated has no melting point. Instead its viscosity is slowly decreased until it is sufficiently fluid to flow.

Surface tension

The apparent pull which the surface of a liquid has whereby it tries to contain the liquid. It is imagined as a tight skin which is always trying to compress the liquid, or as a skin which is stretched by the liquid which it contains. Thus a free or unattached volume of liquid forms itself into a sphere: the volume surrounded by the smallest possible surface area. In reality surface tension is caused by the attraction of the component molecules of the liquid whereby they group themselves into the most compact mass. There is in reality no skin under tension at the surface. This is an apparent phenomenon resulting from the internal stresses. However, the so-called surface tension can be measured and laboratory measurements are made of the surface tensions of molten glazes.

The term comes into the potter's vocabulary in relation to molten glazes. A glaze with a low surface tension quickly creeps into narrow crevices or porous surfaces. This phenomenon is called 'wetting' and is similar to the action of a thin liquid like petrol which can wet a material upon which water would stand as globules. Water has a higher surface tension than petrol.

A glaze with a high surface tension does not 'wet' the pottery body but, if at all loose, tends to curl back or consolidate itself in globules. This phenomenon is called 'crawling'. Stiff or viscous glazes tend to have high surface tensions. Runny or fluid glazes tend to have low surface tensions.

The surface tension of a glaze is directed by its chemical composition. Some constituent oxides make a glaze of low surface tension. An example is potassium oxide (K_2O) which is also an active flux and creates fluid glazes. Some oxides make a glaze of high surface tension. An example is aluminium oxide (Al_2O_3) which also increases a glaze's viscosity. If the glaze oxides are put into a table in the order of their action upon surface tension it will be found that potassium oxide is at one end and aluminium oxide at the other. The oxides between them are in approximately the same order as their action on viscosity. To give a comparison, a table of oxide action on viscosity at approximately 1050°C (1922°F) is also given. It is extracted from the fuller table given under **Viscosity**. On both tables, silica is included in its correct place and is taken as the standard with which the others are compared.

The two tables do not match exactly which means that minor adjustments made to one state do not necessarily affect the other. However their relationship is strong because they depend upon the same actions. These actions are the breaking and making of bonds between oxide molecules especially between an oxide and silica in the creation of linked chains. In a molten glaze the bonds are continually being broken and remade in new combinations.

A rise in temperature brings into action more fluxes and increases the ease with which bonds are broken, thus increasing fluidity. It also lowers the surface tension slightly.

Small amounts of additional oxides interfere with the creation of regularized patterns which have a stiffening effect. They thereby increase fluidity quite markedly but they lower the surface tension only slightly.

A reducing atmosphere often increases fluidity by creating greater interaction with the body and turning iron oxide into a flux. It has no effect upon surface tension.

Lastly, it should be stated that surface tension of the molten glaze is not related to the physical thickness of the glaze layer. It is true that the high surface tension shows most in thick glazes where it can cause crawling; and that a thinner layer of glaze may overcome the problem of crawling; it does not, however, alter the surface tension but gives less opportunity for a rupturing of the glaze layer.

Suspender

An addition to a glaze slop to keep the materials in suspension. Popular suspenders are bentonite with calcium chloride and polymer adhesives. See **Flocculation** and **SCMC**.

Polymer adhesives help to bind a friable glaze to the ware before firing as well as providing slop suspension. Many other adhesives like gelatine, cellulose pastes and resin gums, temporarily thicken a glaze slop and keep it in suspension. However, the most popular suspender is 1% bentonite which is flocculated by the addition of calcium chloride to the water.

Syenite

An igneous rock with less than 10% free silica (quartz). Above this amount of quartz the rock is called a granite. See **Nepheline**.

Symbol
See **Chemical symbol**.

← Increases surface tension		← Increases viscosity →
HIGH SURFACE TENSION		
Aluminium oxide		
Magnesium oxide	**HIGH VISCOSITY**	
Zirconium oxide		
Calcium oxide	Aluminium oxide	
Tin oxide	Zirconium oxide	
Zinc oxide	Tin oxide	
Strontium oxide	Barium oxide	
Barium oxide	Titanium oxide	
SILICA	**SILICA**	
Titanium oxide	Magnesium oxide	
Boron oxide	Calcium oxide	
Lithium oxide	Strontium oxide	
Lead oxide	Zinc oxide	
Sodium oxide	Boron oxide	
↓ Lowers surface tension — Potassium oxide	Lead oxide	
	Lithium oxide	
LOW SURFACE TENSION	Sodium oxide	
	Potassium oxide	↓ Increases fluidity
	LOW VISCOSITY	

T

Tables

See *Appendix of Tables*, page 395.

Talc

Magnesium silicate. French chalk. Steatite. Soapstone. $3MgO.4SiO_2.H_2O$. An insoluble mineral and convenient source of magnesium oxide for bodies and glazes. See *Magnesium oxide*.

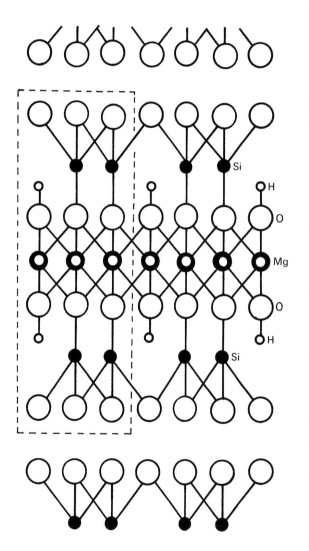

Talc is an idealized mineral which in nature has a variable formula of proportions and nearly always contains some calcium, iron and aluminium. Steatite and soapstone are attempts to name two varieties.

Before the action of magnesium oxide as a catalyst was understood, it was discovered empirically that talc restrained the tendency of the glaze to craze if it was added to the earthenware body. The required action is not that of a flux although some fusion must take place in high temperature bisc firings. Rather it depends upon there being some free silica available which does not fuse. This free silica is often deliberately introduced into the body as powdered quartz. During the bisc firing, some is converted from quartz phase to cristobalite phase by the catalytic action of the magnesium oxide and it remains crystalline. The cristobalite has a high rate of contraction and the body thereby exerts a squeeze upon the glaze which acts against any tendency to craze. See *Silica: conversion* and *Cristobalite*.

Talc is also added to stoneware bodies to increase resistance to thermal shock. At first this appears contradictory to the idea of using it to increase cristobalite. The explanation lies in the composition of the body. The cristobalite earthenware body contains a large proportion of free silica. In some cases as much as 50% of the body will be free silica. Shockproof stoneware bodies must contain as little free silica as possible. They are composed of kaolinite and other aluminous clays. The talc provides a flux which itself is low in expansion rate. This flux involves the free silica left from mullite formation and the silica introduced in the talc. The process is intended to use magnesium oxide as a flux and not as a catalyst. The free silica is thus involved in a melt which, because it is with magnesium oxide, is a viscous melt and one not so destructive to pottery forms as fluid flux/silica melts. By becoming molten, the silica, whether quartz or cristobalite, loses its crystalline nature and is rendered of low thermal expansion. See *Table 26*.

These talc/clay shockproof bodies are called cordierite bodies. Cordierite is a magnesium and iron silicate mineral. The idealized formula attempted by reconstruction in cordierite bodies is $2MgO.2Al_2O_3.5SiO_2$. Some cordierite ware is flameproof which is an extreme test for a pottery body. Cordierite bodies are also used for electrical insulators for high frequencies.

Cordierite bodies have a narrow firing range because there is a necessity to involve the free silica before distorting the ware. They are also difficult to cover with a satisfactory glaze because of their low expansion rates.

Talc in glazes provides unattached magnesium oxide and silica. It is a useful mineral for glazes maturing above 1000°C (1832°F) because it decomposes at 900°C (1652°F) into free magnesium oxide, free silica and water. It can be used to produce opaque and matt glazes as described under *Magnesian matts*. Its popular use is in stoneware glazes, where, after becoming involved in a liquid phase, it reforms as enstatite upon cooling. See *Enstatite*.

Tammann temperature

In 1926 Gustav Tammann (1861–1938) proposed that a powdered solid has a sintering point which is 0·57 of its melting point in °K. Degrees Kelvin (°K) are centigrade measurements of temperature starting at 0°K for theoretical absolute zero which is −273°C. See ***Kelvin***. Sintering points give useful information about when fusion starts and the probable densification of non-glassy engobes.

The Tammann temperature for potassium feldspar is:

$$\text{MP} \quad 1200°\text{C} + 273 = 1473°\text{K}$$
$$1473°\text{K} \times 0·57 = 840°\text{K}$$
$$840°\text{K} - 273 = 567°\text{C Tammann temperature}$$

If two or more materials are involved, the sintering point, or start of fusion for ceramic materials, is proportionate. Therefore the Tammann temperature for a 50/50 mixture of zinc oxide and silica is:

zinc oxide   MP 1970°C gives T.t. of 1006°C
silica   MP 1710°C gives T.t. of 857°C
50/50 mixture has T.t. of 932°C which is half-way.

The next example also gives the melting point of the 50/50 mixture for comparison. This is lower than half-way because of the alkali/acid interaction. The sintering point is still half-way between the two Tammann temperatures:

sodium oxide	MP 900°C	T.t. 396°C
silica	MP 1710°C	T.t. 857°C
50/50 mixture	MP 1037°C	T.t. 626°C

See ***Interaction, Eutectic mixture, Melting point*** and ***Sinter***.

Tea-dust

Describes the decorative surface of glazes where a matt, very fine speckle covers what appears to be a more shiny glaze underneath. As with many of these overall textural effects the origin was Chinese. The term is sometimes limited to effects produced in the original manner using a matt enamel which is dusted onto the glaze. The original colour varied from a mustard yellow to a sage green. However, the description also fits many effects resulting from overloading glazes with metal oxides especially when such glazes are over other glazes or vitrifying slips. There is a variant of tenmoku which has been described as tea-dust.

The following is a tea-dust glaze for 1200°C (2192°F). It is black with brown dust on top.

potassium feldspar	50
china clay	15
flint	5
whiting	15
red iron oxide	5
manganese oxide	5
cobalt oxide	5

Tea marl

A red and green shale of the Triassic Period. It is crumbly and can be reconstituted as a clay by crushing and blunging. It produces a red-burning clay. See ***Marl***.

Teapot

A pot for infusing and serving tea. It is usually a lidded pot of compact form with a spout and handle. The teapot originated in China in the 14th century and was developed from the kettle previously used. It came to Europe in the 17th century as an import with the tea. At first tea was regarded as a medicine and teapots were small, some only 5 cm in diameter. Cheaper tea grown in India and Ceylon during the days of the British Empire resulted in tea becoming the popular drink of 19th-century Britain. Teapots became larger. Some held as much as two gallons and had two spouts. Two-spouted pots either fill two separate cups or have two spouts side by side to fill one cup more quickly.

The development of the teapot, as it is made by individual potters today, can be considered British or even English. The teapot is a symbol of friendliness. First, the society ladies of 18th-century England held their afternoon tea parties. Later, in the 19th century, tea was the alternative stimulant to beer for the working classes. Today the relaxing and confidential aura of tea-drinking remains but it has lost the precious atmosphere which was reflected in the decorative effects of chinoiserie and rococo. The individual potter is able to make teapots which capture this friendliness by the successful integration of the different parts and the harmony of body and glaze. Teapots have developed over 300 years from the Elers pieces of the 17th century which copied Chinese red stoneware. Astbury, Whieldon and Wedgwood each gave some character to the development so that by the 19th century a truly English teapot had developed. In the 20th century, Oriental influence, this time Japanese, added to the character.

The examples shown are sprigged stoneware by Pauline Paterson; oxidized stoneware by Will Levi Marshall; raku with lace resist by Steve Mills; tiger-skin salt glaze by Peter Meanley; composite underglaze patterns by Richard Godfrey; forged-iron-handled porcelain by Joanna Howells; rouletted salt glaze by Jane Hamlyn; salt-glazed porcelain by Michael Casson; and salt-glazed stoneware by Micki Schloessingk, seen in a newly-opened kiln.

The functional points of a teapot are simple, but the satisfactory combination of these points is a challenge to the potter's skill and imagination, especially when some elegance or aesthetic interest is required of this tea-table focal point. The pot must hold sufficient tea, usually four to six cupfuls, keep it hot while the tea infuses, be stable and easily lifted and accurately manoeuvred to pour the tea into the cups. It must, to some degree, strain the tea by holding back the tea leaves in the pot and yet it must be capable of being easily cleaned.

Capacity is usually reckoned in cupfuls. A small teapot holding two cupfuls is a half-pint one. A theoretical form to be considered for the body of the pot is a sphere. This is adjusted in consideration of other factors. The sphere is the form that gives the greatest capacity for a given surface area. This is advantageous as regards the weight of the pot which has to be lifted and controlled. It also gives less surface for heat loss. Boiling water is used to infuse the tea and it is advantageous to keep the tea as hot as possible for the five minutes required for infusion.

A form broader than high gives a larger cross-section for the movement of the tea during this process. The broader form is also more stable. To keep the tea hot during infusion, earthenware is considered better than stoneware or porcelain. Traditionally, red earthenware (which is lower fired and hence more porous and the better insulator) is preferred to white earthenware. Tea connoisseurs declare that they can taste the difference in tea made in a red earthenware pot. It is interesting to note that the raku tea bowl, which is a good insulator, acts as both teapot for infusing and the cup for drinking.

The popular broad body for the pot presents a pleasing rhythm from which may spring the spout and handle. The spout should describe in outline, or indicate in general feeling, the action of the tea as it flows. Analysis of handles, spouts and lids is given separately under these headings.

TEAPOT CLAY. Any red clay which has the combination of properties necessary for making teapots: plasticity for throwing; a long enough working range to allow spouting

and handling before drying; and when fired, to be sufficiently hard to stand up to everyday use; be a good insulator to hold in the heat; and be a rich brown colour under a clear glaze. The North Staffordshire red clay is traditionally a teapot clay.

Technique

The individual way in which each potter carries out a process. Technique is allied to skill. It is developed by establishing a personal relationship with the work and is often the result of repeated progressive actions. Technique cannot be taught or learnt, it can only be acquired. What is taught is a method or a process.

Temper

An addition to clay which improves work-ability, e.g. sand and grog. Temper will also affect the fired result but its introduction is essentially to assist forming and uniform drying. See also **Grog, Workability, Preparation of clay: control of grain size, Filler** and **Grain size**.

Temperature

A means of describing heat. Temperature is measured in degrees Celsius (°C) or degrees Fahrenheit (°F). These are the two common scales used by potters. Five Celsius degrees equal nine Fahrenheit degrees, but, whereas Celsius is based upon 0° as the freezing point and 100° as the boiling point of water, on the Fahrenheit scale the freezing point is 32° and the boiling point 212°.

$$100°C \text{ per hour} = 180°F \text{ per hour}$$

Tables of temperature equivalents and incandescence are included in **Tables 31** and **33**. Celsius is used as standard throughout this book. See also **Heat, Celsius** and **Kelvin**.

TEMPERATURE CONVERSION FORMULAE.

$$\text{Degrees Fahrenheit} = (°C \times \tfrac{9}{5}) + 32$$

$$\text{Degrees Celsius} = (°F - 32) \times \tfrac{5}{9}$$

Tenmoku

Temmoku. A stoneware glaze which is deeply stained by iron oxide. Tenmokus are usually dark brown and black with some rust patches, but occasionally they are yellow, green or purple. Good tenmokus have an expressive depth and variation of colour. This is achieved by the use of a glaze that has some flow. It fills hollows, gives thickness variation on the pot's form and by the use of the correct amount of iron oxide gives an interesting balance of solute and precipitate. The photographs show a jug by Christopher White and a goblet by Frank Hamer. See **Iron oxide: in glazes and Colour plates 67** and **69**.

Tenmokus are either slip glazes made from ferruginous clay and wood ash etc, or feldspathic type glazes, fluxed with wood ash or limestone, to which 4% to 12% of iron oxide has been added. The Far Eastern tenmokus were traditionally fired and cooled quickly and were oxidized. Western counterparts have more often been given some reduction to get a more blue-black colour in the dark parts. Any stoneware glaze which is deeply stained by iron oxide could acceptably be called a tenmoku. Specifically, tenmokus are restricted to shiny glazes of the black or dark brown type and the other matt and mottled effects are given separate names. Calcium oxide is a suitable flux for reduced tenmokus but oxidized tenmokus require sodium, potassium and boron oxides in order to achieve a clean colour. See **Calcium oxide**.

TENMOKU (VARIATIONS). The connoisseur makes many sub-divisions of the tenmoku family of wares. The three main types are called tenmoku, tessha and kaki. Tenmokus are the black and dark brown glazes with a tendency to 'break to rust' on the rims and sharp edges. If the rust-coloured parts spread over more of the glaze causing rust patches, it would be called tessha and if the rust colour covered most of the surface it would be a kaki glaze. The kaki is sometimes given the name persimmon if it is especially bright in colour and shine. The duller kakis are simply called rusts.

Crystallization gives more matt effects amongst which one has been called tea-dust. This is self explanatary and the colour varies from mustard green to black. All the connoisseur names are descriptive. Pigskin is a semi-matt glaze with a dimpled surface. Oil-spot tenmoku has a series of lustrous spots up to 5 mm across which vary with metallic sheen as do oil spots on water. Partridge feather is similar but with smaller bright spots. Hare's fur is of two types: one is like the soft smoky grey under-fur and streaks the dark tenmoku's surface; the other is like the light-coloured tips of the hairs against the darker fur.

TENMOKU (ORIGIN). In China from the Han Dynasty

through the Tang Dynasty (1st to 10th centuries) a development took place involving brown glazed wares. During the Song Dynasty (AD960 to AD1279) the perfection of firing allowed a thicker glaze layer and a more mature glaze. The result was the dark brown stoneware glaze.

The finest examples of this period are the Jian bowls. These are rice and tea bowls rarely wider than 12 cm in diameter and varying from black to rust with many variations of the smoky hare's fur variety. The glaze was either a clay and ash slip or a straight clay slip glaze, which was put on raw ware and once-fired in varying atmospheres. The idea of the rich dark glaze with its infinite possibilities caught the imagination of many potters (though not the imperial court) and the idea spread.

To the north east of Jian in the Province of Fujian is a group of mountains called Tianmu Shan. Japanese Zen Buddhist monks visiting the monastery there used the Jian tea bowls and later took them back to Japan where they were excitedly admired and became known as Tianmu or Tenmoku. These bowls and further developments in Japan were the source of contemplative delight until the development of raku in the 16th century.

Tenorite
Copper oxide ore. CuO. A black, soft ore resulting from the oxidized weathering of other ores. See *Copper ores*.

Tension
Stretch. The act of being pulled to increase size. Glazes are in tension before they craze. The crazing accommodates the stress of tension which existed.

Ternary diagram
Triaxial diagram. See *Eutectic mixture*.

Terracotta
Earthenware ceramics both glazed and unglazed. The word comes from the Italian and means simply 'fired earth' though the word is often used to describe the orange-brown colour of red-burning clay.

Terracotta clay is usually grey or buff which fires to red, but red clays are often referred to as terracotta, and terracottas have been modelled in cream-burning clays also, so the description is quite broad.

The best use of terracotta is in the intimate piece of work where the sensitive quality of direct expression in clay can be used. Some of the finest examples of terracotta are the least pretentious and were made as toys, domestic ornaments and burial offerings. Terracottas have been made throughout the world at pottery centres, being associated more with pottery than with sculpture. When terracotta is used for architectural work it is in the personal detail that it is most successful. It was effectively used in 19th-century Britain in the form of unglazed pieces and in Renaissance Italy as high-relief plaques with coloured glazes.

The photographs are of Scottish and Maltese souvenirs and a large garden urn by Simon Hulbert.

Terra sigillata
Historically, the name for a very fine relief-decorated earthenware with a smooth red gloss finish. The gloss is an exceptionally fine slip coating. The slip is a siliceous illite clay refined by repeated levigations. The ware was fired in a bright oxidizing fire. The technique was developed in the eastern Mediterranean in the 1st century BC and its development spread with the Roman empire. It is often called Samian ware.

This method of producing a shiny burnished surface has been revived for unglazed ceramics and the name colloidal-slip treatment is used synonymously. This popular method of creating a very attractive tactile surface is often combined with the subtle colouring from smoking and sawdust firing. Metallic salts are used to enhance the colour. The surface is finished by a wax polish. See *Burnishing*, *Smoking* and *Metallic salts*.

A terra-sigillata slip can be made from any clay although fine clays are obviously best. The clay should be mixed with a copious amount of water including a small amount of deflocculant to disperse the fine clay particles. A water softener will work as a deflocculant. Thorough mixing is essential to separate the smallest clay particles and put them in suspension. The exceedingly thin slurry is allowed to settle for a couple of days before the all-important, cloudy, top three-quarters of the water is siphoned off. This contains the superfine clay particles which are now flocculated by an acid like calcium chloride, Epsom salt or vinegar to encourage their sedimentation. Settling results in clear water and a very small amount of the required terra-sigillata slip.

Duncan Ayscough sprays the slip onto his pieces in layers, and fires them as shown in *Sawdust firing*.

Tessha

A variation of the tenmoku glaze in which the rust parts spread in patches over about half the surface. The rust colour is due to the crystallization of the red iron oxide upon cooling. See *Iron oxide: in glazes*.

Tetraoxide

An oxide involving four atoms of oxygen with one or three atoms of another element in each molecule. See also *Oxide*.

Theoretical formula

A chemical formula used in calculations because it is simpler than using a chemical analysis. The theoretical formula ignores important 'impurities'. For example flint, which could be 95% silica and 5% calcium carbonate, is given a theoretical formula of SiO_2 as if it were 100% silica. Other common examples of theoretical formulae are:

china clay	$Al_2O_3.2SiO_2.2H_2O$
potassium feldspar	$K_2O.Al_2O_3.6SiO_2$
sodium feldspar	$Na_2O.Al_2O_3.6SiO_2$
dolomite	$CaCO_3.MgCO_3$

Thermal shock

The stress created within a ceramic object by temperature change. Thermal shock is responsible for the occurrence of cracks and is an overall term.

Its normal use refers to sudden changes of temperature such as happen to ovenware. If there is a large difference in temperature between two parts of the same piece of ceramic there is obviously a size difference due to expansion/contraction. This is the cause of the stress.

The ways in which some cracks occur have been given separate names and are called dunting and spalling. Dunting is the result of stress caused by silica (quartz and cristobalite) inversions. These inversions create marked changes in size of the silica and affect the size of the ceramic body containing them. Stresses which are not absorbed result in cracks which are called dunts. Spalling is cracking of kiln brickwork and is the result of both silica inversions and the normal thermal shock. *Dunting* and *Spall* are separate items in this book.

A ceramic body is a poor conductor of heat. When boiling water is poured into a teapot there is a time lag before the heat reaches the outside. In the section of the side of the pot, the inside is expanding with the heat of the boiling water before the outside. Stress is obviously created during this time-lag which may weaken some of the mechanical bonds of the body. When repeated a hundred times, a crack may appear which grows until it is noticeable. The crack may not happen suddenly but it is the result of thermal shock. A crack of this type may start parallel to the surfaces of the pottery body—that is, within the wall of a pot between inside and outside. However it soon angles itself to the surface at a point where the pot wall is thinner. Cracks in teapots often occur around the sectional unevenness of the foot rim. If the thickness is uniform it may be possible to absorb this transient stress an unlimited number of times.

With ovenware the heat or cold may suddenly envelop one side of the pot as it is placed into or withdrawn from the oven. The temperature difference is in this case across the whole pot as well as possibly through the thickness of the pot wall. This thermal shock can create sufficient stress to rupture the pot between the hotter and the colder halves. The actual amounts involved could be as much as 0·25% linear increase as the pot enters a hot oven. This is 5 mm across a 20 cm plate. This amount is sufficient to rupture a pot whose body has insufficient elasticity to absorb the temporary differential.

As with the example of the teapot, ovenware in the form of casseroles and pie dishes may sustain ruptures through thermal shock which are not immediately apparent. If the body is very dense it is likely that a through crack will result, probably very quickly and with an alarming noise. If the body is not dense, the cracking may be slower and one may hear cracking as it takes place. It may be quite slow, lasting a minute or more, as the strain is relieved a part at a time.

A glassy, vitrified part may crack but the crack cannot continue through the body because it is stopped by a space. The stress then builds up against the next glassy part which then cracks as far as the next space. This continues until the stress is eased and the natural elasticity of the body can absorb the remaining stress. An open porous body can therefore absorb a thermal shock better than a dense vitrified body but this does not mean that it has not cracked partially.

The periodic extension of a crack can often happen in a casserole. Sometimes one may hear it take place but fail to see the minute crack. Each time the casserole is used the crack is extended a little. All this is unknown to its owner until the remaining unruptured part gives way. An examination of the crack will often show that it has existed for a long time as can be seen by the way grease and water have entered the crack and discoloured the body.

It is generally known that an open porous body is a better insulator than a dense body. For example, kiln insulation bricks are light and porous. The trapped air provides excellent heat insulation. It follows that a vitrified body and a glaze are better conductors of heat than an open porous body. Conversely, a coarse open body or similarly a fine but porous body will retain its heat when a dense or vitrified body, and certainly a glaze, will have lost its heat. The

porosity acting as insulation makes the porous body slow to warm up and slow to cool down.

When pottery is used in the oven the first part of a pot to warm through is the glaze. This will occur quickly. The second part is the body and this will occur more slowly if the body is porous. When the glaze is warm, but not the body, there exists a stress between the two. The glaze is too big for the body and is under what is called a state of compression forced on it by the body. Most glazes are able to withstand this compression. Ones which cannot do so flake off at sharp corners on rims and handles. The phenomenon is called shivering. The stress must be quite extreme for this to occur. It is unlikely to happen on sound ware. Tell-tale signs will previously have occurred with ware prone to shivering. Such signs would be minor shivering, shelling and inexplicable plate cracks on overfired ware.

The sharp slivers of glaze are a danger with ovenware. It can also happen that if the glaze is very thick inside a wide cooking dish the glaze exerts sufficient pressure to rupture the body and this will take with it the glaze in a sudden shattering of the pot. Pots have been known to shatter suddenly into four or five pieces.

When the body also warms thoroughly it will catch up with the expansion of the glaze. In fact it will overtake it. Many bodies have greater thermal expansion and contraction rates than the glazes which cover them. If the rates are very different, the glaze will now come under tension from the body. The glaze will be too small for the body. Even the most elastic lead glaze has a limit to the amount of tension it can withstand. With any glaze it is only about one-tenth of the stress that it can withstand in the opposite direction under compression. The result is that the glaze ruptures. The body remains intact but the glaze cracks in what is known as crazing. If the stress is not sufficient to cause crazing in the oven it may well become sufficient when the piece of pottery is taken from the oven. At this point the glaze meets the colder air first. Being a relatively good conductor it quickly gives out its heat and in so doing it contracts. The porous body conserves its heat and remains expanded. Few glazes can withstand this treatment which is why ovenware is so frequently crazed.

It should also be remembered that ovenware is often left to soak in water. The porous body takes water into the pores and the body expands as a result. This too puts a tension on the glaze which can cause the crazing to spread.

Some potters like to see a small amount of crazing on their unused ovenware. This is especially true of their stoneware. Although this crazing will get worse with use it is an indication that the glaze is not starting under compression at room temperature. Crazing is considered preferable to shattering and shivering.

Thermal shock is the stress which may or may not result in a crack, in shivering or in crazing. It is bound to exist and cannot be entirely removed. The stress occurs between contiguous parts of ceramic bodies when pots are suddenly warmed or cooled in the kiln or in the oven or when used for hot liquids. Thick pots are more prone to the effects of thermal shock than thin ones. Glazed pots are more prone than unglazed ones. Thick glazes are more prone than thin glazes. Further application of thermal shock theory to pottery-making is discussed under **Ovenware**. A relationship between vitrification and strength is made under **Vitrification**. The cause of cracks is dealt with under **Cracks** and the theory of dunting which is related to thermal shock is dealt with under **Dunting**.

Thermocouple

A probe introduced through the kiln wall into a chamber to measure the temperature. See **Instrumentation** and **Pyrometry**.

Thermoscope

Pyroscope.

Thermotrophy

Thermotropy. The phenomenon of colour change by heat. Apart from the fact that ceramic bodies and glazes are glowing red at temperatures above 600°C (1112°F), they are also undergoing reversible colour changes in the range from room temperature to 600°C (1112°F). On cooling from firing, bodies and glazes do not achieve their final colour until the temperature has fallen below 80°C (176°F). If a kiln is opened when it is hot the difference is sometimes quite startling. Some bodies appear much lighter than their final colour and some glazes appear darker. Glazes containing titanium oxide, especially with tin oxide, appear a yellow buff colour which eventually fades to a pure white at room temperature.

Thivier's earth

A red ochreous sand.

Thixotropy

The property of slips to change fluidity when being left undisturbed; the slip at rest becomes more viscous. Also the ability of wet clays to maintain a given shape. See **Workability**.

All clay suspensions (slips) have this property which is the result of the establishment of mutual attraction bonds between the particles. Thixotropy begins to build up as soon as the slip comes to rest. It usually passes unnoticed but some slips and glaze slops containing clays show pronounced thixotropy if left unstirred for a few days. On first restirring one is tempted to add more water but a thorough stirring returns the suspension to its original fluidity and no extra water is required.

Thixotropy should not be confused with the maturation of a newly-made slip whereby the clay particles are split into smaller pieces by the penetration of water. This naturally produces a less fluid slip. See **Fluidity: of slip and glaze suspension**.

The slip or glaze suspension which exhibits noticeable thixotropy is often one in which a small amount of soluble alkalis has been released into the water. Magnesium oxide and carbonate, some soft alkaline frits and most wood ashes can be responsible for the phenomenon described above.

Large amounts of alkali in the slip usually destroy the property of thixotropy. Therefore, in the preparation of casting slips a balance between fluidity and thixotropy must be achieved. Thixotropy is a valuable property in a casting slip because it enables the newly-formed cast to keep its form without distortion while it is still wet in the mould. Too high a thixotropy, however, would mean that the mould could not be drained after filling because the slip would 'set'.

The two popular deflocculants for casting slips are sodium carbonate and sodium silicate. They both give slips of high fluidity but sodium carbonate has little effect upon a clay's natural thixotropy whereas sodium silicate destroys it. The required thixotropy in the casting slip is therefore achieved by a balanced combination of the two deflocculants.

Flocculated glaze slops are usually thixotropic. The flocculation of the clay particles which causes a higher viscosity also increases the thixotropy. It is a valuable property because it enables a thick layer of glaze to remain steady on the newly-glazed pot prior to being set down for drying. The property is especially valuable on non-porous bisc. Over-flocculated glazes sometimes exhibit too much thixotropy. The fault shows as a glaze which will not smooth out immediately after dipping although it is still wet. The fault is usually evident in the unstirred glaze slop also. It can be corrected by a tiny amount of sodium silicate.

Through firing

A glaze firing of raw ware. The firing has to go through a biscuit stage first and therefore the normal precautions of both biscuit firing and glaze firing are combined, resulting in a longer firing.

All clays are suitable for through firing but one precaution is necessary. A clay which contains a large amount of volatile material, carbon and sulfur, requires a complete oxidation of these before the glaze melts. This is not possible with a soft glaze which starts to fuse at the same temperature as the volatiles burn out. The body is thus sealed and the volatiles will cause blistering and bloating. The traditional lead-glazed earthenwares were often slipped and glazed on one side only for this reason. Only at a few pottery centres were clays available which could be completely sealed and it was at these centres that the most decorative slipwares were made. With stoneware the same precaution at burning out is necessary for, although the glaze has not melted, it has often hardened. The longer, higher firing creates integration of body and glaze and this, together with some vitrification of the body, seals the outer surfaces. Any residual volatiles then trying to escape will cause bloating. See **Black core, Once-fired** and **Raw: raw glazing**.

Throwing

The action of making pots on a quickly rotating wheel using only the hands and, for lubrication, water. It is one of the most exciting, expressive and impressive skills in pottery-making. The process involves centring a spinning lump of plastic clay upon the wheel-head. When the piece is running true, it is opened in the centre, an inside base is formed and the walls of the pot are lifted from the remainder of the clay by a series of upward movements involving the balanced pressure of fingers inside and outside the pot. The wheel-head usually rotates in an anti-clockwise direction which seems to suit most right-handed potters, but some potters, notably in the Far East, use a clockwise direction. The wheel-head is usually horizontal but ones at an angle have been used for throwing large bowls, and upside down ones have been used for large pots where the clay's own weight helps to extend the clay. See also ***Repetition throwing***.

Throwing probably developed from the use of a simple turntable, which was made to rotate freely, and the use of a wet pinching process with water for lubrication. The Egyptians are credited with the first use of the potter's wheel about 3000BC. The people of the eastern Mediterranean used the potter's wheel during their Bronze Age, but elsewhere in the world, the use of the potter's wheel seems to have been an Iron Age innovation at the same time as the use of wheeled carts.

Throwing is a faster method of making pots than any other hand method. It contains all the elements of a great skill: the potter is in direct contact with the material. This reliance on personal skill is its attraction for the individual potter today but industry has almost dispensed with it. Throwing is the most satisfactory way to make variably-shaped hollow forms. Once learnt, the skill can be exploited to make the main part of sculptural and imaginative pieces.

A thrown bowl can be folded at the rim and added to, a method used in many of Janet Hamer's birds. See photograph of the black crowned heron.

Throwing is important, therefore, not because it is a fast method of production but because it is a means of expression. Although each pot can be sufficiently like the last to be called a repeat item, each one is a restatement of an idea and is therefore different. The opportunity for making a gradual improvement in the idea sets throwing above processes which use moulds. Pots made with moulds are limited by the mould and are often conceived in flat profile. Thrown pots are conceived in their three-dimensional existence and are capable of continual development. The best thrown work has a fluidity that speaks of the process of rhythmic manipulation of spinning clay. Photographs are of Nigel Wood, Andrew McGarva, Margaret Frith, David Frith, and two of Peter Wills on a momentum wheel.

THROWING CLAY. Throwing seems to demand of the clay a higher standard of workability, based primarily on plasticity, than does any other forming method. The hand-building processes, which require a well-behaved clay, seem to be capable of more flexibility of technique to cope with peculiarities.

Throwing clay must be plastic—capable of being formed quickly. It must be thixotropic—capable of holding the new form when pressure is released. It must be strong—capable of being pulled and worked without breaking. It must also have friction against the hands so that it can be gripped and lifted. This property is often called 'bite' to differentiate it from the general drag of a short clay which inhibits its sliding through the hands. There is a balance here of two opposing properties which is equated with the potter's skill.

The property of bite is further discussed under **Preparation of clay: control of grain size.** Here is mentioned the fact that a highly plastic clay which is too slippery can often be improved in workability by the addition of a sharp sand or grog. The addition adds bite for throwing and also a resistance to shear which helps the clay to stand up on the wheel.

Within these strict demands there is still room for the personal preference of the potter. Some potters prefer the soapy feel of a clay with little perceptible bite, while others like a strong texture to run through the fingers. Some like the dense heaviness of a de-aired clay, while others like the softer texture of hand-prepared clay.

Tiger skin

A pronounced textural pattern seen on salt- and soda-glazed ware. It is most noticeable on relatively coarse bodies which have received heavier introductions of salt or sodium compounds at higher temperatures. The effect appears as craters or hollows of colourless glaze surrounded by raised beads of glaze which link into curved chains forming a characteristic pattern. The glaze is a very stiff aluminous melt which does not readily smooth over an uneven surface. A mottled effect is first engendered by small-scale variations in the clay and the sprayed effect of sodium oxide attack. Dry craters sometimes remain where the sodium oxide has

been unable to react with a too large particle of silica or aluminium oxide and the surrounding glaze is too stiff to run over it. The pattern is often emphasized by colour in the thicker beads of glaze. This is the result of iron oxide being leached out of the body, or iron or cobalt oxides being leached from slip coatings. The colouring oxide is migrating outwards and only remains in the larger mass of glaze. The jug is by Michael Casson.

The effect is sometimes called leopard skin but the name tiger skin arose in the 18th century when all the leopard family were included as tigers. See also **Orange peel, Salt glaze, Soda firing** and **Colour plate 41**.

Tin ash

A mixture of tin oxide and lead oxide. It is a brown colour but gives white opacity to glazes when the lead oxide fluxes the silicates and the tin oxide remains as suspended particles.

Tin ash was the glaze constituent for the Hispano-Moresque wares and later tin-glazed wares until the 20th century. Lead and tin ores or their metals were roasted together to produce the oxides. There is obvious danger from lead fumes which prohibits the process today.

In consideration of early glaze recipes which contain tin ash one should realize that the proportions of the oxides vary from 50:50 to 85:15, lead oxide:tin oxide.

Tincal

Himalayan borax. See **Borax**.

Tin-glaze

Tin-enamel. See **Maiolica** and **Delft**.

Tin lustre

An iridescent lustre on the surface of a glaze produced by complete reduction of tin oxide.

Tin oxide in glazes normally produces a white opacity which is sullied by reduction. However, if a heavy but quick reduction is effected, as it can be by the raku method, an iridescence is produced on the surface while maintaining the white glaze underneath.

The following raku glaze is effective on a pink body which blushes pleasantly through the glaze and contrasts with it by reducing to black where unglazed:

lead bisilicate	87
ball clay	7
tin oxide	6

Tin oxide

White tin oxide. Tin dioxide. SnO_2 (previously called stannic oxide). The normal or fully-oxidized state of the metal tin. It is purchased as a white powder which is very light in weight. Amounts up to a maximum of 15% give increasing opacity and whiteness as the oxide is suspended in a glaze. It has been used as a glaze opacifier for at least 600 years. The photograph shows a contemporary Spanish piece.

Tin is a metal with a low melting point. It occurs as cassiterite or tin stone, which is the crude ore form of the dioxide. The ore is roasted to oxidize the impurities and is then reduced with carbon to extract the metal. The ore contains arsenic, bismuth, copper, iron and zinc, some of them as sulfides. The tin metal has the lowest melting point and can therefore be extracted by a controlled heat of 232°C (450°F). Tin was one of the earliest metals to be smelted and along with copper gave the alloy bronze. Tin stone and tin pyrites are widely found in the world, but the largest economical deposits are in south-east Asia, west Africa and south America.

There are two types of tin oxide. They are the white dioxide (SnO_2) and the black monoxide (SnO): they were previously called stannic and stannous oxides. Both are stable at room temperatures. The white can be reduced to the black at temperatures above 200°C (392°F). The black is easily reoxidized at temperatures above 700°C (1292°F). Both oxides give opacity to glazes. Both oxides are practically inert below 1150°C (2102°F) being finely divided particles in suspension in the glaze and giving opacity by having a refractive index different from the surrounding glass. Both oxides melt at approximately 1150°C (2102°F) when they begin to dissolve in the glaze. The white tin oxide acts as an acid or anti-flux thereby stiffening the melt and dissolving slowly. The black tin oxide acts as a flux and is quicker to dissolve in the glaze. Both types dissolve more quickly in alkaline glazes.

The black tin oxide gives unpleasant grey cloudiness to a glaze. Opacity is practically lost in high temperature reduction and sometimes reoxidized black tin oxide gives an unpleasant light grey scum on cooling. It is obvious that to use tin oxide in reduction firings is a very expensive way of

producing an unpleasant effect. It is included here for completeness because it may be discovered accidentally.

The white tin oxide gives a pleasing creamy white opacity. The amount required varies according to the glaze composition and the temperature. The effect of some is lost at the higher temperatures. Between 5% and 10% is usually sufficient to turn an otherwise transparent glaze into an opaque one. Some glazes might require as much as 15% but this would be a limit and amounts of tin oxide over 8% have a noticeable anti-fluxing effect upon a glaze. Tin oxide increases the glaze's viscosity resulting in pin-holing and, as an extreme, in crawling and mattness.

Tin oxide is a popular white opacifier in spite of its high price. It holds its place because it gives a more pleasant opacity than its cheaper rivals. A possible drawback is its habit of picking up pink flashes if chromium oxide is present in other glazes in the same kiln. See **Chromium oxide: chrome-tin pink**.

Rival opacifiers which are used because of their relative cheapness give excellent whiteness and opacity but under controlled circumstances. Zirconium oxide and zirconium silicate are popular. The white can be whiter than tin oxide but the quality is glassy. Calcium phosphate sometimes turns grey and even brown. Cerium oxide is limited to low temperatures; similarly antimony oxide, which also dissolves in some glazes and gives yellows with lead silicates. Titanium oxide picks up colour from the body and accentuates colour from any iron present giving creams.

The following glaze for 1050°C (2102°F) uses tin oxide to give a soft creamy white:

cornish stone	12
china clay	10
lead bisilicate	70
tin oxide	8

Tin oxide black

SnO. The grey or black oxide of tin. The normal oxide of tin is the white dioxide (SnO_2). The white is an opacifier giving white glazes and acting as an anti-flux, but reducing atmospheres before and during fusion result in the black tin monoxide. One could expect this to act as an alkaline—that is, a flux—and it will do so above 1200°C (2192°F) and become partially dissolved. However, its action appears slight or slow compared with other fluxes and the reduced tin oxide more often clouds a glaze with an unattractive grey. Very heavy reduction of tin oxide, as by raku, can give some excellent metallic tin lustres. See *Tin lustre*.

Tired clay

Clay that has lost its strength by being overworked. The strength of a clay is related to, but is not the same as, its plasticity. The two factors are part of a clay's workability. See *Workability*.

Plastic clay has strength even though it is soft. It can support its own weight in extended circumstances like wide bowls and tall pots. Clay can also be pushed and pulled into new shapes without breaking. This displays a combination of plasticity, strength and thixotropy as described under Workability.

Plasticity is a measure of the clay's capacity to allow its particles to slide past one another yet keep in contact. The particles are held together partially by the suction that is encouraged by the water between them. It is rather like a pile of wet playing cards which will slide across one another yet stick together. If air enters between the particles, then the clay is more easily ruptured. A tired clay is like this. The plasticity potential is still the same. The particles will slide past one another as before but they can also be separated, and with less force.

Clay becomes tired when it has been overworked. Throwing on the wheel tires the clay as well as the potter. The pressures and frictional actions of blunging, mechanical mixing, wedging and even throwing and pressing, if prolonged, can partly destroy the forces of attraction between the clay particles. The thixotropy which holds wet clay in a shape is temporarily weakened and needs time to establish its bonds again.

The cure for tiredness is a rest. Sometimes a short rest of a day or two is sufficient but usually a longer rest called ageing and souring is needed. Rested clays regain their strength, and previously-thrown clays often seem to have improved in plasticity. Clays which have been constituted from powder by the dough mixing method will certainly be improved by throwing and resting.

There is no rule about how long a clay should rest except the longer the better. A couple of months is the usual time. It should be resting, of course, in its plastic state and preferably with slightly more moisture content than is eventually envisaged. It is always easier to slightly dewater a clay by kneading than to increase the moisture content. Also during the resting period there is hope that the clay will improve in plasticity by sub-division of particles. This will require extra water to fill the new spaces. Wrapping the clay in close-fitting polythene sheets is ideal for the resting.

The rest which improves the strength of the clay consolidates the particles. De-airing the clay by the use of a vacuum pug mill is said to be equivalent to two months rest. However, what de-airing does not do is to encourage the bacteriological growth. This takes time and produces a colloidal gel between the clay particles. This gel increases plasticity. It is called souring and is descriptive of the smell which such clays have. See also *Preparation of clay*.

Titanates

Compounds involving titanium oxide, e.g. lead titanate ($PbO.TiO_2$), zinc titanate ($ZnO.TiO_2$), calcium titanate ($CaO.TiO_2$) also called perowskite, iron titanate ($FeO.TiO_2$) also called ilmenite.

Titanite

Sphene. Calcium silicon titanate. $CaO.SiO_2.TiO_2$. Calcium titanium silicate. $OCaTi(SiO_4)$. A crystalline mineral which separates from glazes and produces crystalline effects including matt surfaces.

Titanium oxide

White titanium oxide. TiO_2. An opacifying oxide which creates crystals within the glaze. In amounts between 5% and 10% of a glaze the titanium oxide gives a pleasant opacity with crystalline soft matt surface. The crystals are very small and cannot be seen separately. Titanium oxide glazes have the power to transmute colour from the body beneath. The colour is incorporated with the crystals and a small amount is enlivened by the light reflected through the crystals.

Titanium oxide is widely distributed in nature in small and large pockets of ores and titanite sands. It also occurs within the structure of many silicates in partial replacement of silica. It accounts for over 1% of the earth's crust. The metal titanium is exceedingly difficult to isolate because it quickly combines with other elements. For example, titanium oxide can be reduced to a monoxide but no further and it quickly regains its full complement of oxygen upon cooling. The metal titanium is used in alloys. It is extracted from the oxide ores anatase, rutile and brookite, and from the titaniferous iron ore, ilmenite. The white titanium oxide is used as a paint pigment and in ceramics.

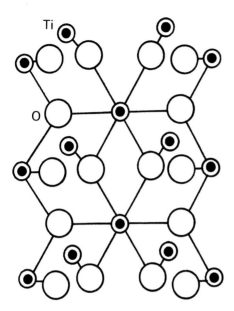

Titanium oxide readily disperses in glazes during fusion but its nuclei are sources of recrystallization as titanates during cooling. Its action is as an acid. It hardens the glaze making it more refractory and has a slight stiffening effect on low-temperature glazes. Small amounts—that is, below 1%—can be completely dissolved. From 1% upwards the recrystallization gives opacity, first as a bluish-white flush, then from approximately 5% a complete opacity. At this amount there is also a matting of the surface. Although 10% to 15% is a usual maximum, as much as 25% can be absorbed by some lead glazes. See also **Crystalline glazes**.

Titanium oxide which is dissolved in a glaze gives a stabilizing effect to the glass structure. It is valuable in lead frits where it lessens the solubility of the lead. The amount is only small, perhaps only 0·1% of the final glaze, but it is sufficient to intensify and stabilize a colour also. Titanium oxide acts in three ways on colours. In small amounts it intensifies the colour making it brighter, e.g. iron oxide can be induced to give bright yellows and oranges. Moderate amounts of titanium oxide (2% to 6%) break up the colouring effect by a mottle. Larger amounts tend to subdue colours but give interesting sparkles to the surface.

Glazes containing titanium oxide with some rutile are subject to the phenomenon of phototrophy. This is the change of colour by the action of light. The amount is only slight. See **Phototrophy**. These glazes are also subject to thermotrophy which is the change of colour by the action of heat. Glazes which are white at room temperature are a yellow colour at temperatures above 150°C (302°F). The colour difference is quite noticeable and can be startling if the kiln is opened when hot. It can also be a disconcerting phenomenon on ovenware.

'T' Material

The trade name for the very light-grey prepared body with white coarse grog manufactured by Morganite Thermal Ceramics Ltd. It is strong and plastic in raw state and increases in strength as it is fired. It vitrifies above 1300°C (2372°F) and is therefore to be considered a refractory clay. It is popular for the handbuilding of pots and models for firings from raku to 1300°C.

Toft dishes

Large slipware dishes made during the late 17th and early 18th century in Staffordshire. They were made by some sixteen different potters of whom Thomas Toft was the outstanding master and over 30 of his dishes are known.

These dishes are deep plates 38 cm to 56 cm across and are richly decorated with figures and animals, scenes and pseudo portraits. Much of the work is heraldic and symbolically royalist. The wide rim gives opportunity for the potter to produce a decorative border. Thomas Toft was especially good at producing a closely criss-crossed yet free border which is called a Toft border.

The dishes were first thrown and turned. Then a layer of white slip was used to cover the red clay. Onto this the outlines were trailed in dark slip and the filling-in done with buff slip. Finally, white was piped onto the outlines as a series of dots, giving a richness and movement to the dark line. The glaze was galena dusted onto the wet slip through a coarse cloth bag. The plates were fired on edge, resting on the rim, which often shows signs of warping. The glaze also has run down in the firing dragging some of the colour from the dark lines which further enhances their richness.

Tokoname

An ancient Japanese centre for the production of water jars and burial urns. The clay fired, in wood-burning kilns, to a dark grey. The pots were often coil built.

Top hat kiln

An intermittent kiln for which the ware is set on a refractory base and the open-based kiln is lowered over the top. The kiln is fired by electricity through overhead cables. The advantages of a top hat kiln are economy of use on alternate bases which can be more easily set in the round.

Tourmaline

A variable mineral associated with quartz and granites. It is often present in cornish stones. Tourmaline is a crystalline borosilicate of aluminium with magnesium, sodium and sufficient traces of iron to render most crystals black.

Transfer decoration

An indirect method of applying repeat onglaze and underglaze decorations. The motif is printed in ceramic colours onto paper or flexible plastic material and transferred from this to the pottery surface. See also **Liverpool, Printing** and **Decal**.

Translucency

The property of porcelain and china which allows light to be seen through the material. It is an attractive effect which is achieved in a white body packed with slow-maturing pure particles of the same or very similar size, usually china clay and feldspar.

Transmutation

The act of changing a glaze's colour. Most potters are aware of how one pot with a glaze containing chromium oxide can colour all the tin-glazed pots in the kiln with pink. Also, to a lesser extent, copper oxide will spread from one pot onto adjacent pots producing greenish flashes or spots, especially with lead glazes. These are usually unintentional transmutations but there are two intentional transmutations of colour in what are called transmutation glazes and transmutation lustres.

TRANSMUTATION GLAZE. A glaze which is opaque but which is capable of picking up the colour from the body or slip beneath it and pulling this colour into the glaze. In this way a decoration on the body becomes a decoration in the glaze. The colouring oxides are drawn into the glaze by the presence of 5% to 15% of titanium oxide. Iron, manganese, copper and cobalt oxides all transmute effectively.

Three example recipes are given for different temperatures:

For 1100°C (2012°F):

feldspar	10
flint	5
lead bisilicate	50
whiting	10
zinc oxide	15
titanium oxide	10

For 1200°C (2192°F):

cornish stone	40
ball clay	10
lead bisilicate	20
whiting	10
zinc oxide	10
titanium oxide	10

For 1250°C (2282°F):

feldspar	50
china clay	15
flint	10
whiting	20
titanium oxide	5

TRANSMUTATION LUSTRE. A lustred surface created on a glaze by transferring metal from an applied paste. The paste is applied to the already-fired surface and given a special firing at a low temperature in a reduction atmosphere. After firing, the coating is cleaned away to reveal the lustre which has been attached to the glaze surface.

Both lead and lead-free glazes will take a transmutation lustre. The important point is that while its structure must be activated during the extra firing in order to capture the lower atoms of the lustre layer, the glaze must not soften or else its surface will be spoilt by the paste. Tin opacified glazes of the 1000°C to 1050°C range (1832°F to 1922°F) are usual. A small percentage of titanium oxide in the glaze assists the capture of the metal.

The composition of the paste depends upon the quality of the lustre to be produced. For solid all-over lustres, a calcined clay with 5% to 30% copper oxide is mixed to a paste with an adhesive. It is brushed onto the glaze in a thick layer. The calcined clay is usually china clay but any non-vitrified clay will do providing it is fine enough to make a paste, is free from fusible matter and has previously been fired a couple of hundred degrees above the temperature at which it is now to be used. For this reason it is called a refractory coating but the term refractory is only relative. The amount of copper oxide varies according to the colouring required and the take-up capacity of the glaze.

Where lustre is to be painted onto a glaze surface in decorative brush strokes, a thinner pigment is prepared often containing raw clay. A typical proportion is 60% clay, 40% copper compound. The Hispano-Moresque lustres of the 14th century were of this type. A red ochre clay was used, sometimes with additional reducing agents like lamp black. The red iron oxide of the ochre assisted the production of the lustre by insulating the reduced lustre from re-oxidation during cooling. Reduction was applied with alternating spasms of oxidation to prevent the glaze from becoming too reduced and to move the copper progressively inwards from pigment to glaze surface. A silver salt was added with the copper compound to produce the particularly fine lustre often called gold lustre though no gold was ever used.

The plate illustrated is by Alan Caiger-Smith who uses this traditional method of painting with an ochre slip containing copper and silver sulfides. See also ***Colour plate 15***.

The firing must be to a temperature lower than the softening point of the glaze, but high enough to effect reduction of the copper compounds and the active capture of the copper by the glaze surface. In practice this limits the firing to between 600°C and 700°C (1112°F and 1292°F). Reduction is effected at the top temperature or during the cooling, the intensity being regulated according to the type of lustre required: rouge flambé, ruby lustre or metallic. The effects are judged by the fishouts.

The refractory coating is washed or rubbed off after the firing. Dry rubbing of thin coatings burnishes the surface which improves the lustre.

Transparent glaze

A glaze in which all the oxides have been involved in the melt and formed irregular chains, there being no crystallization or particles to obstruct the passage of light. Being balanced in flux and glass-former, it is fully fused, flows evenly and has a smooth shiny surface. The transparent glaze recipe is usually simple to understand, there being a main flux like lead oxide or calcium oxide with alumino-silicates like clay and feldspar.

If a transparent glaze is stained by oxides which act as fluxes it will remain transparent. Additions of amphoteric and acidic oxides tend to give opacity. See ***Periodic table***.

A transparent glaze recipe is often used as the basis for a range of glazes. Additions are made of tin oxide, colouring oxides etc. Adjustments to simple recipes like the following are straightforward because each material is acting in its most obvious way.

For raku 1000°C (1832°F):

china clay	5
flint	5
lead bisilicate	90

For earthenware 1100°C (2012°F):

feldspar	10
china clay	10
flint	10
lead bisilicate	65
whiting	5

For 1200°C (2192°F):

potassium feldspar	20
china clay	10
flint	15
lead bisilicate	40
whiting	15

For stoneware 1250°C (2282°F):

potassium feldspar	50
china clay	15
flint	15
whiting	20

For porcelain 1280°C (2336°F):

potassium feldspar	25
china clay	25
flint	25
whiting	25

Trial rings

See ***Bullers rings***.

Triaxial diagram

See ***Eutectic mixture:*** graph 4.

Tridymite

Silica. SiO_2. One of the primary phases of silica. It exists in disordered cristobalite where its unique nine sub-divisions, called forms, 'invert' at different temperatures, thereby smoothing the otherwise sudden size change of pure cristobalite.

Tridymite is introduced into pottery bodies along with cristobalite to produce craze-resistant wares which are also resistant to thermal shock. It is also used in industrial silica refractories. See ***Silica: conversion*** and ***Silica: inversions***.

Trioxide

An oxide involving three atoms of oxygen in each molecule. The other element may be represented by one or two atoms. For example SO_3 and Al_2O_3. In the latter case the other element would be given the prefix di or the oxide is called a sesquioxide. See ***Sesquioxide*** and ***Oxide***.

Trolley kiln

Trolley hearth kiln. An intermittent kiln for which the ware is stacked on a trolley or bogey which runs on rails into the kiln. The advantages are the ease with which setting and drawing can be done around the trolley; and in the use of two or more trolleys so that the kiln structure can be kept in more economical use. Trolley kilns are usually fired by gas or electricity and are between 10 cub. ft and 100 cub. ft capacity.

Tunnel kiln
See *Continuous kiln*.

Turning
Trimming. Skimming. Shaving. Fettling. Removing unwanted clay to achieve a particular form, thin a pot wall or create a foot rim etc. It is usually done on thrown ware and at the leatherhard stage. The unwanted clay is removed in a series of long shavings. The tools are wire loops and sharp blades of metal, wood and plastic.

The throwing wheel is often used for turning and the pot is centred and stuck to the wheel-head by wetting and suction assisted, if necessary, by pieces of clay. Inverted narrow-necked pots are held in a chuck or chum. Simple cylindrical and cup forms are often turned on a horizontal spindle (lathe) by sealing the rim to a mandrel.

The tools need to be kept sharp. A file, stone, emery and glass paper are used. Clay is a very abrasive material and quickly blunts the tools. Some short clays are difficult to turn and tend to crumble rather than allow themselves to be cleanly cut. They are easier to turn if the wheel is rotated for turning in the opposite way to that used for throwing.

TURNING TOOLS. Wire loops and sharp stiff blades capable of cutting thin slices of leatherhard clay. The blade must be stiff enough to cut the shaving of clay without flexing itself. The wire loop must be strong enough to push its way through the clay.

Mild steel is the most popular material for blade tools. Stainless steel is also used but does not take so keen an edge and is thus less suitable for fine clays like porcelain, fine stoneware and fine earthenware. Spring steel, soft mild steel and spring wire can be used for loop tools which are useful for turning soft and coarse clays. Cheap alloy spoons, sharpened by filing the back side towards the edge, are useful for the insides of bowls etc. A file or a rubbing stone is used to sharpen metal tools.

Wooden tools are made from hard dry bamboo or boxwood. They are sharpened with a plane, knife and glass-paper. Similarly, hard plastic sheeting can be sawn to shape and sharpened with glass-paper. These tools are used for the softer clays.

For turning on a horizontal lathe, straight chisel-type metal tools are used. They are sometimes cut to a particular shape for the repetition work of turning foot rims or decorative rings. Photograph of David Frith.

Twaddell
Twaddle. °TW. Degrees Twaddell. Units used to measure the relative densities of solutions and suspensions. This scale provides an expansion of normal r.d. numbers which for potter's solutions and suspensions would fall between 1 and 2 and therefore always involve either fractions or decimals. The portion in excess of 1 is multiplied by 200. This has the effect of making the relative density of water 0°TW and potters' suspensions in the range up to 200°TW. 200°TW would be equivalent to a slip of 200 g per 100 ml or 40 oz pt UK or 33 oz pt US. The scale is named after William Twaddell who made the first hydrometer (Twaddell shot) with this scale.

The formulae concerned are:

$$\text{Degrees Twaddell} = 200 \times (\text{r.d.} - 1)$$

$$\text{Relative Density} = 1 + \frac{°\text{TW}}{200}$$

$$\text{Weight of one UK pt in oz} = \left(1 + \frac{°\text{TW}}{200}\right) \times 20$$

$$°\text{TW} = 200 \times \left(\frac{\text{oz pt UK}}{20} - 1\right)$$

$$°\text{TW} = 200 \times \left(\frac{\text{oz pt US}}{16 \cdot 7} - 1\right)$$

See also *Formula: density*.

Tyg
A 16th- to 19th-century drinking mug, often with more than one handle and, in extreme cases, as many as twelve. Tygs were usually made in a dark-coloured clay, were sometimes decorated with sprigs and glazed with an iron-stained lead glaze.

Tz'u-chou
See *Cizhou*.

U

Ulexite

$NaCaB_5O_9.8H_2O$ or $Na_2O.2CaO.5B_2O_3.16H_2O$. A mineral containing boron oxide, sodium oxide and calcium oxide. It occurs with borax and colemanite in California and with gypsum in Chile. It is also called boronatrocalcite and natroborocalcite, and is in hydrated form. It is used as a source of flux and glass-former in empirical frits.

Underclay

Glum. Hustle. Fireclay from the seam directly under the coal seam. It is sometimes mined with the coal.

Underclay is often softer than other fireclays and for pottery purposes requires less weathering to bring to plastic state. When blunged, sieved and settled, an underclay often makes a good ovenware body. See also *Fireclay*.

Underfired

Fired at a temperature lower than the intended or with insufficient heat-work and showing defects because of this. The defects are:

1. The biscuit is too porous and takes too much glaze from dipping. See *Porosity*.
2. Bisc has no chance to mature in the softer glaze firing and the final ware will probably craze. See *Crazing*.
3. Where body and glaze mature together there is insufficient integration to give full strength to the ware. The glaze may also craze or shell. See *Body-glaze layer*.
4. Underfired glazes are often dull and lifeless with a 'dry' surface which is lighter in colour than anticipated. Transparent and shiny glazes tend to craze because they have not integrated with the body. See also *Fosted*.

Underglaze

U/G. Ceramic colours applied usually on a biscuit and covered with a transparent glaze.

The qualities of underglaze are the intensity and wide range of colour. Its advantage over onglaze decoration is its permanence, it being as permanent as the covering glaze.

Underglaze colours are modified oxides which gain their full colour with the 'wetting' action of the covering glaze. They usually contain a small amount of glaze, referred to as flux, which binds them to the body and integrates them with the glaze above. The photographs show three decorative wall plates using u/g pigments by Frank Hamer.

The pigments are prepared in different ways according to the strength and stability of the colouring oxides. The process involves the establishment of the colour by fusion or calcination of the oxides, followed by grinding. By combining oxides as spinel structures stains are produced which

are relatively stable in glazes and at high temperatures. The colours are mixed with an oil or varnish for application to biscuit, or with a gum to raw ware. Pigments can also be purchased ready mixed usually with polyvinyl acetate adhesive which also acts as an extender to assist flow.

Colour suppliers specify upper temperature limits for the products in their catalogues. The same stain can often be used successfully for underglaze, inglaze, maiolica and glaze staining. Certain colours are more restricted in their temperature range and most are dulled or changed by reduction firing. See **Stain**.

Unity formula
See **Formula: unity**.

Unomi
'Hot water drink'. A Japanese teabowl. Although playing little part as a ceremonial object in the western world, the unomi still provides the opportunity to make a single statement through a simple functional form. The examples are by Kenneth Quick and Ruthanne Tudball.

This type of statement is linked with the attitudes of the whole tea ceremony and contemplative Buddhism. See **Zen**. The ceramic message in a teabowl can be traced back to 10th-century China. See **Tenmoku: origin**. The appreciation of the unomi in stoneware and raku, as we now understand it in the west, is traceable to the perception of Rikiu Sen, the 16th-century Japanese tea master.

Up-draught kiln
A kiln in which the hot gases pass upwards through the ware. It is the simplest form of kiln and does not require a chimney. There is sufficient draw in the tall, tapering chamber itself to pull in air at the fire-mouth, through the fire, combustion space, and into the chamber from whence the exit is through holes in the cover. Heat is conserved in the chamber by a chequered floor and sometimes by a baffle ceiling. The disadvantage of this simple design is that it is difficult to achieve uniformity of temperature throughout the ware as flames tend to short-cut up the most direct passages to the exit, but it makes use of the shorter flames from coal and coke. By the late 18th century the up-draught kiln had been perfected as the Stoke bottle kiln making possible a temperature of 1300°C (2372°F). See **Bottle kiln**.

Uranium oxide
U_3O_8. A colouring oxide which gives yellows, oranges and reds under specific conditions. It was used to modify other colours in the yellow and green range.

The oxide is purchased as a spent oxide which has only a low radio-activity. This continues so that the final glaze is slightly radio-active. Amounts up to 15% are used. A red colour is possible in lead silicate glazes which are low in aluminium oxide, and free from boron oxide. The effect is similar to chrome red but withstands 1050°C (1922°F). Yellow and green are more usual colours. Reduction sullies all uranium colours.

Uranium oxide (U_3O_8) is a combination of other oxides:

$$UO_2 + UO_3 = U_2O_5$$
$$U_2O_5 + UO_3 = U_3O_8$$

This article is included for completeness. The use of uranium oxide is not recommended.

V

Vacuumed clay

Clay which has been subjected to a vacuum. In this state, the air bubbles in the clay explode and are removed. The clay particles are brought into closer contact resulting in an increase in strength. See **De-airing**.

Valency

Valence. The theoretical combining power of an atom. The valency of hydrogen is 1. The valency of oxygen is 2. Two hydrogen atoms are therefore required to combine with one oxygen atom. In symbols this is written as H_2O and the compound is water.

The valency of barium is 2. It therefore combines on equal terms with oxygen to produce barium oxide (BaO).

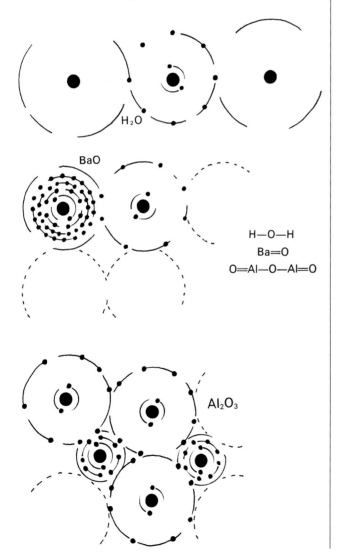

H—O—H
Ba=O
O=Al—O—Al=O

The valency of aluminium is 3. In order to write the symbol for aluminium oxide, it is necessary to think in terms of two atoms of aluminium with a total valency of 6. To combine with this valency of 6, three oxygen atoms, each of valency 2, are required. The chemical symbol for aluminium oxide is therefore written Al_2O_3 which keeps the theoretical atoms in whole numbers. The valency bond number is 6 which is the lowest common multiple of 2 and 3.

Lists of the elements found in pottery materials with their valencies are given in **Tables 17** and **34**. In these Tables some elements are given more than one valency. For example, iron oxide exists as Fe_2O_3 and FeO: valencies 3 and 2. Both iron oxides exist in ceramic fusions and changes one to the other are usually caused by the kiln atmosphere. However all polyvalent oxides change to a lower valency with an increase in temperature and involvement in fusion.

An atom's valency depends upon the number of electrons in the outer layer of the atom. These electrons are available for transferring or sharing with other atoms to form bonds. Also the size of the atom determines how many other atoms of a different size can be packed around it in the creation of bonds. The potential of an atom in this respect is called its co-ordination number. It is not necessary for the potter to understand all the aspects of atomic theory which affect valency. It is sufficient to appreciate their existence and to comprehend the common oxides within the more complex substances which are the raw materials. See also **Atom, Formula: structural, Lattice structure** and **Periodic table**.

Vanadium oxide

Vanadium pentaoxide. V_2O_5. Vanadium trioxide. V_2O_3. A rare metal oxide which gives a weak yellow colour in ceramic fusions. It has stronger staining power when prepared as a stain with tin oxide or zirconium oxide to give yellow, or with zirconium silicate to give blue.

Vanadium oxide occurs as an ore in the United States and South Africa. Vanadium metal is used in steels to improve shock resistance.

Vanadium pentaoxide (V_2O_5) is acidic but vanadium trioxide (V_2O_3) can exist and is alkaline. The stable state is the pentaoxide which can be used as a yellow glaze colourant in amounts up to 10%. The glaze needs to be well fused and glassy before the vanadium oxide is satisfactorily absorbed. Lead glazes are ideal but the colour is never strong and is not so rich as the yellow obtainable from antimony oxide in a lead glaze. The advantage of vanadium oxide is that it can be used at higher temperatures than antimony oxide.

Vanadium stains

Two prepared stains are available: yellow and blue. They are both recent developments which make use of vanadium trioxide as a flux at high temperatures. In the yellow stain the vanadium oxide is combined with tin oxide or zirconium oxide. The yellow is a stronger stain than vanadium oxide alone and is much easier to use.

In the blue stain the vanadium oxide is combined with zircon (zirconium silicate). Like the yellow, this is a stable colour for all temperatures but these stains do tend to be refractory and not easy to dissolve. They are often fritted with soft glasses to render them more usable though this weakens the colouring power slightly.

Vaporization

With the action of heat some body and glaze constituents change from solid or liquid (melted) state to gaseous state. If they then come into contact with suitable compounds some liquefy again and form new compounds. Thus chromium oxide, copper oxide and sometimes cobalt oxide are found to have transferred themselves to new surfaces. Also sodium oxide and boron oxide will be seen to transfer themselves to unglazed surfaces like kiln furniture where they flux the silicates and produce a thin glaze. This is similar to **Salt glaze**, and **Soda firing**.

Some substances remain as vapours and escape from the kiln. See **Volatiles** and **Fumes**.

Raw lead glazes would vaporize above 1000°C (1832°F) with a loss of as much as 10% of the lead oxide content. Fortunately, lead oxide in fritted form does not vaporize so easily and will withstand 1200°C (2192°F) before dissociating from the glaze.

Until the dangers from polluted atmospheres were recognized, some potters made use of volatile lead oxide to give a gloss to delicate modelling where a thick glaze would have obliterated the detail. A saggar was coated inside with raw lead compound and the modelling supported on suitable stilts.

Vapour glazing

There are a number of techniques which make use of the propensity of some glaze fluxes to volatilize at kiln firing temperatures. Zinc oxide, lead oxide, sodium compounds and boron oxide can be introduced into the kiln either through ports during the firing, or in containers placed amongst the ware. The volatile fluxes attack the clay surfaces to form glaze. The most well-known processes use common salt and soda. See **Salt glaze, Soda firing** and **Volatiles**.

Vehicle

Any medium used to assist in applying colour or glaze. The vehicle has no part in the fired formula but burns out in the firing.

Vellum matt

See **Satin matt.**

Vent

A small circular or square sectional opening through the kiln wall or door by which the kiln chamber is ventilated. It is usual to have two vents, one placed low down and the other high up, in order to achieve a track of air into and out of the chamber. When necessary, a vent is closed by a bung, stopper or flap. The usual spyhole serves as a vent in many small kilns.

Vents are opened and closed as part of the adjustment of kiln atmosphere to oxidation and reduction.

Viscosity

The stiffness of a liquid created by the friction amongst its particles and molecules. The term viscosity can be applied to clay slips and glaze slops, and also to molten glazes. Viscous slips are thick and pour with difficulty. Viscous glazes do not move, or move very little, in the firing. The reciprocal of viscosity is fluidity.

It is normal ceramic practice to consider molten glazes in terms of viscosity. A runny glaze will have a low viscosity. A stiff glaze will have a high viscosity. The unit of measurement for viscosity is the poise. A runny glaze of low viscosity might have a rating in the order of 1000 poise. A very stiff glaze of high viscosity would have a rating in the order of 100,000 poise.

Slips, slops and other liquid suspensions are usually considered in terms of fluidity. A runny suspension will have a high fluidity. Glazes and suspensions are dealt with here in consideration of viscosity. They are separately dealt with in consideration of their fluidity under the heading of **Fluidity**.

VISCOSITY OF CLAY AND GLAZE SUSPENSIONS. The viscosity of a slip is a measure of its internal friction. In stirring a slip or other suspension one moves a part of the whole. This part attempts to drag with it the adjacent parts. If the slip is very fluid there is minimal friction and the adjacent parts are said to have a high velocity difference. On the other hand if the slip is very viscous there is a high degree of friction and the velocity difference is kept low. The measurement of the forces required to overcome different frictions and achieve a standard velocity difference between adjacent parts gives values by which different viscosities can be compared.

It is normal practice to talk of suspensions in terms of fluidity. The values of viscosity are translated into values of fluidity by the following formula:

$$\frac{1}{\text{viscosity (poise)}} = \text{fluidity (rhe)}$$

Therefore a viscous slip with a high viscosity value of 500 poise becomes a slip of low fluidity with a value of 0·002 rhe. A runny slip of low viscosity with a value of 10 poise becomes a slip of high fluidity with a value of 0·1 rhe.

The subject is treated more fully under **Fluidity**.

VISCOSITY OF MOLTEN GLAZES. The viscosity of a glaze is measured when the glaze is maturing. It is at this point that it is important to know how it behaves. It is necessary to have movement in a glaze in order that it can mature since maturation is the smoothing out of the glaze after the bubblings of the melting reactions. The glaze must therefore be liquid at this stage but it may be a stiff liquid (of high viscosity) or it may be a very runny liquid (of low viscosity). In order to be a glaze it must, however, have this liquid phase. If there is no liquid phase it cannot be considered a glaze. It would then be like a slip or a body which, however vitreous (glassy), remains a solid and retains its form. Glazes have no form of their own but take the form of the object they cover. They cannot exist alone.

If the glaze is on a horizontal surface when it matures, it must smooth out by finding its own level. This is rather like a lot of lumps of ice which, when they melt to water, run together to form a flat-surfaced pool. Glazes on tiles or contained on shallow plates can be less viscous than other glazes. They are not able to run away, but equally it is more difficult for them to flow together. There are two factors involved: one is gravity which encourages the layer to be flat surfaced and the other is surface tension which encourages a smooth surface around the bulk of the layer. See **Surface tension**.

A glaze on a vertical surface needs to be more viscous than a glaze on a horizontal surface, otherwise it will run down and off the surface under the pull of gravity. Fortunately, the more viscous glaze will still be able to mature and smooth out because the amount of actual movement involved will probably exceed that obtained on a horizontal surface. The ideal glaze for the vertical surface has therefore a higher viscosity than the one for a horizontal surface. This difference is encountered when one tries to use the same glaze on horizontal surfaces like plates and vertical surfaces like coffee pots. It presents a problem familiar to makers of tableware which can only be solved ideally by having different glazes for the different pieces.

The theory of glaze viscosity is explained thus: when part of a liquid moves, as for example when the outer layer of a molten glaze moves downwards with the pull of gravity, it can do so only by breaking its contact with the next adjoining layer within the glaze. The breaking of this grip is called shear. If friction is very high between adjacent molecules then it is impossible for the stress created by gravity to shear the layers. Movement cannot then take place. A glaze like this would be considered to be of extremely high viscosity. On the other hand if there is very little friction it is possible for the outer layer to slide downwards and to drag with it the next layer, and the next etc. The innermost layer is unable to slide because it is held by the friction of the solid body. It is usual to consider the action as one of layers shearing, with each layer moving a similar amount to the next. The outer one therefore moves the furthest. This action is shown in fig. 1.

A glaze which is applied thickly can therefore move further than the same glaze applied thinly but the viscosity

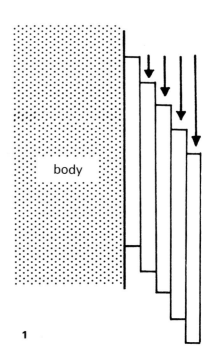

1

of the glaze remains the same. Thus on a vertical surface there are three factors involved in the maturation and production of a smooth surface: gravity pulling against viscosity giving a speed of movement, surface tension, and glaze thickness influencing the amount of movement.

The amount of movement can be seen in many glazes as short pulled lines of colour. An average amount of movement is about 2 mm and this is desirable to smooth over the glaze surface. Glazes of a higher viscosity are required over underglaze colours which have a tendency to be 'pulled' by the glaze. Some decorative glazes which rely upon movement to give their effect can be measured in centimetres of movement. They are of low viscosity and are applied thickly.

Glazes of high viscosity have strong or numerous bonds across neighbouring layers of glaze. In diagrammatical form this is seen as the difference between the glaze of high viscosity in fig. 2 and low viscosity in fig. 3.

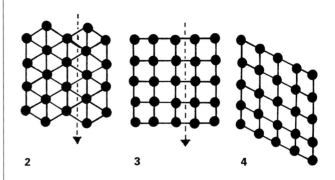

2   **3**   **4**

It is impossible to distort the structure at fig. 2. It can only flow by the breaking and remaking of the bonds down the dotted arrow.

The structure at fig. 3 is more vulnerable. There are fewer

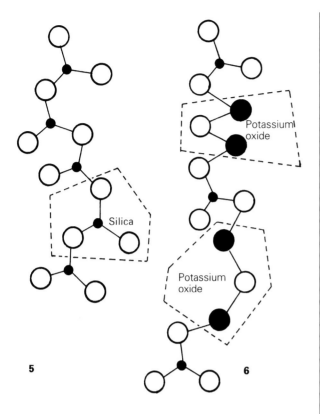

5

6

Silica

Potassium oxide

Potassium oxide

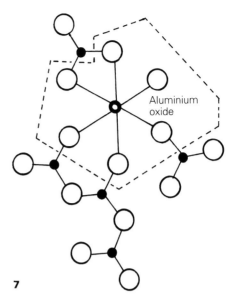

Aluminium oxide

7

bonds to break and the structure can also be distorted as at fig. 4.

These examples are purely diagrammatic but serve to show the factors involved. Molten glazes are a series of flexible chains, considered as silica chains, fig. 5, whose links are joined together in long lengths and also across from chain to chain. Monovalent oxides like potassium oxide provide very flexible links. The flexibility of a chain and also its place of shear is at the oxygen atom. The potassium oxide molecule freed from its own structure and introduced into the silica chain is obviously capable of great flexibility, fig. 6. Compare this with the aluminium oxide molecule where aluminium is in six-fold co-ordination with oxygen. When aluminium oxide is introduced into the silica chain it creates a more rigid structure than existed before, fig. 7.

Potassium oxide and aluminium oxide are at opposite ends of the scale in their influence upon viscosity. Potassium oxide creates fluid melts of low viscosity. Aluminium oxide

introduced into a melt creates a stiffening so that the melt is of high viscosity. The other glaze oxides lie between these two extremes. Their influences on the viscosity of the melt are partly governed by their fluxing actions since flow is a property of fusion. The influences are also partly governed by the type of bonds produced. The oxides can be put in an order of influence upon viscosity for each temperature range. This is shown in the table.

Notes on the table of oxide influence upon viscosity.
Zone A. The oxides on the far left promote the least viscosity. That is, their presence lowers the viscosity of the melt. Each oxide is subject to the law of eutectic mixtures which relates to melting points and thus to viscosity at a given temperature. The number of fluxes present has effect upon viscosity by the law of interaction.
Zone B. The oxides on the left promote less viscosity than those on the right. Each oxide is also subject to the law of eutectic mixtures whereby there is an optimum result beyond which greater amounts of oxide act in the opposite direction and raise the viscosity. The number of fluxes present has effect upon viscosity by the law of interaction.
Neutral zone. The oxides here have little effect upon viscosity and can be included in reasonable amounts without apparent change of viscosity. Silica is included as a mid-way

Table of oxide influence upon viscosity

← ————— *Viscosity lowered* ————— — ————— *Viscosity raised* ————— →

	Zone A	Zone B	Neutral zone	Zone C	
	K_2O Li_2O B_2O_3 NaKO Na_2O	BaO SrO CaO ZnO MgO PbO	TiO_2 SiO_2	SnO_2 ZrO_2 Al_2O_3	over 1250°C over 2280°F
	K_2O Li_2O Na_2O B_2O_3 NaKO	BaO SrO CaO ZnO PbO MgO	TiO_2 SiO_2	SnO_2 ZrO_2 Al_2O_3	1200–1250°C 2190–2280°F
	K_2O Na_2O Li_2O NaKO PbO	B_2O_3 SrO CaO ZnO BaO MgO	TiO_2 SiO_2	SnO_2 ZrO_2 Al_2O_3	1150–1200°C 2100–2190°F
	K_2O Na_2O NaKO Li_2O	PbO B_2O_3 SrO ZnO CaO BaO	MgO SiO_2	TiO_2 SnO_2 ZrO_2 Al_2O_3	1100–1150°C 2010–2100°F
1050–1100°C	K_2O Na_2O NaKO	Li_2O PbO B_2O_3 ZnO SrO CaO	MgO SiO_2	TiO_2 BaO SnO_2 ZrO_2 Al_2O_3	1920–2010°F
1000–1050°C	K_2O NaKO Na_2O	Li_2O PbO B_2O_3 ZnO SrO CaO	MgO SiO_2	TiO_2 BaO SnO_2 ZrO_2 Al_2O_3	1830–1920°F
950–1000°C 1740–1830°F	NaKO	K_2O Na_2O Li_2O PbO B_2O_3 ZnO	MgO SiO_2	TiO_2 BaO SrO CaO SnO_2 ZrO_2 Al_2O_3	
below 950°C below 1740°F		NaKO K_2O Na_2O PbO B_2O_3	Li_2O SiO_2	ZnO TiO_2 MgO BaO SrO CaO SnO_2 ZrO_2 Al_2O_3	

guide. Its amount in a melt obviously affects viscosity and it is taken here as the central norm by which the viscosity is judged.

Zone C. Apart from a slight effect from interaction, all the oxides in this zone raise the viscosity. Aluminium oxide at the far right creates the most viscous glaze melt.

N.B. Other factors to be considered in the balancing of a glaze by alteration of oxides by substitution or addition are: surface tension and rate of thermal expansion/contraction.

Vitrifiable clay

Clay which has a long maturing range and can therefore be fired successfully up to its vitrification point without deformation. This is necessary for the making of stoneware.

The slow maturation is dependent upon the presence of suitable fluxes and anti-fluxes. The suitable fluxes are potassium oxide and sodium oxide whose action starts at around 500°C (932°F) and progresses consistently. About 2% to 5% is sufficient. Unsuitable fluxes are calcium oxide, magnesium oxide etc which have short active periods of fluxing.

There is really only one suitable anti-flux and that is aluminium oxide. An aluminium oxide content of around 30% will satisfactorily check a tendency to fuse too quickly.

Stoneware clays, most ball clays and the least refractory fireclays could be called vitrifiable clays. Some red clays can also be vitrified but most have a tendency to bloat before densification is reached. Porcelain body is a prepared vitrifiable clay.

Vitrification

The furthest stage to which a body can be taken without deformation. At the vitrification point in the firing, a body is usually in a malleable state. That is, it could be deformed by pressure but a pot keeps its form because of the strength of its structure. However more heat-work in the form of higher temperature or prolonged temperature would result in deformation by the pot's own weight and the bloating of the body.

Vitrification is the result of the fluxing of the feldspathoids and free silica in the body. This molten silicate flows into the interstices between the clay particles and attacks and begins to flux them by interaction. See ***Firing: biscuit*** for diagrams. When the whole has cooled, the original clay particles are welded together by a glassy matrix which almost fills all the interstitial spaces. A vitrified body is usually accepted as having a small porosity. When a body has reached the point of being absolutely non-porous it is also so glassy that it fractures more easily.

The graphs show a typical relationship between fired strength and vitrification. Stoneware clays are capable of coming to this point slowly. This is called maturing. Earthenware clays tend to be ones which reach the end point suddenly so that one has to accept a fair amount of porosity. See ***Breakdown***.

Volatiles

Elements and compounds which vaporize during firing. The temperature at which each volatilizes depends upon its involvement at the time so the temperatures given are necessarily approximate and represent the lower end of the range. See also ***Vaporization***.

Complete loss			
water	H_2O	100°C	212°F
nitrogen	N	200°C	392°F
chlorine	Cl	200°C	392°F
hydroxyl group	OH	500°C	932°F
carbon oxides	CO, CO_2	700°C	1292°F
sulfur oxides	SO_2, SO_3	900°C	1652°F
fluorine	F	1000°C	1832°F

Measurable or noticeable loss			
zinc oxide (calcination)	ZnO	950°C	1742°F
lead oxide	PbO	1000°C	1832°F
copper oxide	CuO	1000°C	1832°F
chromium oxide	Cr_2O_3	1050°C	1922°F
sodium oxide	Na_2O	1100°C	2012°F
boron oxide	B_2O_3	1150°C	2102°F

Slight loss			
cobalt oxide	CoO	1100°C	2012°F
barium oxide	BaO	1200°C	2192°F
manganese oxide	MnO	1200°C	2192°F
potassium oxide	K_2O	1200°C	2192°F

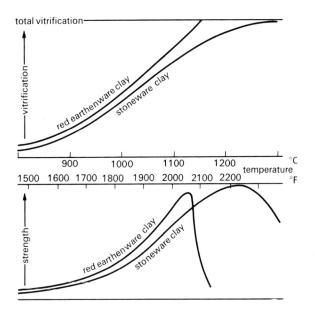

W

Wad (1)

Manganese dioxide ore often containing cobalt oxide. See *Asbolite*. The name is sometimes used for other ores which occur in the form of clusters of cylinders.

Wad (2)

Wadding. A strip or lump of refractory clay used to seal saggars in bungs, support shelves etc. Wad clay is highly refractory and so remains friable and does not fuse to the fireclay shelves, supports etc but can be chipped away after firing. The photograph of Micki Schloessingk's kiln (above) shows the pots set with wads.

WAD BOX. Dod box. A cylindrical box with a plunger which extrudes plastic clay through a tapered nozzle or die. It is used for making wads or snakes for setting saggars etc. See also *Dod box*.

The drawings show the principle of the wad box and the model manufactured by William Boulton Ltd.

Washing soda

Natron. Hydrated sodium carbonate. Soda crystals. $Na_2CO_3.10H_2O$. Soluble sodium salt used as a source of sodium oxide for frit and glaze making. Commercial frit manufacturers use the anhydrous sodium carbonate. Small amounts of dry-powder glaze can be made experimentally for filling hollows on tiles etc which are fired horizontally. See *Sodium oxide: in glazes*.

The molecule of washing soda is about six times the weight of silica. This should be borne in mind when making dry-powder glazes. A glaze to melt at about 1000°C (1832°F) will have equal molecules of sodium oxide and silica and can be made with about six times as much washing sodium oxide as flint. Equal weights give a glaze with one molecule of sodium oxide to every six of silica and this melts at approximately 1200°C (2192°F). These glazes require stabilizing with some clay or feldspar.

Water

H_2O. Most potters appreciate water's importance in providing the lubricant for the clay particles. What is not generally appreciated is that the potter rarely uses distilled or pure water. Spring water and tap water contain dissolved ingredients which help or hinder the potter. Mostly the result is unnoticed but sometimes a water may contain sufficient calcium oxide to cause scumming. This will show on the unglazed parts of the fired ware. In addition, the water may contain salts which soften the clay and affect glaze slops. Some commercial water softeners have a deflocculatory effect. Some potters save the water siphoned from one glaze for mixing with the next. Others settle the throwing water from the wheel and re-use it. Re-used water of this sort can be felt to be sticky or slippery when wet fingers are rubbed together. It is worthwhile considering if there is any particular advantage in re-using water, other than economy, before always using fresh.

Water is analysed in its various functions in clay and as water in glazes and slips. Some other minerals contain water between the chemical structure, e.g. chert and flint, or as part of their chemical structure, e.g. borax and colemanite.

WATER IN CLAY. Water can account for as much as 40% of the weight of plastic clay. This 40% would be made up of about 20% lubricant, 10% to fill the pores between the particles of clay and 10% chemically combined within the clay particles. These three different functions which water performs give rise to a host of names describing the water and the processes involved in its addition or removal. They are here headed: water of plasticity, pore water and bound water. See also **Drying**.

Water of plasticity. Lubricant water. Separate water. This water provides the lubrication for the clay particles and enables them to slide past one another. The quality of plasticity of a clay is dependent upon the size and shape of these clay particles and the amount of other material, e.g. sand, which is present and cannot be plasticized. There is an optimum amount of water of plasticity for each clay. Beyond this amount the clay is too soft and sticky for use.

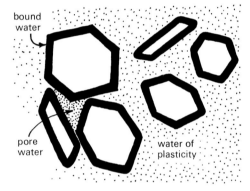

Highly plastic clays (such as ball clays) require more water than low plasticity clays (such as fireclays) to bring them to the plastic state. As much as 30% of the weight of a plastic clay can be water of plasticity. An average clay has 20% but in low plasticity bodies which contain non-plastic materials, like flint and feldspar, the water can be as low as 10%. Apart from the non-plastic materials present, the size of the clay particles is all-important. The most plastic clays have smaller sized particles. These present more surface area per given weight of clay than do large particles. Therefore there is a greater surface area to be surrounded by water in fine clays. This is apparent if one thinks of starting with one large piece which, when broken in two, presents two additional surfaces for the same bulk weight. This reasoning is true down to the exceedingly small particle size of clay where one could put 250,000 particles end to end in an inch. It is helpful to realize the range of particle size. The smallest clay particle from a highly plastic clay would fit about 8000 times into the bulk of a clay particle from a low-plasticity clay.

Clays which require a lot of water of plasticity naturally take longer to dry. They also contain a large bulk of water, which accounts for a considerable shrinkage from plastic to dry state. The water of plasticity can be added quite simply and calculated in pints per hundredweight. It can be removed quite simply by evaporation.

Pore water. Water of formation. Equilibrium moisture content (EMC). Atmospheric water. Water which is locked inside the pores of dry clay. It is held there by capillary action, by the surface tension of the water layer around each particle (this layer being attached to the hydroxyl groups of the clay), and by the imprisoning nature of the surrounding particles. It is water in the sense that it was mixed with the water of plasticity at the plastic stage whereas the bound water is in the form of hydroxyl (OH) groups.

Pore water could account for 12% of the weight of apparently dry clay. The amount varies with the moisture content of the surrounding air, as explained under **Readsorption**. Clay which has been dried in the sun on a warm day will contain very little pore water but always contains some.

Pore water is not completely removed until the clay has reached a temperature higher than the boiling point of water and remained there for some time to dispel the water as steam. The point at which the clay is theoretically bone dry is 120°C (248°F). The early part of a firing is always taken slowly in order to dispel the pore water safely without rupturing the ware. This is called the water-smoking period.

Bound water. Chemically combined water. The water of crystallization, combination, constitution, composition or hydration. Water which is part of the chemical structure of the compound, e.g. in gypsum, copper sulfate and kaolinite. The term usually arises with reference to clay to differentiate between the bound water and the plasticity and pore waters. The water of plasticity dries out from the clay in the atmosphere. The pore water is driven off by heat up to 120°C (248°F) but the bound water remains as part of the clay compound ($Al_2O_3.2SiO_2.2H_2O$) until red heat, 600°C (1112°F).

Bound water accounts for up to 14% of the weight of dry clay and can be seen escaping as water vapour from muffle kilns at red heat. It leaves the clay with little danger of steam pressure rupturing the ware. It is able to do this because the process is a slow one starting at about 450°C (842°F), increasing to 600°C (1112°F) and trailing off to 700°C (1292°F). Also, as the process starts, the clay becomes comparatively open. The pores become clear passages leading out from the interior.

When the bound water has gone, the clay is no longer clay but pot—that is, fired body. This is the ceramic change. The process is also called dehydration, de-hydroxylation, anhydration, decomposition and sometimes, casually, burning off. The last water to escape is in the form of hydroxyl groups attached to the aluminium oxide or gibbsite layer and would theoretically be called the water of constitution. See **Double layer theory**.

WATER IN GLAZES AND SLIPS. The water which is used to make a slop or slip is either a very weak acid or a mildly alkaline solution. The difference is slight and can occur with the water itself or from containers and materials. The effects are quite noticeable and should be understood by the potter in case they occur accidently. The deliberate occasions are given below.

For casting slips the water is an alkaline solution. This deflocculates the clay particles and produces a fluid slip. See **Deflocculation**. The phenomenon also occurs with slip-glazes containing wood ash. See **Wood ash**.

For glaze slops the water is made slightly acidic by the inclusion of calcium chloride. This flocculates the clay content which hinders sedimentation. When required, slips for clay decoration are flocculated slightly to make them dry more quickly. See **Calcium chloride, Flocculation** and **Bentonite**.

Water-glass

Sodium silicate. Various combinations of sodium oxide and silica from $Na_2O.SiO_2$ to $Na_2O.4SiO_2$ which are soluble in water. They can be used in simple glazes.

Water-glass is used commercially as a glue and concrete hardener. The metasilicate is used as a deflocculant in casting slips. See **Deflocculation** and **Sodium silicate**.

Water smoking

Pre-heating. The drying of clay during the early stages of firing. The water-smoking period must be taken slowly and is usually considered as from room temperature to 120°C (248°F). It is popular to take two hours over this period. With primitive firing methods which involve quick firings in open bonfires, the water smoking is done previously over hot charcoal and is called pre-heating.

All air-dried clay contains some atmospheric water held in the pores by adsorption and capillary action. This water is converted to steam at 100°C (212°F), the boiling point of water. It can be seen as water vapour escaping from vents and cracks in the kiln, and it can be felt by the hand in the warm wet air coming from a chimney or vent. When the water-smoking period is over, the vent air from wood-fired and electric kilns will be dry and hot. The vent air from kilns fired by natural and liquid petroleum gases always contains water as end product of combustion so a more skilful judgement is needed in deciding when water smoking is completed.

During damp weather the water held in the pores of air-dried clay could be as much as 4% of the weight of the clay but 1% is a general amount. Compared with an amount of water like 25% water of plasticity, this 1% seems small. Even so, this represents a large volume of steam. Water expands rapidly when converted into steam and because the pores are formed from closely-held clay particles, the escape passages are small. Burnished pottery will also have its surface pores sealed.

If unable to escape, the steam builds up pressure until it blows itself free. Probably every potter has experienced this at some time. The resulting debris is often a shattered pile of flakes, reminiscent of the frost-shattered detritus on the summits of mountains.

The amount of water held in dry clay is dependent upon the humidity of the atmosphere and the type of clay. As a general rule, finer clays, like ball clays, have smaller pores and therefore hold more water against the action of normal drying. See **Drying**.

Wax resist

Wax, either melted or as an emulsion, which is applied to pottery to prevent colour, glaze etc from adhering at that point. See **Resist**. Below, Janet Hamer glazing a ceramic bird (melted wax resist); bowl by Sheila Spencer (emulsion resist).

Weald clay

Wealdon clay. Clays found in the south-east of England associated with the chalks of the Cretaceous System. See **Marl**.

Weathering

The action on clays left in the open air whereby they disintegrate and improve in plasticity. The action is one that is continuous in nature and is partially responsible for the creation of clay from igneous rock and fully responsible for the removal of primary clays to become secondary clays.

Weathering achieves the sub-division of the clay grains or large particles into clay crystals or small particles. The finer the particles, the more plastic will be the clay. Rain, wind and frost are involved; and they can act most quickly upon clays which were once plastic but have lost plasticity by compression and drying, e.g. a shale. Even a shale, which produces a clay of poor plasticity when it is crushed and reconstituted, will have much more plasticity after one winter's weathering. After ten or twenty years of weathering the shale can reach its original potential and achieve the plasticity it had before it was compressed.

Clays with large, orderly crystals are difficult to weather. Such clays are the kaolins. Here it is a case of dividing a large crystal and this is more difficult than making a division between crystals which were held together to form grains. The sub-division of a crystal is a slow process and only possible along lines of weakness in the structure. Such a weakness occurs where some isomorphous substitution of aluminium and silicon has taken place. See ***Disordered kaolinite***.

The quicker processes of weathering which take ten to one hundred years can be simulated and accelerated by blunging to divide the particles. Fireclays, shales and some mudstones can be improved by natural or simulated weathering but china clays, which have never had the finer particles created, require a few million years of weathering to make them plastic. In a fully plastic clay which has the strength to be formed and reformed, the finest particles are held together like a colloidal gel. The violent action of blunging destroys this gel. Its restoration is begun by the addition of chemical additives but time is needed for the structure to achieve the strength of a finely flocculated clay.

There is therefore a limit to the improvement in plasticity that can reasonably be expected of any clay in a potter's lifetime. This limit is the clay's potential. The action of weathering is not magic. It cannot create plasticity where there is no potential. Shales and rock fireclays have a high potential. The potential of china clay is too remote. It is impossible to weather a sand into a clay because it has no potential at all.

Loams contain clay but they also contain a high proportion of sand. Their plasticity potential is low. This is shown in that loam soils have not weathered to plastic clays. In a similar way, it is pointless to try to further weather a surface clay. Even though recognizable as a clay, if it has been exposed for a number of years and still shows insufficient plasticity, it probably has little potential. This is probably due to its low content of plastic clay and/or its high content of kaolinitic clay of large crystal size.

Some prepared bodies come into this category. They are sold as 'clays' for specialized use. This does not require a high plasticity and therefore the body contains only a small amount of plastic clay. However the potential of this plastic clay has been realized in the preparation of the body. One cannot expect weathering to improve the plasticity of such a body.

Weathering also helps to decompose iron pyrites. The resulting iron sulfate is washed away. Other soluble salts are also washed away by weathering. For weathering a clay is spread out on a concrete base or in troughs in an exposed place. About a 10 cm thickness is considered the limit that the action can penetrate. In suitable clay pits it may be possible yearly to build up a pile of clay in 10 cm layers until the stack has had sufficient weathering.

Weathering and plasticizing are also dealt with under ***Preparation of clay***.

Wedging

A hand process of preparing plastic clay which involves mixing and compressing the clay. It is so-called because it packs or thrusts the clay into itself.

A plastic clay must be homogeneous for use. Sometimes the clay required is a mixture of two clays or the clay has been dewatered from a slurry by the use of drying troughs. These clays are not homogeneous. They are composed of harder parts and softer parts. These parts of different consistency must be thoroughly mixed and the air bubbles which are trapped in the clay must be expelled. The process whereby this is achieved is called wedging. It is a general conditioning of the clay and is a process replaced by pugging when working in large amounts. Wedging is often done before ageing or storage. It is followed, either immediately or after storage, by kneading. Kneading achieves the same end except that it does not compress the clay as much. It is also usually concerned with a piece of clay of particular size for the work in hand.

In wedging, a conveniently-sized lump of clay is thrown down onto the wedging bench. This is a stoutly-built, strong table about 70 cm high. The lump of clay is thrown down to form a wedge shape with the wide end towards the potter. This end half is cut off with a wire, lifted, turned over and brought down to meet the other half with force. The whole lump is lifted, knocked onto the bench to regain its lump shape and thrown down to start the process again. The process is repeated fifty times or so until the clay is thoroughly mixed and compressed. Air bubbles are expelled where they lie close to a cut.

The compression of the clay, including the removal of air bubbles, improves the clay's workability. See **Workability**. Some potters use wedging as an initial mixing process and employ kneading for most of the conditioning of the clay. Some wedge only and some knead only: it depends upon the potter's strength and the condition and type of clay.

Wedgwood

Josiah. Born in 1730 into a family of potters in Burslem, England, he became the most famous potter in the world and died in 1795 leaving an important, thriving business. Wedgwood was one of the first industrial potters to organize division of labour for greater production. He was an excellent businessman, had an inventive mind, was a tireless experimenter, and unlike many potters he knew his limitations.

Wedgwood made many friends and these helped him to overcome his deficiencies in taste and education. Thomas Bentley, his partner, was especially helpful and looked after the neo-classical wares while Josiah concentrated on functional ware and perfecting the many ideas current at the time.

Wedgwood's most famous wares are his cream-coloured earthenware, renamed Queen's Ware when Queen Charlotte ordered tea and coffee sets in 1765; Black Basalt or Egyptian Ware made from a black stoneware; Red Stoneware; and Jasper Ware with its finely-modelled white sprigging on a coloured background. See **Creamware**.

Wet ware

Ware put into a glaze firing without prior drying. Biscuit ware absorbs water from the slop as glaze is applied. The early stage of the glaze firing removes this water as vapour. If this is done too quickly, the steam might loosen the glaze layer sufficiently to cause crawling, or even result in pieces of glaze falling from the ware. This would happen when the glaze started to melt and move. Faults arising from this loosening of glazes are termed wet-ware faults.

Wheel

Potter's wheel. A rotating disc on which pots are formed. It is motivated by outside power, electricity etc, or by foot or hand

with the help of a flywheel. Its purpose is to turn the clay while the hands form the pot. The action of the hands is thus applied symmetrically. Where the rotation is produced by foot, mechanical power etc the hands are left free to manipulate the clay. Production is thereby increased.

The wheel-head is usually horizontal but some are at an angle or even horizontal but upside down. These require a different throwing technique but once controlled are a benefit for throwing some forms because the lifting action is assisted by gravity. Wheel-heads at an angle are used for bowls. Wheel-heads upside down are used for large tall forms.

Egypt is credited with being the place of origin of the potter's wheel. It was here that the turntable shaft was the leatherhard trimming (turning) is done with the same wheel direction as the throwing. In such cases throwing is done anti-clockwise and turning is done clockwise. Also after throwing many potters reverse the wheel direction and burnish the leatherhard clay surface. See also **Throwing** and **Turning**. The photographs are of the Shimpo RK10 wheel marketed by Potclays Limited, a Momentum wheel, used by Peter Wills, and a Roma wheel for the disabled marketed by Stow Potters' Wheels.

Whieldon

Thomas. A mid-18th century Staffordshire potter, famous for his marbled ware and tortoise-shell ware. Marbled ware was made by mixing together differently coloured clays. The half-mixed clay was thrown and then turned to remove the slurry and reveal the variegations. Tortoise-shell ware was a cream earthenware with a mottled glaze produced by dabbing the surface with a sponge soaked in cobalt, copper or manganese-coloured glaze. Josiah Wedgwood was partner to Whieldon before setting up his own pottery. See **Creamware**.

Whirler (1)

A heavy turntable used in press-moulding. Because it is heavy the whirler will revolve slowly and steadily. This is essential for accurate press-moulding. To allow both hands to be free to work, the whirler is turned by the stomach. Press-moulders are suitably proportioned for this work.

lengthened about 3000BC and a flywheel added. The flywheel was kicked and later was moved by pulling the edge with the left hand while forming the clay with the right. This led to the anti-clockwise motion for the potter's wheel which is almost universal. Only in parts of Japan and in parts of India was a clockwise motion used.

The clockwise wheel evolved from the use of a flywheel as wheel-head which was motivated by a hand-held stick located in notches near the edge. Holding the stick at its top end in the left hand and locating the other end in a notch the right hand is used to pull the stick towards one. When the wheel is turning sufficiently one can begin throwing. The wheel has to be given periodic impetus during the throwing of a pot.

Most potters learn to throw anti-clockwise and if a power wheel is used it is unlikely to be reversible. However, some experience with throwing clockwise is beneficial because it makes one analyse one's actions thoroughly. Also some clays, notably those containing only a small amount of naturally plastic clay, e.g. special bodies like porcelain, sometimes tire of being turned one way only. Some tear if

Whirler (2)

A faulty plate, saucer etc which will spin round on a central part instead of standing firmly on its foot rim. It is the opposite of a humper.

Thrown plates and dishes tend to become whirlers and, whether turned or unturned, the pull is accentuated by the drying of the rims before the wells. It is often necessary to forcibly depress the bases of overturned plates as they dry. The use of extra grog in the clay for plate-making also helps to overcome the fault.

White

White is achieved in pottery by the use of minerals which are themselves without colourant.

In clays, the usual colourant is iron oxide, traces of which give cream-coloured bodies. The iron stain can be given a bluish tinge by reduction. This is often done with white porcelain. Alternatively, it can be given an over-riding bluish tinge by the addition of cobalt oxide. This method is used in earthenware.

White glazes are opaque glazes using the opacifying oxides of tin, titanium, zinc and zirconium. See *Opacifiers*.

White lead

Basic lead carbonate. $2PbCO_3.Pb(OH)_2$. See *Lead oxide* and *Lead poisoning*.

White-hard clay

White-dry clay. Clay from which the water of plasticity has evaporated at the surface. The term is used even with coloured clays because there is a whiteness about the sharp edges where drying begins. At this stage the outside of the clay is dry but the inside is still damp. White-hard clay is not completely dry and is not theoretically ready for firing. A simple test is to put the clay to the cheek. If it feels cold it is not dry. Dry clay is at air temperature.

It should be remembered that the term dry used here is relative. The air itself contains moisture and the clay will contain an equal amount of moisture. This is called the equilibrium moisture content (EMC). Because of the atmospheric moisture in the pores of the clay the first part of a firing must take place slowly. This is called water smoking. See *Water* and *Drying*.

Whiting

Calcium carbonate. Paris white. $CaCO_3$. Source of calcium oxide for bodies and glazes. Potter's whiting is usually precipitated and is therefore as near to the pure chemical as it is possible to get. For its action during firing see *Calcium oxide*.

Other sources of whiting are crushed limestone, crushed chalk and ground seashells. Musselwhite is whiting made from mussel shells. They contain some chromium compounds which sometimes discolour tin glazes.

Wicket

The entry hole into the kiln chamber whereby the ware is set

and drawn. The wicket is bricked in and clammed over for firing except for spyholes or holes for fishout tests.

Willemite

Wilhelmite. Zinc silicate. Zn_2SiO_4 or $2ZnO.SiO_2$. A crystalline zinc mineral with translucent properties. Similar crystals are formed during the cooling of zinc matt glazes. See *Zinc oxide: crystallizer* and *Crystalline glazes*.

Win

The process of digging or mining a material, especially clay, and transporting it to be processed. Winning is divided into the two operations; getting and transporting.

Wind

Press-moulder's name for air bubbles.

Window dip

The action of dipping a pot sideways into slip or glaze. The best effect is on a swelling form where the 'window' is a complete shape which does not meet the pot rim or foot. The advantage of a window dip is that the window shape has affinity with the form of the pot and makes a good area for a panel decoration.

Witherite

Barium carbonate. $BaCO_3$. A white crystalline mineral associated with lead ores. It is one source of barium oxide for glazes and is also used as an agent for de-scumming clays. See *Barium carbonate*.

Wollastonite

Calcium silicate. $CaSiO_3$ or $CaO.SiO_2$. See *Table 3* for analysis. The natural mineral which combines calcium oxide and silica, and a source of these for glazes. It occurs in such metamorphic rocks as granitized calcareous sandstones. The true mineral is not so difficult to grind but it is still more expensive than using calcium carbonate and silica.

It is of particular use in viscous glazes such as celadons which are susceptible to crawling. It avoids the glaze disturbance caused by the release of carbon dioxide when whiting is used, or water when colemanite is used. See *Crawling*.

The wollastonite crystal forms in glazes during firing from about 1200°C (2192°F) upwards and continues to grow during cooling providing there is a high proportion of calcium oxide and a high proportion of free silica. The crystals give opacity and a matt surface. See *Lime matt* and *Crystalline glazes*.

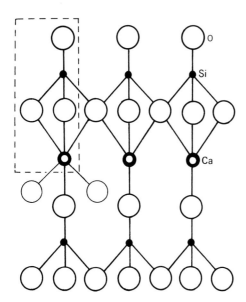

There is more than one explanation of the way in which the silica chain accommodates itself to the six-fold calcium cation. The diagram shows one of the simplest explanations in which a silica chain is linked by isolated cations. Other chains would be accommodated back and front.

Wood ash

The inorganic residue after the combustion of the organic structure of wood. The term is popularly extended to include other vegetable ashes, e.g. grass, reed and straw. Wood ash contains up to 90% alkaline fluxes. See *Table 2*. The remainder is silica and phosphorus oxide which are glass-formers and aluminium oxide which is the important amphoteric oxide. A wood ash is therefore similar to a glaze, and could be called a natural glaze frit. A few wood ashes will make a glaze alone but mostly they are useful constituents and have been so for centuries. See also *Ashes*.

Historically, wood ashes were used as the main flux in Oriental stoneware and porcelain glazes. Wood ash was readily available because the kilns were wood fired. The quality of glaze achieved encourages world-wide use of wood ash even when kilns are fired by other fuels.

Wood ashes vary enormously. They are by far the most variable material that a potter uses. The ashes can be as different, chemically, as chalk and granite. They not only act as glaze fluxes but introduce colour, usually very subtle colour with reduction, and produce crystalline opacity with

interesting flecking. The photographs are of a bottle with beech ash glaze and a teabowl with walnut ash glaze, both by Phil Rogers. See *Recipe Appendix*.

Wood ashes rarely act as practical fluxes below 1150°C (2102°F) because of the calcium compounds present. Amounts added to existing glazes usually provide interesting opacification, colour and crystallization. Above 1150°C (2102°F) wood ashes act as fluxes and amounts over 30% of a glaze will give crystalline opacity also. These statements are necessarily broad, for each ash, even two batches from the same species of tree, will behave uniquely. However, the principles explained under *Eutectic mixture* apply, and many ash glazes crystallize because they contain more than the eutectic amount of flux.

Wood ash is incorporated into a batch by weight as are the other ingredients. The following recipes for 1250°C (2282°F) show amounts varying from 18% to 40%.

Off-white crystalline slip-glaze for porcelain:

potassium feldspar	15
porcelain clay	62
beech ash	18
whiting	5

Olive celadon slip-glaze for stoneware:

potassium feldspar	30
ball clay	15
red clay	20
wood ash	25
whiting	10

Semi-transparent to go on biscuit:

potassium feldspar	50
china clay	10
quartz	10
wood ash	30

Crystalline to go on biscuit:

potassium feldspar	40
china clay	20
wood ash	40

Wood ashes contain soluble compounds: oxides,

carbonates, sulfates and chlorides. These dissolve in the water of the glaze slop and can be detected as a soft feel to the water and in extreme cases as a caustic burning of the skin. These compounds soak into the pottery body during glazing and a small amount remains there to flux the body and increase the body-glaze layer. The rest returns to the surface of the glaze during drying and crystallizes there. During firing these compounds provide extra fluxing.

The effect can be advantageous or a nuisance. Certainly with slip-glazes the solubles deflocculate the clay causing the slop to be thin and slippery. It is then impossible to obtain a sufficiently thick layer on the pot. The addition of calcium chloride or vinegar corrects the deflocculation but the resulting acidic balance of the water only encourages more alkali to dissolve. The slop must be re-balanced each time it is used.

Some, but never all, of the soluble compounds can be removed from the ash by washing. To do this the ash is mixed thoroughly with plenty of water, allowed to settle and the water siphoned off. At this mixing stage, unburnt material and charcoal can be removed because it tends to float. The process of washing, settling and siphoning is repeated until the water is clean and tasteless. The wood ash is sieved through a 6's to 10's mesh progressing to a 60's. This is about the finest practical because wood ash quickly clogs a mesh. Some potters prefer coarse ash because it brings texture to the glaze.

The washed ash is finally settled and dried for use as a glaze constituent. Because it clogs a mesh it is often added to the slop after the other constituents have been sieved.

If wood ash is to be used unwashed it is usually dry-sieved through a coarse sieve and added to the other constituents after they have been sieved. Some potters wash their wood ash after weighing it. There is obviously a loss of weight by this method but ash glazes are variables and often require adjustment by the addition of whiting or silica to the batch after the first test firing.

Wood firing

Firing by the original fuel, wood, is becoming increasingly popular amongst young energetic potters. There is no doubt that it gives a quality to unglazed parts of stoneware, and to a lesser extent earthenware. This is best described as toasting or flashing. It results from the alternate reduction and oxidation of a wood fire and in some cases is enhanced by fly ash. Glazed surfaces also improve having a variety of surface texture and subtle colour. No other fuel gives these qualities. Wood firing combines naturally with salt glazing. The photograph is of a traditional wood-fired slipware platter by Peter and Jill Dick of Coxwold Pottery.

The wood must be absolutely dry. It needs to be prepared and stored at least a year in advance. Large storage space, some under cover, is essential. Preparation is warm exhausting work as is stoking the kiln. However, wood is still the cheapest kiln fuel and is a renewable resource. Fortunately quick-growing softwoods, like spruce and larch, give most heat.

The long flame from wood can be directed around large kilns but the maximum advantage is gained in a climbing, chambered kiln which also has the advantage that it can be side stoked. The photograph below shows John Thies stoking a two-chamber, wood-burning, catenary-arched kiln during the Aberystwyth Festival in 2001.

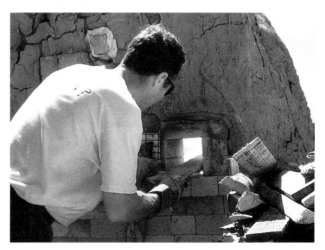

One distinct difference between firing by wood and the use of gas or oil with blown air is the independence of wood firing from electric power. Wood firing depends upon the draw created by the chimney.

Workability

The character of a clay that is a combination of strength, plasticity and thixotropy. It is difficult to analyse because the three properties overlap in the qualities they bring to the clay.

To achieve maximum workability for a clay, it is necessary to understand how the three properties are to be promoted. It is also necessary to know which ones to promote in order to give correct workability for the particular job in hand.

A clay of good workability stands up well to the stress of stretching, as in throwing, pressing and the pulling of handles. This demands a combination of strength and plasticity. A good clay also has the capacity to allow itself to be deformed by a reasonably slight pressure. This is the property of plasticity. Covered by the term thixotropy is the capacity to provide the necessary strength and plasticity when needed. A good clay is often required to have a resistance to shear that is high at a given moment, rather than one that is high over a continuous movement. It is a question of particle attraction rather than frictional drag. This is a similar property to inertia. A clay for throwing and hand-building must reasonably support its own weight. The three properties are described in more detail under **Plasticity, Thixotropy** and **Preparation of clay**. The lack of workability is described under **Short clay**.

The usual potter's tests for workability are a simple deformation test and a tie-a-knot test. In deformation testing, one pushes a piece of clay with the thumb or finger and notes how much initial resistance there is. Also one notes whether the clay went in the way intended and whether it held the intended form. Some poor clays have too much initial resistance and feel hard and bouncy. Some have no resistance and stick to the fingers as one takes off the

pressure, thus spoiling the intended form. Others tear instead of sliding in the shear.

In the tie-a-knot test, a piece of clay is rolled between the palms to give a strip about the thickness of a pencil. This strip is tied in a knot. A good clay will accept this exercise without rupture. The poor clay will rupture if it does not actually break.

WORKABILITY RANGE. The variation of water content that a plastic clay can stand and still remain plastic. If too little water is present the clay is too stiff to work, and if too much water is present the clay becomes too wet and sticky. Red clays and ball clays which have very fine clay particles have better—that is, wider—workability ranges than the coarser clays such as fireclay and china clay. The use of plasticizers such as bentonite while increasing working plasticity do not necessarily increase the workability range. See also **Plasticity**.

Wreathing
A slip-casting fault showing as a rippled surface on the slip side of the cast. See **Casting slip: adjustment**.

Y

Yellow

Yellow colours are produced in different ways in pottery. Each way is individual and works only within limits which are often narrow.

The most positive yellow stain is antimony oxide in a lead glaze. Iron oxide also gives yellows when bleached in a lime matt glaze or restricted by titanium oxide. Vanadium oxide gives yellow in combination with tin oxide or zirconium oxide as a prepared stain. See **Antimony oxide, Iron oxide, Praseodymium oxide** and **Vanadium stains**. Occasionally, bodies containing traces of copper oxide produce bright yellows under lead glazes. Consistency is impossible to establish.

Yellow ochre

Limonite. $2Fe_2O_3.3H_2O$. A soft crumbly variety of iron ore. It sometimes contains some clay and limestone. See **Limonite**.

Yixing

Yi-hsing. I-hsing. A pottery centre near Shanghai in Jiangsu (Kiangsu) province, China. The familiar, reddish stoneware teapots have been made here since the 16th century. They are usually unglazed but are sometimes given a smooth slip finish. The ware is very fine-grained and often decorated with incised inscriptions and sprigging. Tea is sometimes drunk through the spout of small teapots and the tiny ones are used for soy sauce.

The pots are constructed from press-moulded pieces or free formed slabs and the applied decoration very skilfully free-modelled. Each maker completes every stage and produces a number of pots in a day according to their size and ornamentation. The photographs show a teapot maker at her bench in Yixing, and a modern bamboo-shaped teapot.

This ware was imitated in England by the Elers brothers in the 17th century. See **Elers brothers** and **Boccaro**.

Also shown are two teapots made in the prized 'Zisha' or purple clay. This clay has a high iron content, 8·38%, which gives it a dark purplish red colour, and a high kaolin content which enables it to be fired to 1200°C (2192°F). The fired body has 2% porosity considered ideal in a teapot. See **Table** 3 for clay analysis.

Teapot makers are classified in a strict hierarchy. The teapot with an overhead handle was totally hand-shaped by a Master in 1871. The modern chrysanthemum-shaped teapot was made by Mr Shao Shunsheng who is a Junior Master Technician. Not yet experienced enough to be a Senior Master, his work is nevertheless highly regarded. Makers in this grade work in small teams. They design their own work, hand-raise the teapot bodies and only use moulds for spouts. A 'Zisha' teapot design must always obey functional rules although some of them depict fanciful subjects.

Z

Zen

One of the two important schools of Japanese Buddhist thought developed from about AD1200. The other school is Shin. Zen ignores the rituals, objects of devotion and scriptures of other Buddhist schools and concentrates upon freeing the mind of material worries in the path towards Satori (Enlightenment). The acceptance of a direct and immediate approach to spiritualization allows an unbiased acceptance and awareness of good in all its forms. The direct impersonal expression of clay and the various colouring effects of raku and stoneware are thus acceptable for what they are, without reservations of what they might have been. Zen Buddhism is responsible for much of the Western World's understanding of the subtle qualities of Oriental pottery.

Zeta potential

The measurement of the ability of a colloidal clay particle to repel similar particles by electrostatic charge. The potential is measured in millivolts and is mostly dependent upon the distance between the two layers on the outside of the clay particle. See *Double layer theory*.

The outer layer is composed of positive charges and if this layer is at a sufficient distance from the clay particle, then no two particles will ever physically meet. Instead, they will repel each other before the forces of attraction can pull them together and form a bond, fig. 1.

If the so-called 'stand-off distance' of the outer layer is small, the zeta potential will be low. The clay particles are able to link their unsatisfied bonds through the layer and form one large particle, fig. 2. Here the mutual forces of attraction of the two particles overcomes the repulsive force of the outer layers. See *Forces of attraction*.

The zeta potential is considered when making casting slips. The stand-off distance is increased by introducing suitable cations which prefer a large stand-off distance. These substitute themselves for the existing cations of the outer layer. The result is a dispersed or deflocculated state whereby the particles do not stick together but slide past one another, constantly repelling each other. This gives fluidity to the suspension in spite of its high clay content.

Zettlitz clay

Czech kaolin from Karlovy Vary. This was the clay used by Dr Hermann Seger in his tests on refractoriness. It became cone number 35 with the later estimated temperature of 1770°C (3218°F).

Zinc blende

Blende. Sphalerite. Black Jack. Zinc sulfide. ZnS. The main ore of zinc. It occurs in limestones and is often associated with lead sulfide.

Zinc oxide

ZnO. A useful auxiliary flux for oxidized glazes. It is introduced as a clean white powder which gives some opacity in the final glaze and encourages crystal growth if present in large amount. It also has a reputation as an anti-craze. In simple shiny feldspathic glazes a small amount of zinc oxide heightens the colours given by copper and cobalt oxides but in more complex glazes and with other colouring oxides, zinc oxide gives muddy colours. It was thoroughly investigated in the 19th century as an alternative flux to lead oxide. This was the first attempt to overcome lead poisoning in the pottery industry. It resulted in the Bristol glaze named after Bristol in England but now only used commercially in the USA. Though not so poisonous as lead oxide, all zinc compounds are poisonous and should be handled accordingly.

Zinc ores occur with copper, tin and lead in igneous rocks and in replacement lodes in limestone sediments. Zinc metal melts at 419°C (786°F). Coatings of zinc are put on to iron to prevent rusting. This is the galvanized iron which is

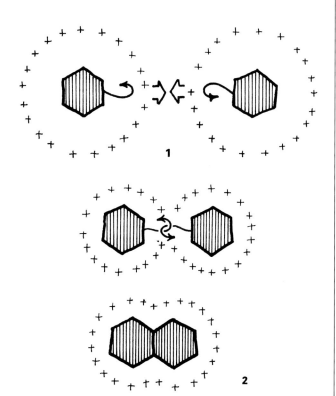

sometimes used for clay storage bins. Damp causes it to tarnish to carbonate but it is reasonably serviceable for clay, with a life of about fifteen years. However, slips and glaze slops tend to attack the coating with detriment to bin and contents. This is accentuated with suspensions which are slightly alkaline or acidic, e.g. casting slips and flocculated glazes. Zinc is used with copper in brass. It is also used in paints and rubber. The common ores are zinc blende, smithsonite, zincite, willemite and hemimorphite.

Zinc oxide is used in glazes as a flux, as a general stabilizer and hardener, as an opacifier, as a crystallizer and as an anti-craze. It is not soluble in water and is, therefore, a useful glaze material although its use can bring difficulties. Its action in small amounts seems always to be beneficial but there is an optimum point for each glaze after which increased amounts give unpredictable results. Some glazes which rely heavily on zinc oxide for fluxing and opacity are fickle and difficult to fire with consistent results.

Zinc oxide has a beneficial effect upon the creation of stable silicates. In the lower temperature glazes, the zinc ion can enter the lattice without loosening it as would a flux (except for exciting other fluxes by interaction). Glazes of simple formula, relying upon a high proportion of a single flux, are obviously affected most.

The zinc oxide also introduces valuable anti-craze properties. It is often substituted for other fluxes of high contraction rate, e.g. sodium, potassium and calcium oxides. It is second only to boron oxide in the 1100°C to 1200°C range (2012°F to 2192°F). See **Glaze fit**. It should be used with due consideration of its other properties regarding opacity and colour response.

There are advantages in the addition to a recipe of zinc oxide but there are also some possible disadvantages apart from its relatively high cost. Zinc oxide can cause crawling and discolouration.

Raw zinc oxide has a high initial shrinkage in the early stages of firing. This is before fusion takes place. This shrinkage can cause cracks in the glaze which are the source of scars when the glaze melts. Zinc oxide glazes have fairly high surface tensions and are therefore prone to crawling. To eradicate the initial shrinkage, the zinc oxide should be calcined before use in a glaze batch. Zinc oxide is unusual in that it does little to lower surface tension yet much to lower viscosity in the molten glaze. See **Viscosity: of glazes** and **Surface tension**.

With sodium, potassium and calcium oxides, the zinc oxide gives clean colours with cobalt and copper oxides. With other fluxes and with other colouring oxides it gives mottled effects which are pleasing but the colours are dull with a muddy opacity. Even a small amount of zinc oxide in a glaze will upset many prepared colours used as stains and underglaze decoration.

ZINC OXIDE FLUX. As a flux, its action can be divided into below 1085°C (1985°F) and above. Above 1085°C it is active as a flux providing it is not reduced by the kiln atmosphere. Even slight reduction is sufficient to extract the oxygen which results in the loss of the zinc also. See later. Its usual use is in the 1150°C to 1250°C range (2102°F to 2282°F) but there is no limit to the temperature at which it can be used. It was at one time considered only as a substitute for lead oxide but it has wider applications as an auxiliary flux that justify its use in spite of its high price. However it cannot be used as the only flux in a glaze. In this way it is similar to calcium oxide. Alone it will not produce a silicate melt below about 1350°C (2462°F) but in the presence of assisting fluxes, e.g. sodium, potassium and calcium oxides, it is very active. It is usual not to exceed 0·3 equivalents of zinc oxide unless crystalline effects are required. It gives a smooth-looking glaze of soft, silky shine and even small additions to a glaze will appreciably alter the glaze surface towards this character.

Below 1085°C (1985°F) the zinc oxide is not an active flux. Yet again it is useful in small amounts because in very small amounts, e.g. up to 1% of a recipe, it seems to have strong interactive influences which result in increased fusion. It can be useful in this way to improve sluggish glazes if its other properties are also desirable. A small amount of borax frit is a more common additive, however.

Zinc oxide, although an active flux, is quite refractory with a melting point of 1975°C (3587°F). This means that there is no upper temperature limit to its use in glazes. Yet, strangely for such a refractory oxide, it is easily reduced to the metal at temperatures above 950°C (1742°F). Unfortunately there is no advantage in this since the metal alone melts at 419°C (786°F) and boils at 925°C (1697°F). Any reduction therefore at 950°C or above, having taken away the oxygen, leaves a boiling metal. The boiling metal volatilizes and is lost. The volatile zinc will condense in the atmosphere of workshop or outside as a poisonous dust. Zinc oxide should therefore be used only in fully oxidized firings.

ZINC OXIDE OPACIFIER. The effectiveness of zinc oxide as an opacifier depends upon the whiteness of its crystal and upon the whiteness of the crystal structures that it encourages. Zinc oxide is unusual, in that, while acting as a flux, it can retain its crystal identity and some of its opacity. Other fluxes, although equally white powders in raw state, become involved completely (dissolved) in the ceramic fusions they engender. Zinc oxide has some amphoteric properties which are seen here because it is acting as both a flux, like calcium oxide, and an anti-flux, like tin oxide. It can fulfil this role in glazes with alkaline fluxes like sodium, potassium and calcium oxides, but if the stronger amphoteric flux boron oxide is present, the zinc oxide is forced into the position of being a flux only. It is then fully involved in fusion and loses its opacity.

Thus zinc oxide can be used as a flux with pleasing opalescent character. Its reflective property as an opacifier is not so high as other opacifiers, but, with zinc oxide, opacity can be increased in a glaze without loss of shine. In fact it is possible to increase the shine and the opacity by the introduction of zinc oxide. This is an advantage compared with the other opacifiers which only act as anti-fluxes and therefore dull the glaze surface.

The following recipe is an opaque white stoneware glaze for 1250°C (2282°F). The zinc oxide acts here as both flux and opacifier.

feldspar	50
china clay	15
flint	10
whiting	10
zinc oxide	10
tin oxide	5

As with its use for a flux, zinc oxide is a beneficial addition to opaque glazes in small amounts where it improves surface shine and adds to the opacity created by other opacifiers. At temperatures below 1085°C (1985°F), it acts as a beneficial filler and opacifier which partially enters fusion giving anti-craze effect and general stability.

ZINC OXIDE CRYSTALLIZER. The crystalline effects from zinc oxide can be divided into those with small crystals, described later as matts, and those with large crystals. The large crystals, looking like frost patterns up to 8 cm across, are produced by zinc oxide and silica. These glazes are usually fired in the 1150°C to 1250°C range (2102°F to 2282°F) and cooled very slowly in the range from 1140°C to 1010°C (2084°F to 1850°F). The cooling over this period may last a few days.

During cooling, the zinc oxide seeks the free silica to form zinc-silicate crystals of willemite ($2ZnO.SiO_2$). It will be seen that little free silica is actually required. There is only one molecule of silica to every two of zinc oxide. Yet for these large crystals to form it is necessary for the glaze to be very fluid. This means a minimum of stiffeners, especially aluminium oxide. Zinc crystalline glazes therefore contain a minimum of china clay and are runny glazes high in free silica although the free silica is not required for the crystals. See also **Crystalline glazes**.

Consideration of these facts can be made in the molecular formula. The aluminium oxide equivalent must not exceed one-fifth of the fluxes excluding zinc oxide. The silica equivalent must be at least a total of two products: zinc oxide equivalent times one and aluminium oxide equivalent times ten. Successful glazes have been made without aluminium oxide. In such cases titanium or zirconium oxide is introduced to give some viscosity and crystal nuclei.

Small crystals give a matt surface. A matt glaze can be produced by the introduction of a separately prepared spinel of zinc aluminate. If the zinc oxide is introduced raw into a glaze, however, it will seek to crystallize with the free silica as in the crystalline glazes previously described.

Small willemite crystals form readily, encouraged by the fact that the zinc oxide retains its crystal identity in the glaze. In fluid glazes which contain boron oxide, a small amount of titanium oxide will act as a catalyst by providing nuclei from which crystals can grow. It is not necessary to slow down the cooling rate. Most kilns cool sufficiently slowly to allow these crystals to form. See **Satin matt**. Neither is it necessary to limit the amount of aluminium oxide present unless the particularly smooth satin finish is required. Most glazes are still sufficiently fluid in the 1050°C to 900°C range (1922°F to 1652°F) when these small crystals form and there will be sufficient free silica for the willemite. A high aluminium oxide content will inhibit only the growth of large crystals. Small crystals will give matts and can form in high aluminium oxide glazes. In fact, a matting agent can be prepared from zinc oxide and china clay of equal weights. The mixture is calcined at 650°C (1202°F) and reground. It can be added to earthenware glazes in amounts up to 25% of the recipe.

The following recipe is for a crystalline matt glaze to be fired at 1100°C (2012°F):

feldspar	10
flint	5
whiting	10
lead bisilicate	50
zinc oxide	15
titanium oxide	10

It is a decorative glaze with transmutation properties arising from the titanium oxide. In order to get full fusion and yet allow crystals to grow, a high proportion of lead bisilicate is used. A thick layer produces the best results but the glaze is rather fluid and runs down the pot in the firing. Bulbous pots with narrow feet require a much thinner application on the lower half. The titanium oxide is present to increase the number of crystals. If a slow cooling glaze with very large crystals is required, the titanium oxide should be reduced and the flint increased. See **Crystalline glazes**.

Zincite

Red zinc oxide. ZnO. A zinc oxide ore which is orange in colour due to manganese impurity.

Zinc silicate

Willemite. $2ZnO.SiO_2$. A naturally occurring crystalline compound and also the crystal which forms as large crystals in crystalline glazes. See **Crystalline glazes**.

Zircon

See **Zirconium silicate**.

Zirconium oxide

ZrO_2. An opacifier which is similar in properties to tin oxide. Amounts of up to 15% can be added to transparent glazes to give increasing opacity and whiteness. Zirconium oxide is highly refractory and can be used at all temperatures.

Zirconium is a metal with a high melting point. It is used in alloys. It occurs in the silicate mineral zircon which is also cut as a gemstone. Zirconium oxide is used in paints and ceramics as a white opacifier. It is also used as a

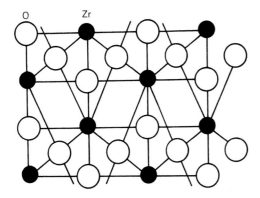

refractory acidic stabilizer in frits, especially frits involving colours.

Zirconium oxide is often introduced into glazes as a substitute opacifier for the more expensive tin oxide. The effects are similar and therefore the substitution can be weight for weight. Most potters find that complete substitution gives a glaze of different quality which is not so pleasing as the original. The whiteness from zirconium oxide is more dead-white and harsh. It lacks the soft quality of tin oxide which gives a creamy white or a bluey milk white. The advantages of zirconium oxide as an opacifier over tin oxide are that it is not influenced adversely by reduction and is not subject to chromium flashing. It is also cheaper. Substitution by zirconium oxide for half of the tin oxide content in a glaze gives a satisfactory white glaze with only a little loss of quality and often some gain in a soft surface shine.

Different qualities of opacity and surface texture can result from the use of different fluxes. Although zirconium oxide does not fully enter the fusion but remains suspended, it responds to the different fluxes. Lead oxide gives a pleasing pastel softness in the following glaze which can be used as a maiolica. It is an unusual glaze in that it does not contain any clay. It is for 1100°C (2012°F):

feldspar	33
flint	6
lead bisilicate	50
zirconium oxide	11

Zirconium oxide is prepared from the mineral zirconium silicate. The silicate is therefore cheaper and introduces more zirconium oxide for an equivalent sum of money. It also disperses the zirconium oxide more widely in the glaze, an effect which renders a better opacity. This dispersion is improved by the use of a critical particle size around 0·2 micrometres. Zirconium silicate is marketed as an opacifier ground to this size and coated with dispersal medium to prevent coagulation. There are various trade names.

Zirconium silicate

Zircon. $ZrO_2.SiO_2$. A mineral associated with igneous rocks. It is highly refractory and harder than quartz. Large crystals which are colourless can be cut as gemstones. The sparkle is second only to diamond. In ceramics it is used to introduce zirconium oxide and silica into glazes and bodies. See *Zirconium oxide*.

It is often easier to disperse zirconium oxide in a glaze by using the silicate rather than the oxide. Amounts are easily related to recipes which use zirconium oxide by considering the silicate as two thirds zirconium oxide and one third silica. Adjustments will be necessary in the silica of the recipe. For example, the following is a semi-opaque zirconium oxide glaze for 1250°C (2282°F) rewritten for zirconium silicate:

feldspar	36	feldspar	36
china clay	9	china clay	9
flint	26	flint	23
whiting	23	whiting	23
zirconium oxide	6	zirconium silicate	9

When zirconium silicate is used it is sometimes found that there is too much silica present. The best whites often form where there is little free silica. To overcome this some zirconium oxide is used in conjunction with the zirconium silicate. Alternatively, extra aluminium oxide is introduced to occupy the free silica.

If zirconium silicate is found to be too refractory in glazes then a little zinc oxide is added to increase fusion without loss of opacity.

Zirconium silicate is highly refractory with a melting point of 2550°C (4622°F). It makes an excellent bat wash when mixed with 10% of china clay. It is also strong and is used for making kiln shelves and other furniture. Its physical hardness enables sintered pellets to be used as grinding media in ball mills etc. The photograph shows Podmore and Sons' vibro-energy mills which use zirconium-silicate grinding medium for grinding zirconium-silicate opacifiers to sub-micrometre size.

APPENDIX OF TABLES

Table 1
Standard abbreviations

At No	Atomic number	cub	cubic
AW	Atomic weight	cwt	hundredweight(s) avoirdupois
BS	British Standard	fl oz	fluid ounce(s)
°C	Degrees Celsius	ft	foot (feet)
CF	Conversion factor	gal	gallon(s)
EMC	Equilibrium moisture content	g	gram(s)
°F	Degrees Fahrenheit	imp	imperial measure
H	Hardness on Mohs' Scale	in	inch(es)
I/G	Inglaze colour	kg	kilo(s) or kilogram(s)
°K	Degrees Kelvin	l	litre(s)
MF	Molecular formula	lb	pound(s) avoirdupois
MP	Melting point	m	metre(s)
MW	Molecular weight	ml	millilitre(s) (equivalent to cc)
O/E	Onglaze enamel	mm	millimetre(s)
O/G	Onglaze colour	oz	ounce(s) avoirdupois
°TW	Degrees Twaddell	oz pt	ounces per pint
U/G	Underglaze colour		(correctly weight of one pint in ounces)
UK	United Kingdom	pt	pint(s)
US/USA	United States of America	qt	quart(s)
avdp	avoirdupois	r.d.	relative density
cc	cubic centimetre(s) also written cm³	wt	weight
	(equivalent to ml)	yd	yard(s)
cm	centimetre(s)		

Table 2
Simplified ultimate analyses of vegetable ashes and bone ash
t = trace. See articles on **Ashes**, **Bone ash** and **Wood ash**.

Tree/Plant	SiO_2	Al_2O_3	P_2O_5	CaO	MgO	K_2O	Na_2O	Fe_2O_3	MnO
Ash	24	1	7	27	12	17	8	4	t
Apple	2		5	65	6	15	6	1	
Beech	6		5	56	11	17	4	1	
Birch	8	4	4	45	11	18	9	1	t
Bracken & fern	33	10	6	12	8	26	3	1	1
Elder	14		13	38	16	17	2	t	t
Grass (lawn)	59	11	5	10	5	5	3	2	t
Grass (meadow)	58	3	4	10	5	15	4	1	t
Hazel	10	t	4	26	15	35	10	t	t
Heather	41		5	21	10	12	9	2	
Ivy	12	t	6	25	8	26	20	3	
Larch	11	1	8	27	8	21	9	4	11
Oak	10	1	10	51	9	11	6	1	1
Scots pine	18	5	7	32	6	18	6	4	4
Spruce	4		7	55	10	14	10	t	
Straw (barley)	57		5	8	3	22	5		
Straw (oat)	49		5	7	4	30	4	1	
Straw (wheat)	70		5	6	4	13	2	t	
Willow	5	t	10	21	9	51	3	1	t
Bone ash	3		42	54	1			t	

Table 3
Simplified ultimate analyses of some common materials
Where two analyses are given they show the possible range. Amounts below 0·4% are marked t for trace.
Seven glazes are included for comparison.

Material	SiO_2	TiO_2	Al_2O_3	Fe_2O_3	B_2O_3	CaO	MgO	K_2O	Na_2O	Li_2O	loss
Clays:											
Albany slip	57	1	15	6		6	3	2	1		9
Ball clay	47	1	33	1		t	t	2	t		16
	70	1	19	1		t	t	2	t		7
Boulder clay	67		23	3		3		2			2
China clay	46	t	38	1		1	1	1	t		13
	47		39								14
Fireclay	44		39	2		1	t				14
	71	1	19	1		1	t	t	t		7
Malm	44		15	6		15	2	1			17
	77		11	1		5		2			4
Red clay	56		24	6		1	3	1			9
	60	1	20	9		1	1	1	t		7
Stoneware clay	44		38	3		t	t	t	t		15
	68	1	22	t		1	t	2	1		5
Zisha clay	59	1	20	9		t	1	3	t		7
Feldspars:											
Potassium feldspar	65		18					17			
	68		18	t		1	t	10	3		t
Sodium feldspar	66		21			1		3	9		t
	69		19						12		
Lime feldspar	43		37			20					
Mixed feldspar	64		20	t		2	t	9	5		t
	67		19	t		t	t	7	7		
FFF feldspar	67		19	t		t	t	9	5		
Plagioclase feldspars:											
Oligoclase	66		22			2			10		
Andesine	62		24			5			9		
Labradorite	57		27			9			7		
Bytownite	51		31			14			4		
Feldspathoids:											
Basalt	49	2	14	11		8	10	1	2		3
Cornish stone	71	t	17	t		2	t	7	2		1
	79	t	12	t		t	t	4	4		1
Granite	70		18			1		9	1		1
Lepidolite	48		29	t		t	t	17	1	3	2
	54		25	t		t	t	8	2	5	6
Nepheline syenite	53		29	2		t	t	7	7		2
	56		25	t		1	1	9	8		t
Petalite	76		16	t		1	1	1	1	4	
	78		18	t		t	t	t	t	4	
Spodumene	63		28	1		t	t	1	1	6	t
	64		29	t		t	t	t	t	7	t
Other materials:											
Colemanite	5		t	t	44	26	t				25
					51	27					22
Dolomite	1		1	t		29	19	t	t	t	50
	4		t	t		33	22				41
Talc	52	t	7	2		t	31				8
	63						32				5
Wollastonite	50	1	1	1		47	t				

continued

Table 3 continued

Material	SiO$_2$	TiO$_2$	Al$_2$O$_3$	Fe$_2$O$_3$	B$_2$O$_3$	CaO	MgO	K$_2$O	Na$_2$O	PbO	loss
Glasses, frits and glazes:											
Cullet	71		2		3	8	2	1	13		
	74		0		0	5	2	1	18		
Lead monosilicate	21									79	
Lead bisilicate	35									65	
Lead sesquisilicate	31									69	
Leadless 1000°C	44		10		22	15		6	3		
Leadless 1100°C	54		11		15	13		7			
Leadless 1200°C	66		13		4	11	1	5			
Leadless 1300°C	71		14		2	8	1	4			
High lead 900°C	46		3		6	5				40	
High lead 1000°C	50		7		7	5		2	3	26	
High lead 1100°C	51		8		9	4		4	4	20	

Table 4
Harrison pyrometric cones
(Potterycrafts Ltd, Stoke-on-Trent, England, UK)

Squatting temperatures when heated at 150°C/hr (270°F/hr)

Cone no.	°C	°F	Cone no.	°C	°F
018	720	1328	04C	1090	1994
017	770	1418	04D	1100	2012
016	795	1463	03	1115	2039
015	805	1481	02	1125	2057
014	830	1526	01	1145	2093
013	860	1580	1	1160	2120
012	885	1625	2	1165	2129
010	910	1670	3	1170	2138
09	930	1706	4	1190	2174
08	950	1742	5	1205	2201
07	990	1814	6	1230	2246
06	1015	1859	7	1250	2282
05	1040	1904	8	1260	2300
04	1060	1940	9	1285	2345
04A	1070	1958	10	1305	2381
04B	1080	1976	11	1325	2417

Table 5
Harrison Minibars
(Potterycrafts Ltd, Stoke-on-Trent, England, UK)

Bending temperatures based on a rise of 150°C/hr (270°F/hr)

Bar no.	°C	°F	Bar no.	°C	°F	Bar no.	°C	°F
018	720	1328	04	1060	1940	3	1170	2138
017	770	1418	04B	1080	1976	4	1190	2174
016	795	1463	04D	1100	2012	5	1205	2201
015	805	1481	03	1115	2039	6	1230	2246
014	830	1526	02	1125	2057	7	1250	2282
013	860	1580	01	1145	2093	8	1260	2300
012	885	1625	1	1160	2120	9	1285	2345
09	930	1706	2	1165	2129	10	1305	2381
08	950	1742						
07	990	1814						
06	1015	1859						
05	1040	1904						

Table 6
Orton pyrometric cones
(Orton Ceramic Foundation, Westerville, Ohio, USA)

Cone no.	*Large cones; squatting temperatures when heated at:* 60°C/hr	108°F/hr	150°C/hr	270°F/hr	Cone no.	*Large cones; squatting temperatures when heated at:* 60°C/hr	108°F/hr	150°C/hr	270°F/hr
022	576*	1069*	586*	1086*	04	1050	1922	1060	1940
021	602	1116	614	1137	03	1086	1987	1101	2014
020	625	1157	635	1175	02	1101	2014	1120	2048
019	668	1234	683	1261	01	1117	2043	1137	2079
018	696	1285	717	1323	1	1136	2077	1154	2109
017	727	1341	747	1377	2	1142	2088	1162	2124
016	764	1407	792	1458	3	1152	2106	1168	2134
015	790	1454	804	1479	4	1168	2134	1186	2167
014	834	1533	838	1540	5	1177	2151	1196	2185
013	836*	1537*	861*	1582*	6	1201	2194	1222	2232
012	856*	1573*	872*	1602*	7	1215	2219	1240	2264
011	872*	1602*	883*	1621*	8	1236	2257	1263	2305
010	880*	1616*	890*	1634*	9	1260	2300	1280	2336
09	915	1679	923	1693	10	1285	2345	1305	2381
08	945	1733	955	1751	11	1294	2361	1315	2399
07	973	1783	984	1803	12	1306	2383	1326	2419
06	991	1816	999	1830	13	1321	2410	1346	2455
05	1031	1888	1046	1915	14	1388	2530	1366	2491

1 The temperature equivalents shown for the large cones may be used as a guideline for determining deformation temperatures of self-supporting cones. However the self-supporting cones may deform at approximately 2°C higher than the large cones depending on the mounting height of the large cones.

2 *These temperatures are approximate. They were not determined at the National Bureau of Standards.

Table 7
Orton pyrometric cones
(Orton Ceramic Foundation, Westerville, Ohio, USA)

Cone no.	*Small cones; squatting temperatures when heated at:* 300°C/hr	540°F/hr	Cone no.	*Small cones; squatting temperatures when heated at:* 300°C/hr	540°F/hr	Cone no.	*Small cones; squatting temperatures when heated at:* 300°C/hr	540°F/hr
022	630*	1165*	010	919	1686	3	1196	2185
021	643	1189	09	955	1751	4	1209	2208
020	666	1231	08	983	1801	5	1221	2230
019	723	1333	07	1008	1846	6	1255	2291
018	752	1386	06	1023	1873	7	1264	2307
017	784	1443	05	1062	1944	8	1300	2372
016	825	1517	04	1098	2008	9	1317	2403
015	843	1549	03	1131	2068	10	1330	2426
014	870*	1596*	02	1148	2098	11	1336	2437
013	880*	1615*	01	1178	2152	12	1355	2471
012	900*	1650*	1	1179	2154			
011	915*	1680*	2	1179	2154			

1. The temperature equivalents shown for small cones may be used as a guideline for determining deformation temperatures of Orton pyrometric bars. However, Orton pyrometric bars were intended solely for use in automatic shut-off devices. They are not to be mounted in plaques or pats and used on a kiln shelf. Orton pyrometric bars were designed to deform in a shut-off when an Orton self-supporting cone of the same number is properly deformed on the kiln shelf.

2. *These temperatures are approximate. They were not determined at the National Bureau of Standards.

Table 8
Seger pyrometric cones
(Staatliche Porzellan-Manufaktur Berlin distributed by H. Welte Ing GmbH & Co. Hürth-Hermülheim, Germany)

Large cones; squatting temperatures when heated at 150°C/hr (270°F/hr)				*Large cones; squatting temperatures when heated at 150°C/hr (270°F/hr)*				*Large cones; squatting temperatures when heated at 150°C/hr (270°F/hr)*		
Cone no.	°C	°F		Cone no.	°C	°F		Cone no.	°C	°F
022	595	1103		010a	920	1688		3a	1170	2138
021	640	1184		09a	935	1715		4a	1195	2183
020	660	1220		08a	955	1751		5a	1215	2219
019	685	1265		07a	970	1778		6a	1240	2264
018	705	1301		06a	990	1814		7	1260	2300
017	730	1346		05a	1000	1832		8	1280	2336
016	755	1391		04a	1025	1877		9	1300	2372
015a	780	1436		03a	1055	1931		10	1320	2408
014a	805	1481		02a	1085	1985		11	1340	2444
013a	835	1535		01a	1105	2021		12	1360	2480
012a	860	1580		1a	1125	2057		13	1380	2516
011a	900	1652		2a	1150	2102		14	1400	2552

Small cones; squatting temperatures when heated at 150°C/hr (270°F/hr)				*Small cones; squatting temperatures when heated at 150°C/hr (270°F/hr)*				*Small cones; squatting temperatures when heated at 150°C/hr (270°F/hr)*		
Cone no.	°C	°F		Cone no.	°C	°F		Cone no.	°C	°F
022	605	1121		010a	925	1697		3a	1185	2165
021	650	1202		09a	940	1724		4a	1220	2228
020	675	1247		08a	965	1769		5a	1230	2246
019	695	1283		07a	975	1787		6a	1260	2300
018	715	1319		06a	995	1823		7	1270	2318
017	735	1355		05a	1010	1850		8	1295	2363
016	760	1400		04a	1055	1931		9	1315	2399
015a	785	1445		03a	1070	1958		10	1330	2426
014a	815	1499		02a	1100	2012		11	1350	2462
013a	845	1553		01a	1125	2057		12	1375	2507
012a	890	1634		1a	1145	2093		13	1395	2543
011a	900	1652		2a	1165	2129		14	1410	2570

Table 9
Bullers bars
(Taylor Tunnicliff Ltd, Stoke-on-Trent, England, UK)

Approximate bending temperature when heated at 80°C/hr (144°F/hr)				*Approximate bending temperature when heated at 80°C/hr (144°F/hr)*				*Approximate bending temperature when heated at 80°C/hr (144°F/hr)*		
Bar no.	°C	°F		Bar no.	°C	°F		Bar no.	°C	°F
1	590	1094		15	940	1724		29	1220	2228
2	610	1130		16	965	1769		30	1240	2264
3	625	1157		17	990	1814		31	1260	2300
4	650	1202		18	1015	1859		32	1280	2336
5	685	1265		19	1045	1913		33	1300	2372
6	715	1319		20	1075	1967		34	1320	2408
7	745	1373		21	1095	2003		35	1340	2444
8	775	1427		22	1115	2039		36	1365	2489
9	800	1472		23	1130	2066		37	1395	2543
10	820	1508		24	1145	2093		38	1425	2597
11	845	1553		25	1160	2120		39	1450	2642
12	870	1598		26	1175	2147		40	1475	2687
13	890	1634		27	1190	2174		41	1500	2732
14	915	1679		28	1205	2201		42	1525	2777

Tables concerning densities and contents of suspensions
See *Formula: Brongniart's* and *Tables 19 and 23.*

Table 10
Slips and glazes (Metric measures)
(Dry materials averaging r.d. 2·5)

Slop wt g/100 ml	Contents g dry	ml water	Approx percentages dry – water	ml water per 100 g dry material
140	66·7	73·3	48 – 52	109
145	75	70	52 – 48	93
150	83·3	66·7	56 – 44	80
155	91·7	63·3	59 – 41	69
160	100	60	63 – 37	60

Table 11
Slips and glazes (Imperial measures)
(r.d. 2·5)

oz pt imp	oz dry	fl oz water	Approx percentages dry – water	Approx pints per 100 oz of dry material for usual suspensions
25	8·3	16·7	33 – 67	
26	10	16	39 – 61	
27	11·7	15·3	43 – 57	
28	13·3	14·7	48 – 52	5·5
29	15	14	52 – 48	4·7
30	16·7	13·3	56 – 44	4
31	18·3	12·7	59 – 41	3·5
32	20	12	63 – 37	
33	21·7	11·3	66 – 34	
34	23·3	10· 7	69 – 31	

Table 12
Low sol glazes (Imperial measures)
(r.d. 3·0)

oz pt imp	oz dry	fl oz water	Approx Percentages dry – water	Approx pints per 100 oz of dry material for usual suspensions
25	7·5	17·5	30 – 70	
26	9	17	35 – 65	
27	10·5	16·5	39 – 61	
28	12	16	43 – 57	
29	13·5	15·5	47 – 53	
30	15	15	50 – 50	5
31	16·5	14·5	53 – 47	4·4
32	18	14	56 – 44	3·9
33	19·5	13·5	59 – 41	3·5

Table 13
High-lead glazes (Imperial measures)
(r.d. 4·0)

oz pt imp	oz dry	fl oz water	Approx percentages dry – water	Approx pints per 100 oz of dry material for usual suspensions
27	9·3	17·7	34 – 66	
28	10·7	17·3	38 – 62	
29	12	17	41 – 59	
30	13·3	16·7	44 – 56	
31	14·7	16·3	47 – 53	
32	16	16	50 – 50	5
33	17·3	15·7	52 – 48	4·5
34	18·7	15·3	55 – 45	4·1
35	20	15	57 – 43	3·75

Table 14
Slips and glazes (US measures)
(r.d. 2·5)

oz pt US	oz dry	oz water (fl oz)	Approx percentages dry – water	Approx US pints per 100 oz of dry material
23	10·5	12·5 (12)	46 – 54	
24	12·2	11·8 (11·3)	51 – 49	5·8
25	13·8	11·2 (10·8)	55 – 45	4·9
26	15·5	10·5 (10)	60 – 40	4
27	17·2	9·8 (9·4)	64 – 36	

Table 15
Low sol glazes (Metric measures)
(r.d. 3·0)

Slop wt g/100 ml	g dry	ml water	Approx percentages dry – water	ml water per 100 g dry material
150	75	75	50 – 50	100
155	82·5	72·5	53 – 47	88
160	90	70	56 – 44	78
165	97·5	67·5	59 – 41	69
170	105	65	62 – 38	62

Table 16
High-lead glazes (Metric measures)
(r.d. 4·0)

Slop wt g/100 ml	g dry	ml water	Approx percentages dry – water	ml water per 100 g dry material
160	80	80	50 – 50	100
165	87	78	53 – 47	90
170	93	77	55 – 45	83
175	100	75	57 – 43	75
180	107	73	59 – 41	68

Table 17
Table of elements
See also *Table 34*.

Element	Symbol	AW	Valency (rarely)	Element	Symbol	AW	Valency (rarely)
Aluminium	Al	27·0	3	Magnesium	Mg	24·3	2
Antimony	Sb	121·8	3 (4 and 5)	Manganese	Mn	54·9	2, 3 and 4
Arsenic	As	74·9	3 (5)	Nickel	Ni	58·7	2 and 4
Barium	Ba	137·3	2 (4)	Nitrogen	N	14·0	3 (1, 2, 4 and 5)
Beryllium	Be	9·0	2	Oxygen	O	16·0	2
Bismuth	Bi	209·0	3 (5)	Phosphorus	P	31·0	3 and 5 (4)
Boron	B	10·8	3	Platinum	Pt	195·1	—
Cadmium	Cd	112·4	2	Potassium	K	39·1	1 (3, 4 and 5)
Calcium	Ca	40·1	2 (4)	Praseodymium	Pr	140·9	4 (3)
Carbon	C	12·0	2 and 4	Selenium	Se	79·0	—
Cerium	Ce	140·1	4 (3)	Silicon	Si	28·1	4 (2)
Chlorine	Cl	35·5	1 (4, 6 and 7)	Silver	Ag	107·9	—
Chromium	Cr	52·0	3 (2, 4 and 6)	Sodium	Na	23·0	1 (2)
Cobalt	Co	58·9	2 and 3	Strontium	Sr	87·6	2 (4)
Copper	Cu	63·5	1 and 2	Sulfur	S	32·1	2 and 4
Fluorine	F	19·0	1	Tin	Sn	118·7	2 and 4
Germanium	Ge	72·6	4	Titanium	Ti	47·9	4 (3)
Gold	Au	197·0	—	Uranium	U	238·0	3, 4 and 5
Hydrogen	H	1·0	1 (2)	Vanadium	V	50·9	2, 3, 4, and 5
Iron	Fe	55·8	2 and 3	Zinc	Zn	65·4	2
Lead	Pb	207·2	2 and 4 (3)	Zirconium	Zr	91·2	4
Lithium	Li	6·9	1				

Table 18
List of capacity equivalents
See also *Formula*.

Note that there are two systems involving fluid ounces, pints and gallons; the imperial measure, formerly official in the United Kingdom, and the US measure used in the United States of America. All the other measures in ounces and pounds avoirdupois, inches and feet, and the metric system are universal. The cubic yards, feet and inches are reserved for measurement of solids but are useful in calculating the capacity of pots.

1 cubic metre	= 1 stere	1 cc = 1 ml	= 0·06102 cub in	1 US gal	= 3·7853 litres
	= 1000 litres		= 0·0352 imp fl oz		= 0·8327 imp gal
1 litre	= 1000 cc (ml)		= 0·0338 US fl oz		= 231 cub in
1 cc	= 1000 cubic mm			1 US pt	= 0·4732 litre
		1 cub ft	= 28·317 litres		= 473·2 ml
1 cub yd	= 27 cub ft		= 6·237 imp gal		= 0·8327 imp pt
1 cub ft	= 1728 cub in		= 7·481 US gal		= 16·6528 imp fl oz
		1 cub in	= 16·387 cc		= 28·875 cub in
1 imp gal	= 4 imp qt		= 0·5768 imp fl oz	1 US fl oz	= 29·573 ml
	= 8 imp pt		= 0·5539 US fl oz		= 1·0408 imp fl oz
1 imp pt	= 20 imp fl oz				= 1·805 cub in
		1 imp gal	= 4·5461 litres		
1 US gal	= 8 US pt		= 0·1603 cub ft	wt of 1 imp pt	
1 US pt	= 16 US fl oz		= 1·201 US gal	of water	= 20·042 oz
		1 imp pt	= 0·5683 litre	wt of 1 US pt	
1 litre	= 0·2199 imp gal		= 568·3 ml	of water	= 16·705 oz
	= 1·7598 imp pt		= 1·201 US pt		
	= 35·196 imp fl oz		= 19·22 US fl oz		
	= 0·2642 US gal		= 34·677 cub in		
	= 2·1132 US pt	1 imp fl oz	= 28·412 ml		
	= 33·8112 US fl oz		= 0·961 US fl oz		
	= 61·025 cub in		= 1·734 cub in		

Footnote. The SI units based on the m.k.s. units (metre, kilogram, second) are now recommended worldwide. This edition of the Dictionary is in step with their adoption.

Table 19
Slop weight equivalents
See *Formula: density, Calculations* and
Tables 10 to 16, and 23.

g/100 ml	oz pt imp	oz pt US	r.d.	°TW
110	22	18·3	1·10	20
114	22·8	19	1·14	28
115	23	19·2	1·15	30
120	24	20	1·20	40
125	25	20·8	1·25	50
126	25·2	21	1·26	52
130	26	21·7	1·30	60
132	26·4	22	1·32	64
135	27	22·5	1·35	70
138	27·6	23	1·38	76
140	28	23·3	1·40	80
144	28·8	24	1·44	88
145	29	24·2	1·45	90
150	30	25	1·50	100
155	31	25·8	1·55	110
156	31·2	26	1·56	112
160	32	26·7	1·60	120
162	32·4	27	1·62	124
165	33	27·5	1·65	130
168	33·6	28	1·68	136
170	34	28·3	1·70	140
174	34·8	29	1·74	148
175	35	29·2	1·75	150
180	36	30	1·80	160
185	37	30·8	1·85	170

Table 20
List of weight equivalents

1 tonne	=	1000 kg
1 kg	=	1000 g
1 g	=	0·001 kg

gross or long measure (imperial)

1 ton	=	20 cwt
	=	2240 lb
1 cwt	=	112 lb
1 lb	=	16 oz
1 oz	=	0·0625 lb

net or short measure (US)

1 ton	=	20 cwt
	=	2000 lb
1 cwt	=	100 lb

1 tonne	=	2204·61 lb
	=	0·9842 ton
1 kg	=	2·2046 lb
1 g	=	0·0353 oz

1 gross cwt	=	50·803 kg
1 net cwt	=	45·359 kg
1 lb	=	453·6 g
	=	0·4536 kg
1 oz	=	28·35 g

Table 21
List of length equivalents

1 metre	=	100 centimetres
1 centimetre	=	10 millimetres
1 yard	=	3 feet
	=	36 inches
1 foot	=	12 inches
1 inch	=	0·0833 feet
1 metre	=	1·0936 yards
	=	3·2808 feet
	=	39·3696 inches
1 centimetre	=	0·3937 inches
1 yard	=	0·9144 metre
1 foot	=	30·48 centimetres
1 inch	=	2·54 centimetres

To convert from inches into centimetres multiply by 2·54
To convert from centimetres to inches multiply by 0·3937

Table 22
Capacity factors

To convert from:	into:	multiply by:
imp pints	US pints	1·201
imp pints	litres	0·5683
imp fl oz	ml	28·412
US pints	imp pints	0·8327
US pints	litres	0·4732
US fl oz	ml	29·573
litres	imp pints	1·7598
litres	US pints	2·1132

Table 23
Density factors
See also *Formula: density* and *Tables 10 to 16, and 19.*

To convert from:	into:	multiply by:
oz pt imp	oz pt US	0·8327
oz pt imp	g/ml	0·0499
oz pt US	oz pt imp	1·201
oz pt US	g/ml	0·0599
g/ml	oz pt imp	20·042
g/ml	oz pt US	16·705

Table 24
Dry weight factors

To convert from:	into:	multiply by:
ounces	grams	28·35
pounds	kilograms	0·4536
gross cwts (imp)	kilograms	50·803
net cwts (US)	kilograms	45·36
grams	ounces	0·0353
kilograms	pounds	2·2046
kilograms	gross cwts (imp)	0·0196
kilograms	net cwts (US)	0·0221

Table 25
Table of oxide effect on surface tension
See **Surface tension**.

HIGH SURFACE TENSION

Aluminium oxide
Magnesium oxide
Zirconium oxide
Calcium oxide
Tin oxide
Zinc oxide
Strontium oxide
Barium oxide
Silica
Titanium oxide
Boron oxide
Lithium oxide
Lead oxide
Sodium oxide
Potassium oxide

LOW SURFACE TENSION

Table 26
Table of thermal expansion and contraction
(approximately proportionate)
For use of table see **Glaze fit**.

HIGH EXPANSION

Na_2O
(If the list were proportionate there would be a gap
here equal to the list from B_2O_3 to CuO)
K_2O
SiO_2 crystalline cristobalite $\alpha\beta$ includes inversion
(If the list were proportionate there would be a gap
here equal to the list from B_2O_3 to PbO)
CaO, SrO
ThO_2
Cr_2O_3
BaO, BeO
CoO
SiO_2 crystalline quartz α no inversion
PbO, NiO, Fe_2O_3, TiO_2, CeO_2
Typical lead glass
Sb_2O_3
Typical sodium glass
Typical white earthenware body
Li_2O, P_2O_5, As_2O_3
ZnO
Typical earthenware glaze
Typical stoneware body and glaze
CuO, MnO
Typical grog
MgO
Porcelain body
Top-quality firebrick
Sillimanite
SnO_2, ZrO_2
Al_2O_3
SiO_2 fused in bodies or glazes
B_2O_3

LOW EXPANSION

Table 27
Table of acceptable limits for unity formulae of glazes

	R_2O_3	R_2O_3 with B_2O_3	RO_2
Lead glazes			
900°–1000°C 1652°–1832°F	0·1 to 0·3	to 1·0	1·5 to 3·0
1000°–1100°C 1832°–2012°F	0·1 to 0·35	to 1·0	1·7 to 3·2
1100°–1200°C 2012°–2192°F	0·2 to 0·4	to 1·0	2·0 to 3·2
Leadless glazes			
900°–1000°C 1652°–1832°F	0·1 to 0·4	to 2·4	1·0 to 3·0
1000°–1100°C 1832°–2012°F	0·2 to 0·5	to 1·5	2·0 to 3·5
1100°–1200°C 2012°–2192°F	0·3 to 0·6	to 1·0	2·0 to 4·0
1200°–1300°C 2192°–2372°F	0·4 to 0·7	to 1·0	1·5 to 2·5 (crystalline) 2·7 to 7·0 (full fusion)

Table 28
Mohs' Scale of hardness
For use see **Mohs' Scale**.

SOFT

1	Talc
2	Gypsum
3	Calcite
4	Fluorspar
5	Apatite
6	Orthoclase
7	Quartz
8	Topaz
9	Corundum
10	Diamond

HARD

Table 29
Effective ranges of glaze oxides
See article on each oxide for details.

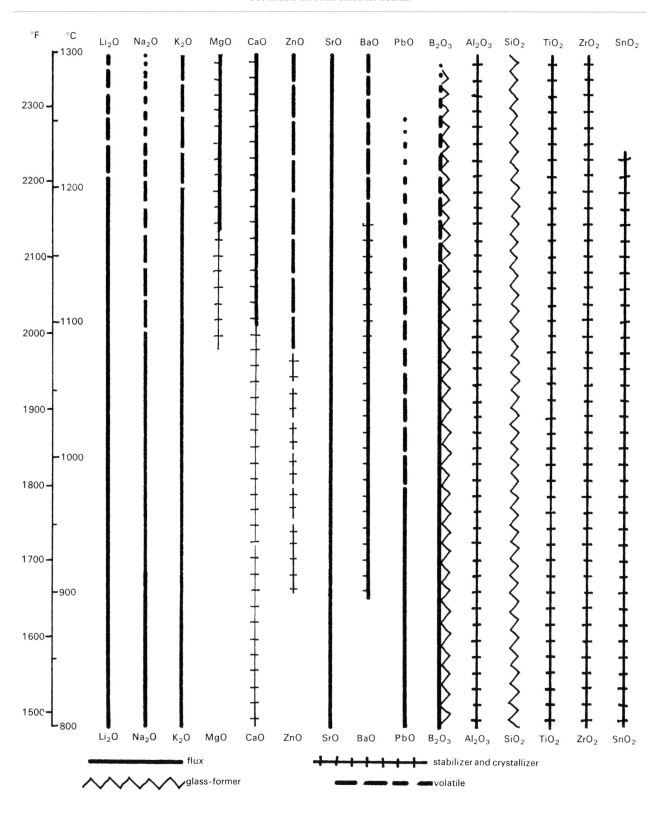

Table 30
Table of mineral constants

MP and D = Melting temperatures and decomposition temperatures which give some indication of behaviour but are often lowered by interaction. The relevant articles must be read in conjunction with this table.

CF = Conversion Factor. A batch weight multiplied by the CF gives the weight of oxides entering fusion.

* = Variables—typical examples given.

MW = Molecular weight. r.d. = Relative density. H = Hardness on Mohs' scale.

Name	Chemical formula	MW	r.d.	H		MP°C		MP°F	CF	Oxides entering fusion
Alabaster	$CaSO_4.2H_2O$	172·2	2·3	3	D	1450	D	2642	0·326	CaO
Albite (sodium feldspar)	$Na_2O.Al_2O_3.6SiO_2$	524·6	2·6	6·5		1170		2138	0·118	Na_2O
									0·194	Al_2O_3
									0·688	SiO_2
Aluminium oxide	Al_2O_3	102·0	3·8	9		2050		3722	1·0	Al_2O_3
Amblygonite	$Li.AlF.PO_4$	147·9	3·0	6	D	1100	D	2012	0·101	Li_2O
									0·245	Al_2O_3
									0·480	P_2O_5
Anatase	TiO_2	79·9	3·8	6·5		1560		2840	1·0	TiO_2
Andalusite	$Al_2O_3.SiO_2$	162·1	3·2	7·5		1380		2516	0·629	Al_2O_3
									0·371	SiO_2
Andesine (plagioclase feldspar)	$\left.\begin{array}{l}0.6Na_2O\\0.4CaO\end{array}\right\}Al_2O_3.4\cdot4SiO_2$*	426·1	2·7	6·5		1350		2462	0·087	Na_2O
									0·053	CaO
									0·239	Al_2O_3
									0·621	SiO_2
Anhydrite (calcium sulfate)	$CaSO_4$	136·2	2·9	3·5	D	1450	D	2642	0·412	CaO
Anorthite (lime feldspar)	$CaO.Al_2O_3.2SiO_2$	278·3	2·8	6·5		1550		2822	0·202	CaO
									0·366	Al_2O_3
									0·432	SiO_2
Anorthoclase (mixed feldspar)	$NaKO.Al_2O_3.6SiO_2$	540·7	2·6	6·5		1190		2174	0·144	NaKO
									0·189	Al_2O_3
									0·667	SiO_2
Antimonate of lead	$Pb_3(SbO_4)_2$	993·2				800		1472	0·664	PbO
									0·294	Sb_2O_3
Antimony oxide	Sb_2O_3	291·6	5·5			650		1202	1·0	Sb_2O_3
Apatite	$CaF_2.3Ca_3(PO_4)_2$	1009·0	3·2	5	D	1300	D	2372	0·556	CaO
									0·422	P_2O_5
Aragonite	$CaCO_3$	100·1	2·9	4	D	825	D	1517	0·561	CaO
Azurite	$2CuCO_3.Cu(OH)_2$	344·5	3·7	4	D	500	D	932	0·689	CuO
Barium carbonate	$BaCO_3$	197·3	4·4		D	1450	D	2642	0·777	BaO
					reduced—D	900	D	1652		
Barium oxide	BaO	153·3	5·0			1923		3493	1·0	BaO
Barytes (barium sulfate)	$BaSO_4$	233·4	4·5	3·5	D	1350	D	2462	0·657	BaO
Barytocalcite	$BaCO_3.CaCO_3$*	297·4			D	900	D	1652	0·515	BaO
									0·189	CaO
Bauxite	$Al_2O_3.2H_2O$	138·0	2·5	3	D	300	D	572	0·739	Al_2O_3
Bentonite	$Al_2O_3.4SiO_2.H_2O$*	360·4			D	600	D	1112	0·283	Al_2O_3
									0·667	SiO_2
Beryllium oxide	BeO	25·0	3·0			2500		4532	1·0	BeO
Bismuth oxide	Bi_2O_3	466·0	9·0			850		1562	1·0	Bi_2O_3
Bone ash	$Ca_3(PO_4)_2$*	310·3	3·1			1670		3038	0·542	CaO
									0·458	P_2O_5
Boracite	$6MgO.MgCl_2.8B_2O_3$*	893·9	2·9	7	D	900	D	1652	0·316	MgO
									0·623	B_2O_3
Borax	$Na_2B_4O_7.10H_2O$	381·2	2·5	2	D	350	D	662	0·163	Na_2O
									0·365	B_2O_3
Boric acid	$B(OH)_3$	61·8	1·5		D	200	D	392	0·563	B_2O_3
Boron oxide	B_2O_3	69·6	1·8			700		1292	1·0	B_2O_3
Brookite	TiO_2	79·9				1830		3326	1·0	TiO_2

Name	Chemical formula	MW	r.d.	H		MP°C		MP°F	CF	Oxides entering fusion
Bytownite (plagioclase feldspar)	$0{\cdot}8CaO$ } $Al_2O_3.2{\cdot}8SiO_2$* $0{\cdot}2Na_2O$ }	327·6	2·7	6·5		1500		2732	0·137 0·038 0·311 0·514	CaO Na$_2$O Al$_2$O$_3$ SiO$_2$
Calcite	$CaCO_3$	100·1	2·7	3	D	825	D	1517	0·561	CaO
Calcium borate	$Ca(BO_2)_2$	125·7				1100		2012	0·446 0·554	CaO B$_2$O$_3$
Calcium carbonate	$CaCO_3$	100·1	2·8	3	D	825	D	1517	0·561	CaO
Calcium chloride	$CaCl_2$	111·1	2·15		D	780	D	1436	0·505	CaO
Calcium fluoride	CaF_2	78·1	3·2		D	1360	D	2480	0·718	CaO
Calcium oxide	CaO	56·1	3·3			2570		4658	1·0	CaO
Calcium phosphate	$Ca_3(PO_4)_2$	310·3	3·2			1730		3146	0·542 0·458	CaO P$_2$O$_5$
Calcium sulfate	$CaSO_4$	136·2	2·9	3·5	D	1450	D	2642	0·412	CaO
Cassiterite	SnO_2	150·7	6·7	7		1150		2102	1·0	SnO$_2$
Celestine	$SrSO_4$	183·7	3·9	3·5	D	1300	D	2372	0·564	SrO
Celsian (barium feldspar)	$BaO.Al_2O_3.2SiO_2$	375·5	3·4	6·5		1500		2732	0·408 0·272 0·320	BaO Al$_2$O$_3$ SiO$_2$
Cerium oxide	CeO_2	172·1	7·3			1950		3542	1·0	CeO$_2$
Chalk	$CaCO_3$	100·1	2·7	2·5	D	825	D	1517	0·561	CaO
China clay	$Al_2O_3.2SiO_2.2H_2O$*	258·2	2·5	2·0	D	600	D	1112	0·395 0·466	Al$_2$O$_3$ SiO$_2$
Chromite	$FeO.Cr_2O_3$	223·8	4·4	5·5		2000		3632	0·357 0·679	Fe$_2$O$_3$ Cr$_2$O$_3$
Chromium oxide	Cr_2O_3	152·0	5·2			2265		4109	1·0	Cr$_2$O$_3$
Cobalt carbonate	$CoCO_3$	118·9	4·0		D	800	D	1472	0·630	CoO
Cobalt carbonate basic	$CoCO_3.Co(OH)_2$	211·8	3·7		D	800	D	1472	0·707	CoO
Cobalt hydroxide	$Co(OH)_2$	92·9			D	120	D	248	0·806	CoO
Cobalt oxide	CoO	74·9	5·7			1805		3281	1·0	CoO
Cobalt oxide	Co_3O_4	240·7	6·0		D	900	D	1652	0·934	CoO
Colemanite	$2CaO.3B_2O_3.5H_2O$*	411·0	2·3	4·5	D	800	D	1472	0·273 0·508	CaO B$_2$O$_3$
Copper carbonate	$CuCO_3$	123·5	5·0		D	500	D	932	0·644	CuO
Copper carbonate basic	$CuCO_3.Cu(OH)_2$	221·0	4·0		D	500	D	932	0·719	CuO
Copper oxide black	CuO	79·5	6·4			1148		2098	1·0	CuO
Copper oxide red	Cu_2O	143·0	6·0			1230		2246	1·112	CuO
Copper sulfate	$CuSO_4.5H_2O$	249·6	2·3		D	650	D	1202	0·319	CuO
Cordierite	$2MgO.2Al_2O_3.5SiO_2$					1540		2804		
Cristobalite	SiO_2	60·1	2·3			1710		3110	1·0	SiO$_2$
Crocus martis	$FeSO_4$	151·9			D	1200	D	2192	1·051	Fe$_2$O$_3$
Cryolite	Na_3AlF_6	210·0	3·0	2·5	D	1000	D	1832	0·443 0·243 0·543	Na$_2$O Al$_2$O$_3$ F$_2$
Cuprite	Cu_2O	143·0	5·8	4·0		1230		2246	1·112	CuO
Diaspore	$Al_2O_3.H_2O$	120·0	2·9	3·5	D	350	D	662	0·850	Al$_2$O$_3$
Diopside	$CaMg(SiO_3)_2$	216·6	3·3			1392		2538	0·259 0·186 0·555	CaO MgO SiO$_2$
Dolomite	$CaMg(CO_3)_2$	184·4	2·8	4	D	800	D	1472	0·304 0·219	CaO MgO
Enstatite	$MgSiO_3$	100·4				1550		2822	0·401 0·599	MgO SiO$_2$
Epsom salt	$MgSO_4.7H_2O$	246·4	1·7		D	1127	D	2061	0·163	MgO
Feldspar barium (celsian)	$BaO.Al_2O_3.2SiO_2$	375·5	3·4	6·5		1500		2732	0·408 0·272 0·320	BaO Al$_2$O$_3$ SiO$_2$
Feldspar lime (anorthite)	$CaO.Al_2O_3.2SiO_2$	278·3	2·8	6·5		1550		2822	0·202 0·366 0·432	CaO Al$_2$O$_3$ SiO$_2$

continued

Name	Chemical formula	MW	r.d.	H	MP°C		MP°F	CF	Oxides entering fusion
Feldspar mixed (anorthoclase)	NaKO. Al_2O_3.$6SiO_2$	540·7	2·6	6·5	1190		2174	0·144 0·189 0·667	NaKO Al_2O_3 SiO_2
Feldspar plagioclase (see Andesine, Bytownite, Labradorite, Oligoclase, Hyalophane under this table)									
Feldspar potassium (orthoclase)	K_2O.Al_2O_3.$6SiO_2$	556·8	2·5	6	1200		2192	0·169 0·183 0·648	K_2O Al_2O_3 SiO_2
Feldspar sodium (albite)	Na_2O.Al_2O_3.$6SiO_2$	524·6	2·6	6·5	1170		2138	0·118 0·194 0.688	Na_2O Al_2O_3 SiO_2
Flint	SiO_2	60·1	2·6	7	1600		2912	0·985 0·015	SiO_2 CaO
Fluorspar	CaF_2	78·1	3·2	4	D 1330	D	2426	0·718	CaO
Germanium oxide	GeO_2	104·6	4·3		1115		2039	1·0	GeO_2
Gibbsite	$Al(OH)_3$	78·0	2·4	3	D 300	D	572	0·654	Al_2O_3
Gypsum	$CaSO_4$.$2H_2O$	172·2	2·3	2	D 1450	D	2642	0·412	CaO
Haematite	Fe_2O_3	159·6	4·9	6·5	1457		2655	0·990	Fe_2O_3
Hemimorphite	$2ZnO$.SiO_2.H_2O*	240·9	3·4	5	D 200	D	392	0·676 0·249	ZnO SiO_2
Hyalophane (barium feldspar)	K_2O.BaO.$2Al_2O_3$.$8SiO_2$*	932·3	2·6	6	1350		2462	0·101 0·164 0·219 0·516	K_2O BaO Al_2O_3 SiO_2
Ilmenite	$FeTiO_3$*	151·7	4·8	6	1365		2489	0·526 0·527	Fe_2O_3 TiO_2
Iron carbonate	$FeCO_3$	115·8	3·8		D 450	D	842	0·689	Fe_2O_3
Iron chromate	$FeCrO_3$	155·8	5·0		1700		3092	0·512 0·488	Fe_2O_3 Cr_2O_3
Iron oxide black	FeO	71·8	5·7		1420		2588 *reduced—*	1·111 1·0	Fe_2O_3 FeO
Iron oxide red	Fe_2O_3	159·6	5·3		1565		2849	1·0	Fe_2O_3
Iron pyrites	FeS_2	120·0	4·9	6·5	D 510	D	950	0·665	Fe_2O_3
Iron spangles	Fe_3O_4	231·4	5·2		D 1538	D	2800	0·311 0·689	FeO Fe_2O_3
Iron sulfate	$FeSO_4$.$7H_2O$	277·9	1·9		D 1200	D	2192	0·287	Fe_2O_3
Iron titanate	$FeTiO_3$	151·7	4·8	6	1365		2489	0·526 0·527	Fe_2O_3 TiO_2
Kalium soda	NaKO	78·1			700		1292	1·0	NaKO
Kaolinite	$Al_2Si_2O_5(OH)_4$	258·2	2·6	2·5	D 600	D	1112	0·395 0·466	Al_2O_3 SiO_2
Kyanite	Al_2O_3.SiO_2	162·1	3·6	4/7	1350		2462	0·629 0·371	Al_2O_3 SiO_2
Labradorite (plagioclase feldspar)	0·6CaO } Al_2O_3.$3·6SiO_2$* 0·4Na_2O	376·9	2·7	6	1400		2552	0·089 0·066 0.271 0.574	CaO Na_2O Al_2O_3 SiO_2
Lead bisilicate	PbO.$2SiO_2$	343·4	4·5		900		1652	0·649 0·351	PbO SiO_2
Lead monosilicate	PbO.SiO_2	283·3			800		1472	0·788 0·212	PbO SiO_2
Lead orthosilicate	$2PbO$.SiO_2	506·5			750		1382	0·881 0·119	PbO SiO_2
Lead oxide	PbO	223·2	9·3		880		1616	1·0	PbO
Lead sesquisilicate	$2PbO$.$3SiO_2$	626·7			850		1562	0·712 0·288	PbO SiO_2
Lepidolite	Li_2F_2.Al_2O_3.$3SiO_2$*	334·1	2·8	3	D 1200	D	2192	0·089 0·305 0·539	Li_2O Al_2O_3 SiO_2
Leucite	$KAlSi_2O_6$	218·3	2·5	6	1350		2462	0·216 0·234 0·550	K_2O Al_2O_3 SiO_2

Name	Chemical formula	MW	r.d.	H		MP°C		MP°F	CF	Oxides entering fusion
Limestone	$CaCO_3$	100·1	2·6	3·5	D	825	D	1517	0·561	CaO
Limonite	$2Fe_2O_3.3H_2O$	373·2	3·8	5·5	D	200	D	392	0·855	Fe_2O_3
Lithium oxide	Li_2O	29·8	2·0			1700		3092	1·0	Li_2O
Lithium carbonate	Li_2CO_3	73·8	2·1		D	650	D	1202	0·404	Li_2O
Magnesium oxide (periclase)	MgO	40·3	3·5			2800		5072	1·0	MgO
Magnesium carbonate (magnesite)	$MgCO_3$	84·3	3·0	4·5	D	350	D	662	0·478	MgO
Magnesium carbonate light	$3MgCO_3.Mg(OH)_2.3H_2O$	365·2			D	410	D	770	0·441	MgO
Magnesium sulfate	$MgSO_4$	120·4	2·7		D	1127	D	2061	0·335	MgO
Magnetite	Fe_3O_4	231·4	5·1	6·5	D	1538	D	2800	1·035	Fe_2O_3
Malachite	$CuCO_3.Cu(OH)_2$	221·0	3·9	4	D	500	D	932	0·719	CuO
Manganese carbonate	$MnCO_3$	114·9	3·6		D	300	D	572	0·615	MnO
Manganese dioxide (pyrolusite)	MnO_2	86·9	4·9		D	1080	D	1976	1·0	MnO_2
						above 1080°C—			0·816	MnO
Manganite	MnO(OH)	87·9	4·3	4	D	200	D	392	0·807	MnO
Manganese monoxide	MnO	70·9	5·3			1650		3002	1·0	MnO
Marcasite	FeS_2	120·0	4·7	6·5	D	510	D	950	0·665	Fe_2O_3
Metakaolin	$Al_2O_3.2SiO_2$	222·2				1770		3218	0·459	Al_2O_3
									0·541	SiO_2
Microcline (potassium feldspar)	$K_2O.Al_2O_3.6SiO_2$	556·8	2·5	6		1200		2192	0·169	K_2O
									0·183	Al_2O_3
									0·648	SiO_2
Mullite	$3Al_2O_3.2SiO_2$	426·2	3·2			1810		3190	0·718	Al_2O_3
									0·282	SiO_2
Natrium potassa	NaKO	78·1				700		1292	1·0	NaKO
Natron	$Na_2CO_3.10H_2O*$	286·0	1·4	1·5	D	860	D	1580	0·217	Na_2O
Nepheline	$K_2O.3Na_2O.4Al_2O_3.9SiO_2$	1229·1	2·6	6		1200		2192	0·077	K_2O
									0·151	Na_2O
									0·332	Al_2O_3
									0·440	SiO_2
Nepheline syenite	$K_2O.3Na_2O.4Al_2O_3.8SiO_2$	1169·0	2·6	6		1200		2192	0·081	K_2O
									0·159	Na_2O
									0·349	Al_2O_3
									0·411	SiO_2
Nickel oxide	NiO	74·7	6·7			1990		3614	1·0	NiO
Oligoclase (plagioclase feldspar)	$0.8Na_2O$ }$Al_2O_3.5.2SiO_2*$ $0.2CaO$ }	475·3	2·7	6·5		1250		2282	0·104	Na_2O
									0·024	CaO
									0·215	Al_2O_3
									0·657	SiO_2
Oolite	$CaCO_3$	100·1	2·7	3	D	825	D	1517	0·561	CaO
Orthoclase (potassium feldspar)	$K_2O.Al_2O_3.6SiO_2$	556·8	2·5	6		1200		2192	0·169	K_2O
									0·183	Al_2O_3
									0·648	SiO_2
Petalite (lithium feldspathoid)	$Li_2O.Al_2O_3.8SiO_2$	612·6	2·4	6·5		1300		2372	0·049	Li_2O
									0·166	Al_2O_3
									0·785	SiO_2
Phosphorite	$Ca_3(PO_4)_2$	310·3	3·2	5		1730		3146	0·542	CaO
									0·458	P_2O_5
Phosphorus oxide	P_2O_5	142·0	2·4			580		1076	1·0	P_2O_5
Plaster of Paris	$2CaSO_4.H_2O$	290·4			D	1450	D	2642	0·386	CaO
Potassium oxide	K_2O	94·2	2·32			700		1291	1·0	K_2O
Potassium carbonate	K_2CO_3	138·2	2·4		D	895	D	1643	0·682	K_2O
Potassium dichromate	$K_2Cr_2O_7$	294·2	2·7		D	500	D	932	0·320	K_2O
									0·517	Cr_2O_3
Potassium permanganate	$KMnO_4$	158·0	2·7		D	240	D	464	0·298	K_2O
									0·449	MnO
Praseodymium oxide	PrO_2	172·9							1·0	PrO_2

continued

Name	Chemical formula	MW	r.d.	H		MP°C		MP°F	CF	Oxides entering fusion
Pyrite	FeS_2	120·0	4·9	6·5	D	510	D	950	0·665	Fe_2O_3
Pyrolusite	MnO_2	86·9	4·9	2·5	D	1080	D	1976	0·816	MnO
Quartz	SiO_2	60·1	2·7	7		1710		3110	1·0	SiO_2
Red ochre	Fe_2O_3	159·6	3·5	2		1565		2849	1·0	Fe_2O_3
Rutile	TiO_2	79·9	4·3	6·5		1825		3317	1·0	TiO_2
Siderite	$FeCO_3$	115·8	3·8	4·5	D	450	D	842	0·689	Fe_2O_3
Silica	SiO_2	60·1	2·7	7		1710		3110	1·0	SiO_2
Silicon carbide	SiC	40·1	3·2	9·8	D	2700	D	4892	1·499	SiO_2
Sillimanite	$Al_2O_3.SiO_2$	162·1	3·2	7		1545		2813	0·629	Al_2O_3
									0·371	SiO_2
Smithsonite	$ZnCO_3$	125·4	4·3	5	D	300	D	572	0·649	ZnO
Sodalite (sodium feldspathoid)	$3NaAlSiO_4.NaCl$	484·8	2·2	6		1200		2192	0·256	Na_2O
									0·316	Al_2O_3
									0·372	SiO_2
Sodium bicarbonate	$NaHCO_3$	84·0	2·16		D	270	D	518	0·369	Na_2O
Sodium carbonate (soda ash)	Na_2CO_3	106·0	2·5		D	860	D	1580	0·585	Na_2O
Sodium chloride	$NaCl$	58·5	2·17			800		1472	0·529	Na_2O
Sodium oxide	Na_2O	62·0	2·3			900		1652	1·0	Na_2O
Sodium silicate (waterglass)	Na_2SiO_3	122·2	2·4			1100		2012	0·508	Na_2O
									0·492	SiO_2
Spodumene (lithium feldspathoid)	$Li_2O.Al_2O_3.4SiO_2$	372·2	3·1	6·5		1400		2552	0·080	Li_2O
									0·274	Al_2O_3
									0·646	SiO_2
Strontianite (strontium carbonate)	$SrCO_3$	147·6	3·6	4	D	1075	D	1967	0·702	SrO
Strontium oxide	SrO	103·6	4·7			2430		4406	1·0	SrO
Talc	$3MgO.4SiO_2.H_2O$	379·3	2·7	1	D	900	D	1652	0·319	MgO
					MP	1300	MP	2372	0·634	SiO_2
Tin oxide white	SnO_2	150·7	6·8			1150		2102	1·0	SnO_2
Tin oxide black	SnO	134·7	6·5	*oxidizes*—700				1291	1·119	SnO_2
Titanite (sphene)	$CaO.TiO_2.SiO_2$	196·1	3·5	5·5		1385		2525	0·286	CaO
									0·407	TiO_2
									0·307	SiO_2
Titanium oxide	TiO_2	79·9	4·2	6·5		1830		3326	1·0	TiO_2
Tridymite	SiO_2	60·1	2·3	7		1700		3092	1·0	SiO_2
Ulexite	$NaCaB_5O_9.8H_2O$	405·1	1·65	1	D	300	D	572	0·077	Na_2O
									0·138	CaO
									0·429	B_2O_3
Uranium oxide	U_3O_8	842·0	7·3			2176		3949	1·0	U_3O_8
Vanadium oxide	V_2O_5	181·8	3·4			690		1274	1·0	V_2O_5
Washing soda	$Na_2CO_3.10H_2O$	286·0	1·5		D	860	D	1580	0·217	Na_2O
Whiting	$CaCO_3$	100·1	2·8	3	D	825	D	1517	0·561	CaO
Willemite	Zn_2SiO_4	222·9	4	5		1200		2192	0·730	ZnO
									0·270	SiO_2
Witherite	$BaCO_3$	197·3	4·3	3·7	D	1450	D	2642	0·777	BaO
				reduced—	D	900	D	1652		
Wollastonite	$CaSiO_3$	116·2	2·8	5		1545		2813	0·483	CaO
									0·517	SiO_2
Yellow ochre	$2Fe_2O_3.3H_2O*$	373·2	3·5	5	D	200	D	392	0·855	Fe_2O_3
Zinc blende	ZnS	97·5	4·1	4·0	D	1020	D	1868	0·835	ZnO
Zinc oxide (zincite)	ZnO	81·4	5·7	4·5		1975		3578	1·0	ZnO
Zirconium oxide	ZrO_2	123·2	5·5			2700		4892	1·0	ZrO_2
Zirconium silicate (zircon)	$ZrSiO_4$	183·3	4·5	7·5		2550		4622	0·672	ZrO_2
									0·328	SiO_2

Table 31
Table of incandescence
See *Temperature* and *Incandescence*.

°C	°F	Kiln interior glow: muffle and other kilns firing and cooling	Kiln interior glow: electric kilns firing only	°C	°F	Kiln interior glow: muffle and other kilns firing and cooling	Kiln interior glow: electric kilns firing only
1400	2552	blue-white		650	1202		
1350	2462			600	1112	first visible red	dull red
1300	2372	white	white	550	1022	black	
1250	2282	yellow	yellow-white	500	932		first visible red
1200	2192	bright orange	light yellow	450	842		black
1150	2102			400	752		
1100	2012	orange	bright orange	350	662		
1050	1922	bright red	orange	300	572	hottest domestic oven	
1000	1832		bright red	250	482		
950	1742			200	392		
900	1652	deep red		150	302		
850	1562			100	212		
800	1472		deep red	50	122		
750	1382			0	32		
700	1292	dull red					

Table 32
Conversion of temperatures
See also *Celsius*, *Fahrenheit*, *Kelvin* and *Calculations*.

$$°C = \frac{(°F - 32) \times 5}{9} \qquad °F = \frac{9(°K - 273)}{5} + 32$$

$$°C = °K - 273 \qquad °K = °C + 273$$

$$°F = \frac{°C \times 9}{5} + 32 \qquad °K = \frac{5(°F - 32)}{9} + 273$$

Table 33
List of temperature equivalents
See *Temperature*.

°C	°F	°C	°F	°C	°F	°C	°F	°C	°F	°C	°F
2000	3632	1280	2336	1180	2156	1090	1994	850	1562	450	842
1900	3452	1270	2318	1177	2150	1080	1976	816	1500	400	752
1800	3272	1260	2300	1170	2138	1070	1958	800	1472	350	662
1700	3092	1250	2282	1160	2120	1060	1940	760	1400	300	572
1600	2912	1240	2264	1150	2102	1050	1922	750	1382	250	482
1500	2732	1232	2250	1149	2100	1038	1900	704	1300	200	392
1400	2552	1230	2246	1140	2084	1000	1832	700	1292	120	248
1350	2462	1220	2228	1130	2066	982	1800	650	1202	100	212
1316	2400	1210	2210	1120	2048	950	1742	600	1112	0	32
1300	2372	1204	2200	1110	2030	927	1700	573	1063		
1290	2354	1200	2192	1100	2012	900	1652	550	1022		
1288	2350	1190	2174	1093	2000	871	1600	500	932		

Table 34
Valency table
See *Valency* and *Table 17*.

	Valency 1 (monovalent)		Valency 2 (divalent)		Valency 3 (trivalent)		Valency 4 (tetravalent)		Valency 5 (pentavalent)	
Metals	Copper	Cu	Copper	Cu	Aluminium	Al	Cerium	Ce		
	Lithium	Li	Cobalt	Co	Cobalt	Co				
	Potassium	K	Manganese	Mn	Manganese	Mn	Manganese	Mn		
	Sodium	Na	Iron	Fe	Iron	Fe	Titanium	Ti		
			Nickel	Ni	Arsenic	As	Nickel (rare)	Ni		
			Lead	Pb	Antimony	Sb	Lead	Pb		
			Vanadium	V	Vanadium	V	Vanadium	V	Vanadium	V
			Beryllium	Be	Uranium	U	Uranium	U	Uranium	U
			Barium	Ba	Boron	B	Zirconium	Zr		
			Calcium	Ca	Chromium	Cr	Praseodymium	Pr		
			Tin	Sn			Tin	Sn		
			Magnesium	Mg						
			Strontium	Sr						
			Zinc	Zn	Bismuth	Bi				
Non-metals	Chlorine	Cl	Oxygen	O	Nitrogen	N	Silicon	Si	Phosphorus	P
	Fluorine	F	Sulfur	S	Phosphorus	P	Sulfur	S		
	Hydrogen	H	Carbon	C			Carbon	C		
Radicals	Hydroxide	OH	Carbonate	CO_3	Phosphate	PO_4				
	Nitrate	NO_3	Sulfate	SO_4	Arsenate	AsO_4				
	Chlorate	ClO_3	Sulfite	SO_3						
	Bicarbonate	HCO_3								

Table 35
Atomic to visible particle sizes compared with wavelengths of electromagnetic radiation

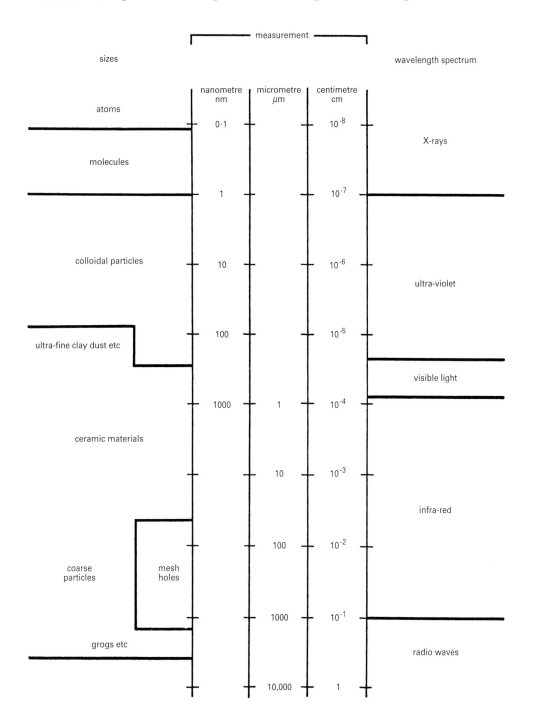

Table 36
Periodic table of elements
For use see *Periodic table*.

Table 37a
Potter's periodic table
For use see *Periodic table*.

	1	2	3	4	5	6	7	8	9	10	11	12	13	14	15	16	17	18	
2	Li_2O	BeO											B_2O_3	C	N	O	F		1
3	Na_2O	MgO											Al_2O_3	SiO_2	P_2O_5	S	Cl		2
4	K_2O	CaO		TiO_2	V_2O_3 V_2O_5	Cr_2O_3	MnO MnO_2	FeO Fe_2O_3	CoO	NiO	Cu Cu_2O CuO	ZnO		GeO_2	As_2O_3	Se SeO_2			3
5		SrO		ZrO_2	Nb	Mo		Ru	Rh	Pd	Ag	Cd CdO		SnO_2	Sb_2O_3	Te			4
6		BaO	CeO_2 PrO_2	Hf	Ta	W_3O_8 WO_3	Re	Os	Ir	Pt	Au			PbO	Bi Bi_2O_3				5
7			U_3O_8																6
																			7

10	11	12	13	14	15	16	17	18	
								Noble gases	
	hydrogen						Halogens	helium	1
	1 H							2 He	
			boron	carbon	nitrogen	oxygen	fluorine	neon	2
			5 B	6 C	7 N	8 O	9 F	10 Ne	
			aluminium	silicon	phosphorus	sulfur	chlorine	argon	3
			13 Al	14 Si	15 P	16 S	17 Cl	18 Ar	
nickel	copper	zinc		germanium	arsenic	selenium	bromine	krypton	4
28 Ni	29 Cu	30 Zn	31 Ga	32 Ge	33 As	34 Se	35 Br	36 Kr	
palladium	silver	cadmium		tin	antimony	tellurium	iodine	xenon	5
46 Pd	47 Ag	48 Cd	49 In	50 Sn	51 Sb	52 Te	53 I	54 Xe	
platinum	gold			lead	bismuth			radon	6
78 Pt	79 Au	80 Hg	81 Tl	82 Pb	83 Bi	84 Po	85 At	86 Rn	
110 Uun	111 Uuu	112 Uub	113 Uut	114 Uuq	115 UUp	116 Uuh	117 Uus	118 Uuo	7

64 Gd	65 Tb	66 Dy	67 Ho	68 Er	69 Tm	70 Yb	71 Lu		6
96 Cm	97 Bk	98 Cf	99 Es	100 Fm	101 Md	102 No	103 Lr		7

Table 37b
Potter's periodic table - alkaline and acidic oxides
For use see *Periodic table*.

Table 38
Common oxides and carbonates with alternative names
See also note on nomenclature on page ix.

Potter's descriptive name	Chemical formula	Stock system name	Definitive name	Other names	Mineral name	
Aluminium oxide	Al_2O_3	aluminium (III) oxide	dialuminium trioxide	alumina aluminium sesquioxide	corundum	
Antimony oxide	Sb_2O_3	antimony (III) oxide	diantimony trioxide	stibium sesquioxide		
Barium oxide	BaO	barium (II) oxide	barium oxide	baria		
Barium carbonate	$BaCO_3$	barium (II) carbonate	barium carbonate		witherite	
Boron oxide	B_2O_3	boron (III) oxide	diboron trioxide	boric oxide boron trioxide boron sesquioxide		
Calcium oxide	CaO	calcium (II) oxide	calcium oxide	lime calcia		
Calcium carbonate	$CaCO_3$	calcium (II) carbonate	calcium carbonate	lime carbonate of lime	whiting chalk calcite argonite	oolite marble calcspar limestone
Cerium oxide	CeO_2	cerium (IV) oxide	cerium dioxide	ceria		
Chromium oxide	Cr_2O_3	chromium (III) oxide	dichromium trioxide	chrome oxide chromia		
Cobalt oxide	CoO	cobalt (II) oxide	cobalt monoxide	cobaltous oxide		
Black Cobalt oxide	Co_3O_4	cobalt (II, III) oxide	tricobalt tetraoxide	cobaltosic oxide cobalto-cobaltic oxide		
Grey Cobalt oxide	Co_2O_3	cobalt (III) oxide	dicobalt trioxide	cobalt sesquioxide		
Cobalt carbonate	$CoCO_3$	cobalt (II) carbonate	cobalt carbonate			
Black Copper oxide	CuO	copper (II) oxide	copper monoxide	cupric oxide	tenorite	
Red Copper oxide	Cu_2O	copper (I) oxide	dicopper monoxide	cuprous oxide copper sub-oxide	cuprite	
Copper carbonate	$CuCO_3$	copper (II) carbonate	copper carbonate	green copper carbonate	malachite azurite	
Black Iron oxide	FeO	iron (II) oxide	iron monoxide	ferrous oxide		
Red Iron oxide	Fe_2O_3	iron (III) oxide	diiron trioxide	ferric oxide iron sesquioxide	haematite	
Magnetic Iron oxide	Fe_3O_4	iron (II, III) oxide	triiron tetraoxide	ferroso-ferric oxide ferrosic oxide iron proto-sesquioxide black magnetic oxide iron spangles	magnetite	
Iron carbonate	$FeCO_3$	iron (II) carbonate	iron carbonate		siderite chalybite	
Iron chromate	$FeCrO_3$	iron(III) chromium(III) oxide	iron chromium trioxide		chromite	
Lead oxide	PbO	lead (II) oxide	lead monoxide	plumbus oxide litharge		
Lead oxide	Pb_3O_4	lead (II, II, IV) oxide	trilead tetraoxide	red lead lead tetroxide minium		
Lithium oxide	Li_2O	lithium (I) oxide	dilithium oxide	lithia		
Lithium carbonate	Li_2CO_3	lithium (I) carbonate	dilithium carbonate			
Magnesium oxide	MgO	magnesium (II) oxide	magnesium oxide	magnesia	periclase	
Magnesium carbonate	$MgCO_3$	magnesium (II) carbonate	magnesium carbonate		magnesite	
Green Manganese oxide	MnO	manganese (II) oxide	manganese monoxide	manganous oxide		
Black Manganese oxide	MnO_2	manganese (IV) oxide	manganese dioxide		pyrolusite	
Manganese carbonate	$MnCO_3$	manganese (II) carbonate	manganese carbonate		rhodochrosite	
Nickel oxide	NiO	nickel (II) oxide	nickel monoxide	nickelous oxide		
Phosphorus oxide	P_2O_5	phosphorus (V) oxide	diphosphorus pentaoxide	phosphorus pentoxide phosphoric oxide		
Potassium oxide	K_2O	potassium (I) oxide	dipotassium oxide	potassa potash kalium oxide		

Potter's descriptive name	Chemical formula	Stock system name	Definitive name	Other names	Mineral name
Potassium carbonate	K_2CO_3	potassium (I) carbonate	dipotassium carbonate	potash pearl ash	
Praseodymium oxide	PrO_2	praseodymium (IV) oxide	praseodymium dioxide		
Silica	SiO_2	silicon (IV) oxide	silicon dioxide	silica	quartz
Sodium oxide	Na_2O	sodium (I) oxide	disodium oxide	soda natrium oxide	
Sodium carbonate	Na_2CO_3	sodium (I) carbonate	disodium carbonate	soda ash sal soda	
Strontium oxide	SrO	strontium (II) oxide	strontium oxide	strontia	
Strontium carbonate	$SrCO_3$	strontium (II) carbonate	strontium carbonate		strontianite
White Tin oxide	SnO_2	tin (IV) oxide	tin dioxide	stannic oxide	cassiterite tin stone
Black Tin oxide	SnO	tin (II) oxide	tin monoxide	stannous oxide	
Titanium oxide	TiO_2	titanium (IV) oxide	titanium dioxide	titania	anatase brookite
Vanadium oxide	V_2O_5	vanadium (V) oxide	divanadium pentaoxide	vanadium pentoxide	
Zinc oxide	ZnO	zinc (II) oxide	zinc oxide		zincite
Zirconium oxide	ZrO_2	zirconium (IV) oxide	zirconium dioxide	zirconia	

Table 39
Analyses of some insulating refractories
t = trace.   LOI = Loss on ignition

Material	Al_2O_3	SiO_2	TiO_2	B_2O_3	Fe_2O_3	CaO	MgO	Alks.	Other
General purpose firebrick	42·6	52·4	1·4		2·7	0·4	0·1	0·4	
Aluminous firebrick	52·1	40·9	1·7		3·1				
Semi-silica firebrick	15·0	80·7	1·2		2·0	0·7	0·3	0·3	
Hot-face insulating brick. 28 grade	61·1	35·7	0·2		1·0	0·6	0·2	1·2	
High temperature insulating brick. 23 grade	37·32	51·34	0·35		1·62	7·28	0·43	1·66	
Low thermal mass brick	39·0	44·0	1·1		0·6	14·6	0·1	0·4	
Ceramic fibre paper and blanket 1260°C (2300°F) grade	51·7	47·6		0·15	0·02			0·3	0·2
Fibre blanket 1420°C (2588°F) grade	62·3	37·2	t		t			0·5	
Fibre board	43·5	45·6			0·9	1·4		0·3	*Inorganic* 0·3 *LOI* 8·0
Low bio-persistance fibre		70 to 80	t			t	18 to 27		
Castable refractory	31·9	50·8	1·4		6·2	7·8	0·5	1·4	
Refractory insulating cement	39·0	60·2		0·8					
Vermiculite bricks	Vermiculite (exfoliated biotite) 75% + bentonite 25%								
Diatomite, moler and silex bricks	[Diatom remains or rice waste ash]	mainly SiO_2 + CaO, Fe_2O_3, Plastic clay, Volcanic ash							

Table 40
Energy equivalents

kilowatt hour	kWh	1	0·0003	0·0176	0·7457	0·0012	0·0003
Btu per hour	Btu/h	3413	1	60	2545	3·97	0·95
Btu per minute	Btu/min	56·88	0·017	1	42·42	0·066	0·016
horse-power hour	HPh	1·341	0·0004	0·0236	1	0·00156	0·0004
kilogram calories	kcal/h	860	0·252	15·12	641·2	1	0·2389
kilojoules kJ	(kilowatt seconds)	3600	1·055	63·3	2684	4·187	1

Example of use: To convert 150,000 Btu/h into kWh find Btu/h unity on the table (column 2). Note the corresponding figure for kWh in the same column (0·0003). Multiply 150,000 Btu/h by 0·0003 = 45 kWh.

Table 41
Pressure equivalents

Units

atmosphere		1								
inches of mercury		29·92	1							
inches of water "wc (water column)	in w.g.	406·8	13·6	1	0·394	27·68	1·736	393·7	4·014	401·4
centimetres of water	cm H_2O	1033	34·53	2·54	1	70·31	4·464	1000	10·2	1019
pounds per square inch	p.s.i.	14·67	0·491	0·036	0·014	1	0·063	14·22	0·145	14·51
ounces per square inch	oz/in²	234·7	7·856	0·576	0·224	16	1	227·5	2·32	232·2
kilograms per square centimetre	kg/cm²	1·033	0·035	0·003	0·001	0·07	0·004	1	0·01	1·019
kilopascals	kPa	101·3	3·386	0·249	0·098	6·895	0·43	98·1	1	100·1
bars (now superseded by kg/cm²)		1·013	0·034	0·003	0·001	0·069	0·004	0·981	0·009	1

Example use of Table: To convert 5 p.s.i. into kg/cm² find p.s.i. unity on table (column 5). Note the corresponding figure for kg/cm² in the same column (0·07). Multiply 5 p.s.i. by 0·07 = 0·35 kg/cm².

Table 42
Mesh sizes

Micrometres are used for International Standard measurements
2000 micrometres = 2 millimetres = approx ¹⁄₁₂ inch

Aperture in micrometres	UK mesh number	USA mesh number	Canada mesh number	Germany mesh number
2000	8	10	10	—
1000	16	18	18	6
500	30	35	35	12
355	44	45	45	—
250	60	60	60	24
180	85	80	80	—
150	100	100	100	40
125	120	120	120	—
106	150	140	140	—
90	170	170	170	—
75	200	200	200	80
63	240	230	230	—
53	300	270	270	110
45	350	325	325	—

Table 43
Conversion scales

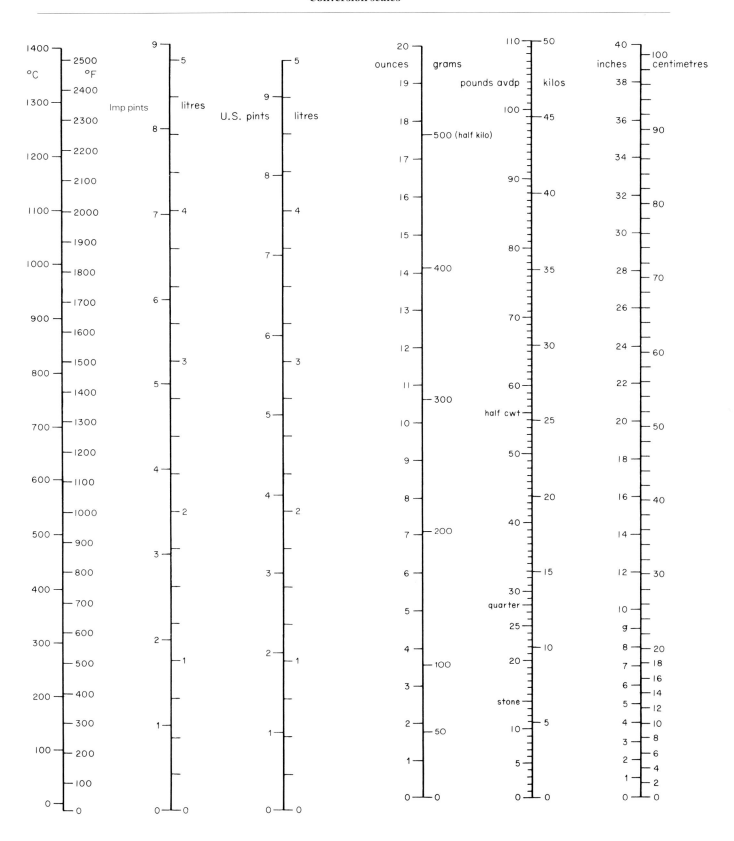

BIBLIOGRAPHY

Books on ceramics, all aspects

T. Birks: *Pottery* (A&C Black 1988)

G. Bliss: *Potter's Question and Answer Book* (A&C Black 1999)

M. Cardew: *Pioneer Pottery* (A&C Black/American Ceramic Society 2002)

J. Connell: *Potter's Guide to Ceramic Surfaces* (Krause 2002)

A. Copeland: *Ceramics Museums of Europe* (Artists Travel Guides 1999)

R. Fournier: *Illustrated Dictionary of Practical Pottery* (A&C Black 1992)

R. and S. Fournier: *Guide to Collections of Studio Pottery in the British Isles* (Ceramic Review 1994)

B. Leach: *A Potter's Book* (Transatlantic 1973)

D. Rhodes: *Clay and Glazes for the Potter* (A&C Black 1973)

A. Young: *Setting up a Pottery Workshop* (A&C Black/American Ceramic Society 1999)

R. Zakin: *Electric Kiln Ceramics* (A&C Black 1994/Krause 1981)

Books on glazes and science

M. Bailey: *Glazes Cone 6* (A&C Black/University of Pennsylvania Press 2001)

M. Clinton: *Lustres* (Batsford 1992)

D. Creber: *Crystalline Glazes* (A&C Black/University of Pennsylvania Press 1997)

G. Daly: *Glazes and Glazing Techniques* (A&C Black 1998/Kangaroo Press 1995)

H. Fraser: *Glazes for the Craft Potter* (A&C Black 1979)

H. Fraser: *Ceramic Faults and their Remedies* (A&C Black 1986)

P. Ilsley: *Macro-Crystalline Glazes* (Crowood Press 1999)

A. Isaacs, J. Daintith, E. Martin (Ed.): *Concise Science Dictionary* (Oxford University Press 1991)

G. J. Leigh (Ed): *Nomenclature of Inorganic Chemistry* (Blackwell Scientific Publications 1990)

P. Rogers: *Ash Glazes* (A&C Black/Krause 1991)

D. Scott: *Clay and Glazes in Studio Ceramics* (Crowood Press 1998)

R. Tichane: *Celadon Blues* (Krause 1999)

R. Tudball: *Soda Glazing* (A&C Black/University of Pennsylvania Press 1995)

N. Wood: *Chinese Glazes* (A&C Black/University of Pennsylvania Press/G & B 1999)

Books on kilns and firing

H. Fraser: *Ceramics Handbook: The Electric Kiln* (A&C Black 1994/University of Pennsylvania Press 2000)

I. Gregory: *Kiln Building* (A&C Black/Gentle Breeze Publishing 1995)

N. Lou: *The Art of Firing* (A&C Black/Gentle Breeze Publishing/G & B 1998)

C. Minogue and R. Sanderson: *Wood-fired Ceramics* (A&C Black/University of Pennsylvania Press 2000)

F. Olsen: *The Kiln Book* (A&C Black/Krause 1983)

J. Perryman: *Smoke-fired Pottery* (A&C Black 1995)

F. Tristram: *Single Firing* (A&C Black/Gentle Breeze Publishing 1996)

J.Troy: *Wood-fired Stoneware and Porcelain* (Krause 1995)

Books on making and techniques

T. Andrews: *Raku* (A&C Black 1994)

S. Banfman: *Raku* (A&C Black/Krause 1991)

P. Beard: *Resist and Masking Techniques* (A&C Black/University of Pennsylvania Press 1996)

R. Cochrane: *Salt-glaze Ceramics* (Crowood Press 2001)

J. Colclough: *Mould Making* (A&C Black/Gentle Breeze Publishing 1999)

D. E. Frith: *Mold Making for Ceramics* (A&C Black/Krause 1992)

R. Gault: *Paper Clay* (A&C Black/University of Pennsylvania Press 1998)

J. Gibson: *Pottery Decoration* (A&C Black 1987/Overlook Press/G & B 1997)

L. Green: *Painting with Smoke–David Roberts–Raku Potter* (Smith Settle 2000)

I. Gregory: *Sculptural Ceramics* (A&C Black/Krause 1992)

M. Hardy: *Handbuilding* (A&C Black/University of Pennsylvania Press 2000)

P. King: *Architectural Ceramics for the Studio Potter* (Lark Books 2000)

A. Lightwood: *Paperclay* (Crowood Press 2000)

C. Minogue: *Impressed and Incised Ceramics* (A&C Black/Gentle Breeze Publishing 1996)

M. Ostermann: *The New Maiolica* (A&C Black/University of Pennsylvania Press 1999)

D. Panciolo: *Extruded Ceramics* (A&C Black 2000)

J. Robison: *Large-scale Ceramics* (A&C Black 1997)

P. Rogers: *Throwing Pots* (A&C Black 1995)

P. Scott: *Ceramics and Print* (A&C Black 1994/Kangaroo Press 1995)

P. Scott: *Painted Clay* (A&C Black 2001)

J. Troy: *Salt-glazed Ceramics* (Watson-Guptill 1977)

S. Wardell: *Slipcasting* (A&C Black/G & B 1997)

M. Wondrausch: *Mary Wondrausch on Slipware* (A&C Black 1986/American Ceramic Society 2001)

Books on historical and contemporary ceramics and their making

T. Birks: *Lucie Rie* (Alphabooks 1988)

B. Blandino: *Coiled Pottery* (A&C Black 1984)

B. Blandino: *The Figure in Fired Clay* (A&C Black 2001/Overlook Press 2002)

A. Caiger-Smith: *Pottery People and Time. A Workshop in Action* (Richard Dennis 1995)

A. Caiger-Smith: *Lustre Pottery, technique, tradition and innovation in Islam and the Western World* (Herbert Press/Faber & Faber 1985)

L. Camusso and S. Bortone (Ed.) *Ceramics of the World* (Macdonald Illustrated 1991)

V. and M. Eden: *Slipware* (A&C Black/University of Pennsylvania Press 1999)

M. Flynn: *Ceramic Figures* (directory of artists) (A&C Black/Rutgers University Press 2002)

K. Hessenberg: *Ceramics for Gardens and Landscapes* (A&C Black/Krause/G & B 2000)

P. Lane: *Contemporary Porcelain* (A&C Black/Krause 1995)

E. Levin: *History of American Ceramics* (Abrams 1988)

M. Lungley: *Gardenware* (Crowood Press 1999)

R. Hopper: *Functional Pottery* (A & C Black/Krause 2000)

D. Jones: *Raku, investigations into Fire* (Crowood Press 1999)

A. McGarva: *Country Pottery* (A&C Black 2000)

J. Mansfield: *Salt-glaze Ceramics* (A&C Black 1991/Krause 1992)

J. Mansfield: *Contemporary Ceramic Art in Australia and New Zealand* (Craftsman House 1995)

S. Peterson: *Smashing Glazes* (North Light Books 2001)

Publications on health and safety

Control of Substances Hazardous to Health Regulations (UK 1988)

Health and Safety at Work Act (UK 1974)

Pottery (Health and Welfare) Regulations (UK 1950) *amended by COSHH*

BS 4163 *Recommendations for health and safety in workshops of schools and colleges*

BS 6748 *A specification for permissible limits of metal release from glazed ceramic ware*

BS 2092 *Protection of eyes regulation*

HMSO 1975 *Safety in the operation of ceramic kilns*

HMSO 1979 *Ceramic health and safety report*

Department of Education and Science Memorandum 517 on the use of certain types of glazes in the teaching of pottery

Department of Education and Science Memorandum 2/65 on the use of poisonous substances

Institute of Ceramics: *Health and Safety in Ceramics* (Pergamon 1981)

Institute of Ceramics: *Safety in Ceramic Education*

T. Challis and G. Roberts: Caution, a guide to safe practice in the arts and crafts (Sunderland Polytechnic 1984)

T. Challis and G. Roberts: *Health and Safety* (AN Publication)

Lead Industries Assoc. Inc. NY: *Facts about lead glazes for art potters and hobbyists*

Dept of Consumer and Corporate Affairs, Canada: *Lead in glazes* (1971)

Note: Catalogues from suppliers of materials etc. often give full information on their products including safety precautions.

Periodicals

American Ceramics (Harry Dennis, 15 W. 44th St, NY 10036, USA)

American Craft (The American Crafts Council, New York)

Ceramic Arts and Crafts (Livonia, Michigan)

Ceramic Review (25 Foubert's Place, London, W1F 7QF)

Ceramics Art and Perception (120 Glenmore Road, Paddington, Sydney, NSW 2021, Australia)

Ceramics in Society (2 Bartholomew St West, Exeter EX4 3AJ)

Ceramics Monthly (P.O. Box 12448, Columbus, OH, 43212-9988, USA)

Ceramics Technical (120 Glenmore Rd, Paddington, Sydney, NSW 2021, Australia)

Contact Quarterly (Alberta Potters' Assoc., P.O. Box 1050, Edmonton, Alberta T5J 2M1)

Craft Australia (Crafts Council of Australia, 27 King St, Sydney 2000)

Crafts (Crafts Council, 44a Pentonville Rd, London N1 9BY)

Crefft (Welsh Arts Council, Museum Place, Cardiff CF1 3NX)

Glas & Keramiek (Postbus 14, NL-5720 A.A.Asten, Netherlands)

Keramiek (Gildstraat 200, 3572 EW Utrecht, Netherlands)

Keramik Magazin (Steinfelder Strasse 10, D-8770 Lohr am Main, Germany)

Keram: Ki Techni (P.O. Box 80653, 185 10 Piraeus, Greece)

La Revue de la Céramique et du Verre (61 Rue Marconi, 62880 Vendin-le-Vieil, France)

Neue Keramik (Unter den Eichen 90, D-2205 Berlin 45, Germany)

New Zealand Potter (Box 147, Albany, New Zealand)

Pottery in Australia (2/68 Alexander St, Crows Nest, NSW 2065, Australia)

Studio Potter (Box 70, Goffstown, NH 03045, USA. Tel. 603-774-3582)

Studio Potter Network Newsletter (69 High St, Exeter, NH 03833, USA. Tel. 603-772-6323)

Information on outlets, craft fairs etc

Craft Guide (annual), Craftsman Magazine Publication, PO Box 5, Driffield, East Yorkshire YO25 8JD

Regional Pottery and Craft Societies organize or have knowledge of most important events.

APPENDIX OF SUPPLIERS

General suppliers of all materials and equipment

United Kingdom
Bath Potters' Supplies, Westfield Ind Est, Unit 18, Radstock BA3 4XE. Tel. 01225-337046
Briar Wheels and Supplies Ltd, Whitsbury Rd, Fordingbridge, Hants SP6 1NQ. Tel. 01425-652991
Ceramatech Ltd, Units 16 & 17 Frontier Works, 33 Queen Street, London N17 8JA. Tel. 0208-885-4492
Potclays Ltd, Brick Kiln Lane, Etruria, Stoke-on-Trent ST4 7BP. Tel. 01782-219816
Potterycrafts Ltd, Campbell Rd, Stoke-on-Trent ST4 4ET. Tel. 01782-745000
Scarva Pottery Supplies, Unit 20, Scarva Rd Ind Est, Banbridge, County Down BT32 3QD. Tel. 028-406-69699

United States of America
Axner Pottery Supply, 490 Kane Court, Oviedo, FL 32765.Tel. 800-843-7057
Leslie Ceramics Supply Co, 1212 San Pablo Ave, Berkeley, CA 94706.Tel. 510-524-7363
Standard Ceramic Supply Co, Box 4435, Pittsburgh, PA 15205. Tel. 412-276-6333

Australia
Potters Equipment Pty Ltd, 13/42 New Street, Ringwood, VIC 3134. Tel. 03-9870-7533

Canada
Tucker's Pottery Supplies Inc, 15 West Pearce St, Unit 7, Richmond Hill, Ontario L4B 1H6. Tel. 416-889-7705
Plainsman Clay Ltd, PO Box 1266, 702 Wood St, Medicine Hat, Alberta T1A 7M9. Tel. 403-527-8535

Specialist suppliers of clay and materials

United Kingdom
W G Ball Ltd, Longton Mill, Anchor Rd, Longton, Stoke-on-Trent ST3 1JW. Tel. 01782-313956
W J Doble, Newdowns Sand & Clay Pits, St Agnes, Cornwall TR5 0ST. Tel. 01872-552979
Imerys Minerals Ltd, John Keay House, St Austell PL25 4DJ. Tel. 01726-74482
Morganite Thermal Ceramics Ltd, Liverpool Rd, Neston, South Wirral L64 3RE. Tel. 0151-336-3911
The Potter's Connection Ltd, Chadwick St, Longton, Stoke-on-Trent ST3 1PJ. Tel. 01782-598-729
Spencroft Ceramics Ltd, Spencroft Rd, Holditch Ind Est, Newcastle, Staffs ST5 9JB. Tel. 01782-627004
Valentine Clays, The Sliphouse, Birches Head Rd, Stoke-on-Trent ST1 6LH. Tel. 01782-271200
WBB Minerals, Brookside Hall, Congleton Rd, Sandbach, Cheshire CW11 4TF. Tel. 01270-752752
Whitfield & Son Ltd, Marsh Trees House, Marsh Parade, Newcastle, Staffs ST5 1BT. Tel. 01782-622666

United States of America
Aardvark Clay & Supplies Inc, 1400 E Pomona St, Santa Ana, CA 92705-4812. Tel. 714-541-4157
American Art Clay Co Inc, 4717 W 16th St, Indianapolis, IN 46222. Tel. 317-244-6871
Archie Bray Foundation, 2915 Country Club Ave, Helena, MT 59601. Tel. 406-442-2521
A R T Studio Clay Co Inc, 9320 Michigan Ave, Sturtevant, WI 53177. Tel. 877-278-2529
Axner Pottery Supply, PO Box 621484, Oviedo, FL 32765. Tel. 800-843-7057
Cedar Heights Clay Co, Div of Resco Products Inc, PO Box 295, Oak Hill, OH 45656. Tel. 614-682-7794
Continental Clay Co, 1101 Stinson Blvd NE, Minneapolis, MN 55413. Tel. 612-331-9332
Laguna Clay Co, 14400 Lomitas Ave, City of Industry, CA 91746. Tel. 800-452-4862
Miami Clay Co, 270 NE 183 St, Miami Garden Drive, FL 33179. Tel. 305-266-6024
Minnesota Clay Co, Normandale Tech Center, Bloomington, MN 55439. Tel. 952-884-9101

Australia
Blackwattle Pottery, PO Box 510, Ingleburn, NSW 2565. Tel. 02-9829-5555
Keane Ceramics Pty Ltd, 177 Debenham Road Sth, Somersby, NSW 2250. Tel. 02-4340-1069
Porcelain Clays, PO Box 84, Erskineville, NSW 2043. Tel. 02-9516-2487

Canada
Pottery Supply House, 1120 Speers Rd, Oakville, Ontario L6L 2X4. Tel. 905-827-1129

Suppliers of pottery equipment

United Kingdom
Acme Marls Ltd, Bournes Bank, Stoke-on-Trent ST6 3DW. Tel. 01782-577757
Co-bam Ltd, Pleasant St, Burslem, Stoke-on-Trent ST6 3DL. Tel. 01782-577136
Edwards and Jones Ltd, Whittle Rd, Meir, Longton, Stoke-on-Trent ST3 7QD. Tel. 01782-599000
Longton Light Alloys incorporating Gladstone Eng Co Ltd, Foxley Lane, Milton, Stoke-on-Trent ST2 7EH. Tel. 01782-536615
Potters' Mate (Lotus Wheelhead), Cust Hall, Toppesfield, Halstead, Essex CO9 4EB. Tel. 01787-237704
Stow Potters' Wheels, 2 Gawcombe, Church Westcote, Oxford OX7 6SS. Tel. 01239-654300

Valentine's Clay Products, Sliphouse, Birches Head Road, Hanley, Stoke-on-Trent ST1 6LH. Tel. 01782-271200

United States of America

American Art Clay, 4717 W 16th St, Indianapolis, IN 46222. Tel. 317-244-6871

Kickwheel Pottery Supply, 6477 Peachtree Indust Blvd, Atlanta, GA 30360. Tel. 800-241-1895

Shimpo Ceramics, 1701 Glenlake Avenue, Itasca, IL 60143-1072. Tel. 630-924-7138

Soldner Equipment, PO 90, Aspen, CO 81612. Tel. 303-925-3742

Australia

Venco Products, G P & G E Hill Pty Ltd, 29 Owen Rd, Kelmscott, WA 6111. Tel. 09-399-5265

Walker Ceramics, 55 Lusher Road, Croydon, VIC 3136. Tel. 03-9725-7255

Canada

Culpepper Ceramics Source, Box 36102, Calgary, Alberta T3E 3C6. Tel. 403-686-3221

New Zealand

Coastal Ceramics, 124 Rimu Rd, Paraparaumu, 6010. Tel. 0-4298-4377

Japan

Nidec-Shimpo Corp, 1 Terada, Kohtari, Nagaokakyo-City, Kyoto, 617-0833. Tel. 075-958-3608

Specialist suppliers of kilns and kiln building materials

United Kingdom

Peter Barnes Refractories, Unit 37/38 Cwmdu Trading Est, Fforest Fach, Swansea SA5 8JE Tel. 01792-588703

Cromartie Kilns Ltd, Dept CR, Park Hall Rd, Longton, Stoke-on-Trent ST3 5AY. Tel. 01782-313947

Gibbons Refractories Ltd, Dudley Works, Cooper's Bank Rd, Brierley Hill, West Midlands DY5 4TY. Tel. 01384-255141

Goodfellow Cambridge Ltd, Ermine Business Park, Huntingdon PE29 6WR. Tel. 01480-424800

Kilncare, 30 Norbury Ave, Stoke-on-Trent ST2 7BJ. Tel. 01782-535915

Kilns and Furnaces Ltd, Keele St, Stoke-on-Trent, Staffs ST6 5AS. Tel. 01782-813621

Laser Kilns Ltd, Unit C9, Angel Rd Works, Advent Way, London N18 3AH. Tel. 0208-803-1016

MPK Insulation Ltd, Hythe Works, Colchester, Essex CO2 8JU. Tel. 01246-459868

Polybond Ltd (Furnascote Div), 42–44 Warsash Rd, Warsash, Southampton SO31 9HX. Tel. 01489-885272

Saffil Ltd, Tanhouse Lane, Widnes, Cheshire WA8 0RY. Tel. 01514-226700

Ray Scott (Sayvit Kilns), Fordham Thermal Systems, Fordham Pottery, 37 Mildenhall Rd, Fordham, CB7 5NP. Tel. 01638-721644

Stanton Kilns, Foley Works, Fenton, Stoke-on-Trent ST4 3DE. Tel. 01782-599395

United States of America

Bailey Pottery Equipment Corp, CPO 1577, Kingston, NY 12401. Tel. 800-431-6067

Bluebird Manufacturing Inc, Box 2307, Fort Collins, CO 80522-2307. Tel. 970-484-3243

Crucible Kilns, 35 S Hanford St, Seattle, WA 98134-1807. Tel. 206-587-0570

Goodfellow Corporation, 800 Lancaster Ave, Berwyn, PA 19312-1780

Industrial Insulations Inc, 10509 Business Drive, Fontana, CA 92337. Tel. 800-551-0277

Olsen Kiln Kits, Pinyon Crest, Box 205, Mountain Center, CA 92361. Tel. 619-349-3291

Paragon Industries Inc, 2011 South Town East Blvd, Mesquite, TX 75149-1122. Tel. 800-876-4328

Randall Wheel and Pottery, 505 University Avenue, Number 39, Rochester, NY 14607. Tel. 716-461-0136

Skutt Ceramic Products, 6441 SE Johnson Creek Blvd, Portland, OR 97206-9594. Tel.503-774-6000

Unifrax Corporation, 2351 Whirlpool St, Niagara Falls, NY 14305-2413. Tel. 716-278-3800

Australia

Ceramic Supply Co Pty Ltd, 1/17–19 Pavesi Street, Guildford, NSW 2161. Tel. 02-9892-1566

Canada

Euclid's Kilns and Elements, 1120 Speers Rd, Oakville, ON L6L 2X4. Tel. 800-296-5456

Sweden

Kanthal International, Box 502, 73427, Hallstahammar

Suppliers of kiln instruments

United Kingdom

Celtic Kilncare Ltd, Celtic Hse, Langland Way, Newport NP19 4PT. Tel. 01633-271455

The Industrial Pyrometer Co Ltd, 66–76 Gooch St, Birmingham B5 6QY. Tel. 0121-622-3511

Stafford Instruments Ltd, 2 Morris Drive, Stafford ST16 3YE. Tel. 01785-604561

United States of America

W P Dawson Inc (Kiln Sitter), 399 Thor Place, Brea, CA 92821. Tel. 714-529-2813

Krueger Pottery Inc, 8153 Big Bend, St Louis, MO 63119. Tel. 800-358-0180

Australia

Australian Oxytrol Systems Pty Ltd (oxygen probe), 85 Wood St, Eaglehawk, VIC 3556. Tel. 03-5446-1530

Clayworks Pty Ltd, 6 Johnston Court, Dandenong, VIC 3175. Tel. 03-9791-6749

Suppliers of pyrometric cones

United Kingdom
　　Taylor Tunnicliff Ltd (for Bullers bars and rings),
　　　　Normacot Road, Longton, Stoke-on-Trent ST3 1PA.
　　　　Tel. 01782-501174
United States of America
　　Orton Ceramic Foundation, PO Box 2760, Westerville,
　　　　OH 43086-9026. Tel. 614-895-2663
Germany
　　Staatliche Porzellan-Manufaktur Berlin (Seger cones),
　　　　Wegelystrasse 1, D10623 Berlin, distributed by H
　　　　Welte Ing GmbH & Co, Max-Planck-Strasse 7, D 5030
　　　　Hürth-Hermülheim. Tel. 02233-7-50-05

Suppliers of computer programs

United Kingdom
　　Victor Bryant, Terracotta Software, 20 Latchmere Rd,
　　　　Kingston KT2 STW. Tel. 0208-546-6685
　　David Hewitt, 7 Fairfield Rd, Caerleon, Newport
　　　　NP18 3DQ
　　Chris Hogg, 17 St Sulien, Luxulyan, Bodmin
　　　　PL30 5EB
United States of America
　　Richard Zakin, Tyler Hall, SUNY, Oswego, NY 13126.
　　　　Tel. 315-343-7381
Canada
　　Tony Hansen, 134 Upland Drive, Medicine Hat, Alberta
　　　　T1A 3N7. Tel. 403-527-2826

Suppliers of safety equipment

　　3M UK Plc, 3M Centre, Cain Rd, Bracknell, Berkshire
　　　　RG12 8HT. Tel. 08705-360036
　　RS Components UK, Lammas Rd, Weldon Ind Est, Corby,
　　　　Northants NN17 9RS. Tel. 01536-444041

Suppliers of films and videos

United Kingdom
　　Deborah Baynes, Nether Hall, Shotley, Ipswich IP9 1PW.
　　Ceramics Invision, Cae Bedw, Brilley, Whitney-on-Wye,
　　　　Herefordshire HR3 6JH. Tel. 01497-831542
Australia
　　Old Lithgow Pottery, Silcock St, Lithgow, NSW 2790.
　　　　Tel. 02-6351-4483
Germany
　　International Catalogue of Films on Ceramics, Dorfstr
　　　　14, 17194 Klein, Luchow. Tel. 39933-71836

Archives

　　Ceramics Archive, School of Art, University of Wales,
　　　　Buarth Mawr, Aberystwyth SY23 1NG. Tel. 01970-
　　　　622460

APPENDIX OF ADDRESSES FOR STANDARDS AND SAFETY

United Kingdom
　　National Back Pain Association, The Old Office Block,
　　　　16 Elm Tree Rd, Teddington TW11 8ST.
　　　　Tel. 0208-977-5474
　　CERAM Research Ltd, Queens Rd, Penkhull, Stoke-on-
　　　　Trent ST4 7LQ. Tel 01782-764444
　　British Safety Council, National Safety Centre, 70
　　　　Chancellors Rd, London W6 9RS. Tel. 0208-741-
　　　　1231
　　British Standards Institution, 389 Chiswick High Road,
　　　　London W4 4AL. Tel. 0208-996-9000
　　Health and Safety Executive, Ceramics Industry
　　　　Advisory Committee, The Marches House, The
　　　　Midway, Newcastle, Staffs ST5 1DT. Tel. 01782-
　　　　602300
　　HMSO Books, Freepost, London SW8 5DR
　　ROSPA, The Royal Society for the Prevention of
　　　　Accidents, 353 Bristol Rd, Edgbaston, Birmingham
　　　　B5 7ST. Tel. 0121-248-2000
United States of America
　　Center for Safety in the Arts, 5 Beekman St, Suite 1030,
　　　　New York, NY 10038. Tel. 212-227-6220

GREEN ADDRESSES

　　Centre for Alternative Technology, Pantperthog,
　　　　Machynlleth, Powys SY20 9AZ
　　Department for Environment, Food & Rural Affairs,
　　　　Nobel House, 17 Smith Square, London SW1P 3JR
　　Friends of the Earth, 26–28 Underwood St, London
　　　　N1 7JQ
　　Renewable Energy Enquiries Bureau, ETSU, Building
　　　　156, Harwell Laboratory, Didcot, Oxfordshire
　　　　OX11 0RA

APPENDIX OF INTERNET RESOURCES FOR POTTERS

Compiled by Ron Parker: www.ronparkerceramics.com

General information and link directories

www.ceramics.org/clayart/
American Ceramics Society, Clayart page: Here, you can search or browse the archives. For more information on Clayart, see the Discussion Groups section below.

http://art.sdsu.edu/ceramicsweb/index.html
San Diego State University ceramics site includes databases of glaze recipes and material analyses, health and safety information, links to other ceramics Web sites, and educational materials.

www.clayzee.com
Clayzee is a comprehensive directory on all things ceramic.

www.ukpotters.co.uk
UK Potters site provides a good range of links to other sites for potters.

www.ceramics.com
Resources dedicated to the professional interested in ceramics and minerals. Site includes an interactive periodic table of the elements.

www.studiopottery.com
The Pottery Studio aims to include examples of work from all British potters and potteries. There are presently about 4000 pages.

www.studiopottery.co.uk
An information site linking potters, galleries and collectors of studio ceramics.

http://bubl.ac.uk/link
A catalogue of selected Internet resources covering all academic subject areas and catalogued according to the Dewey Decimal Classification.

www.e-yakimono.net
This Japanese site is an information centre with good links to Japanese pottery sites.

www.ceramique.com
This is a French reference site for ceramics. It also has useful links to other, mainly French, sites.

www.ceramicstoday.com
A non-profit forum for international ceramic art on the Web. It evolved from Claynet and ceramics.about.com.

www.pottersdictionary.com
Links to all the sites in this list, selected from thousands of sites with information for potters.

Magazines

www.ceramic-review.com
Ceramic Review – the journal of the Craft Potters Association, UK. Articles published are practical, technical and experiential.

www.ceramicsmonthly.org
Ceramics Monthly – the magazine of the American Ceramics Society on ceramic art and craft.

www.ceramicart.com.au
Ceramics: Art and Perception – Australian magazine dedicated to ceramic art
Ceramics Technical – by the same publisher, devoted to research in the field of ceramics.

Historic potteries

www.leachpottery.com
Bernard Leach settled in St Ives on his return from Japan in 1920. There, with the help of his friend, Shoji Hamada, he started the now famous Leach Pottery.

www.winchcombepottery.co.uk
The present Winchcombe Pottery was started by Michael Cardew in 1926, when he left St Ives. He had been Leach's first student.

www.wenfordbridge.com
During the 1930s, Michael Cardew moved his family to Cornwall, 'where the light was right'. There, he opened the Wenford Bridge Pottery, and developed his own career.

Festival

www.internationalceramicsfestival.co.uk
International Ceramics Festival, Aberystwyth: Every alternate year (since 1986) some of the world's leading potters and ceramic artists gather for demonstrations, lectures and discussions.

Discussion groups: e-mail and newsgroups

www.acers.org/cic/clayart
Clayart: E-mail discussions range from materials and techniques, to business advice and philosophy. There is information on how to use the site, and search the Clayart archives.

http://groups.google.com
Here you can search for topics already discussed on any news group, as well as pottery. These archived discussions can be read without a special 'newsreader' – including:

rec.crafts.pottery
This is the major pottery newsgroup. You can subscribe to a group, or you can just watch the discussion. You can then take part, if and when you feel ready.

Associations

www.ceramic-review.co.uk
Craft Potters Association: The major organization for craft potters in the UK. (Accessed via the magazine site.)

www.acers.org
American Ceramic Society: The US organization dedicated to the advancement of ceramics.

http://ceramicsireland.org
Craft Potters Society of Ireland: A source of information for potters at home and abroad.

www.potteryinaustralia.com
Potters' Society of Australia: The society also produces the journal *Pottery in Australia*.

www.nvk-keramiek.nl
The Dutch Ceramists Association: This site also has an extensive potter's links section.

www.kalkspatz.ceramic.de
German Potter's Association: The site has a travel guide, and a potter's German – English dictionary.

www.craftinfo.org.nz/community/moreinfo/craft_potters.htm
New Zealand Craft Resource: The resource for crafts and craft artists, including potters.

www.southwalespotters.org.uk
South Wales Potters: One of the largest regional ceramics societies (and the first) in the UK.

Museums and galleries

http://ceramicsmuseum.alfred.edu
Schein-Joseph International Museum of Ceramic Art, at Alfred University New York, houses nearly 8000 ceramic and glass objects, from ancient pottery shards to contemporary sculpture.

www.stoke.gov.uk/museums
The Museums of the Potteries: This site includes the Stoke-on-Trent City Museum and Art Gallery, the Etruria Museum, and the Gladstone working pottery museum.

www.aber.ac.uk/ceramics
Aberystwyth University Arts Centre: one of the major studio ceramics collections in the UK. It has fine examples of pottery by Bernard Leach, other early studio potters, and contemporary potters.

www.ashmol.ox.ac.uk
The Ashmolean, Britain's oldest public museum, has one of the world's finest ceramics collections. Its Potweb project aims to create an online catalogue of the entire ceramic collection.

www.vam.ac.uk
The Victoria & Albert is Britain's National Museum of Art and Design, with an excellent ceramics collection. It claims to be the greatest museum of applied and decorative arts in the world.

www.asia.si.edu
Smithsonian's Freer and Sackler galleries form the USA's national museum of Asian art. The galleries offer one of the West's most refined collections of Asian art.

www.moco.or.jp/en
The Museum of Oriental Ceramics, Osaka, is dedicated to collecting, exhibiting and researching oriental ceramics. It has some 2000 pieces of oriental ceramics.

www.asiasociety.org/arts/ceramics
The Asia Society is America's leading institution dedicated to fostering understanding of Asia. A selection from the society's ceramics collection is on the Web site.

www.ruffordcraftcentre.org.uk
Rufford Arts Centre's Web site aims to be the best for British pottery and ceramics.

The Internet is in a permanent state of change, but the listed sites were all operational in October 2003.

RECIPE APPENDIX

These recipes are personal recipes quoted from the potters concerned. Some are batch recipes in actual weights. Others are percentages or numbers convenient to the originator. These recipes complement the more basic recipes in the body of the book.

To convert a batch recipe to a percentage so that it can be compared better with other recipes, first ensure that all the item weights are of the same scale, that is, all pounds, all ounces, all kilograms or all grams. Then divide each item weight by the total weight and multiply by 100. For example:

borax frit	63 lb 8 oz $\longrightarrow$	63·5
china clay	10 lb 0 oz $\longrightarrow$	10
	total	73·5

% of borax frit $\dfrac{63\cdot5}{73\cdot5} \times 100 = 86\cdot4\%$

% of china clay $\dfrac{10}{73\cdot5} \times 100 = 13\cdot6\%$

To convert percentage recipe to batch recipe see example in **Calculations**. To convert avoirdupois to metric or vice versa see **Formula**.

John Alliston

Bronze matt surface treatment. Slop dip on biscuit. Oxidation to 1260°C (2300°F). See **Colour plate 38**.

china clay	5
manganese oxide	7
copper oxide	1

Clay body. Dough mix, pug, sour/age, de-air pug before use. See **Extrusion**.

fireclay	112
red clay	60
Hyplas 71	56
china clay	21
sand	24
vinegar	

Mike Bailey

The following four glazes were designed to be fired within a range from 1220°C to 1250°C (2228°F to 2282°F) oxidized. Explanations on adaptations for temperature variations are given in Mike Bailey's book *Glazes for Cone 6*. Three of these recipes are illustrated on test tiles shown on colour plates: Orange red (**Colour plate 67**); Bright turquoise blue (**Colour plate 82**) and Deep green (**Colour plate 82**), plus Light turquoise (on a square dish on **Colour plate 82**).

Orange red. (upper range to cone 8)

potassium feldspar	44·5
bentonite	2·0
bone ash	14·2
flint/quartz	16·0
china clay	10·1
talc	10·6
lithium carbonate	2·6
red iron oxide	10·7

Bright turquoise blue.

potassium feldspar	49
HP71 ball clay	9
bentonite	1
barium carbonate	27
whiting	14
copper carbonate	2·5

Deep green.

potassium feldspar	30
standard borax frit Potclays 2263	10
china clay	14
barium carbonate	17
whiting	5
flint/quartz	24
copper carbonate	4

Light turquoise.

sodium feldspar	15
high alkaline frit Potclays 2275	47
china clay	5
bentonite	2
lithium carbonate	2
whiting	6
zinc oxide	5
quartz	18
copper oxide	2

Turquoise raku glaze.

high alkaline frit Potclays 2275	85
china clay	13
bentonite	2
copper carbonate	4

Rob Bibby

White glaze for maiolica firing at 1100°C (2012°F). See illustrations under *Printing* and *Colour plate 17*.

lead bisilicate	65
calcium borate frit	10
china clay	10
flint	5
tin oxide	10
zirconium silicate	4

Daphne Carnegy

Tin glaze for maiolica on thrown red earthenware body based on Alan Caiger-Smith's original recipe. Oxides and underglaze stains are often mixed for painting on the raw glaze. Otherwise oxides are used for blues, greens, browns and blacks, and underglaze stains are used for yellows, reds and purples. Firing temperature 1060°C to 1140°C (1940°F to 2084°F). See *Maiolica*.

lead bisilicate	60
standard borax frit	9
cornish stone	15
china clay	5

tin oxide	7
zirconium silicate	7
zinc oxide	2
bentonite	2

Sue Carr

These two shiny glazes are fired on 'David Leach' porcelain body with heavy reduction for 1½ hours from cone 012, then light reduction to cone 10. See article on *Porcelain*.

Bright red glaze.

sodium feldspar	40
flint	20
whiting	15
borax frit	25
kaolin	5
copper oxide	1·5
tin oxide	3·5

Pink glaze.

potassium feldspar	35
ball clay	17
kaolin	12
whiting	12
flint	7
barium carbonate	17
copper oxide	2

Michael Casson

Clay for salt-glazed pots which we call 'Harry Davis Mix'.

ball clay	75
china clay	24
cornish stone	1

Slips used on wood-fired salt-glaze ware at 1300°C (2372°F). See photographs under *Green issues, Salt glaze* and *Colour plates 52* and *54*.

Tan slip.

HSN ball clay	50
porcelain china clay	50
nepheline syenite	5

Rutile slip.

nepheline syenite	50
SMD ball clay	50
rutile	10

Sheila Casson

Glazes for porcelain.

Magnesium glaze.

cornish stone	33
whiting	7
china clay	6
ball clay	4
magnesium carbonate	2

Dolomite glaze with tin oxide.

potassium feldspar	6 lb 4 oz
sodium feldspar	6 lb 4 oz
dolomite	5 lb 10 oz
whiting	14 oz
tin oxide	1 lb 0 oz

These two glazes are often used in a 50/50 mix over the vitreous slips listed below. The firing is reduced in a propane kiln to 1280°C (2336°F). See photograph under **Sgraffito**.

Vitreous iron slip.

cornish stone	60
ball clay	35
china clay	5
red iron oxide	100

Vitreous blue slip.

red clay	100
manganese oxide	32
cobalt oxide	15
red iron oxide	59

Blue slip for use on stoneware clay to be salt glazed at 1300°C (2372°F) in propane reduction kiln.

nepheline syenite	50
SMD ball clay	50
cobalt oxide	1
red iron oxide	2·25

Tan slip for salt-glazing.

porcelain clay	
potassium feldspar	} equal parts
ball clay (CY)	

Stoneware glazes to be fired to 1300°C in propane reduction kiln.

Shino glaze applied at green state and incised for inlay after biscuit.

petalite	38
nepheline syenite	38
AT ball clay	10
Hyplas ball clay	14

Green celadon glaze.

cornish stone	40
feldspar	6·6
whiting	13·5
quartz	13·5
porcelain body	20
red iron oxide	1

Derek Clarkson

Limoges and David Leach porcelain bodies are used and usually fired to 1280°C (2336°F) in an electric kiln. Cooling is precisely controlled to give crystal-growing periods of up to 6 hours. See **Crystalline glazes**.

Basic recipe to which colouring is added. See **Colour plate 11**.

Ferro frit 3110	51·50
zinc oxide	20·75
flint	20·55
titanium oxide	6·20
china clay	0·25
aluminium oxide	0·75

Glaze for left-hand pot shown in **Colour plate 10**.

Degussa frit 90208m	75·00 g
titanium oxide	1·25 g
copper carbonate	2·50 g

Glaze for right-hand pot in **Colour plate 10**.

Degussa frit 90208m	75·00 g
titanium oxide	1·65 g
copper carbonate	3·50 g

Glaze for pot shown in **Colour plate 12**.

Degussa frit 90208m	47·60 g
calcined zinc oxide	27·90 g
flint	34·50 g
china clay	0·33 g
titanium oxide	6·90 g
cobalt carbonate	0·15 g
copper carbonate	2·00 g

manganese oxide 1·70 g
crystal-growing period 5hrs 53mins at 1065°C (1949°F).

Glaze for pot shown in **Colour plate 75**.

Degussa frit 90208m	70·20 g
cobalt carbonate	0·15 g
red iron oxide	0·20 g

Rosemary Cochrane

Recipes for use prior to salt glazing in oil-fired reduction. See photographs under **Jug** and **Colour plate 6**.
  Slip to be applied at leatherhard stage giving pale peach to deep orange according to clays used and salting.

Hyplas or other ball clay	50
china clay	50

Blue slip.

HVAR ball clay	70
china clay	30
cobalt oxide	2·5
red iron oxide	1·5

Blue engobe (Suzy Atkins) for trailed decoration.

nepheline syenite	70
AT ball clay	5
HVAR ball clay	25
cobalt oxide	1

Blue glaze (Walter Keeler) applied to raw ware. 1280°C (2336°F).

potassium feldspar	50
ball clay	30
dolomite	20
cobalt carbonate	0·65
copper carbonate	0·5

Shino glaze (Jane Hamlyn) applied to raw ware. 1260°C to 1280°C (2300°F to 2336°F). Used especially on insides of pots.

nepheline syenite	33
ball clay	33
potassium feldspar	33

Delan Cookson

Blue glaze recipe for oxidized porcelain at 1280°C (2336°F). The glaze is extremely variable and not suitable for domestic ware. It requires a fast firing and cooling. See **Barium oxide, Copper oxides** and **Colour plate 16**.

nepheline syenite	34
feldspar	5
china clay	12
flint	7
barium carbonate	34
whiting	5
lithium carbonate	3
copper carbonate	1·7

Emmanuel Cooper

Glaze recipe for oxidized porcelain. Electric kiln 1260°C (2300°F).

feldspar	40
dolomite	8
whiting	22
china clay	20
flint	10
tin oxide	6

The dolomite must be refined and not raw, otherwise the glaze will be matt instead of shiny. Colouring oxides painted under the glaze will burn through and become integrated. See **Colour plate 19**.
  Stoneware glazes developed for oxidation firing in electric kilns. See **Nickel oxide** and **Barium carbonate**.

Nickel blue glaze 1200°C (2192°F).

feldspar	52
whiting	5
barium carbonate	15
zinc oxide	12
china clay	6
flint	10
nickel oxide	2

Pink/blue matt glaze 1250°C to 1280°C (2282°F to 2336°F).

feldspar	35
barium carbonate	40
zinc oxide	15
china clay	5
flint	5
nickel oxide	1 to 3

Recipe for glaze ECZ for 1280°C (2336°F) reduced. 'This is a glaze I have used for many years in reduction, and although it can sometimes be a bit difficult to apply, it gives a good pale blue and silky smooth surface.' See **Colour plate 67**.

cornish stone	50
whiting	23
zinc oxide	3
quartz	10
china clay	14
red iron oxide	0·5

Molly Curley

Uses Emmanuel Cooper's transparent glaze recipe for slipware.

lead bisilicate	5 lb
borax frit	10 lb
cornish stone	2 lb
ball clay	1 lb
flint	2 lb

Add red iron oxide 10 oz and manganese oxide 1 oz for honey glaze giving yellows and greeny blues. Applied on 950°C (1742°F) biscuit. Fired to 1140°C (2084°F), with ½ hour soak, in electric kiln.

Jack Doherty

Additions to Valentine's standard porcelain body to make coloured body for inlay work. See *Agate* and *Inlay*.

Textured silver/grey.

| rutile ore (unsieved) | 3 to 5% |

Pale yellow.

| manganese carbonate | 3% |

Pale pink.

| Deancraft Salmon stain | 1% |

Coloured slips for soda firing from Jack Doherty. 'For the past few years the coloured clays which I use have been developed for soda firing. In practice this means that I have been using fewer commercial body stains, instead using combinations of oxides modified with materials such as aluminium oxide and flint. I have also found interesting colour and texture by mixing different ball clays and china clays with the basic porcelain body and using as an inlay.'

Dark sea green.

chromium oxide	35
cobalt oxide	10
tin oxide	15

| flint | 15 |
| aluminium oxide | 25 |

Orange/Russet.

ball clay	33
china clay	33
porcelain	33

Peach.

| porcelain | 90 |
| titanium oxide | 10 |

Jack built a 510 litre kiln for soda firing. The catenary arch structure was built by ramming the mixed castable into a former made from 15 mm plywood. The door blocks were also cast with this mixture.

an aggregate grog using a wide range of grog sizes (dust to 5 mm)	4 parts
fireclay	4 parts
sawdust/wood chippings	4 parts
aluminium hydrate	1 part
cement	1 part

Joan Doherty

Transparent raku glaze for use on white body. See photograph under *Raku*.

| borax frit | 85 |
| china clay | 15 |

Derek Emms

These glazes are used on 'David Leach' porcelain, Pot-clays 1147, and fired to 1285°C (2345°F), Harrison Bell cone 9, reducing from 980°C (1796°F). See photograph under *Jun*.

Pale blue opalescent jun glaze.

feldspar	40
flint	30
whiting	20
borax frit	10
talc	5
china clay	2
red iron oxide	1

Tenmoku glaze.

| feldspar (waterground) | 60 |
| flint | 22 |

whiting	10
HVAR ball clay	8
synthetic red iron oxide	6·5

Blue-green celadon glaze.

feldspar (waterground)	40
flint	30
wollastonite	20
china clay	10
Molochite (200's)	5
zinc oxide	5
synthetic red iron oxide	0·5
[jar milled for 2½ hours]	

Avril Farley

Avril Farley fires to between 1245°C and 1265°C (2273°F and 2309°F) holding the cooling temperature below 1100°C (2012°F) for the crystal-growing period. Double axe-head shapes appear between 1090°C and 1060°C (1994°F and 1940°F), the softer, puff-ball/floral shapes at temperatures below this. See **Crystalline glazes** and **Colour plates 9, 42** and **74**.

Glaze recipe.

Ferro frit 3110	47
calcined zinc oxide	23
calcined china clay	3
flint	23
titanium oxide	4

Plus bentonite or CMC 2% to 3% to make brushable. Oxides/carbonates of copper, cobalt and manganese are used up to 8% in total.

David Frith

Pale green celadon glaze. Reduction fired to 1280°C (2336°F). The minerals are ball-milled for 4 hours.

cornish stone	80
ball clay (AT)	10
whiting	10
talc	6
black iron oxide	1

Kaki glaze for reduction firing to 1280°C.

feldspar	30
quartz	30
china clay	20
whiting	5

| dolomite | 2 |
| red iron oxide | 5 |

Margaret Frith

Pale blue celadon glaze (Yingqing) for stoneware and porcelain. The glaze minerals are ball-milled for 4 hours and the glaze is fired in a reduction atmosphere to 1280°C (2336°F).

quartz	28
china clay	27
cornish stone	23
whiting	22
red iron oxide	0·75

Carolyn Genders

Slip to go on ungrogged white earthenware body and fired with matt transparent glaze to 1120°C to 1160°C (2048°F to 2120°F). See **Coiling**.

ball clay	30
potassium feldspar	30
white body	30
frit	10
colouring	10–20%

Matt transparent glaze.

lead bisilicate	61
cornish stone	9
china clay	35
whiting	5

Frank Hamer

Stoneware dolomite glaze for 1260°C (2300°F) reduced. See photographs under **Dolomite matt** and **Goblet**.

potassium feldspar	50
china clay	23
whiting	6
dolomite	15
high expansion borax frit	6

Stoneware semi-transparent glaze for 1280°C (2336°F) reduced. This glaze has a fatty quality where thick and varies its surface according to underlying colour. See photographs under **Underglaze**.

| potassium feldspar | 46 |
| china clay | 15 |

flint	11
whiting	15
dolomite	8
low expansion frit	6
zirconium silicate	6·5

Janet Hamer

Vitrifying black slip/glaze for stoneware or porcelain cone 7 to 9, oxidized or with light reduction.

ball clay	76
whiting	14
red iron oxide	5
copper carbonate	2
cobalt carbonate	9
low expansion frit	7
potassium feldspar	18
china clay	3
flint	3
zinc oxide	0·4

Vitrifying blue slip/glaze for cone 9 oxidized or reduced. Very dark blue with soft shine. Good on porcelain.

BBV ball clay	92
dolomite	20
cobalt oxide	3
iron oxide	2
copper carbonate	0·25

Celadon glaze. Orton cone 9 well down. Reduced from 1060°C (1940°F). Grey/green matt when cooler, clear green when hotter. Blue jun areas where thick, high fired and well reduced. Crawls if temperature rise is bumpy. See photographs under *Celadon*.

potassium feldspar	43
china clay	2
quartz	30
whiting	20
talc	4
colemanite	1
black iron oxide	1
Molochite flour	1

Dolomite glaze. Good on porcelain and stoneware at Orton cone 9. Needs reduction to be smooth on medium-coarse stoneware. See photograph under *Dolomite matt*.

potassium feldspar	25
sodium feldspar	27
china clay	18
whiting	5
dolomite	25
borax frit	5

Copper glaze for high-temperature lustre. Fired oxidized to 1220°C (2228°F). Reduced with wood when cooling from 970°C to 500°C (1778°F to 932°F). Needs heavy reduction. See photograph under *Lustres*.

potassium feldspar	19
china clay	8
flint	16
whiting	18
lead bisilicate	19
standard borax frit	19
copper carbonate	4
bentonite	1

Clear yellow glaze for oxidation. The manganese oxide mellows the harshness of the praseodymium yellow but beware, praseodymium stains vary in strength. Soft pale green in reduction.

potassium feldspar	44
china clay	13
flint	13
whiting	16
manganese oxide	2
praseodymium stain	6
red iron oxide	0·5

Michael and Barbara Hawkins

The white firing porcellaneous body for throwing is mixed in a dough mixer and de-aired in a pug mill.

Hyplas 71	75%
standard porcelain powder	23·5%
Minomex (nepheline syenite)	1·5%

Glazes are fired to 1300°C (1372°F) (Cone 10 to 11) with reduction from 980°C (1796°F).

potassium feldspar	19,600 g
whiting	8,160 g
china clay	4,800 g
flint	9,600 g
zirconium silicate	6,000 g

FFF feldspar	20,000 g
dolomite	6,000 g
china clay	7,560 g
zirconium silicate	6,400 g
bentonite	400 g

The Hawkins use lustres fired to 820°C (1508°F).

Cookson-Matthey	dark blue
	12% gold
Heraeus	mother-of-pearl
	10% bright gold

Alan Heaps

High-temperature earthenware semi-matt glaze pulling colour from Potclays 1129 St Paul's clay.

lead bisilicate	100
china clay	50
whiting	25
tin oxide	5
dolomite	5
vanadium oxide	2

Joanna Howells

Ash glaze for porcelain, reduction fired to 1300°C (2372°F). See *Coffee pot*.

potassium feldspar	32
whiting	32
china clay	16
silica	16·8
wood ash	32

Glaze for teapot. See *Teapot*.

flint	16·05
china clay	11·9
dolomite	5·3
wollastonite	17·6
cornish stone	63·2
bentonite	2·0

Sophia Hughes

Turquoise glaze for firing in an electric kiln to 1280°C (2336°F).

nepheline syenite	43
barium carbonate	35
whiting	5
china clay	5
flint	12
copper carbonate	2
bentonite	0·5

Jude Jelfs

Unglazed black slip, 1095°C (2003°F), waxed while still warm from kiln using beeswax polish. See photograph under *Black*.

china clay	50
HVAR ball clay	50

low temperature borax frit	30
black stain	22·5

David Jones

Raku base glaze. See *Raku* and *Colour plate 33*.

alkaline frit	85
china clay	10
bentonite	5

Add cobalt oxide 3, or silver nitrate 1, or copper oxide 1, or gold chloride 0·25.

Copper matt coating.

copper carbonate	90
china clay	5
bentonite	5

Jonathan Keep

Decoration engobe to paint on biscuited semi-porcelain (Potclays 1144), cover with transparent glaze and fire to 1220°C (2228°F) oxidized in electric kiln.

semi-porcelain body	50
FFF feldspar	35
body/glaze stain	15 (or less)

Transparent cone 6 glaze.

FFF feldspar	40
china clay	10
flint	25
whiting	18
gerstley borate	8

Chrome-tin pink glaze, cone 6 1220°C oxidized. See *Chromium oxide*.

FFF feldspar	40
china clay	5
quartz	10
whiting	20
gerstley borate	5
lithium carbonate	5
tin oxide	5
chromium oxide	0·4

Dolomite matt glaze, Cone 6 1220°C oxidized. See *Dolomite matt*.

FFF feldspar	45
china clay	25

quartz	5
dolomite	20
whiting	5

Bristol type glaze, Cone 6 1220°C oxidized. See **Bristol**.

FFF feldspar	50
china clay	15
quartz	20
whiting	10
zinc oxide	10
tin oxide	5

White barium textured glaze, Cone 6 1220°C oxidized. See **Barium oxide**.

nepheline syenite	55
china clay	5
whiting	12
zinc oxide	8
tin oxide	2
barium carbonate	20

Turquoise runny glaze, Cone 6 1220°C oxidized. See **Copper oxides**.

nepheline syenite	80
barium carbonate	10
lithium carbonate	8
bentonite	2
copper carbonate	2

Anne Lightwood

Basic porcelain body which is stained at slip stage with up to 10% of W. G. Ball body stains, underglaze colours or oxides. See **Lamination**.

Grolleg china clay	45
Hyplas ball clay	20
potassium feldspar	20
quartz	15
bentonite	2
Molochite	2 to 5

Christine McCole

Glaze for large oven dish for wood firing with reduction at 1280°C (2336°F). See **Colour plate 67**.

sodium feldspar	25
dolomite	15
HVAR ball clay	25
bone ash	10

quartz	25
plus red iron oxide	10%

Andrew McGarva

Cone 10 stoneware glaze for decoration in oxides painted onto the unfired glaze. See photographs under **Oxide, Bowl, Press-moulding** and **Throwing**.

potassium feldspar	2
nepheline syenite	2
ball clay	1

Stephen Mills

See photograph under **Teapot**.

Raku body.

Potclays 1106 White St Thomas	50
Potclays 1112 Ivanhoe	50

Raku glaze (Dave Roberts recipe).

calcium borate frit	40
Potterycrafts P2955 borax frit	40
china clay	15
tin oxide	5

John Pollex

Transparent glaze for slipware on Medcol red earthenware clay.

lead sesquisilicate	8600 g
china clay	1400 g
potassium feldspar	500 g
flint	800 g
whiting	250 g

Add red iron oxide 150 and iron spangles 175 (unsieved) for traditional amber glaze.

Jim Robison

Jim Robison uses variously coloured slips over grogged bodies and once fires to cone 8 with reduction from 1080°C (1976°F). Glazes are sprayed and multiple layers are built up. See **Colour plates 30** and **31, Outdoor ceramics** and **Slabbing**.

Ash glaze.

mixed ash	10 lb
china clay	9 lb
potassium feldspar	2½ lb
whiting	2½ lb
added colours include	
copper oxide	3%
cobalt oxide	1%
yellow ochre	6%

Matt glaze.

potassium feldspar	20
whiting	35
china clay	35
ball clay	10

Satin white glaze.

potassium feldspar	29·5
nepheline syenite	29·5
china clay	11·0
whiting	13·5
dolomite	3·0
zinc oxide	3·0
bentonite	0·5
zirconium silicate	5·0
tin oxide	5·0

Phil Rogers

Ash glaze for use over white slip. Fired reduction 1280°C (2336°F). See photographs under **Wood ash, Stoneware** and **Colour plate 5**.

specific wood ash	2000
cornish stone	600
feldspar	600
whiting	250
china clay	300
quartz	300

White slip.

SMD ball clay	2
Molochite	1

Micki Schloessingk

Stoneware clays for salt glaze. See **Colour plate 45**.

1. Terres et Cendres du Berry. Pyrite (with pyrites). La Borne, France.

2. Terre a gres St Amand en Puisaye, France.
3. Porcelaine (dure) Limoges, France.

Various combinations of the above or used on their own. Firing temperature 1320°C (2408°F), cone 12, reducing/neutral atmosphere.
Bat wash: aluminium oxide 3 parts, china clay 1 part.
Wadding: aluminium oxide 2 parts, fine Molochite 2 parts, china clay 1 part, plus wallpaper paste.

Josie Walter

Transparent glaze for slipware. See photograph under **Earthenware**.

lead bisilicate	75
borax frit	5
potassium feldspar	10
finely powdered red clay	10
bentonite	4

Raw glaze applied at leatherhard stage to Valentine's medium red earthenware clay. Fired to cone 03 in an electric kiln. Add 1% red iron oxide for warmer colour particularly over green slip.

White slip.

TWVD ball clay	100%

Black slip.

thick brown slip (collected from water bowl after throwing)	4 pints
red iron oxide	1½ oz
cobalt oxide	1 oz
nickel oxide	1 oz
manganese oxide	1 oz

Green slip.

TWVD ball clay	100
copper oxide	3

Dark blue slip.

TWVD ball clay	100
cobalt oxide	3.5

Blue, pink and grey slips are made by adding 10 parts Mereswann underglaze stains to 100 parts TWVD ball clay.

John Wheeldon

Recipe for black basalt body firing to cone 7. See **Colour plates 60** and **63**.

HVAR ball clay	55
china clay	15
Molochite	30
manganese oxide	3·3
red iron oxide	3·3
copper oxide	1·6
cobalt oxide	1·6

Glaze for cone 7 over basalt body.

cornish stone	12·5
nepheline syenite	12·5
quartz	25
whiting	25
china clay	25

Lustres from Heraeus and Cookson-Matthey are then applied and fired to 720°C (1328°F) cone 018.

Peter Wills

Glazes for porcelain in an electric kiln.

Bronze fires up to 1285°C (2345°F) and probably has a wide range below this temperature. See **Manganese oxide**.

manganese oxide	75
copper oxide	25
FFF feldspar	50
barium carbonate	50
bentonite	10

White glaze for 1280°C (2336°F) between matt and glossy, not for domestic ware.

FFF feldspar	70
barium carbonate	15
whiting	15
tin oxide	7
bentonite	5

Chrome-tin pink. See **Colour plate 29**.

FFF feldspar		62
whiting		28
flint		10
colemanite		5
china clay		5
tin oxide		5
bentonite		5
chromium oxide	(deep red)	0·5%
	(deep pink)	0·1%
	(light salmon pink)	0·04%

Mary Wondrausch

Bideford pipe clay sieved 100's is the white slip to go on Fremington clay and be covered with this transparent glaze. See **Slipware**.

lead sesquisilicate	7500
china clay	1800
flint	600

Add red iron oxide 1% for pale honey and 2% for dark honey.